# DEPRIVATION AND HEALTH IN SCOTLAND

# DEPRIVATION AND HEALTH IN SCOTLAND

Vera Carstairs
Russell Morris

**ABERDEEN UNIVERSITY PRESS**
Member of Maxwell Macmillan Pergamon Publishing Corporation

First published 1991
Aberdeen University Press

**British Library Cataloguing in Publication Data**

Carstairs, Vera
    Deprivation and health in Scotland
    1. Scotland.   Health Services
    I. Title
    362. 109411

    ISBN 0-08-037979-6

Typeset by Logotechnics, Sheffield–Zürich
Printed by Athenaeum Press Ltd, Newcastle-upon-Tyne

# Contents

# List of Tables

# List of Figures

# ACKNOWLEDGEMENTS

The analysis of the material which appears in this book was made possible by financial support from the Chief Scientist, Scottish Home and Health Department. Mortality data and social class populations by age were supplied by the General Register Office Scotland, and other population and census indicators assembled from the 1981 Census small area statistics output. (The Census Office for Scotland plans to include the deprivation score reported here as part of the output from the 1991 Census.) The remaining data were supplied by the Information and Statistics Division of the Common Services Agency of the Scottish Health Service. We are grateful to all of these agencies. We also wish to thank Brian Jarman and Mahdavi Bajekal for calculation of the deprivation scores for English Wards, Dr Robert Elton and Dr Geoffrey Cohen for statistical advice, and Dr Leo Kinlen for comment on the cancer data. Doctors Michael Heasman and Graham Scott gave valuable advice and constructive criticism on the material and its organisation. Finally Anne Elder deciphered and typed successive drafts of the chapters.

Differentials in health and the associated risk factors has given rise to an enormous literature in recent years and we offer apologies to all those people whose relevant papers we have failed to mention in this publication.

Outlines of postcode sector maps belong to the Post Office and maps may be obtained from Bartholomews. Outlines for health boards and local government districts have been supplied by the Scottish Development Department. Computer maps have used the LINEMAP suite of programmes developed by the Northern health boards' operational research unit; these are available from Mr F Nimmo, Grampian health board.

Data from the GRO are published by permission of the Controller of her Majesty's Stationery Office. Permission to reproduce other material has been given by the Office of Population Censuses and Surveys, the Lancet, the British Medical Journal and Scottish Medical Journal, Community Medicine and Croom Helm.

CHAPTER 1

# Introduction and Methods

Inequalities in health has been a focus of debate in the arena of health and social policy over a considerable period. Since 1911 successive decennial reports of the Registrars General for England and Wales and Scotland[1] have analysed death rates for the population of working age in relation to social class, as determined by occupation, as well as by occupation itself. More recently the examination of differences has extended to include infant mortality and information on self-reported health state from population sample surveys: the General Household Survey[2] and the Health and Lifestyle report.[3] The evidence, which shows strong gradients in health and mortality measures with lower social classes exhibiting considerably enhanced levels of mortality and illness than those in upper social classes, has been amply documented and we do not intend to review it again. The publication of the Black Report[4] 1980 gave this evidence a higher profile and brought the debate into greater prominence; after reviewing the evidence from many studies the working group came to the conclusion that the main influence on the inequalities in health which were observed lay in the material circumstances and conditions in which people live. The report also spelt out its conclusions in respect of policy — not only for health, social services and social security but also for fiscal and other strategic areas. This publication was followed by The Health Divide — the final report from the Health Education Council in 1987[4] which updated some of the previous information and examined new material. The issues raised have provided the stimulus for a number of specific studies focusing on social factors such as unemployment and housing in relation to health, and to area studies which examine the inequalities for areas within Britain. The debate is not confined to Britain however; the first of the targets for the year 2000 drawn up by the World Health Organisation and endorsed by thirty-three member countries in the European Region relates to equity in health and sets targets which include a 25 per cent reduction in the differences in health status which exist between groups within countries as well as between countries of the Region.

The available evidence on equalities in the main uses the measure of social class as the indicator of differences in social status between individuals. Social class has come to be so universally employed in the data which chart 'inequalities in health' — in fact more commonly 'in death' — owing to the inclusion of occupation in the details on the death certificate, occupation providing the basis for classifying to a social class. Successive analyses of mortality by social class (as well as by

1

occupation) have shown the familiar picture of a general increase in mortality rates through the range from 'upper' to 'lower' social classes which provide most of the fuel for the debate. Doubts have recently been expressed about the value of social class however which relate both to its contemporary value and its utility in measuring change over time: [5,6] in the latest decennial report less emphasis was placed on analysis by social class and more by occupation groups, due to 'serious reservations about the quality of the data and about the concept and use of social class classified in this way'.[7] These reservations relate in the main to numerator/denominator bias — that is the lack of agreement in recording of occupation on the death certificate (the numerator event) and in the census record that provides the population denominators — which arises in the more detailed information that is recorded on the census, since the individuals concerned are in a position to supply this for themselves. Information on the death record tends to be less specific and more occupations fall into the residual categories of the classification, so that these occupation may show erroneously high mortality compared with related occupations. While this problem affects occupational analysis in particular, it is also present for social class and led the authors of the most recent occupational mortality report to conclude that much of the excess mortality for social class V which emerges may be due to the high ratio seen for the residual occupation unit of labourers and unskilled workers. This extreme bias in social class V will, of course, result in mortality being artificially lowered in occupations in other social classes.

In addition to this bias, the recording of occupation for women on death certificates is at a relatively low level although analysis by husband's occupation (for married women) or by head of household (for children) overcomes some of the problems.

Differentials for retired people has also not featured prominently in social class analysis of mortality due to the unreliability of occupational recording for those no longer in work, and with the use of last occupation rather than main lifetime occupation in the records being a focus for criticism.

Some of the problems described are being overcome by means of the Longitudinal Survey (LS) which has selected a one per cent sample of individuals from the 1971 Census (in England and Wales) and links subsequent events, deaths and others, to information recorded on the census record, including social class as well as other social characteristics.[8] More reliable estimates of social class differentials in mortality emerge from use of this method, including for the elderly.[9] The LS does not extend to include Scotland however. For the analysis of other health events the value of social class is diminished by the difficulties experienced in collecting sufficiently detailed occupational data on routine medical records such as hospital admissions, in particular for persons not in employment.

Many researchers have turned therefore to measures which describe the area of residence using socio-economic data from the census which are available for many area levels on a consistent and comparable basis, and measurement of the concept of deprivation has been one of the products of these methodological innovations.

## *Area-based Analysis*

Area-based analysis profits from the introduction of the postcode system in recent years with postcodes providing a convenient means of allocating an area reference based on the address of an individual and being used for this purpose for the registration procedures of births, deaths and marriages, and throughout the health service in respect of hospital admissions and similar events. Given a full unit postcode an address may be allocated to a range of area levels using the central postcode directories maintained by the Registrar General for Scotland and the Office of Population Censuses and Surveys.[10] The postcode sector, of course, forms part of the postcode as shown in the format below, which, with a few exceptions, is uniform throughout the country.

| EH | 37 | 5 | UQ |
|------|----------|--------|------|
| area | district | sector | unit |

The unit consists of an area of a postman's delivery and, in residential areas, contains around 35 persons. The analysis in this instance is conducted at the level of the sector, which gives a population of sufficient size (av. c.5000) to provide reasonably reliable rates in respect of most health events.

The census provides both the population data, used in the calculation of rates, and the area characteristics, in this case for postcode sectors, this being one of the area levels for which the small area statistics output from the census is available in Scotland, although not in England and Wales. It is possible therefore to locate all the events to the sector in which the individual resides, calculate the rates using sector populations, which are available by age and sex, and relate these rates to the characteristics of the sector using variables contained in the Census SAS output; in this analysis characteristics are selected and combined to locate a sector on a dimension ranging from very affluent to very deprived.

The correlation of the deprivation score with the health measures provides one main statistical technique (see Appendix A1) and the correlations reported are all Pearson's product-moment correlation (r).

The analysis is carried out mostly in respect of 1010 postcode sectors but with some variation on this number (see Appendix A3 and the text for more detail). Sectors vary in size from small numbers up to nearly 20,000 and for statistical purposes the correlation analysis is weighted by the population size of each sector (see Appendix A4). This procedure effectively reduces the impact of small sectors (often with very extreme values) and gives greater weight to the larger sectors for which the events data are more robust and more reliable. For some of the health measures with lower numbers of events the association with deprivation is examined over the 56 local government districts in Scotland.

Data are reported for categories of deprivation (see chapter 2) postcode sectors, local government districts and health boards and in addition some data are also aggregated and examined for groups of health boards: West, East and Rural. The West covers the area of Strathclyde Region and includes Ayr & Arran, Argyll & Clyde, Greater Glasgow and Lanarkshire health boards. Rural boards comprise Borders, Dumfries & Galloway, Highland and the Islands ( which are dealt with as a group). Other East coast boards - Fife, Grampian, Lothian and Tayside — as well as Forth Valley (Central Region) comprise the group of Eastern boards.

Much of the data exhibit differences which are explored on this area basis, and tables for health boards are printed in this order to enable these differences to be more clearly seen.

## Health and Population Data

The health measures examined comprise a wide range of records which are routinely collected and include all events occurring in the Scottish population: death registrations, NHS hospital discharge records, including births in hospital, the cancer register which holds a record for every individual identified as having the disease, and information from the census for people of working age reporting themselves as not in a job because of temporary or permanent sickness. The data have been assembled for a number of years around the census in order to provide substantial numbers for analysis at postcode level (table 1.1). For the examination of differentials in causes of death and in infant deaths the data-set is extended to include all deaths occurring in the six years from 1980 to 1985. Further detail on the database is given in Appendix A1.

Mortality data have been supplied by the Registrar General for Scotland, population data and the area characteristics come from the 1981 Census Small Area Statistics output [11] and all remaining data have been made available by the Information & Statistics Division of the Common Services Agency which maintains the national health services databases for Scotland. [12]

The events data are all calculated as standardised rates or ratios, thus effectively excluding variation which is due to differences in the age and sex structure of the populations (see Appendix A6). The standardised mortality ratio (SMR) provides the main statistic in the analysis of mortality; it shows whether the level of events for an area is above or below that which would be expected from the age and sex composition of the population. Scotland always equals 100; above this level mortality is higher than expected and vice versa. Ratios for other types of event are calculated in the same way. SMRs are calculated for the age groups 0-64 and 65 and over as well as all ages in order to observe the influence of deprivation on mortality and other health measures at younger and older ages.

For some record types a small percentage of records could not be allocated to a postcode sector. These deficits are detailed in Appendix A and in the relevant chapters of the publication. In addition all records for Fife residents are excluded from analyses of hospital data as the health board was not supplying full postcodes for its own residents in 1981.

## Measuring Deprivation

A measure of deprivation provides one of the main bases for analysis and we now go on to consider both concepts, definition and measurement.

No clear cut and universally accepted definition of deprivation exists and commentators have criticised the lack of a sound conceptual base and an underlying theory in the selection of indicators. [13] Our approach attempts to locate areas (and populations in them) on a dimension which reflects the access people have to material resources which (to quote Townsend) 'permit individuals to play the roles, participate in relationships and follow the customary behaviour which is expected of them by virtue of their membership in society'. [14] Of course, since we are looking at people located at all points on this dimension, from extreme prosperity to extreme disadvantage, the term 'deprivation' is somewhat of a misnomer to describe this range in circumstances. It serves however as convenient shorthand for what would otherwise require a more complex label and since it has come to be used in this manner in recent years we follow the usage which has been established while acknowledging this as a slight abuse of the English language.

The variations in social and economic circumstances which exist between areas were first brought into prominence by a report on the 1971 census data which proved to be fundamental to the development of subsequent analysis in relation to deprivation [15] and which concluded that 'the problems of the Scottish cities, especially stand out most starkly': in 1971 Scotland had 53.6% of the Enumeration Districts in Great Britain with overcrowded households, 34.5% with men unemployed, 35.9% with no car and 21.9% with low social group (socio-economic group 11) compared with having only 11% of all Enumeration Districts. These characteristics are those which feature in our measure of deprivation but others have chosen to select other indicators. Census data provide the only source of objective and uniform data for the entire population and since measurement of access to material resources is constrained by the data available from that source there is continuing debate as regards the appropriate composition of 2 deprivation measure, as well as of the statistical techniques which may be used to combine individual variables into an index, i.e. a single score which summarises the scores on the individual variables. The composition of a number of (deprivation) measures which have achieved some prominence following the 1981 census, all of which use the census as their source of data, exemplify the lack of consistency which exists. Some of these have been defined specifically in relation to health while others, designed in a different context, have been appropriated into the health field. Among these is the measure devised by the Department of the Environment (DOE) in the context of urban policy. Although not drawn up in relation to health the DOE measure was among those considered as measures of social deprivation by the Department of Health and Social Security in its recent review of the resource allocation formula in England and Wales. [16]

The DOE method combined the indicators listed below to give measures of variation in deprivation between local government districts in England and Wales:

> Persons unemployed
> Overcrowded households
> Single parent households
> Households lacking exclusive use of basic amenities
> Pensioners living alone
> Residents with head of household born in
> New Commonwealth or Pakistan
> Population change
> Standardised mortality ratio

The DOE 'note' ranks districts on all of these indicators but also derives four indexes - basic, economic, housing and social - which do not include the last two indicators above (population change and mortality) but attach different weightings to some of the indicators e.g. the economic index weights unemployment times four. Two indicators which are often included in deprivation measures - car ownership and being in a low social class - are omitted, the latter being excluded due to 10% data from the census* not being available when the report was prepared. [17]

---

* occupation, industry, workplace are only coded for 10% of records

These two items are also absent from the comparable measure devised by the Scottish Development Department (SDD) which is based on twelve indicators divided into three sections. [18] The weights used in this index are derived from a principal components analysis; the weight attaching to the area value on each indicator is the coefficient factor score on factor one, determined over all Enumeration Districts (EDs) in Scotland, as shown below:

|  | Weights |
|---|---|
| **Housing** | |
| Amenity deficiency | -.038 |
| Overcrowding | .179 |
| Vacant dwellings | -.034 |
| Level & access (old) | .027 |
| Level & access (<5) | .140 |
| **Economic** | |
| Unemployment | .218 |
| Youth unemployment | .204 |
| Permanent sick | .162 |
| Low earning SEG's# | .170 |
| **Socio-demographic** | |
| Single parents | .185 |
| Large households | .125 |
| Elderly households | -.006 |

#comparable to social class 4 and 5

These weights are very different to those to be seen later in the Jarman score, elderly households for instance making an insignificant contribution to the SDD score.

Another measure drawn up by SDD [19] was used to classify individual households on the basis of the presence within the household of the six indicators of:

Unemployment of head of household
Low SEG of head of household
Overcrowded households
Large family - 4 or more dependant children
Single parent household
All elderly household

We refer again to this measure in examining deprivation in Scotland in chapter 2; like the one above it contains a number of demographic indicators as well as those which describe the circumstances of the household. This would expose it to the same criticism that has been directed at the DOE approach by Townsend on the basis that it includes and gives great weight to a number of demographic categories which may be at risk of being deprived, but which should not be identified in this way since it is important to maintain the distinction between the measurement of conditions in an area and the kinds of people experiencing those conditions. He argues that it is wrong in principle to include demographic sub-groups of the population in a definition of deprivation even if many people in these groups are deprived, since it is the deprived condition, not their status, which has to be measured. Definitions such as that of the DOE are in danger therefore of double-counting, or of labelling as in some degree deprived areas which in most people's reckoning would not fall into this category, for instance affluent retirement areas which happen to have a high proportion of pensioners living alone.

The same criticism may be directed at the Jarman score which calculates 'underprivileged area scores' (UPAs) for the electoral wards in England and Wales. [20] The index is constructed by weighting the ward values for the indicators listed below by the weights shown:

|  | weight |
| --- | --- |
| Elderly living alone | 6.62 |
| Population aged under five | 4.64 |
| One-parent families | 3.01 |
| Social class V | 3.74 |
| Unemployed | 3.34 |
| Overcrowded | 2.88 |
| Changing address within the past year | 2.68 |
| Ethnic minorities | 2.50 |

The weights used in this case are those emerging from a survey of general practitioners in which they were invited to allocate a score to each of the indicators to represent the demand on general practitioner services and the resulting index is again composed both of socio-economic conditions and of demographic sub-groups. Large weights are attached to both the elderly and young children. Although devised originally in relation to primary care the Jarman measure was also used by DHSS in its review of the resource allocation methods; [16] it has also been employed in the examination of admission rates to mental illness hospitals in England and Wales, in a report [21] which also suggests use of the UPA scores as a weighting factor for resource allocation for acute psychiatric services.

In terms of need for primary care services it is possible to defend the inclusion of the demographic categories in the UPA scores but the labelling of this measure as 'underprivilege' is in danger of confusing the concept, and in this context the resulting measure is open to the same criticism as that levelled at the DOE index. Townsend also finds the measures resulting from both of these two exercises lacking in what may be considered as 'face validity' since districts within the Northern Region are not included among the most deprived areas in England, and this appears to fly in the face of most observation and experience. [14]

Criticism of the Jarman score has also been voiced by Scott-Samuel who proposed use of the measure of permanent sickness as an objective indicator of need for primary health care [22] and subsequently used a range of census variables (see list below) to explain differences in the permanent sickness rates in the 33 wards of Merseyside and Cheshire. The ten variables which explained more than 25 percent of the variance, were combined into a single measure together with 'permanent sickness' to offer an alternative to the Jarman score as an indicator of need for primary care:

persons temporarily sick
households overcrowded
households severely overcrowded
households owner occupied

households rented from Local Authority
households no car
men 16-64 unemployed
women 16-59 unemployed
households 3 or more dependant children
single-parent families

This list appears to fall into the error of double counting, by duplication of the tenure and overcrowding variables for instance, while the inclusion of the two indicators of temporarily and permanently sick take this measure into a different dimension from that of material deprivation.

A contribution to the development of the concept of deprivation is made by Townsend in proposing a distinction between material and social forms of deprivation, the latter relating essentially to roles and relationships, membership in society and social contacts. Universal measures are not readily available for these and their relationships to health state is not well documented although the nature and extent of social interaction is increasingly gaining credence as one of the determinants of health state. [23] Material deprivation on the other hand entails lack of those goods and services, resources and amenities and of a physical environment which are customary in society; census measures can provide at least some insight into these conditions although by no means all aspects of material deprivation can be made operational using information from this source.

Four indicators were selected by Townsend to represent material deprivation in his analysis of health measures in wards within the Northern Region: [24]

economically active who are unemployed
households with no car
households not owner occupied
households overcrowded

We consider some material from this report and compare the mortality levels with those in Scotland in chapter 3. Together with the DOE and Jarman measures the Townsend indicator was included in the recent review of RAWP methodology. [16]

Excluded from this list, but included in our own index, is a measure of social class, which Townsend excludes on the same conceptual basis as his objections to the inclusion of other demographic sub-groups. Unlike the other sub-groups, however, we believe that being in a low social class, equally with being unemployed, places families in a position of poor access to material resources in a way that cannot be said for being aged under 5 or over 65. Our lack of agreement on this particular indicator only exemplifies the absence of a coherent approach which is universally recognised, to the concept and measurement of deprivation.

In his approach to defining the various concepts involved, Townsend seeks to establish a distinction between deprivation and poverty, [14] maintaining that people may experience one or more forms of deprivation without being in poverty; but concedes nevertheless that people experiencing severe forms of deprivation are likely to have very little income and little or no other resources. Since the availability of financial resources is a main determinant of access to material goods and services our own view is that the gradations from 'affluent' to 'severely deprived' which are observed in the population are largely a reflection of the level of income and wealth - and that the dimension that is observed could equally well be achieved by measurement of financial resources.

Using a variety of statistical techniques most of these measures combine information for a number of variables into a single score. Thunhurst however has argued against the use of a single index and for the retention of techniques which 'retain the multi-dimensionality of the problem space'. [25] He (and his collaborators) identified three types of indicators; direct, indirect and interpretative, comprising 13 specific variables, but despite the title of his publication it is not clear in the text by what process the relevance of these variables to the determination of health planning was established.

The selection of variables for inclusion in our own index is based upon previous work which examined health and deprivation in the wards of Glasgow and Edinburgh. [26] The seven indicators included in that instance were based on a list used by the Scottish Development Department in identifying areas for priority treatment in respect of planning. The present analysis excludes a variable relating to the absence of household amenities since, although still relevant, the housing stock improved between 1971 and 1981 to a position where few households live in accommodation lacking facilities: in 1981 97.2% of households in Scotland had exclusive use of a bath or shower and toilet. [27] Households with one to three rooms are excluded since we prefer the measure of overcrowding which relates persons to the rooms available. The population economically active also is not included since the age structure of the population could have a large impact on this measure, more retired people resulting in fewer economically active.

The variables finally selected are those listed below:

Overcrowding: Persons in private households living at a density of >1 person per room as a proportion of all persons in private households

Male unemployment: Proportion of economically active males who are seeking work

Low social class: Proportion of all persons in private households with head of household in social class 4 or 5

No car: Proportion of all persons in private households with no car

Each of these indicators we believe to represent or be determinant of material disadvantage. Both living in overcrowded accommodation and not owning a car may reflect lack of material resources although it might be argued that public housing policies and rent subsidies are designed to ensure adequate space standards even for those with low incomes. Car ownership, it has been suggested is useful as a surrogate for current income [24] and also confers benefits in terms of access to other resources. It might be argued that in city areas, with good access to public transport, owning a car is not a necessary aim; experience and observation suggest however that despite the ready availability of public transport (or perhaps as a reflection of its inconvenience and cost) ownership of a car is something that families do wish to achieve. In country areas car ownership may be more of a necessity and its value as a discriminator between urban and rural areas is diminished although there is considerable variability within the rural areas themselves.

Being in low social class — i.e. in semi-skilled or unskilled occupations — indicates earnings at the lower end of the income scale. [28] Although joint incomes in a household are now more common than in the past this will be true also for households at other positions on the occupational range and where the head of household is in low social class even joint incomes are likely to remain actively low, with all that implies in relation to access to material resources and the ability to make choices in life. Unemployment also is likely to result in reduced incomes and straitened circumstances and moreover to impose other pressures on individuals through loss of self-esteem, and on families through the problems and tensions generated.

Variables which merely reflect demographic factors are not included in our measure (although they have been used by others) since we do not believe that being elderly, or aged under 5 or in a large family are by themselves an indication of deprivation. Housing tenure also does not feature in our list of indicators since this is considered to be of lesser value in Scotland which has a higher proportion of its housing stock in the public sector and lesser variation between areas than occurs in England and Wales. Housing tenure is, nevertheless, found to be associated with the deprivation measure. The index of deprivation could have been extended to include a number of other variables which also might appear relevant, but many of the candidates are very highly inter-correlated with one another and some of them are essentially variations on a similar theme (e.g. overcrowding and occupancy norm). Many of them may be seen, in the correlation matrix at B1.1, to be highly associated with the deprivation score and with the four variables actually included in the index, (as below) and their influence is thus implicitly included in the score:

occupancy norm with overcrowding
females unemployed with males unemployed
16-24 unemployed with males unemployed
one parent household with males unemployed
not having higher qualification with low social class

Preliminary exploration of the data also suggested that the inclusion of other variables added little to the power of the index to explain the variations observed in mortality (see Appendix A8) and it was concluded that there was little to be gained, either conceptually or in practice in defining the index on a more complex basis.

It may be noted that unlike a number of other measures considered all four variables are calculated on the basis of individuals not households; this is considered preferable for the purpose of the analysis of events which relate to individuals but in practice the differences from using the two approaches are likely to be small.

Despite the considerable difference which can be seen in the selection of variables, as also in the statistical treatment of the various measures which we have considered elsewhere in detail [29] there is considerable agreement between our own measure, DEP, and others, which, together with their performance in explaining the variation in a number of health variables within Scotland is considered in chapter 10.

Scottish DEP fulfils the requirement for rigourous definition by including only variables which measure those circumstances of the population which may be interpreted as conferring or denying access to material benefit, and will be seen to function well in explaining variations in health.

## Calculation of the Deprivation Score

The deprivation score is an unweighted combination of four standardises variables, the resultant variable giving a summary statistic (a Z-score) for an area (see also Appendix A8). The method first of all calculates the values of the variables listed for all postcode sectors and then the means and standard deviations, as seen in table 1.2.

The deprivation score can be computed for postcode sectors (or other areas) once the population weighted means and standard deviations have been determined. For example, the score for the postcode sector EH41 3 (Haddington), which has a population of 5000 is calculated from the values for the component variables (see Table 1.2.)

The variables for EH41.3 are all somewhat lower than the Scotland means and the combined score is in the negative - more affluent - half of the distribution. Scores may be positive or negative, the former indicating greater deprivation and the latter great affluence. For larger areas - Local Government Districts and Health Boards - area scores are derived by multiplying the component sector scores by their populations and summing to area level, this sum then being divided by area total population to give the area score.

# Background to the Report

This analysis has been stimulated by the continuing discussion on inequalities in health and the opportunities offered by the area-based approach to provide unique evidence for a wide range of measures of health.

Only limited evidence has been available so far on the variations in health by social factors within Scotland, the decennial Occupational Mortality reports of the Registrars' General providing the main evidence in respect of mortality in persons of working age.[7] A previous report had shown strong gradients in mortality by deprivation within Glasgow and Edinburgh[26] and Greater Glasgow Health Board and Lothian Region have examined health problems for small areas within their boundaries[30,31] but this publication breaks new ground in providing a comprehensive and detailed examination of the health differentials within Scotland as a whole as observed not only in mortality but in a range of other measures of the health of the population. Scotland's position at the more adverse end of the spectrum of mortality and deprivation within Great Britain is also examined.

Although the need to document the way in which health varies in the population in Scotland provides the main rationale for this analysis another significant impetus was the need to explore issues which have been the subject of debate over many years in relation to the resource allocation formula for the health service[32] which aims to distribute the total funds available to health boards in relation to need. In the absence of good data on geographical differentials in morbidity or need for health care the formula incorporates as a proxy the mortality experience of the population aged 0-64, the SMRO-64 being used as a weighting factor in the estimation of requirements for that section of the population in respect of various parts of the hospital and community services. Questions have been raised however whether deprivation creates a need for health care which is not fully taken into account in the mortality data and whether a component for deprivation should form part of the formula. This analysis examines these issues and also the question of the weighting, or elasticity, which should be attributed to the SMR values, in the form of the relationship observed between mortality and need for hospital services.

The report considers in the second chapter the way in which deprivation is distributed in Scotland, and also how Scotland fares compared with England and Wales. The pattern for the all causes mortality is presented in chapter 3, at a number of area levels; while some of these facts are relatively well-known the rates for postcode sectors focus down on the impact of mortality within the local government and health board areas which provide the usual basis for examination. Within Scotland, the West/East divide appears as marked as the North/South in England and Wales. Scotland's position vis-à-vis England and Wales is also examined. The way in which mortality varies in relation to deprivation provides the subject matter of chapter 4. While the influence is strongest in young adults the differentials are still maintained in older age groups. Area deprivation is shown to have an influence on mortality differentials by social class, and it is suggested that Scotland's greater mortality compared with England and Wales may be due in part to its more adverse socio-economic circumstances. Causes of deaths are considered in chapter 5, with the variations by deprivations showing that not all causes are affected equally, although a high proportion do reflect the environmental influence. The evidence is amplified in chapter 6 which is concerned with a number of measures of morbidity in the population, with the gradients for specific sites of cancer showing close agreement with those for deaths from the same causes. Information on temporary and permanent sickness in the population suggests that the differentials in sickness experience may be more extreme than those for mortality. Chapter 7 turns to considering how (general) hospital resources are used in relation to deprivation, bringing in consideration of the local supply of services and the impact distance from services may have on their use. The relationships emerging provide a basis for considering (in chapter 8) how these would impinge on the allocation of resources to health boards in the context of providing an equitable distribution in relation to the needs of the population. These empirical findings suggest a potential major impact on the funding for some boards compared with the present position.

In chapter 9 data relating to various aspects of illness and death are brought together and the theoretical constructs which have been advanced to explain differentials in health provide a basis to examine the evidence which emerges from this analysis as also do other studies which help in understanding why health should differ according to the area in which people live. The utility of the measure of deprivation used by us is compared with others in chapter 10. The benefits and some of the problem of area-based methods as a tool for epidemiological analysis are examined; this approach may claim to overcome many of the limitations inherent in the social class approach, based on individuals, and moreover exhibits much greater discrimination between populations than does social class, thus providing a more powerful basis for explaining differentials in health.

The evidence which emerges from this analysis shows clearly the more adverse health experience of the population living in deprived areas in Scotland compared with those in more affluent circumstances starting at birth and continuing through to death. This evidence has implications for the development of policies, the determination of planning strategies and the allocation of resources not only within the health service but also within other areas of social policy, at both national and local level. The detailed data on individual postcode sectors as well as the methods used, provide a basis for mounting specific local programmes and for monitoring changes which may occur, and may be of value to other researchers in the area of health epidemiology. We believe the data in this report will be of value both to planners and practitioners at local level as well as to researchers and to 'students' of the politics of health and others concerned with the development of policies to improve health in the population of Scotland.

TABLE 1.1    HEALTH MEASURES: NOS. OF EVENTS

|  | Years | No. of events (thous.) |
|---|---|---|
| Deaths | 1980-82 | 190 |
|  | 1980-85* | 380 |
| Perinatal & infant deaths | 1980-85* | 5 |
| General hospitals | 1981 |  |
| - discharges |  | 618 |
| - bed-days |  | 8200 |
| Maternity hospitals | 1980-82 |  |
| - deliveries |  | 182 |
| Mental hospitals | 1980-82 |  |
| - admissions |  | 76 |
| Cancer registrations | 1979-82 | 95 |
| Temporarily sick | 1981 | 37 |
| Permanently sick | 1981 | 77 |

*The data set hes been augmented to permit more robust analysis of cause-specific and perinatal and infant deaths

TABLE 1.2    CALCULATION OF DEPRIVATION SCORE

|  | EH41.3 | $\bar{x}$ | S.D. |  |
|---|---|---|---|---|
| Overcrowding | 0.22 | 0.25 | 0.11 | N.B. Means and |
| Male unemployment | 0.08 | 0.13 | 0.07 | standard deviations |
| Low social class | 0.23 | 0.24 | 0.10 | for all Scotland |
| No car | 0.27 | 0.41 | 0.19 | postcode sectors |

Deprivation Score

$$=(.22-.25)/.11 \quad + \quad (.08-.13)/.07 \quad + \quad (.23-.24)/.10 \quad + \quad (.27-.41)/.19$$

$$= \quad -0.27 \quad + \quad -0.71 \quad + \quad -0.10 \quad + \quad -0.74$$

$$= \quad -1.82$$

CHAPTER 2

# Deprivation within Scotland

The calculation of the deprivation score has already been described in chapter 1. The distribution of deprivation at various area levels in Scotland provides the main topic for this chapter; its relationship to the urban/rural character of the area is also considered as is deprivation in Scotland compared with that in England and Wales.

The deprivation score (DEP) for 1,010 sectors has a mean of zero and a standard deviation of 3.6. The scores range from -8.48 to +12.82, as shown in Fig. 2.1, and are fairly normally distributed for the population although the tail is somewhat longer at the positive (more deprived) end of the scale. Since the distribution does not exhibit absolute normality the population is not distributed equally on either side of the mean and 56% is found below the mean (more affluent) and 44% above the mean (more deprived).

In order to exclude extreme values which may result from small populations much of the data is presented for postcode sectors (PCS) with more than 500 population. The exclusion of the small PCS causes a loss of 180 sectors but only 33,231 population, 0.66% of the total. It also has the effect of excluding some extreme values and reducing the range in the scores to -7.31 to +12.27.

All of the statistical analysis is carried out using the actual deprivation score for PCS but for some purposes it is more convenient and understandable to present data in relation to a limited range of categories of deprivation and the extended distribution was therefore collapsed into the seven categories as shown in Figure 2.1. These categories were designed to retain discrimination between the characteristics rather than to ensure equality of numbers within classes, and the use of septiles (or quintiles) was not considered appropriate for this purpose. The seven classes therefore are unequal but maintain the discriminatory features of the distribution. Twenty-five per cent of the population are in the middle range of -1 to +1, and 6% to 7% at the two extremes of the distribution. The class intervals contain populations roughly within plus or minus 0.3, 0.8, 1.5 or more than 1.5 standard deviations of the mean. The class boundaries are arbitrary and other methods of determining them would result in some variations in the output measures which are reported on the basis of these categories but would not effect changes in the general patterns observed.

# The Components of Deprivation

The values for the individual variable and the deprivation scores for the seven deprivation categories (in table 2.1 and Fig. 2.2) all, of course, exhibit a strong gradient with increasing deprivation, not having a car for instance rising from 13.3% in the most affluent to 79.4% in the most deprived areas, and unemployment from 4.0% to 30.6%. The differential in the values between affluent and deprived areas is most marked however for low social class, the population in the most deprived category being eight times that in the most affluent. These data show very clearly the more favourable conditions of those living in affluent areas compared with the greater adversity (in these terms) which exists in deprived areas. (See Table 2.1)

The difference is also seen in the summary mean deprivation score for each of the deprivation categories with a range from -6.02 to +8.36, this of course being somewhat less than for PCS (from -7.3 to +12.3); the range from most affluent to most deprived reduces as PCS are aggregated up to larger units (table 2.2) whether on the basis of their characteristics or into administrative areas.

The range in the individual census variables shows a similar pattern (table 2.3) being least at the largest area level of health board, and greatest for PCS.

Variability was greatest for not owning a car (S.D. 18.3) and lowest for unemployment (S.D. 7.2). (See Table 2.3)

The individual components of the deprivation index vary fairly considerably from area to area as can be seen in table 2.4 for the three groups of health boards. Western boards have the highest proportions of population with no car, unemployed and overcrowded although the proportion in social class 4 and 5 is just higher in rural boards; otherwise these had the lowest average values, although they were not much different to the eastern group in respect to unemployment or overcrowding.

All the variables exhibit more variability between sectors, as shown by the standard deviations (table 2.4) in Western boards than Eastern boards (with almost equal numbers of sectors), and lower variability on all measures in the rural boards (as is also the case for the overall measure of deprivation - see table 2.12).

Although car ownership is highest overall in rural boards it can be seen from inspection of the minimum values (in Appendix table B2.1a) that there are sectors in Western and Eastern boards wit higher levels of car ownership (3.4% with no car) than any sector in the rural boards (9.2%). However the maximum value (for PCS) for not owning a car is much lower at 55% in rural areas than in any PCS in the West or East which have values up to 89%.

Data for individual health boards and local government districts (tables B2.1a,b) show car ownership as highest in the Islands (26% having no car) and lowest in Glasgow health board (57%) and varying from less than 20% in the LGDs of Gordon, Kincardine and Deeside, Bearsden & Milngavie and Eastwood to over 50% in Inverclyde, Clydebank, Glasgow City and Monklands. While car ownership shows some link to the urban/rural character of the area there is nevertheless diversity within these and sectors with both low and high values are found scattered throughout urban (West/East) as well as rural areas.

Male unemployment was lowest in Grampian (6.3%) and highest in Glasgow health board at 18.1%; two districts in Grampian (Gordon and Kincardine & Deeside) had unemployment levels below 5% as did Bearsden and Eastwood in Glasgow, and Shetland; at the same time unemployment was highest also within Glasgow health board, in Glasgow City (21%), followed by Monklands (18%) in

Lanarkshire health board. Four districts - Clydebank, Cumberland, Monklands and Motherwell - had no sectors with less than 10% male unemployed - while many sectors had unemployment below 5% including within the City of Glasgow which also, together with Renfrew, had sectors with the highest values of 39% (table B2.2b).

Overcrowding varied from 16% in the Borders to 33% in Glasgow, (tables B2.3) and between LGDs from less than 10% in Eastwood and 11% in Bearsden and Milngavie, up to 30% or more in Renfrew, Inverclyde, Clydebank, Glasgow City, Motherwell and Monklands, which had the highest value of 38%. Minimum PCS values were very varied and ranged from around 2% in Edinburgh city and Eastwood, to 20% or more in Clydebank, Hamilton, Monklands and Motherwell. Sectors with the highest level of overcrowding, of more than 50%, were found in Inverclyde and Renfrew, Glasgow city and Monklands.

The proportion of population in low social class (tables B2.4) was least in Lothian, Fife and Highland health boards (21 - 22%) and highest in Borders, the Islands and Dumfries & Galloway (28%). It varied more for LGDs, from 6% in Bearsden and Milngavie and Eastwood, up to 30% or more in Berwickshire, in Glasgow City and Banff and Buchan. Sectors with below 1% in low social class were found in eight districts while some, mainly rural, districts had no sector with less than 20% in social class 4 and 5. Maximum values ranged from less than 15% in one PCS (Bearsden and Milngavie) to 55% within Glasgow City and 63% within Renfrew.

# Deprivation at Area Levels

## Health Boards

Deprivation is most severe in Western boards with Glasgow's average score of 2.50 vastly exceeding that of any other board (table 2.5 and Fig. 2.3); Lanark (0.87) is next followed by Argyll and Clyde (0.49), the Western Isles (0.26) and Ayr and Arran (0.05). All other health boards are below the mean for Scotland, although it should be noted that the mean itself is influenced by the large proportion of population in the boards above the mean. Of the remaining mainland boards Tayside is the least affluent (-0.55) followed by Forth Valley (-0.91) and Lothian (-0.94); Dumfries (-1.22), Fife (-1.17), the Borders (-1.80) and Highland (-1.82) come next in order, with Grampian (-1.95) coming at the most affluent end of the scale, together with both Orkney and Shetland. There could however be some slight systematic bias in the score for rural boards since car ownership is at a higher level and will tend to produce a more favourable score in rural communities than may be justified vis-à-vis urban areas.

## Local Government Districts

The deprivation scores (DEP) for local government districts (LGDs) give a more disaggregated picture of the distribution of deprivation with scores ranging from 4.08 to -5.65 (fig.2.4). Table 2.6 shows the range for districts within health boards, with boards ranked on their overall deprivation score.

Not surprisingly deprived LGDs (with a positive score) are found in the main in health boards which also have positive scores, the exception being Tayside (within which Dundee City has a positive score) and Lothian which contains the deprived district of West Lothian; both boards are in the more affluent part of the distribution (i.e. with negative scores) although Tayside only just so.

All of the western boards plus Tayside and Lothian have districts with positive deprivation scores; in all other boards all districts have negative scores. Only twelve districts have positive scores however (due to the large proportion of total population residing in these); in relative terms districts with low negative scores can be considered as more deprived also.

Glasgow City with a value of 4.08 far exceeds the deprivation score for any other district, the next highest values being Monklands (2.95) and Motherwell (2.34) in Lanarkshire (table 2.7). All except three of the most deprived districts are to be found in the four health boards in the Strathclyde region. Outside of this region the most severe deprivation is found in Dundee City, with West Lothian being the only other district on the Eastern side of the country with a positive score and Western Isles the only district in the group of rural boards. (See Table 2.7)

Glasgow health board contains not only the most deprived but also the most affluent districts within it and only Glasgow of the four Strathclyde health boards contains districts which fall within the most affluent quintile in Scotland (see Table 2.7, 1st Quintile): Eastwood and Bearsden and Milngavie (the top two districts) are followed by two in Grampian — Gordon and Kincardine and Deeside, these four districts being well separated from the next group. The first, most affluent, quintile contains mainly Northern districts, with the notable exception of three districts within Greater Glasgow health board.

Districts falling within the other three quintiles are also listed in Table 2.7. The next most deprived (4th) quintile contains a mixture of districts from West, East and rural; the urban areas in both West and East tend to be smaller conglomerates of population than in the most deprived. Edinburgh and Aberdeen cities however are found in the middle range (3rd quintile), distancing them very considerably from Glasgow and Dundee; this middle range contains mainly areas within the central belt although both Caithness and Argyll & Bute also appear. In the second quintile the districts are predominantly rural and mostly confined to the more southerly half of Scotland although Inverness and Sutherland also appear.

## Local government districts: deprived households

Deprivation scores are computed on an area basis — i.e. the prevalence of a particular characteristic within a sector. The use of such scores for an area is often criticised on the basis of the implication this carries that the population within an area shares equally in the characteristics that are observed (i.e. is homogeneous). This is certainly not the case and neither are all deprived households to be found in deprived areas, nor do all the households in an area have similar measures on the indicators. The prevalence of deprivation within households is nevertheless strongly correlated with the level of deprivation in an area (in this case local government district), as is apparent using data from an analysis carried out at household level by the Registrar General for the Scottish Development Department[1] based on the six indicators below:

> unemployment of the head of household
> low SEG of head of household
> overcrowded households

large family - 4 or more dependent children
single parent household
all elderly household

Households were described as multiply deprived if they qualified on two of these measures and as severely deprived if they qualified on three. While one might debate the inclusion of the last three 'indirect' variables in this list it is nevertheless instructive to note the very high agreement between the deprivation score and the % of households deprived, districts with more deprived scores having greater concentrations of multiply and severely deprived households, and vice versa (table 2.8). The values for the ten most deprived and most affluent districts are shown below:

| Deprived District | DEP score | % households multiply deprived | % households severely deprived |
|---|---|---|---|
| Glasgow city | 4.07 | 29 | 4.7 |
| Monklands | 2.94 | 25 | 4.5 |
| Motherwell | 2.33 | 25 | 3.8 |
| Clydebank | 2.25 | 23 | 3.3 |
| Inverclyde | 1.95 | 23 | 3.2 |
| Cumnock & Doon Valley | 1.24 | 21 | 2.3 |
| Dundee city | 0.89 | 24 | 2.7 |
| Cunninghame | 0.85 | 20 | 2.6 |
| Renfrew | 0.62 | 21 | 3.0 |
| Hamilton | 0.51 | 19 | 2.6 |
| **Affluent Districts** | | | |
| Eastwood | -5.65 | 6 | 0.4 |
| Bearsden & Milngavie | -5.51 | 6 | 0.5 |
| Gordon | -4.07 | 11 | 0.8 |
| Kincardine & Deeside | -3.81 | 14 | 0.8 |
| N.E.Fife | -2.64 | 16 | 1.1 |
| Shetland | -2.46 | 14 | 1.4 |
| Nairn | -2.41 | 17 | 1.5 |
| Badenoch & Strathspey | -2.40 | 17 | 1.2 |
| Ross & Cromarty | -2.31 | 16 | 1.3 |
| Orkney | -2.30 | 14 | 1.1 |

The very considerable agreement between these measures is clear, with deprived districts having a greater proportion of households which would be counted as deprived and vice versa at the affluent end of the spectrum (figure 2.5). DEP correlates very highly with the prevalence of deprived households, the coefficients being 0.967 for multiply deprived and 0.936 for severely deprived. The values shown suggest that not more than about 25% of households are deprived on two variable and less than 5% on three in the most deprived district. Local government districts are large and mostly heterogeneous areas however; the present analysis at postcode sector level reduces the heterogeneity in the population - the smaller the area level the greater the range in the deprivation scores. (Table 2.2)

The regression equations which describe the relationships between the measures may be utilised to estimate the percent. of households that are multiply or severely deprived at the extremes of the range for postcode sectors:

% households multiply deprived   =   19.638  +  DEP  x  2.204
% households severely deprived   =    2.357  +  DEP  x  0.50

The level of deprived households at PCS level is estimated from these equations as below:

|  | %<br>multiply<br>deprived | %<br>severely<br>deprived |
|---|---|---|
| most deprived PCS,<br>DEP = +12.27 | 46.6 | 8.5 |
| least deprived PCS,<br>DEP = -7.37 | 3.4 | 0 |

These values suggest greater concentrations of deprived households in some sectors than in the most deprived district (Glasgow City). At PCS level however the level of affluence only slightly exceeds that in the most affluent district and the prevalence of deprived households shows only a minor change.

These data have been analysed also by Knox[2] who was able to look at combinations of different indicators at different area levels and show that the profile of disadvantage varies, with the more urban areas being characterised by combinations involving low socio-economic status, unemployment, overcrowding and single-parent families while at the other end of the spectrum rural areas are dominated by low socio-economic state and pensioner households. Using the SDD measure of deprivation which creates a score over a combination of 12 indicators for EDs he found 51% of households in the worst 1% of EDs to be multiply deprived and 17% severely deprived, a somewhat higher level than the estimate given above for the most deprived sector, which is closer to the values for the worst 5% of EDs at 41.5% and 10.7% respectively. These data suggest, as would be expected, that pockets of more severe deprivation will be found within postcode sectors, and this is shown by our own data which computes the area measure for EDs and shows that these are spread on either side of the DEPCAT of the sector but with few affluent EDs being found in more deprived sectors and few deprived in affluent sectors (Appendix A3).

## Postcode Sectors

The distribution for postcode sectors by deprivation within health boards not surprisingly finds a high proportion of deprived PCS to be located within Glasgow health board (table 2.9): 32 of the 40 sectors at the most extreme level, and 31 of the 77 sectors in category 6. The eight remaining sectors at DEPCAT 7 are spread between Argyll & Clyde (3), Ayr & Arran (1), Lothian (2) and Tayside (2) but all except the Borders and Highland have at least one PCS in category 6. Fifty per cent of the population in Glasgow live in sectors within the two most deprived categories (table 2.10 & fig. 2.6) with Lanarkshire health board having the next highest proportion of deprived population (21%) followed by Argyll & Clyde (19%) and Ayr & Arran (13%). On the Eastern side of Scotland only Lothian

(10%) and Tayside (16%) have a discernible proportion of population at this level and only Dumfries & Galloway of the rural areas (4%).

At the other (affluent) end of the spectrum PCS are more widely distributed among health boards with eight of the mainland boards having some PCS in the most affluent category, and all boards at the next level (table 2.9). Lothian has the largest number of sectors at level 1 or 2 (40) but Glasgow is also well represented with 29, as are Grampian (29) and Tayside (24).

Grampian has the highest proportion of population at the two most affluent levels (39%) followed by Orkney (43%) and Tayside and Lothian with 28% (table 2.10). Lanark with 4% is well below the level of other mainland boards. Most boards can be seen to have some population at each level of deprivation, the exceptions being Borders, with population in only three categories and Highland in only four; the islands exhibit marked differences, the Western Isles showing greatest deprivation and Orkney least (table 2.10). These results are grouped into areas in table 2.11 where the greater deprivation in West, greater relative affluence in the East and the lesser variation in Rural areas are apparent.

The range for PCS within health boards and LGDs, in Appendix table B2.5a,b shows the most deprived postcode sector (with more than 500 population) with a score of 12.27, is found in Renfrew, followed by one with a score 11.97 in Glasgow City. These are followed, at some distance, by a PCS in Edinburgh (7.62), Inverclyde (7.43), Dundee City (6.19) and Cunninghame (6.13). PCS with scores between 5 and 6 are found in Hamilton, Monklands and Motherwell and in West Lothian. Lesser deprived values are found in rural areas, the highest scores being in the Western Isles (4.09) and Wigtown (3.0).

The most favourable sector score is also found within Glasgow health board (within Eastwood district -7.31) followed by Grampian (Aberdeen City -7.17, Kincardine and Deeside -7.37) and Lothian (Edinburgh City -7.16). Most districts have at least one PCS with a positive (deprived) score, as shown by the maximum value in Appendix table B2.5b, although there are a few districts where this is not the case. Since all districts have at least one PCS with a negative (affluent) score there is a range between affluent and deprived in most districts; the exceptions are those where both the lowest and highest scores for PCS are negative (more affluent), as listed below:

> Bearsden & Milngavie
> N.E.Fife
> Gordon
> Kincardine & Deeside
> Berwickshire
> Ettrick & Lauderdale
> Stewartry
> Badenoch & Strathspey
> Inverness
> Nairn
> Ross & Cromarty
> Sutherland
> Orkney
> Shetland

With the exception of Bearsden and Milngavie these are all rural areas. It should be noted that the number of PCS in some districts is very low.

The variation in deprivation is greatest in Western boards (as shown by the standard deviation) and lower in the rural than in the Eastern boards (table 2.12); with fewer PCS in total rural areas are inherently more likely to have greater variability but this consideration does not affect the differences seen between the West and East.

Within boards the variation of PCS in terms of DEP (table B2.5a) is greatest in Glasgow and then Argyll and Clyde, followed by Tayside and Lothian. DEPCAT values are mapped for PCS within health boards at figure 2.7.

Deprivation scores and individual components are listed at Appendix B2.6.

## Deprivation and the urban/rural nature of the area

It appears from these deprivation values for LGDs and PCS that deprivation is strongly linked to the urban or rural characteristics of the area, and this link is explored further: an urban/rural score was calculated for each postcode sector and LGD using the urban/rural indicator assigned by the census office for each ED, as follows:

part of a continuous urban block with a population of:

1    1 million or more
2    100,000 < 1 million
3    10,000 < 100,000
4    1,000 < 10,000
5    a rural area or continuous urban block of less than 1,000 population.

(gaps of 1km or more are taken to represent a break in the continuity of built-up areas.)

Urban/rural values were derived by summing the populations for EDs within PCS and LGDs, weighted by the codes 1-5 as above. The measure may thus vary between 1 and 5 although in most cases the value was in fact discrete for PCS since there is tendency for EDs within PCS to be similar in character. This is obviously not the case for LGDs which contain areas that are more diverse.

The values for LGDs have been shown in table 2.8; inevitably in view of the scoring system these are somewhat arbitrary since only the Glasgow conurbation and districts attaching to it can be labelled as most urban, with a score of one (i.e. 1 million or more population) with the other three cities in Scotland attracting scores of two or more. An alternative measure is that of population density (i.e. persons per hectare) which varies between 0.02 in Sutherland to 38.0 in Glasgow. There is general but not precise agreement between these two measures — all areas with U/R scores of four or more have densities below one person per hectare while the most urban value (1.0) and greatest density (38) is found in Glasgow City, with Aberdeen, Edinburgh and Dundee having densities well below that level at 11, 17, and 8. Some districts with U/R values between 1 and 2 however have densities below these levels: Eastwood 4.6, Monklands 6.8 and Renfrew 6.7 although Bearsden and Milngavie, one of the two most affluent districts, has a density of 11 — similar to Aberdeen.

Clearly density is a more precise measure, since U/R values are derived from rankings, but the latter may capture information about the way in which the population clusters together that reflects a different dimension to that obtained by spreading the population over the entire area whether habitable or not.

The correlation between U/R and density is fairly strong, at -0.789 (density falls in value as rurality increases) and is slightly stronger at 0.756 between density and DEP than between U/R and DEP at -0.663 (r over 56 LGDs).

Correlation between the DEP and the U/R scores shows this to be -0.431 at PCS level and -0.663 LGD level, thus confirming this association. That it is not complete is apparent from the greater affluence seen in Bearsden and Milngavie and Eastwood despite their very urban score (table 2.8) and the intermediate DEP scores (mostly in the fourth quintile) for LGDs such as Banff, Lochaber, Wigtown, Skye and Lochalsh and the Western Isles despite their rural or very rural scores on that measure.

As might be expected the U/R score for postcode sectors shows an association with the deprivation score, which falls from +1.31 (more deprived) in the most urban group of sectors to -2.45 in the most rural (table 2.13). The characteristics or urban and rural areas in Scotland are seen in table 2.14 (3) and suggest that:

> more older people are found at either end of the distribution - i.e. in both the most urban and most rural areas

> persons born outside the U.K. account for only 2.8% in comparison with 16.7% in England and Wales), the proportion being highest in the three most urban bands, followed by the most rural areas

> owner occupation increases with rurality

> cars per household shows a distinct trend with increasing rurality and public transport declines as 2 means of getting to work

> unemployment is highest in the most urban areas

> the proportion working in manufacturing industry shows no particular trend except that it is lowest in the most rural band

> the percentage in social classes 1 and 2 is lowest at the most urban level and highest at the most rural, with little variation in between (our own data however - see Figure 2.2 — show high proportions in social classes 4 and 5 in rural health boards).

## England & Wales and Scotland

Deprivation scores were computed for the wards of England & Wales, using the Scottish means and standard deviations (table 2.15) to ensure that the scores are absolutely comparable. The means of the four variables were also calculated on an England and Wales basis to show the difference in circumstances between the two countries. Data for overcrowding were however found not to be comparable due to the count of rooms being on a different basis in the two countries. An estimate of the effect of this discrepancy was made using a table giving the count of rooms for a sample of households on the 1971 basis (as used in England & Wales in 1981) and on the 1981 basis, (4) which resulted in a reduction in the overcrowding measure from 25.3% to 15.8%. It was necessary however to scale up the value for England & Wales to make it comparable with the Scottish data and the value shown differs from published data. The mean values are in all cases much lower in England and Wales than in Scotland, with the discrepancy being most marked for overcrowding, for which an almost three-fold difference occurs for persons living at a level of more than one person per room.

Given the higher level of all these variables in Scotland then it is clear that the country exhibits more adverse conditions than does England and Wales as a whole, a position which had already been noted in 1971 in the first major analysis of deprivation at small area level which concluded that 'the problems of the Scottish cities, especially Clydeside, stand out most starkly': in 1971 Scotland had 53.6% of the Enumeration Districts (EDs) with overcrowded households, 34.5% with men unemployed, 35.9% with no car and 21.9% with low social group (SEG11) compared with having only 11% of all EDs. (5)

The mean deprivation score for England and Wales on the Scotland basis is -3.3 (compared with a mean of zero for Scotland) - well within the more affluent half of the distribution and nearly (0.90) one standard deviation from the mean. Almost 22% of the population in England and Wales are living at levels of affluence which are attained by only 6% in Scotland, and 18% in Scotland are living at levels of deprivation experienced by only between 4% and 5% in England and Wales (table 2.15).

These findings serve to underline the essentially relative nature of this score: 45% of the population of Scotland is living in areas with positive scores, i.e. in the more deprived half of the Scottish distribution, but in relation to the mean value of -3.3 for England and Wales over 80% would be found in areas with scores which indicate greater deprivation, i.e. within the more deprived half of this distribution, compared with around 47% in England and Wales. Clearly the differentials observed between the two countries in 1971 at national level still persist in 1981.

TABLE 2.1   CENSUS VARIABLES BY DEPRIVATION CATEGORY

| | DEPCAT | | | | | | | |
| | Affluent | | | | Deprived | | | |
| | 1 | 2 | 3 | 4 | 5 | 6 | 7 | All |
| | % | % | % | % | % | % | % | % |
| No car | 13.3 | 23.4 | 30.8 | 41.8 | 50.4 | 61.9 | 79.4 | 41.3 |
| Male unemployment | 4.0 | 5.8 | 8.3 | 11.5 | 15.9 | 20.3 | 30.6 | 12.5 |
| Low social class | 5.2 | 13.7 | 20.2 | 25.2 | 29.0 | 34.0 | 42.7 | 24.0 |
| Overcrowding | 8.0 | 14.1 | 19.6 | 25.0 | 31.2 | 38.4 | 48.4 | 25.4 |
| DEPscore | -6.02 | -3.86 | -2.01 | -0.24 | 1.96 | 4.28 | 8.36 | |

TABLE 2.2   RANGE IN DEPRIVATION SCORES BY AREA LEVEL

| | Most affluent | Most deprived |
|---|---|---|
| Postcode sectors (PCS) | -7.3 | +12.3 |
| Deprivation categories (DEPCAT) | -6.02 | +8.36 |
| Local government districts (LGD) | -5.65 | +4.07 |
| Health boards (HB) | -1.95 | +2.50 |

TABLE 2.3    RANGE IN CENSUS VARIABLES BY AREA LEVEL

|       | No Car | Male Unemployment | Overcrowding | Low social class |
|-------|--------|-------------------|--------------|------------------|
|       | %      | %                 | %            | %                |
| PCS   | 3.4-92.6 | 0.5-52.7        | 1.7-59.8     | 0.0-71.4         |
| LGD   | 13.5-65.5 | 3.2-20.9       | 9.5-38.4     | 6.3-33.3         |
| HB    | 26.4-56.8 | 6.3-18.1       | 16.1-32.8    | 21.1-28.2        |
| S.D.  | 18.3   | 7.2               | 11.3         | 10.1             |

TABLE 2.4    CENSUS VARIABLE STATISTICS FOR HEALTH BOARD GROUPS

|               | Area | | | | | |
|               | West | | East | | Rural | |
|---------------|------|------|------|------|------|------|
| Variable      | Mean | S.D. | Mean | S.D. | Mean | S.D. |
| No car        | 47.9 | 19.4 | 37.0 | 15.8 | 28.6 | 8.6  |
| Male unemployment | 15.9 | 7.7 | 9.7 | 5.4 | 8.7 | 3.8 |
| Overcrowding  | 30.1 | 12.5 | 21.7 | 8.6  | 19.4 | 5.3  |
| Low social class | 25.1 | 11.1 | 22.5 | 9.3 | 25.8 | 6.9 |
| No. of sectors* |    | 338  |      | 337  |      | 135  |

*sectors with pop.>500 and excluding institutional sectors

TABLE 2.5    DEPRIVATION SCORE FOR HEALTH BOARDS

| Area | Population | Dep. Score | Sectors |
|------|------------|------------|---------|
|      | Mean       | No.        |         |
| WEST | 2,374,475  | 1.35       | 479     |
| Argyll & Clyde | 444,576 | 0.49 | 118 |
| Ayr & Arran | 375,064 | 0.05 | 91 |
| Greater Glasgow | 986,818 | 2.50 | 173 |
| Lanarkshire | 568,017 | 0.87 | 97 |
| EAST | 2,161,514 | -1.12 | 447 |
| Fife | 324,755 | -1.18 | 60 |
| Forth Valley | 268,056 | -0.91 | 62 |
| Grampian | 462,888 | -1.95 | 88 |
| Lothian | 723,108 | -0.94 | 147 |
| Tayside | 382,707 | -0.55 | 90 |
| RURAL | 497,976 | -1.57 | 213 |
| Borders | 97,218 | -1.80 | 45 |
| Dumfries &Galloway | 141,863 | -1.22 | 49 |
| Highland | 186,997 | -1.82 | 103 |
| The Islands | 71,898 | -1.26 | 16 |
| SCOTLAND | 5,033,965 | 0.00 | 1139 |

TABLE 2.6    RANGE OF DEPRIVATION SCORES FOR LOCAL GOVERNMENT DISTRICTS
WITHIN HEALTH BOARDS

|  | HB Value | Range for LG Districts | |
|---|---|---|---|
|  |  | Deprived | Affluent |
| Greater Glasgow | 2.50 | 4.08 | -5.65 |
| Lanarkshire | 0.87 | 2.94 | -1.39 |
| Argyll & Clyde | 0.49 | 1.95 | -1.38 |
| Western Isles | 0.26 | - | - |
| Ayrshire & Arran | 0.05 | 1.24 | -1.35 |
| Tayside | -0.55 | 0.89 | -2.05 |
| Forth Valley | -0.91 | -0.40 | -1.79 |
| Lothian | -0.94 | 0.26 | -1.58 |
| Fife | -1.18 | -0.39 | -2.64 |
| Dumfries & Galloway | -1.22 | -0.67 | -1.88 |
| Borders | -1.80 | -1.55 | -2.06 |
| Highland | -1.82 | -0.45 | -2.40 |
| Grampian | -1.95 | -0.80 | -3.81 |
| Orkney | -2.30 | - | - |
| Shetland | -2.46 | - | - |

TABLE 2.7    DEPRIVATION SCORES FOR LOCAL GOVERNMENT DISTRICTS

| LGD | DEPscore | H.B. |
|---|---|---|
| **5th quintile: most deprived** | | |
| Glasgow City | 4.08 | Glasgow |
| Monklands | 2.95 | Lanark |
| Motherwell | 2.34 | Lanark |
| Clydebank | 2.25 | Glasgow |
| Inverclyde | 1.95 | Argyll & Clyde |
| Cumnock & Doon Valley | 1.24 | Ayr & Arran |
| Dundee City | 0.89 | Tayside |
| Cunninghame | 0.85 | Ayr & Arran |
| Renfrew | 0.62 | Argyll & Clyde |
| Hamilton | 0.52 | Lanark |
| Western Isles | 0.26 | Western Isles |
| West Lothian | 0.26 | Lothian |
| **1st quintile: most affluent LGDs** | | |
| Eastwood | -5.65 | Glasgow |
| Bearsden & Milngavie | -5.51 | Glasgow |
| Gordon | -4.07 | Grampian |
| Kincardine & Deeside | -3.81 | Grampian |
| N.E. Fife | -2.64 | Fife |
| Badenoch & Strathspey | -2.52 | Highland |
| Shetland | -2.46 | Shetland |
| Nairn | -2.42 | Highland |
| Ross & Cromarty | -2.31 | Highland |
| Strathkelvin | -2.30 | Glasgow |
| Orkney | -2.30 | Orkney |

TABLE 2.7   DEPRIVATION SCORES FOR LOCAL GOVERNMENT DISTRICTS CONTD.

| LGD | DEPscore | H.B. | |
|---|---|---|---|
| **4th quintile** | | | |
| Kilmarnock & Loudon | 0.00 | Wigton | -0.67 |
| Dumbarton | -0.22 | Banff & Buchan | -0.80 |
| Kirkaldy | -0.39 | Skye & Lochalsh | -0.84 |
| Falkirk | -0.40 | Nithsdale | -1.02 |
| Lochaber | -0.46 | Clackmannan | -1.02 |
| Cumbernauld | -0.66 | | |
| **3rd quintile** | | | |
| Edinburgh | -1.10 | Dunfermline | -1.38 |
| Caithness | -1.32 | Aberdeen | -1.41 |
| Kyle & Carrick | -1.35 | Angus | -1.46 |
| Clydesdale | -1.36 | Midlothian | -1.51 |
| East Kilbride | -1.36 | Roxburgh | -1.55 |
| Argyll & Bute | -1.38 | | |
| **2nd quintile** | | | |
| East Lothian | -1.58 | Stewartry | -1.88 |
| Annan & Eskdale | -1.59 | Perth & Kinross | -2.05 |
| Stirling | -1.79 | Ettrick & Lauderdale | -2.06 |
| Berwick | -1.81 | Inverness | -2.08 |
| Moray | -1.84 | Sutherland | -2.11 |
| Tweeddale | -1.86 | | |

TABLE 2.8   MULTIPLY AND SEVERELY DEPRIVED HOUSEHOLDS, DEP SCORE AND URBAN/RURAL SCORE FOR LOCAL GOVERNMENT DISTRICTS

| | % Multiply Deprived | % Severely Deprived | Deprivation Score | Urban/rural Value |
|---|---|---|---|---|
| **WEST** | | | | |
| Argyll & Clyde | | | | |
| Argyll & Bute | 18 | 1.8 | -1.38 | 4.42 |
| Dumbarton | 17 | 1.9 | -0.22 | 3.17 |
| Inverclyde | 23 | 3.2 | 1.95 | 2.17 |
| Renfrew | 21 | 3.0 | 0.62 | 1.45 |
| Ayr & Arran | | | | |
| Cumnock & Doon Valley | 21 | 2.3 | 1.24 | 4.13 |
| Cunninghame | 20 | 2.6 | 0.85 | 3.34 |
| Kilmarnock & Loudon | 21 | 2.3 | 0.00 | 3.44 |
| Kyle & Carrick | 17 | 1.6 | -1.35 | 3.41 |
| Greater Glasgow | | | | |
| Bearsden & Milngavie | 6 | 0.4 | -5.51 | 1.04 |
| Clydebank | 23 | 3.3 | 2.25 | 1.01 |
| Eastwood | 6 | 0.5 | -5.65 | 1.08 |
| Glasgow City | 29 | 4.7 | 4.08 | 1.00 |
| Strathkelvin | 13 | 1.4 | -2.30 | 2.50 |

Lanarkshire
| | | | | |
|---|---|---|---|---|
| Clydesdale | 17 | 2.4 | -1.36 | 4.22 |
| Cumbertnauld | 15 | 1.9 | -0.66 | 3.12 |
| East Kilbride | 15 | 1.3 | -1.36 | 3.15 |
| Hamilton | 19 | 2.6 | 0.52 | 2.32 |
| Monklands | 25 | 4.5 | 2.95 | 1.21 |
| Motherwell | 25 | 3.8 | 2.34 | 2.23 |

EAST

Fife
| | | | | |
|---|---|---|---|---|
| Dumfermline | 16 | 1.8 | -1.38 | 3.45 |
| Kirkcaldy | 19 | 2.0 | -0.39 | 3.25 |
| N.E. Fife | 16 | 1.1 | -2.64 | 4.16 |

Forth Valley
| | | | | |
|---|---|---|---|---|
| Clackmannan | 16 | 1.6 | -1.05 | 3.53 |
| Falkirk | 17 | 1.5 | -0.40 | 2.46 |
| Stirling | 18 | 2.3 | -1.79 | 3.79 |

Grampian
| | | | | |
|---|---|---|---|---|
| Aberdeen City | 17 | 1.8 | -1.41 | 2.16 |
| Banff & Buchan | 17 | 1.7 | -0.80 | 4.04 |
| Gordon | 11 | 0.8 | -4.07 | 4.64 |
| Kincardine & Deeside | 14 | 0.8 | -3.81 | 4.62 |
| Moray | 16 | 1.2 | -1.84 | 4.01 |

Lothian
| | | | | |
|---|---|---|---|---|
| East Lothian | 17 | 1.4 | -1.58 | 3.53 |
| Edinburgh City | 17 | 2.0 | -1.10 | 2.09 |
| Midlothian | 15 | 1.5 | -1.51 | 3.27 |
| West Lothian | 20 | 2.2 | 0.26 | 3.49 |

Tayside
| | | | | |
|---|---|---|---|---|
| Angus | 16 | 1.3 | -1.46 | 3.69 |
| Dundee City | 24 | 2.7 | 0.89 | 2.10 |
| Perth & Kinross | 16 | 0.1 | -2.05 | 3.94 |

RURAL

Borders
| | | | | |
|---|---|---|---|---|
| Berwickshire | 16 | 0.6 | -1.81 | 4.60 |
| Ettrick & Lauderdale | 17 | 1.3 | -2.06 | 3.84 |
| Roxburgh | 19 | 1.5 | -1.55 | 3.78 |
| Tweeddale | 16 | 0.8 | -1.86 | 4.36 |

Dumfries & Galloway
| | | | | |
|---|---|---|---|---|
| Annan & Eskdale | 16 | 1.5 | -1.59 | 4.36 |
| Nithsdale | 17 | 1.9 | -1.02 | 3.68 |
| Stewartry | 17 | 1.8 | -1.88 | 4.52 |
| Wigtown | 19 | 2.8 | -0.67 | 4.49 |

Highland
| | | | | |
|---|---|---|---|---|
| Badenoch & Strathspey | 17 | 1.2 | -2.52 | 4.53 |
| Caithness | 17 | 1.4 | -1.32 | 4.39 |
| Inverness | 14 | 1.6 | -2.08 | 3.59 |
| Lochaber | 19 | 1.3 | -0.46 | 3.86 |
| Nairn | 17 | 1.5 | -2.42 | 4.24 |
| Ross & Cromarty | 16 | 1.3 | -2.30 | 4.47 |
| Skye & Lochalsh | 19 | 0.9 | -0.84 | 4.86 |
| Sutherland | 20 | 1.5 | -2.11 | 4.76 |

Islands
| | | | | |
|---|---|---|---|---|
| Orkney | 14 | 1.1 | -2.30 | 4.59 |
| Shetland | 14 | 1.4 | -2.46 | 4.69 |
| Western Isles | 25 | 2.4 | 0.26 | 4.81 |

TABLE 2.9    POSTCODE SECTORS BY DEPRIVATION CATEGORY WITHIN HEALTH BOARDS

| Health Board | Number of Sectors* | | | | | | | |
| --- | --- | --- | --- | --- | --- | --- | --- | --- |
| | | Affluent | | | | | Deprived | |
| | Total | 1 | 2 | 3 | 4 | 5 | 6 | 7 |
| Argyll & Clyde | 78 | 7 | 12 | 17 | 19 | 12 | 8 | 3 |
| Ayr & Arran | 72 | 3 | 9 | 16 | 19 | 17 | 7 | 1 |
| Borders | 28 | - | 6 | 15 | 7 | - | - | - |
| Dumfries & Galloway | 35 | - | 5 | 20 | 7 | 2 | 1 | - |
| Fife | 50 | 4 | 4 | 19 | 18 | 4 | 1 | - |
| Forth Valley | 45 | 4 | 8 | 10 | 13 | 8 | 2 | - |
| Grampian | 64 | 6 | 23 | 17 | 16 | 1 | 1 | - |
| Greater Glasgow | 135 | 17 | 12 | 14 | 13 | 16 | 31 | 32 |
| Highland | 59 | - | 15 | 28 | 14 | 2 | - | - |
| Lanarkshire | 63 | - | 3 | 15 | 17 | 15 | 13 | - |
| Lothian | 117 | 19 | 21 | 20 | 34 | 14 | 7 | 2 |
| Tayside | 70 | 6 | 18 | 20 | 11 | 9 | 4 | 2 |
| Islands | 14 | - | 2 | 5 | 4 | 1 | 2 | - |
| SCOTLAND | 830 | 66 | 138 | 216 | 192 | 101 | 77 | 40 |

*with more than 500 population

TABLE 2.10    POPULATION DISTRIBUTION BY DEPRIVATION CATEGORY

| Health Board | Percent of total population in health boards | | | | | | |
| --- | --- | --- | --- | --- | --- | --- | --- |
| | Affluent | | | | | Deprived | |
| | 1 | 2 | 3 | 4 | 5 | 6 | 7 |
| Argyll & Clyde | 7 | 9 | 16 | 25 | 25 | 14 | 5 |
| Ayrshire & Arran | 3 | 11 | 15 | 28 | 28 | 13 | - |
| Borders | - | 14 | 54 | 32 | - | - | - |
| Dumfries & Galloway | - | 15 | 52 | 19 | 10 | 4 | - |
| Fife | 6 | 5 | 43 | 36 | 7 | 2 | - |
| Forth Valley | 5 | 16 | 19 | 35 | 21 | 4 | - |
| Grampian | 4 | 35 | 22 | 34 | 2 | 3 | |
| Greater Glasgow | 10 | 8 | 11 | 9 | 12 | 23 | 27 |
| Highland | - | 22 | 46 | 28 | 4 | - | - |
| Lanarkshire | - | 4 | 24 | 27 | 23 | 21 | - |
| Lothian | 12 | 16 | 15 | 35 | 12 | 6 | 4 |
| Tayside | 6 | 22 | 20 | 18 | 18 | 9 | 7 |
| Orkney | - | 43 | 57 | - | - | - | - |
| Shetland | - | 3 | 97 | - | - | - | - |
| Western Isles | - | - | 7 | 75 | 5 | 12 | - |
| SCOTLAND | 6 | 14 | 22 | 25 | 15 | 11 | 7 |

TABLE 2.11    DISTRIBUTION OF POSTCODE SECTORS BY DEPCAT WITHIN HEALTH
BOARD GROUPS

|   |   | DEPCAT | | | | | | | |
|   |   | Affluent | | | | | Deprived | | |
|   |   | 1 | 2 | 3 | 4 | 5 | 6 | 7 | All |
| (a) | number | | | | | | | | |
|   | WEST | 27 | 36 | 62 | 68 | 60 | 59 | 36 | 348 |
|   | EAST | 39 | 74 | 86 | 92 | 36 | 15 | 4 | 346 |
|   | RURAL | - | 28 | 68 | 32 | 5 | 3 | - | 136 |
|   |   | 66 | 138 | 216 | 192 | 101 | 77 | 40 | 830 |
| (b) | percent | | | | | | | | |
|   | WEST | 41 | 26 | 29 | 35 | 59 | 77 | 90 | 42 |
|   | EAST | 59 | 53 | 40 | 48 | 36 | 19 | 10 | 42 |
|   | RURAL | - | 21 | 31 | 17 | 5 | 4 | - | 60 |
|   |   | 100 | 100 | 100 | 100 | 100 | 100 | 100 | 100 |
| (c) | percent | | | | | | | | |
|   | WEST | 8 | 10 | 18 | 20 | 17 | 17 | 10 | 100 |
|   | EAST | 11 | 21 | 25 | 27 | 11 | 4 | 1 | 100 |
|   | RURAL | - | 21 | 50 | 24 | 4 | 2 | - | 100 |

TABLE 2.12    DEPRIVATION SCORE STATISTICS FOR HEALTH BOARD GROUPS

| Area | Deprivation Score | | | | No. of Sectors |
|   | Mean | Stan. Dev. | Minimum | Maximum | |
| WEST | 1.34 | 4.02 | -7.31 | 12.27 | 338 |
| EAST | -1.08 | 2.82 | -7.17 | 7.62 | 337 |
| RURAL | -1.55 | 1.62 | -4.51 | 4.09 | 135 |
| SCOTLAND | 0.02 | 3.59 | -7.31 | 12.27 | 810 |

Notes:    Sectors >500 excluding 20 with large institutional populations

TABLE 2.13    DEPRIVATION FOR URBAN AND RURAL AREAS
(POSTCODE SECTORS GROUPED)

|   | U/R Value | Mean | Pop.Th. | DEP Score |
|---|---|---|---|---|
| Urban | 1 < 2 1 | 1.03 | 1611 | 1.31 |
|   | 2 < 3 | 2.07 | 1063 | 0.26 |
|   | 3 < 4 | 3.18 | 1224 | -0.39 |
|   | 4 < 5 | 4.17 | 892 | -1.48 |
| Rural | 5 | 5.0 | 242 | -2.45 |

TABLE 2.14    SELECTED CHARACTERISTICS OF URBAN AND RURAL AREAS (SCOTLAND)

| Areas population size in thousands | % of usual residents | | % of households owner-occupied | cars per household | % travelling to work by public transport | % of men 16-64 unemployed | % working in manufacturing | % in social class 1 and 2 |
|---|---|---|---|---|---|---|---|---|
| | Pensionable age and over | Born outside UK | | | | | | |
| All urban areas | 16.7 | 2.8 | 33.3 | 0.59 | 29.7 | 15.1 | 25.2 | 19.2 |
| 500-499 | 18.7 | 3.6 | 24.9 | 0.35 | 50.6 | 24.3 | 25.0 | 11.6 |
| 200-499 | 20.0 | 4.5 | 53.2 | 0.56 | 41.5 | 11.1 | 16.3 | 26.2 |
| 100-199 | 18.5 | 3.3 | 31.3 | 0.57 | 34.1 | 12.6 | 23.0 | 20.2 |
| 50-99 | 15.1 | 2.0 | 23.7 | 0.55 | 30.7 | 17.2 | 31.1 | 16.7 |
| 20-49 | 14.3 | 2.3 | 31.8 | 0.65 | 23.6 | 14.7 | 28.2 | 20.1 |
| 10-19 | 15.4 | 2.1 | 34.1 | 0.67 | 21.3 | 12.8 | 26.9 | 20.5 |
| 5-9 | 16.7 | 2.5 | 36.1 | 0.69 | 17.4 | 11.5 | 24.0 | 20.5 |
| 2-4.9 | 16.1 | 2.3 | 37.2 | 0.75 | 18.5 | 11.2 | 24.5 | 22.3 |
| under 2 | 19.4 | 2.4 | 40.0 | 0.76 | 18.6 | 10.7 | 21.0 | 19.9 |
| Rural areas | 17.9 | 2.9 | 46.8 | 1.05 | 9.2 | 8.6 | 13.5 | 32.3 |

Source: ref.3

TABLE 2.15   DEPRIVATION COMPONENT VALUES FOR ENGLAND AND WALES AND
SCOTLAND

|  | England & Wales | Scotland |
|---|---|---|
|  | % | % |
| Males unemployed | 8.7 | 12.5 |
| Persons overcrowded | 9.3* | 25.3 |
| Persons no car | 24.4 | 41.2 |
| Low Social class | 19.8 | 24.1 |

*value amended to adjust for different basis for calculation of rooms in England and Wales and
Scotland in 1981 Census

TABLE 2.16   POPULATION LIVING AT DIFFERING LEVELS OF DEPRIVATION: ENGLAND
AND WALES AND SCOTLAND

| DEPCAT | England & Wales | Scotland |
|---|---|---|
|  | % | % |
| 1 Affluent | 21.6 | 6.1 |
| 2 | 30.4 | 13.7 |
| 3 | 21.7 | 21.8 |
| 4 | 14.7 | 25.5 |
| 5 | 7.6 | 14.8 |
| 6 | 3.6 | 11.4 |
| 7 Deprived | 1.0 | 6.8 |

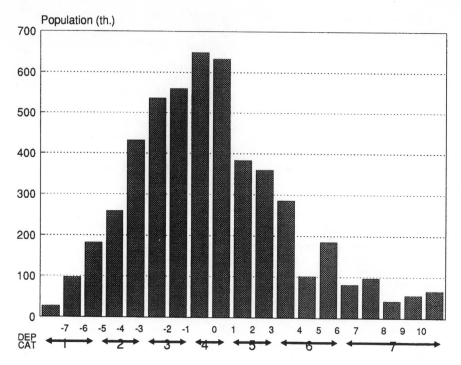

FIGURE 2.1    DEPRIVATION SCORE DISTRIBUTION

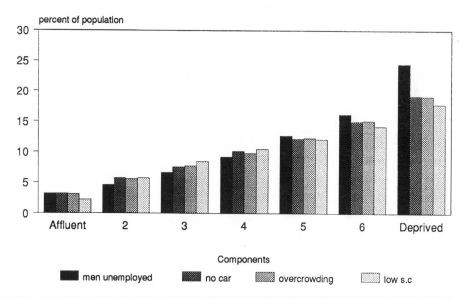

FIGURE 2.2    DEPRIVATION COMPONENTS BY DEPCAT

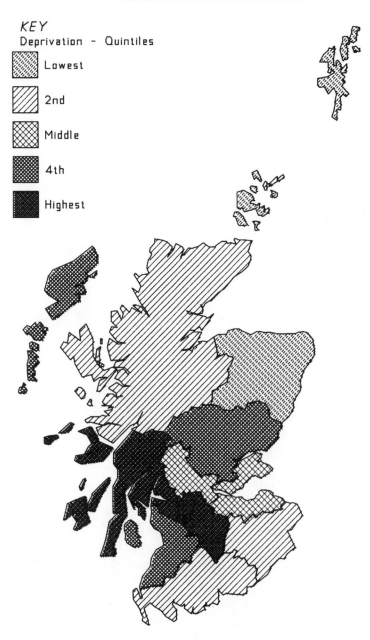

KEY
Deprivation - Quintiles

▨ Lowest

▨ 2nd

▨ Middle

▨ 4th

■ Highest

FIGURE 2.3   HEALTH BOARDS DEPRIVATION SCORE

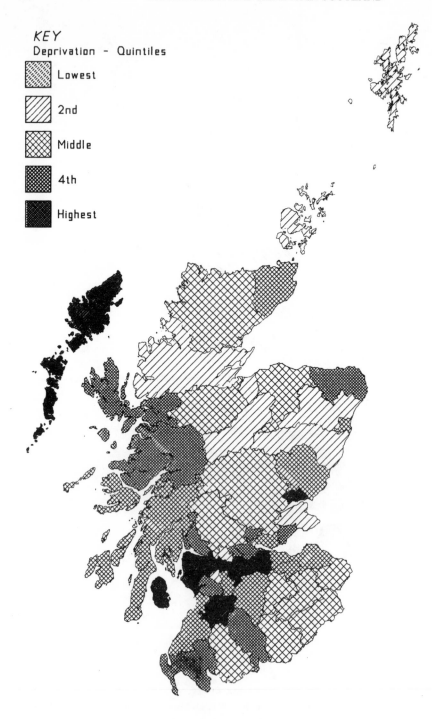

FIGURE 2.4    LOCAL GOVERNMENT DISTRICTS DEPRIVATION SCORE

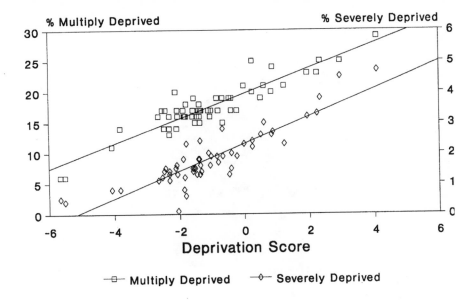

FIGURE 2.5   DEPRIVATION SCORE V MULTIPLY + SEVERELY DEPRIVED HOUSEHOLDS
OVER 56 DISTRICTS

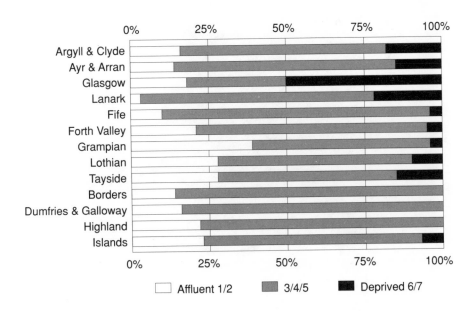

FIGURE 2.6   HEALTH BOARD POPULATIONS: PERCENT BY DEPCAP

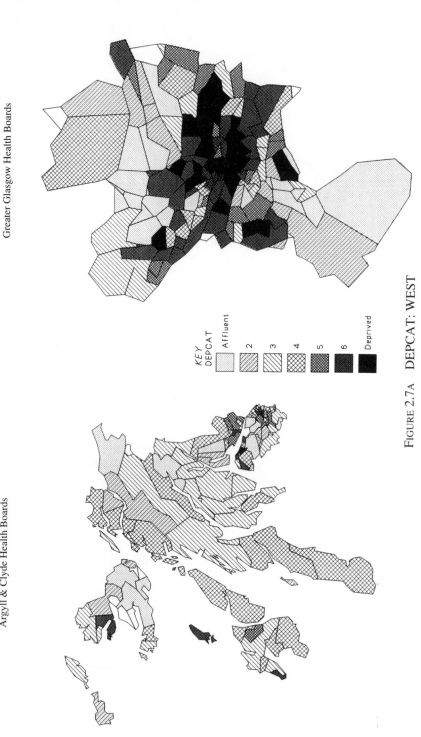

FIGURE 2.7A   DEPCAT: WEST

Lanarkshire Health Boards

Aryshire & Arran Health Boards

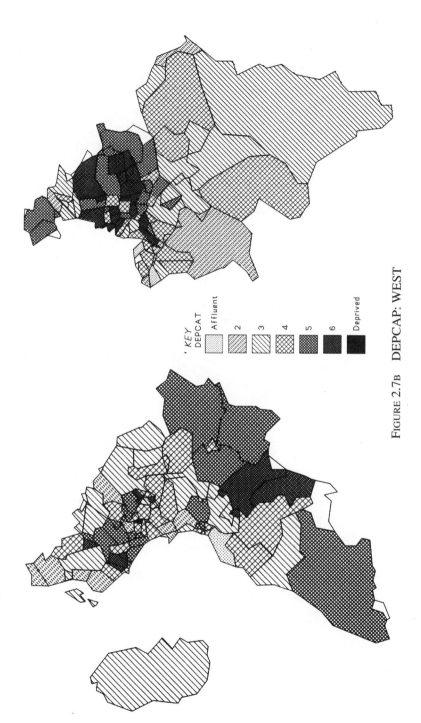

FIGURE 2.7B    DEPCAP: WEST

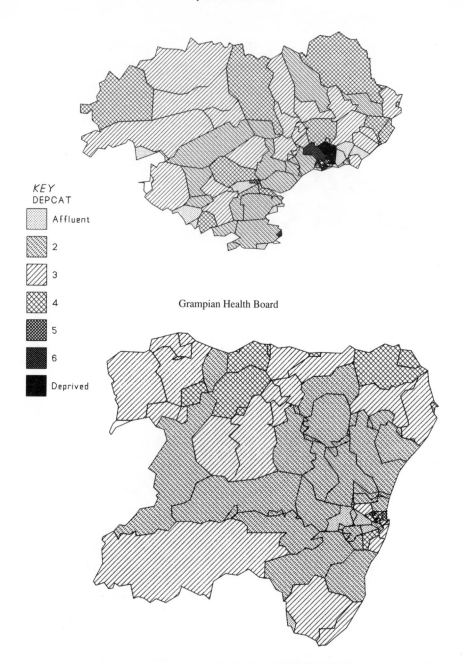

Tayside Health Board

Grampian Health Board

KEY
DEPCAT

Affluent

2

3

4

5

6

Deprived

FIGURE 2.7C    DEPCAT: EAST

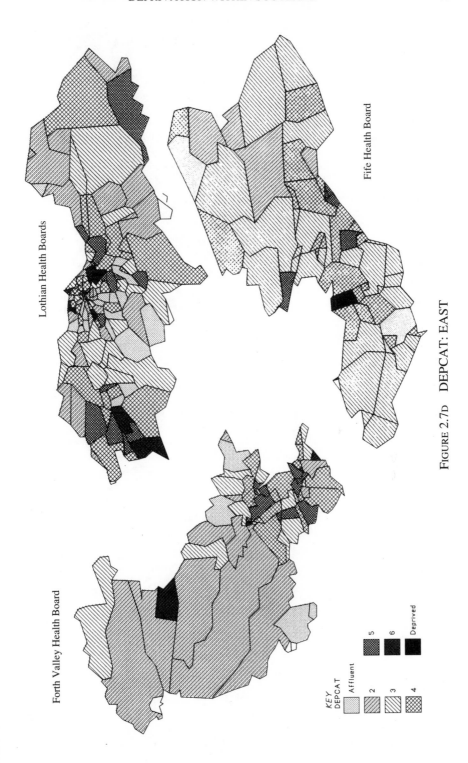

Fife Health Board

Lothian Health Boards

Forth Valley Health Board

KEY
DEPCAT

Affluent
2
3
4

5
6
Deprived

FIGURE 2.7D   DEPCAT: EAST

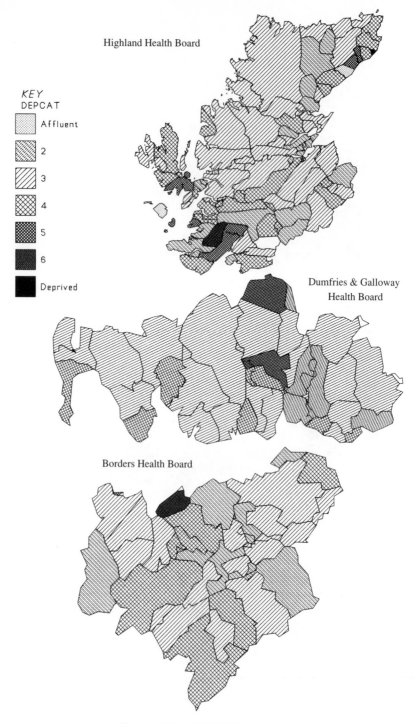

FIGURE 2.7E    DEPCAP: RURAL

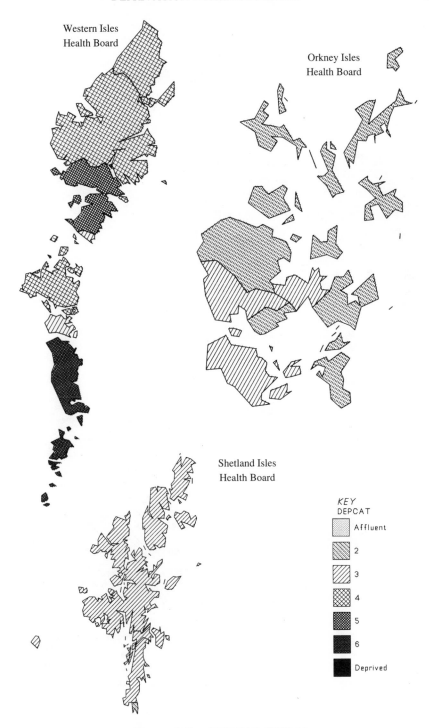

FIGURE 2.7F    DEPCAP: RURAL

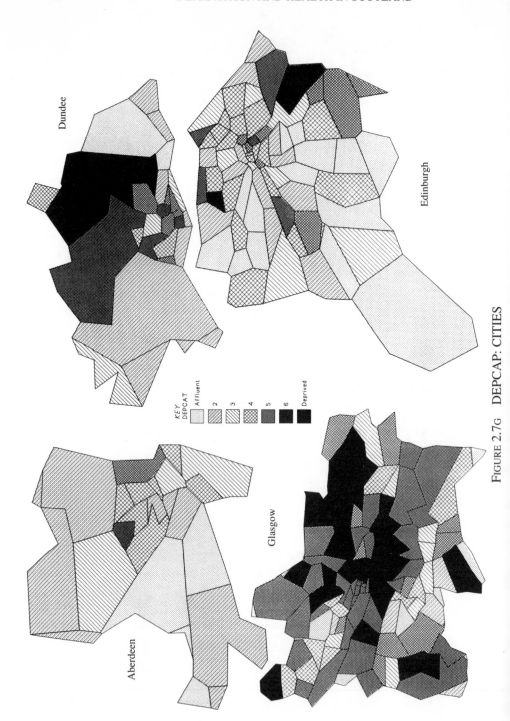

FIGURE 2.7G   DEPCAP: CITIES

# Mortality in Scotland 1980-82

This chapter deals with the geographical distribution of mortality in Scotland and serves to set the scene for the examination of deprivation in relation to mortality. Much of the material it presents for health boards and local government districts will be well-known to readers of the Registrar General's annual report[1] but the data for postcode sectors which are presented later in the chapter are not so readily available since counts of deaths by postcode sector for each year are produced only in microfiche. Moreover the combination of data over a period of three years in this analysis serves to make the sector values more reliable, while the population data for postcode sectors enable standardised rates to be calculated. The chapter also brings together published data comparing mortality in Scotland with that in England and Wales, and examines the levels of mortality in postcode sectors in Scotland in relation to those in the wards of the Northern Region.

## Health Boards and Local Government Districts

The pattern of overall mortality in Scotland is well known, being highest in the four boards which comprise the Strathclyde region, all four boards having SMRs above 100 at all ages, 0-64 and 65 and over (table 3.1, fig. 3.1), with Glasgow having the highest rate at all ages and 0-64, followed by Argyll & Clyde, but with lesser variation between these four boards at age 65 and over. Apart from these four health boards SMRs are higher in Highland than in other areas. Mortality is lowest in Grampian, Borders and Tayside at all ages and 0-64; and at 65 and over in the Islands, in Dumfries & Galloway, and Grampian. It is notable that the pattern of high or low mortality tends to persist for both age groups; areas with low mortality at 0-64 also tend to have low mortality at 65 and over, and vice versa.

Within local government districts (LGDs) mortality is again highest in the West — but not in all districts. At all ages SMRs are highest (table 3.2) in Glasgow City, Inverclyde, and Monklands (110 or more), all within Strathclyde region; two districts within Glasgow health board however — Bearsden & Milngavie and Eastwood — exhibit the lowest mortality in Scotland, in each of the three age groups, with Strathkelvin and East Kilbride in the West also being below the national average. While all health boards in the East and Rural areas have SMRs

43

below 100 (with the one exception of Highland at 0-64) the picture is much more diversified at LGD level with Caithness displaying higher mortality than in many of the districts of Strathclyde, as also does Wigtown; within Highland also the LGDs of Lochaber and Nairn have five out of six values above the mean. Clackmannan, Kirkcaldy and West Lothian also just exceed 100 on all three measures.

At 0-64 the range of SMRs is more extreme, with Glasgow City and Inverclyde again having the highest values (124, 122) followed by Caithness, Cunninghame, Monklands and Motherwell (110-120). Several districts have SMRs below 80. These are mainly rural, with Bearsden & Milngavie and Eastwood (at 68) being the exceptions. For the age group 65 and over there are no values over 110, Cumnock & Doon Valley, Kilmarnock and Loudoun and Monklands having the highest values of 109 to 110 with Renfrew, Inverclyde, Glasgow City, Cumbernauld, Hamilton and Motherwell in the West having values between 105 and 109 as well as the Rural districts of Wigtown, Caithness and Nairn. Bearsden & Milngavie and Eastwood both with SMRs below 85 are again at the lowest extreme of the distribution, with N.E.Fife, Gordon, Berwickshire, Annandale and Eskdale, and Stewartry, (all rural districts) falling between 85 and 90.

Figure 3.2 for LGDs shows the pattern of generally higher mortality on the West side of Scotland and the central belt extending West from Lothian. The North East of Scotland and parts of the Highlands are an exception to the generally lower mortality seen on the East side for all three age-groups. The age/sex specific mortality rates (fig. 3.3 and table 3.10) show the familiar picture of mortality increasing with age, and at each age group being considerably higher for men than women, this differential being greatest at the age group 45-54.

## Mortality at Postcode Sector Level

The frequency distributions of SMRs for PCS are seen in table 3.3 for the 810 sectors with more than 500 population and excluding institutional sectors (see Appendix A5). At all ages 51% of SMRs fall within the band of 90<110, and 56% at 65 and over. The distribution is more dispersed at 0-64 with only 30% in this band. Due to small populations for some sectors (and hence low numbers of deaths) not all of the values which fall outwith this middle band are significant (part b). At all ages 263 (32%) SMRs are significant (at the 5% level), 205 (25%) at 0-64, and 171 (21%) at 65 and over. Mapped values for sectors within health boards appear in figure 3.4.

The inequalities in mortality which have already been observed at health board and local government district level may be explored in more detail by examining the geographical distribution of PCS with low and high SMRs within Scotland.

These SMRs will be found listed for each sector at Appendix table B3.1, and the variation of SMRs for PCS within health board groups, health boards and local government districts at Appendix tables B3.2-4.

High mortality, at health board and local government district level, has been shown to occur mainly in Western areas, although there are exceptions to this general picture. Postcode sectors show pockets of high and low mortality throughout the country although a higher proportion of sectors with high SMRs are in Western areas, and in particular within Glasgow health board. The full distribution of sector values is seen in table B3.3. We consider here however only the SMRs which are significantly different (at the five percent level) which provides a more reliable picture of the variation in death rates. These are shown in detail in Appendix tables B3.6 and summarised in table 3.4.

The distribution of these SMRs shows all boards to have at least one sector with a significantly low SMR value of less than 90 (table 3.4a). Three boards - Grampian, Lothian and Tayside - have more than 20% of sectors (>500 pop.) with low values, and, at the other extreme, four boards - Argyll & Clyde, Ayrshire & Arran, Highland and Lanarkshire - only five percent or less. At the upper end of the distribution (>110) Western boards overall have 33% of sectors in this range, Eastern six percent and Rural boards five percent. Glasgow health board has by far the highest proportion of its sectors with high SMRs (44%), with Argyll & Clyde, Ayrshire & Arran and Lanarkshire following with between 20% and 30%. Outside of the West only Forth Valley produces more than 10% of sectors with SMRs of more than 110, other boards having smaller proportions.

At 0-64, (table 3.3a) there being fewer deaths, SMRs generally require more extreme values to reach a formal level of statistical significance, and only 25% do so. The pattern for health boards is repeated nevertheless with Borders as well as Grampian, Lothian and Tayside having 18% or more of their sectors with low values (<90); Glasgow however is only just below this level with 14% below 90. At the upper end of the distribution, 42% of sectors in Glasgow exhibit significantly high values, followed (as for all ages) by Argyll & Clyde, Ayrshire & Arran and Lanarkshire all with more than 10%.

Only Borders has no sectors with high death rates in this age group while in Dumfries & Galloway only two of its 35 sectors lie outside the normal range, i.e. significantly different from 100, whether high or low.

The vast difference between the Western boards and others is readily seen in tables 3.5. Only 23% of low SMRs (all ages) are found in the West and 64% in the East (part a). In contrast 81% of the high values are found in Western boards and only 14% in the East. At 0-64, 63% of low values are in the East (part a) and 29% in the West, while 81% of high values again are in the West and only 12% in the East. At 65 and over the pattern is similar.

The table also shows (part b) that 33% of all sectors in the West have significantly high mortality compared with five to six percent of sectors in the East or Rural board at all ages, and this pattern is also apparent at age 0-64 and at 65 and over. The association between the SMRs 0-64 and 65 and over (over PCS) is seen to be positive and fairly strong, at 0.52 (table 3.6), indicating that areas which have high mortality at younger ages also tend to have higher mortality in the elderly. The close correspondence between mortality at 15-59 and 60 and over for the postcode sectors of Greater Glasgow health board has been noted elsewhere.[2]

Thus in areas of excess mortality at younger ages the vulnerability of the population is apparently not exhausted by this experience, older people in these area still having lower life expectancy.

The more extended distribution (Appendix table B3.6) shows that there were 29 sectors at the younger age group (0-64) with significantly high SMR values of 150 or more and these sectors are listed below:

Argyll & Clyde Health Board
  Inverclyde LGD
  PA 14.6 163, PA 15.1 174, PA 15.2 175
  Renfrew
  PA 3.1 166

Glasgow Health Board
  Glasgow City
  G3.8 177, G5.9 165, G20.9 158, G21.2 170, G22.5 164, G31.1 162
  G31.3 165, G31.4 154, G31.5 163, G33.1 169, G40.1 197, G40.4 195,
  G41.1 199, G42.7 177, G51.3 151, G73.1 159

Highland Health Board
  Caithness
  KW3.6 214
  Inverness
  IV1.1 204, PH32.4 210
  Sutherland
  KW8.6 174

Lothian Health Board
  Edinburgh City
  EH6.5 152, EH16.4 158

Tayside Health Board
  Dundee City
  DD1.5 151

Western Isles Health Board
  PA80.5 184, PA81.5 154

The excess mortality at younger ages is particularly marked in Glasgow City which accounts for 16 of the 29 values over 150. Figure 3.5 shows the particular concentration of high mortality in central sectors in the city.

  Seven of the remaining high values are to be found in urban areas and six in boards in the rural group; many of these however are based on fairly small numbers of deaths (see Appendix B3.1).

## England and Wales and the Northern Region

Mortality levels in Scotland exceed those in England and Wales by a level of 15% and these differentials have persisted over many years. Data for 1981 and 1985 (table 3.7) show the variation within countries of the United Kingdom, overall mortality for both Scotland and Northern Ireland being greater than for England and Wales. Although the differential has fallen slightly between 1981 and 1987, Scotland's position vis-à-vis other countries of the U.K. has worsened since its SMRs, both male and female, now exceed all three countries whereas in 1981 Northern Ireland was in the most unfavourable position.

  For people of working age data from the Decennial Occupational Mortality Supplement for 1979-83[4] show the considerable excess of mortality in Scotland (on a Great Britain basis); with SMRs of 124 for males and 130 for married women mortality far exceeds England and Wales, or the region with highest mortality within it — the North — with SMRs of 115 for men and 112 for married women (table 3.8, fig. 3.5).

Social class data paint the same picture and highlight the enhanced mortality in the Clydeside conurbation (table 3.9): for each social class - with the exception of class 4 for men - the SMRs are higher in Scotland than the North and higher again for Clydeside. The general pattern is the same for married women as for men, although, with the exception of social class V the differentials between Scotland and the North and other areas are even more pronounced for women, as would be expected from the higher overall value.

Excess mortality is not left behind by Scots moving to England or Wales, SMRs of 118 being reported in 1979-83 for both males and females born in Scotland, a level exceeded only by people of Irish origin among the countries of birth examined. The excess was greatest among young adults, particularly men, with an SMR of 135 at 20-49, but also persisted into old age being 16% above the England and Wales mean for men aged 70 and over. Both the Scots and Irish immigrants exhibited higher mortality in the 1980s than the average levels in England and Wales in the 1970s. [5]

The higher mortality in Scotland compared with England and Wales is also seen in the age/sex specific rates (table 3.10), the excess being apparent for both males and females from 35-64.

Mortality in Scotland in the younger age group may be compared with that in the Northern Region in more detail, and for this purpose the SMRs for Scottish sectors are calculated using the England and Wales death rates for 1980-82 seen in table 3.10 for age/sex groups below age 65. Standardising on this basis produces an overall SMR (male plus female) of 125 for Scotland compared with 100 for England and Wales. For the 810 sectors with more than 500 population in Scotland the SMRs calculated on this basis may be compared with those for the 678 wards in the Northern Region with populations ranging from 500 to 15,500. [6] Values for the Scottish sectors now reflect the 25% greater mortality and the effect is to shift the distribution upwards (table 3.11). On this (England and Wales = 100) basis only 18% of values would be less than 90 compared with 26% on the Scotland basis and 62% over 110 compared with 29% (table 3.4a). Compared with the wards in the Northern Region a smaller proportion of sectors in Scotland is found at the lower end of the distribution (<90) and more at the upper end: 62% over 110 compared with 49% in the North and, of these, 17% over 150 in comparison with eight percent in the North, with 41 (5%) of sectors in Scotland attaining values over 180 and 13 (2%) in the North, and only two of the 678 wards in the North reaching a level of 200 or more compared with 30 of the sectors in Scotland.

The high levels of premature mortality found in some sectors in Scotland, in Glasgow City in particular, are thus seen to be more extreme than in the worst wards in the Northern Region which, together with the North West, exhibits the highest mortality within England and Wales.

TABLE 3.1    SMRs FOR HEALTH BOARDS AND GROUPS OF BOARDS 1980-82

|                      | All ages | 0-64  | 65+   |
|----------------------|----------|-------|-------|
| WEST                 | 106.5    | 110.1 | 105.1 |
|                      |          |       |       |
| Argyll & Clyde       | 106.7    | 108.0 | 106.2 |
| Ayr & Arran          | 104.6    | 103.8 | 104.8 |
| Greater Glasgow      | 107.5    | 115.4 | 104.8 |
| Lanarkshire          | 105.4    | 106.3 | 105.0 |
|                      |          |       |       |
| EAST                 | 94.5     | 90.1  | 95.9  |
|                      |          |       |       |
| Fife                 | 97.3     | 96.9  | 97.4  |
| Forth Valley         | 97.7     | 96.1  | 98.3  |
| Grampian             | 92.0     | 83.5  | 94.7  |
| Lothian              | 94.3     | 91.2  | 95.3  |
| Tayside              | 93.6     | 86.9  | 95.9  |
|                      |          |       |       |
| RURAL                | 95.9     | 94.4  | 96.4  |
|                      |          |       |       |
| Borders              | 93.3     | 81.5  | 96.4  |
| Dumfries & Galloway  | 94.7     | 96.4  | 94.2  |
| Highland             | 99.5     | 100.1 | 99.3  |
| Islands              | 94.0     | 93.6  | 94.1  |

TABLE 3.2    SMRs FOR LOCAL GOVERNMENT DISTRICTS 1980-82

|                        | All ages | 0-64  | 65+   |
|------------------------|----------|-------|-------|
| WEST                   |          |       |       |
|                        |          |       |       |
| Argyll & Clyde         |          |       |       |
|                        |          |       |       |
| Argyll & Bute          | 102.8    | 100.0 | 103.8 |
| Dumbarton              | 102.7    | 98.9  | 104.2 |
| Inverclyde             | 111.3    | 122.5 | 107.0 |
| Renfrew                | 107.6    | 106.7 | 107.9 |
|                        |          |       |       |
| Ayr & Arran            |          |       |       |
|                        |          |       |       |
| Cumnock & Doon Valley  | 109.8    | 108.6 | 110.3 |
| Cunninghame            | 105.4    | 112.3 | 103.0 |
| Kilmarnock & Loudoun   | 107.6    | 103.2 | 109.2 |
| Kyle & Carrick         | 100.1    | 93.0  | 102.3 |
|                        |          |       |       |
| Greater Glasgow        |          |       |       |
|                        |          |       |       |
| Bearsden & Milngavie   | 79.7     | 68.0  | 84.5  |
| Clydebank              | 105.8    | 108.9 | 104.5 |
| Eastwood               | 79.1     | 67.7  | 83.0  |
| Glasgow City           | 111.6    | 124.2 | 107.5 |
| Strathkelvin           | 95.9     | 88.2  | 99.5  |

Lanarkshire

| | | | |
|---|---|---|---|
| Cumbernauld | 104.9 | 101.0 | 107.6 |
| East Kilbride | 90.6 | 84.6 | 94.0 |
| Hamilton | 106.0 | 105.9 | 106.0 |
| Clydesdale | 100.3 | 103.0 | 99.6 |
| Monklands | 110.3 | 112.2 | 109.3 |
| Motherwell | 107.6 | 117.3 | 107.4 |

EAST

Fife

| | | | |
|---|---|---|---|
| Dunfermline | 100.7 | 99.4 | 101.2 |
| Kirkcaldy | 101.8 | 101.7 | 101.8 |
| N.E. Fife | 84.2 | 80.1 | 85.2 |

Forth Valley

| | | | |
|---|---|---|---|
| Clackmannan | 103.9 | 102.5 | 104.5 |
| Falkirk | 96.4 | 97.7 | 95.8 |
| Stirling | 96.8 | 89.2 | 99.5 |

Grampian

| | | | |
|---|---|---|---|
| Aberdeen City | 96.3 | 86.9 | 99.3 |
| Banff & Buchan | 91.4 | 85.4 | 93.4 |
| Gordon | 82.0 | 70.6 | 85.6 |
| Kincardine & Deeside | 86.6 | 72.7 | 90.7 |
| Moray | 91.4˙ | 87.4 | 92.6 |

Lothian

| | | | |
|---|---|---|---|
| East Lothian | 90.0 | 86.1 | 91.2 |
| Edinburgh City | 93.4 | 89.8 | 94.4 |
| Midlothian | 96.3 | 85.5 | 101.3 |
| West Lothian | 101.4 | 103.0 | 100.6 |

Tayside

| | | | |
|---|---|---|---|
| Angus | 91.2 | 76.3 | 95.6 |
| Dundee City | 95.1 | 91.4 | 96.3 |
| Perth & Kinross | 93.2 | 85.1 | 95.5 |

RURAL

Borders

| | | | |
|---|---|---|---|
| Berwickshire | 87.3 | 78.8 | 89.5 |
| Ettrick & Lauderdale | 94.6 | 89.6 | 96.3 |
| Roxburgh | 96.0 | 79.4 | 100.5 |
| Tweeddale | 91.5 | 72.1 | 96.1 |

Dumfries & Galloway

| | | | |
|---|---|---|---|
| Annan & Eskdale | 86.9 | 89.9 | 85.8 |
| Nithsdale | 96.7 | 100.0 | 95.6 |
| Stewartry | 87.7 | 84.3 | 88.5 |
| Wigtown | 106.7 | 106.5 | 106.7 |

TABLE 3.2   SMRs FOR LOCAL GOVERNMENT DISTRICTS 1980-82 CONTD.

|  | All ages | 0-64 | 65+ |
|---|---|---|---|
| **Highland** | | | |
| Badenoch & Strathspey | 96.2 | 93.9 | 97.0 |
| Caithness | 108.5 | 111.8 | 107.2 |
| Inverness | 97.9 | 98.1 | 97.9 |
| Lochaber | 103.4 | 107.6 | 102.0 |
| Nairn | 102.5 | 92.6 | 105.2 |
| Ross & Cromarty | 96.2 | 93.5 | 97.1 |
| Skye & Lochalsh | 93.9 | 106.7 | 93.3 |
| Sutherland | 98.6 | 100.7 | 98.0 |
| **Islands** | | | |
| Orkney Isles | 92.0 | 97.3 | 90.5 |
| Shetland Isles | 91.1 | 76.5 | 95.4 |
| Western Isles | 96.7 | 103.9 | 95.4 |

TABLE 3.3   DISTRIBUTION OF SMRs BY POSTCODE SECTORS*

|  | All ages | | 0-64 | | 65+ | |
|---|---|---|---|---|---|---|
|  | No. | % | No. | % | No. | % |
| *(a) all SMRs* | | | | | | |
| < 70 | 23 | 3 | 124 | 15 | 18 | 2 |
| 70< 80 | 45 | 6 | 89 | 11 | 43 | 5 |
| 80< 90 | 159 | 20 | 126 | 16 | 117 | 14 |
| 90<110 | 410 | 51 | 240 | 30 | 450 | 56 |
| 110<120 | 93 | 11 | 88 | 11 | 113 | 14 |
| 120<130 | 47 | 6 | 47 | 6 | 41 | 5 |
| 130+ | 33 | 4 | 96 | 12 | 28 | 3 |
| n= | 810 | 100 | 810 | 100 | 810 | 100 |
| *(b) Significantly high or low SMRs* | | | | | | |
| < 70 | 18 | 7 | 71 | 35 | 15 | 9 |
| 70< 80 | 37 | 14 | 24 | 12 | 24 | 14 |
| 80< 90 | 65 | 25 | 3 | 1 | 35 | 20 |
| 90<110 | 4 | 2 | - | - | 3 | 2 |
| 110<120 | 66 | 25 | 3 | 1 | 38 | 22 |
| 120<130 | 43 | 16 | 21 | 10 | 32 | 19 |
| 130+ | 30 | 11 | 83 | 40 | 24 | 14 |
| n= | 263 | 100 | 205 | 100 | 171 | 100 |

*excludes sectors <500 population and institutional sectors

TABLE 3.4A    SECTOR SMRS WITH SIGNIFICANTLY HIGH OR LOW VALUES*

| (a) All ages | LOW SMRs < 90 | | | High SMRs > 110 | |
|---|---|---|---|---|---|
| | No. Sectors | No. | % of sectors | No. | % of sectors |
| WEST | 338 | 28 | 8 | 112 | 33 |
| Argyll & Clyde | 77 | 3 | 4 | 22 | 29 |
| Ayrshire & Arran | 71 | 3 | 4 | 16 | 23 |
| Greater Glasgow | 128 | 19 | 15 | 56 | 44 |
| Lanarkshire | 62 | 3 | 5 | 18 | 29 |
| EAST | 337 | 77 | 23 | 20 | 6 |
| Fife | 49 | 5 | 10 | 4 | 8 |
| Forth Valley | 44 | 5 | 11 | 5 | 11 |
| Grampian | 62 | 20 | 32 | 1 | 2 |
| Lothian | 113 | 26 | 23 | 5 | 4 |
| Tayside | 69 | 21 | 30 | 5 | 7 |
| RURAL | 135 | 15 | 11 | 7 | 5 |
| Borders | 27 | 5 | 19 | 1 | 4 |
| Dumfries & Galloway | 35 | 6 | 17 | 2 | 6 |
| Highland | 59 | 3 | 5 | 4 | 7 |
| Islands | 14 | 1 | 7 | - | - |
| ALL | 810 | 120 | 15 | 139 | 17 |

*excludes institutional sectors and < 500 population and significant SMRs 90 < 110 p = < 0.05

TABLE 3.4B    SECTOR SMRS WITH SIGNIFICANTLY HIGH OR LOW VALUES*

| (b) 0-64 | | LOW SMRs < 90 | | High SMRs > 110 | |
|---|---|---|---|---|---|
| | No. Sectors | No. | % of sectors | No. | % of sectors |
| WEST | 338 | 28 | 8 | 87 | 26 |
| Argyll & Clyde | 77 | 4 | 5 | 15 | 19 |
| Ayrshire & Arran | 71 | 2 | 3 | 8 | 11 |
| Greater Glasgow | 128 | 18 | 14 | 54 | 42 |
| Lanarkshire | 62 | 4 | 6 | 10 | 16 |
| EAST | 337 | 62 | 18 | 13 | 4 |
| Fife | 49 | 3 | 6 | 4 | 8 |
| Forth Valley | 44 | 5 | 11 | 3 | 7 |
| Grampian | 62 | 16 | 26 | 1 | 2 |
| Lothian | 113 | 20 | 18 | 4 | 4 |
| Tayside | 69 | 18 | 26 | 1 | 1 |
| RURAL | 135 | 8 | 6 | 7 | 5 |
| Borders | 27 | 5 | 19 | - | - |
| Dumfries & Galloway | 35 | 1 | 3 | 1 | 3 |
| Highland | 59 | 1 | 2 | 4 | 7 |
| Islands | 14 | 1 | 7 | 2 | 14 |
| ALL | 86 | 98 | 12 | 107 | 13 |

*excludes institutional sectors and < 500 population and significant SMRs 90 < 110 p = < 0.05

TABLE 3.5    HIGH/LOW SECTOR SMRs BY HEALTH BOARD GROUPS
(P = <0.05)

| | All ages | | 0-64 | | 65+ | |
|---|---|---|---|---|---|---|
| | <90 | 110+ | <90 | 110+ | <90 | 110+ |
| | % | % | % | % | % | % |
| (a) percent of significant SMRs | | | | | | |
| West | 23 | 81 | 29 | 81 | 23 | 78 |
| East | 64 | 14 | 63 | 12 | 55 | 16 |
| Rural | 13 | 5 | 8 | 7 | 22 | 6 |
| 100% = | 120 | 138 | 98 | 107 | 94 | 168 |

| (b) percent all sectors* | | | | |
|---|---|---|---|---|
| all ages | West | East | Rural | All |
| <90 | 8 | 23 | 11 | 14 |
| 110+ | 33 | 6 | 5 | 17 |
| 0-64 | | | | |
| <90 | 8 | 18 | 6 | 12 |
| 110+ | 25 | 4 | 5 | 13 |
| 65+ | | | | |
| <90 | 5 | 12 | 12 | 9 |
| 110+ | 22 | 4 | 4 | 11 |
| 100% = | 338 | 337 | 135 | 810 |

* more than 500 population;    excludes institutional sectors
excludes sig. SMRs 90 < 110

TABLE 3.6    CORRELATION OF AGE-SMRs

| | all ages | 0-64 | 65+ |
|---|---|---|---|
| all ages | 1.0 | | |
| 0-64 | 0.81 | 1.0 | |
| 65+ | 0.90 | 0.52 | 1.0 |

TABLE 3.7    SMRs ALL AGES FOR COUNTRIES OF THE UNITED KINGDOM
U.K. = 100

| | E | W | S | NI | E | W | S | NI |
|---|---|---|---|---|---|---|---|---|
| 1981 All causes | 98 | 104 | 115 | 116 | 98 | 103 | 114 | 116 |
| 1987 All causes | 98 | 103 | 116 | 111 | 98 | 101 | 113 | 110 |

Source: OPCS Mortality Statistics. (ref.3)

TABLE 3.8    SMRs FOR REGIONS OF ENGLAND, WALES AND SCOTLAND
1979-80, 1982-83

|  | Males 20-64 | Married Women 20-59 |  |
|---|---|---|---|
| Great Britain | 100 | 100 | |
| England and Wales | 97 | 97 | |
| Wales | 105 | 105 | |
| Scotland | 124 | 130 | |
| Clydeside | 138 | 145 | |
| North | 115 | 112 | |
| North West | 114 | 113 | |
| Yorks & Humberside | 105 | 104 | |
| West Midlands | 103 | 101 | |
| East Midlands | 95 | 96 | |
| South East | 87 | 88 | |
| South West | 87 | 87 | |
| East Anglia | 78 | 80 | |

Source: OPCS Occupational Mortality 1979-80, 1982-83, (ref.4)

TABLE 3.9    AGE-STANDARDISED SMRs 1979-80, 1982-83 BY SOCIAL CLASS

| Social class | GB | E&W | North | Scotland | Clydeside | Rem. Scotland |
|---|---|---|---|---|---|---|
| (a) Males 20 - 64 | | | | | | |
| 1 | 66 | 65 | 70 | 74 | 74 | 73 |
| 2 | 74 | 73 | 81 | 88 | 92 | 82 |
| 3M | 93 | 91 | 105 | 109 | 119 | 101 |
| 3NM | 105 | 101 | 113 | 135 | 153 | 119 |
| 4 | 114 | 112 | 135 | 131 | 148 | 118 |
| 5 | 165 | 159 | 185 | 215 | 256 | 165 |
| All | 100 = 5.57/1000 | 95 | 115 | 124 | 138 | 110 |
| (b) Married women 20 - 59 | | | | | | |
| 1 | 73 | 72 | 65 | 84 | 87 | 78 |
| 2 | 81 | 79 | 87 | 100 | 105 | 95 |
| 3M | 90 | 88 | 95 | 113 | 114 | 110 |
| 3NM | 108 | 104 | 110 | 141 | 161 | 121 |
| 4 | 121 | 118 | 144 | 150 | 168 | 135 |
| 5 | 157 | 150 | 185 | 212 | 236 | 187 |
| All | 100 = 2.23/1000 | 97 | 112 | 130 | 145 | 116 |

Source:    OPCS Occupational Mortality 1979-80, 1982-83, (ref.4)
Tables GD 19, GD 27

TABLE 3.10   MORTALITY RATES PER 1,000 POPULATION
SCOTLAND AND ENGLAND AND WALES 1980-82

| | Scotland | | England and Wales | |
|---|---|---|---|---|
| | M | F | M | F |
| 0 - 4 | 3.3 | 2.5 | 3.1 | 2.4 |
| 5 - 14 | 0.3 | 0.2 | 0.3 | 0.2 |
| 15 - 24 | 1.0 | 0.3 | 0.8 | 0.3 |
| 25 - 34 | 1.1 | 0.6 | 0.9 | 0.5 |
| 35 - 44 | 2.6 | 1.6 | 1.8 | 1.3 |
| 45 - 54 | 8.0 | 4.9 | 6.1 | 3.7 |
| 55 - 64 | 21.9 | 12.3 | 17.7 | 9.6 |
| 65 - 74 | 53.2 | 30.2 | 48.1 | 25.2 |
| 75+ | 134.9 | 99.1 | 122.5 | 90.3 |

Source: (E & W) OPCS, Mortality Statistics (ref 3)

TABLE 3.11   DISTRIBUTION OF SMRs 0-64, NORTHERN REGION WARDS AND
POSTCODE SECTORS IN SCOTLAND, 1980-82, ENGLAND AND WALES = 100

| | North % | | Scotland % | |
|---|---|---|---|---|
| < 50 | 4 | ⎫ | 1 | ⎫ |
| 50< 60 | 2 | ⎪ | 2 | ⎪ |
| 60< 70 | 3 | ⎬ 24 | 3 | ⎬ 18 |
| 70< 80 | 6 | ⎪ | 6 | ⎪ |
| 80< 90 | 9 | ⎭ | 6 | ⎭ |
| 90<100 | 14 | ⎫ 26 | 10 | ⎫ 21 |
| 100<110 | 12 | ⎭ | 11 | ⎭ |
| 110<120 | 14 | ⎫ | 13 | ⎫ |
| 120<130 | 13 | ⎬ 41 | 13 | ⎬ 45 |
| 130<140 | 8 | ⎪ | 10 | ⎪ |
| 140<150 | 6 | ⎭ | 9 | ⎭ |
| 150<160 | 3 | ⎫ | 5 | ⎫ |
| 160<170 | 2 | ⎬ 8 | 3 | ⎬ 17 |
| 170<180 | 1 | ⎪ | 4 | ⎪ |
| 180+ | 2 | ⎭ | 5 | ⎭ |
| n= | 678 | | 810 | |

Source: (Northern Region): (ref. 6)

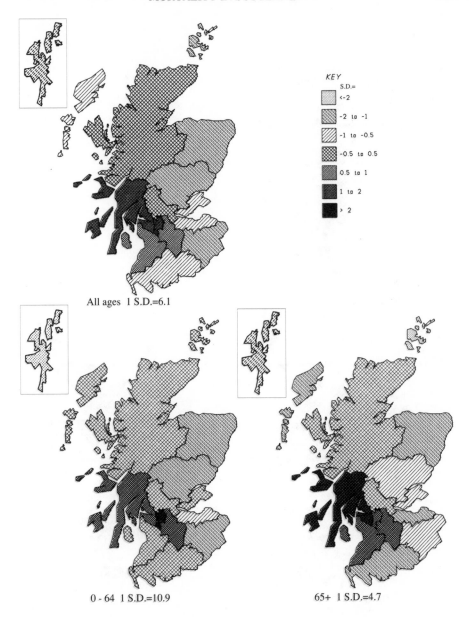

KEY

S.D.=

<-2

-2 to -1

-1 to -0.5

-0.5 to 0.5

0.5 to 1

1 to 2

> 2

All ages  1 S.D.=6.1

0 - 64  1 S.D.=10.9          65+  1 S.D.=4.7

FIGURE 3.1    SMRs for Health Boards 1980 - 82

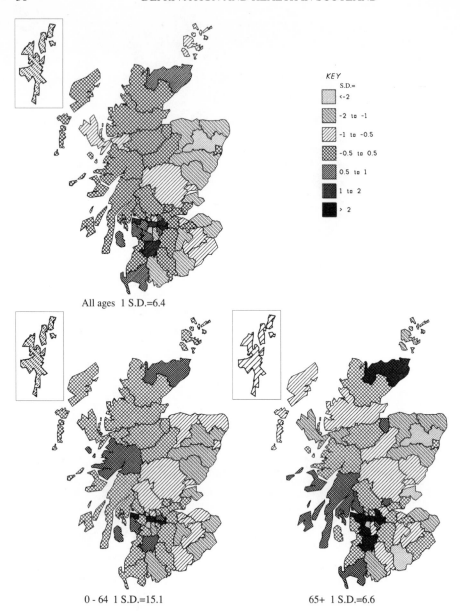

All ages  1 S.D.=6.4

KEY
S.D.=
<-2
-2 to -1
-1 to -0.5
-0.5 to 0.5
0.5 to 1
1 to 2
> 2

0 - 64  1 S.D.=15.1                65+  1 S.D.=6.6

FIGURE 3.2    SMRs FOR LOCAL GOVERNMENT DISTRICTS 1980 - 82

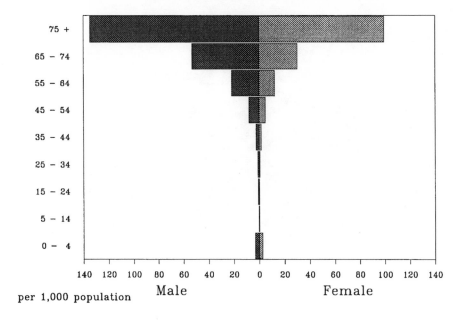

FIGURE 3.3    MORTALITY RATE BY AGE AND SEX, SCOTLAND 1980-82

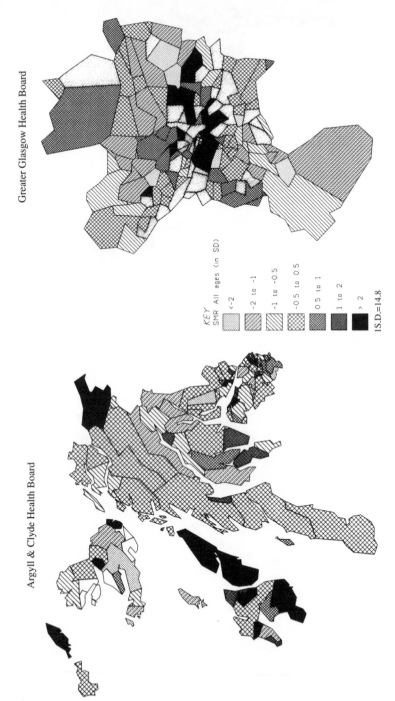

Greater Glasgow Health Board

1 S.D.=14.8

Argyll & Clyde Health Board

KEY
SMR All ages (in SD)

< -2
-2 to -1
-1 to -0.5
-0.5 to 0.5
0.5 to 1
1 to 2
> 2

1S.D.=14.8

FIGURE 3.4A    SMRs ALL AGES: WEST

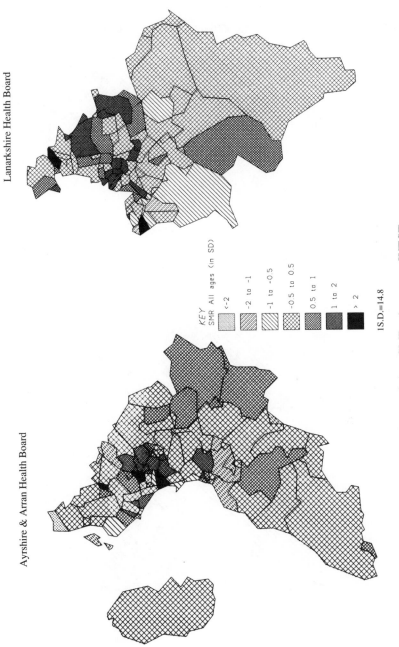

1 S.D.=14.8

Lanarkshire Health Board

Ayrshire & Arran Health Board

KEY
SMR All ages (in SD)

< -2
-2 to -1
-1 to -0.5
-0.5 to 0.5
0.5 to 1
1 to 2
> 2

1S.D.=14.8

FIGURE 3.4B    SMRs ALL AGES: WEST

Tayside Health Board

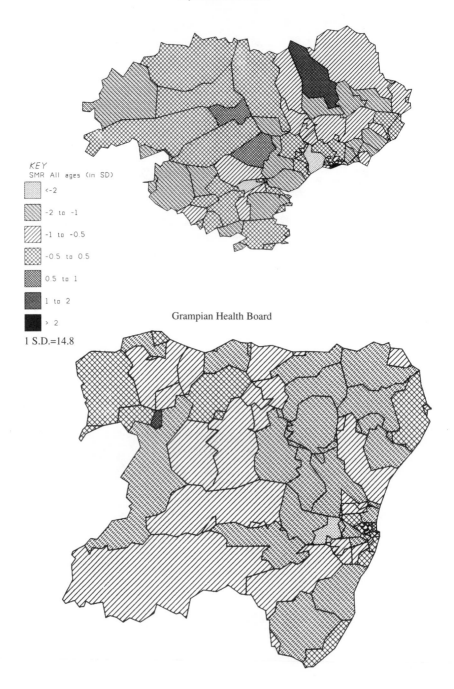

KEY
SMR All ages (in SD)

□ < -2
□ -2 to -1
□ -1 to -0.5
□ -0.5 to 0.5
■ 0.5 to 1
■ 1 to 2
■ > 2

1 S.D.=14.8

Grampian Health Board

FIGURE 3.4c    SMRs ALL AGES: EAST

Lothian Health Board

Fife Health Board

Forth Valley Health Board

KEY
SMR All ages (in SD)

<2
-2 to -1
-1 to -0.5
-0.5 to 0.5
0.5 to 1
1 to 2
> 2

1 S.D.=14.8

FIGURE 3.4D    SMRs ALL AGES: EAST

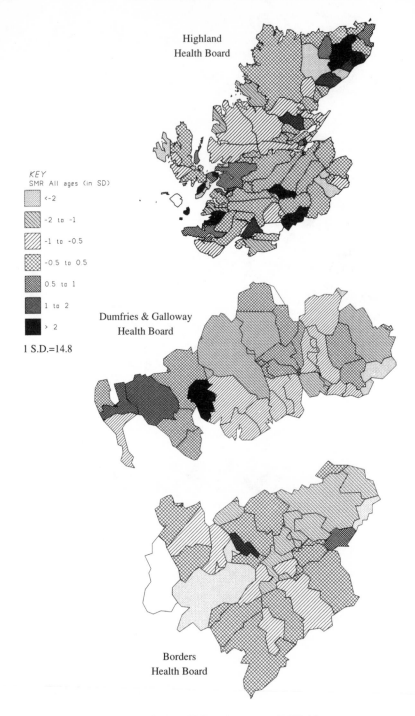

FIGURE 3.4E    SMRS ALL AGES: RURAL

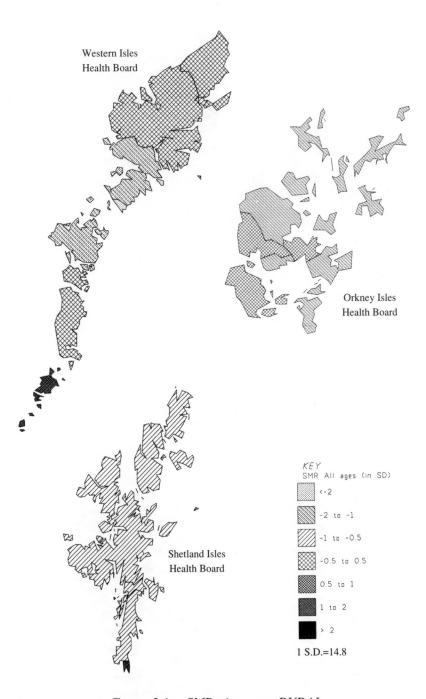

KEY
SMR All ages (in SD)

- <-2
- -2 to -1
- -1 to -0.5
- -0.5 to 0.5
- 0.5 to 1
- 1 to 2
- > 2

1 S.D.=14.8

FIGURE 3.4F   SMRs ALL AGES: RURAL

FIGURE 3.4G   SMRs ALL AGES: CITIES

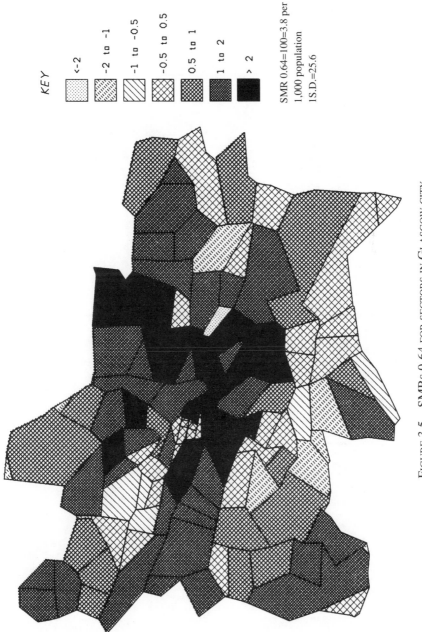

KEY

<-2

-2 to -1

-1 to -0.5

-0.5 to 0.5

0.5 to 1

1 to 2

> 2

SMR 0.64=100=3.8 per
1,000 population
1S.D.=25.6

FIGURE 3.5    SMRs 0-64 FOR SECTORS IN GLASGOW CITY

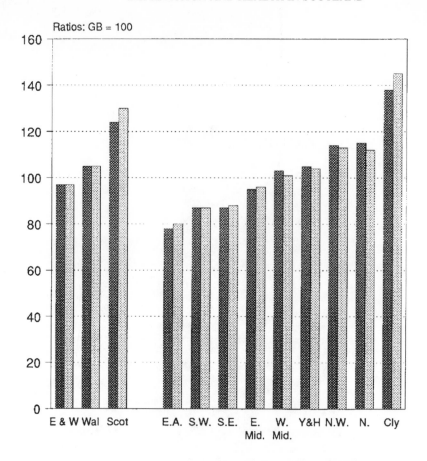

Ratios: GB = 100

Source Occupational Mortality Report

FIGURE 3.6    SMRs FOR REGIONS 1979-83

# CHAPTER 4

# Mortality and Deprivation

Mortality and deprivation are strongly associated as can be seen from the scatter diagrams in Fig. 4.1 and the strong correlations: 0.72 at all ages, 0.75 at 0-64 and 0.53 at 65 and over (table 4.1). The correlation coefficients are seen to be slightly lower with the individual variables composing the index (although by very little for 'no car' with SMR 0-64), and to be very much higher with deprivation than with the social class measure (% of population with head in social class 4 or 5). For all three mortality measures, no car and male unemployment correlate more highly than low social class and overcrowding. Association with a range of other variables shows the SMR all ages and 0-64 to be highly correlated (0.67 and 0.72) with the proportion of the population (in private households) who are unable to work because of permanent sickness and just slightly less so with the temporarily sick. As one might expect, mortality is negatively correlated with the proportion of the population having higher qualifications and owning housing, and, to a lesser degree, with the population who were born outside Scotland but in the U.K., and with the level of migration into the area within the previous year.

## *Gradients in Mortality*

Figure 4.1 presents the scatter diagrams and table 4.2 (and Figure 4.2) summarise the information in these to show the very considerable gradients from affluent to deprived areas: death rates at 0-64 are more than twice as high in the most deprived areas than in the most affluent, and even for the elderly the gradient may be observed although the order of difference is only 1.3 times.

For comparison these gradients are also shown for quintiles of the distribution in table 4.3, and can be observed to exhibit a much less extended range, particularly at 0-64, compared with DEPCAT which provides a more informative basis for disclosing differentials in mortality within the population than does this more conventional distribution. Around 7% of the population are found in categories with extreme affluence or deprivation, compared with 20% on the quintile basis.

The correlations seen in table 4.1 for the age group 0-64 are similar to those reported for the wards in the Northern Region of England[1] although it should be noted that neither the definition of the variables in the deprivation index nor the statistical techniques used to derive this measure are exactly the same. The pattern is essentially the same in both areas, although all of the coefficients are higher in Scotland than in the North, i.e. the relationship is more strongly observed. (Table 4.4)

In this age group in both of these analyses the combined deprivation measure explains rather more of the variation in mortality ($R^2$ = 56% Scotland, 38% North) than any individual indicator, although no car and unemployment are close runners-up. In both results low social class provides a less effective explanatory variable although the correlation coefficient for Scotland (0.62) is the same as for the overall deprivation measure in the North; the lower correlation in Townsend's analysis (0.57) may be influenced by the inclusion of social class 3 manual in this indicator which is not included in his overall measure.

## Variation by Age and Sex

The enhanced mortality data for 1980-85 were used to examine the gradients by age and sex for the seven deprivation categories (table 4.5, Fig. 4.3). Despite the six years of data the numbers remain relatively modest at younger ages, 5-14, 15-24, and at these ages the pattern is not clear. It is present however for the 0-4 age group, being stronger for females than males and particularly strong at the age groups 25-34 and 35-44, the ratio between the most affluent and most deprived areas being greatest for females 25-34 at 3.9. Except at this age group and 0-4 the ratio is generally greater in males than in females in the age groups under 65. After age 35-44 the differential slowly diminishes, but nevertheless continues and, although small, is still apparent in the age group 75 and over.

Although the 1980-85 data contains years which are getting remote from the census, with the exception of the age groups 5-14 and 15-24 the data are remarkably similar to those for 1980-82, based on half the number of deaths (see Appendix table B4.1). The effect of using six years data has been, in general, to effect some regression to the mean, i.e. the values for the most affluent and most deprived sectors tend to be less extreme than in the data based on three years only.

## Comparison with other studies

The gradients at 0-64 may be compared with those for social class (for 1979-80, 1982-83) for men aged 20-64 and married women 20-59, from the Occupational Mortality decennial supplement.[2] (Table 4.6)

These data present a similar picture but with lesser consistency in the gradients than those by deprivation category, lower ratios in social class 4 than in DEPCAT 6 and ratios in social class 5 which are much higher than in the most deprived category. Of course not all deaths and population can be allocated to a social class which may affect the data, but overestimation of the ratios for social class 5 has also been suggested due to numerator/denominator bias, individuals being described with less specific occupations on the death certificate than on the census thus inflating the number of deaths in the residual occupations and in social class 5.[2]

Greater reliance has been placed on social class analysis from the Longitudinal Study (LS), which has been designed to overcome this particular problem, any death in the sample being attributed to the same social class as recorded for the individual at the 1971 Census. For men aged 15-64 at that time the ratio between social class 1 and social class 5 increased from 1.4 in 1971-75, to 1.9 for deaths in 1976-81, and 1.8 in 1981-85, with the highest SMR value of 129 in social class 5 occurring in the latest period.[3]

RANGE AND RATIO IN MORTALITY GRADIENTS FOR MEN AGES 15-64 IN 1971, ENGLAND & WALES (LS)

| Deaths in: | Range | Ratio |
|---|---|---|
| 1971-75 | 79-111 | 1.4 |
| 1976-81 | 64-119 | 1.9 |
| 1981-85 | 72-129 | 1.8 |

These ratios and the SMR values for the lowest social group are less than those observed in the gradients by deprivation for the population aged 0-64 (table 4.2) or for men aged 20-64 in table 4.6.

At older ages the 'first reliable estimates' of social class gradients in England & Wales are also supplied by the Longitudinal Study, again for men, for deaths in the period 1976-81.[4]

RANGE AND RATIOS IN MORTALITY GRADIENTS FOR OLDER MEN

| | 65-74 | | 75+ | |
| | Range | Ratio | Range | Ratio |
|---|---|---|---|---|
| Scotland (1980-82) | 81-124 | 1.6 | 96-110 | 1.2 |
| England & Wales (1976-81)* | 68-109 | 1.5 | 73-116 | 1.6 |

*age in 1971

These data exhibit a ratio between extremes of the social class categories which is similar to that between the most affluent and most deprived DEPCATs for men aged 65-74, although the range in the values is very different. At 75 and over the range is much wider in the LS data, and these observations have resulted in the comment that 'mortality gradients after retirement are almost as steep as those found in the later stages of working life'[4] but this is not borne out by the Scottish data which show a continuing diminution from 45-54, with very little range remaining at age 75 and over. (Table 4.5)

Many factors, including the time scale, country and completeness of the data, may affect the possibilities of true comparison. The LS is free of the numerator/denominator bias which exists in the Occupational Mortality decennial supplement but suffers from other bias due to some proportion of the population, and hence deaths, not being classified to an occupation (and thus to a social class).

In younger men (15-64) mortality was much higher in the non-classified, and, in part, the non-classified accounts for the more restricted gradients found in the social class data from this source in the period from 1971-75. Later data show that the effects of these (health-related) exclusions tend to wear off.[3] In older men (deaths in 1976-81) mortality for those not classified was high at 65-74, with an SMR of 162, but at 75 and over had a low values of only 103. It is possible therefore that both of these values (high and low) are exerting some influence on the range observed by social class in these two age groups. Another factor to take into account is that many deaths will fall into an older age group than that which applied at the time of the 1971 census.

Townsend's data provide the only substantial and accessible body of data for comparison with a deprivation-based analysis and, for men and women combined, the ratio of 2.2 in the mortality gradients by DEP at 0-64 is the same as that reported by him[1] in relation to the worst and best deciles on his overall health index, although lower than the ratio of 2.8 reported for deciles when ranked by the SMR 0-64. On this latter basis Townsend also found the range in variation greatest and relative death rates highest in the North in the two decades leading up to retirement, 45-54, 55-64, with the range between the worst and best deciles also being wider at 0-14 than at 15-44, whereas in Scotland the widest range appears in the two decades 25-34 and 35-44. These data for the North are slightly difficult to interpret on a comparative basis however since the wards are ranked on the health measure and since almost 80% of deaths in the age range 0-64 actually occur between 45 and 64 it is perhaps not surprising that the gradients are widest in these two age-groups. Townsend and his colleagues do indeed show that 'higher premature mortality at every quintile step corresponds with higher unemployment, greater overcrowding and lower levels of car ownership and owner occupation', but nevertheless the suspicion must arise that the gradients could look slightly different if ranked on the basis of deprivation.

## Mortality, Social Class and Deprivation

For a sub-set of the data it proved possible to examine deaths by social class of the individual in relation to the deprivation value of the area. This analysis, for deaths in 1980-82 and for males aged 20-64, was made possible by the supply of additional population tables by age and social class (at 10% level) for postcode sectors. The analysis is confined to men since the proportion of women classified to a social class on the census is much lower than for men; 16% of women aged 20-64 in Scotland are not assigned to an occupation (whether own or husband's) compared with 8% of men in the same age-group, and occupation is also less well recorded on the death certificate: only 3% of certificates for men aged 20-64 fail to record an occupation compared with 23% for women (own or husband's occupation) in the same age group.[2] Fewer women would have an own occupation on either document. Both populations and deaths by age and social class were aggregated for all postcode sectors within a category of deprivation and death rates by age and SMRs for the age group 20-64 were calculated, the overall death rate being 6.75 per 1000 for the population group.

The SMRs by social class and by deprivation (table 4.7) show that the gradients are very similar. The differences are that (except at 20-24) the gradients by deprivation category increase consistently from the most affluent to most deprived level whereas there are some exceptions in the social class data; and that the values for social class 5 always exceed those for the most severe deprivation category. (It may be noted that 7% of the population is to be found in the lowest categories on both classifications). Since PCS within the lowest deprivation category are unlikely to be comprised 100% of population in social class 5 this observation is not unexpected, but over-estimation of the rates for social class 5 [2] means that the high values must be interpreted with caution.

The data (table 4.7) are consistent in showing that the influence of low social class/deprivation is most extreme in the age groups 25-44 on both measures as is also seen in table 4.5, although again the general unreliability of social class 5 rates must be borne in mind.

For each social class there exists a gradient in mortality by deprivation category (table 4.8) with mortality ratios increasing from the most affluent to the most deprived areas in a mainly consistent fashion.

Some population in each social class is to be found at each level of deprivation (table 4.9) although, as one would expect, there is a strong association between the two measures, affluent areas having a higher proportion of people in social classes 1, 2 and 3 non-manual, and deprived areas more in manual social classes 3, 4 and 5. The death rates by deprivation categories may be standardised for differences both in the social class composition and in the age structure of the population, and the differentials seen between affluent and deprived areas are diminished to some degree by this procedure, the range changing from 64 to 146 (table 4.7B) when standardised by age alone, to 77 to 132 when social class is also taken into account (Fig, 4.4). A strong gradient remains nevertheless with the most deprived category having a rate 70% greater than the most affluent compared with 123% greater for the age-standardised value. Of course social classes are not homogeneous [5] and some of the trend in mortality seen may be explained by different occupational groups within a social class living in different types of areas and having differing mortality experience. The data strongly suggest however that the area characteristics continue to exert a considerable influence over and above that due to the social class characteristics of the population in the area. [6]

## The Distribution of SMRs by Deprivation

### Sector level

The distribution of SMRs at postcode sector level by deprivation category underlines the strong association between these two measures. In the most affluent areas 81% of SMRs all ages are less than 90 while in the most deprived areas 89% are over 110 (table 4.10, Fig. 4.5a). Fifty percent of all values fall between 90 and 110 and the middle categories of deprivation (3, 4 and 5) all have more than 50% in this band. The transition from lesser to greater mortality with increasing deprivation is clearly seen in categories 3 and 5 with the former having only 7% of the SMR values above 110 and the latter only 5% below 90.

At 0-64 the picture is repeated (Fig. 4.5b) with greater emphasis, a higher proportion having more extreme values; 97% of SMRs in the most affluent sectors are below 90 (and 71% below 70), with the most deprived areas having 97% above

110, and 81% greater than 130. (The more extended distributions for the age SMRs may be seen in Appendix tables B4.2/3/4 part (a)).

At 65 and over the values are less extreme and 56% are to be found in the middle band. The same pattern still persists nevertheless with affluent sectors having a higher proportion of low SMRs and high SMRs being more common in deprived categories.

The pattern for SMR values which are significant at the 95% level is even more dramatic. At all ages 32% (259) of sector values differ significantly. Of the 120 values below 90, 74 (62%) are found in the two most affluent categories, and none in the two most deprived categories (table 4.11).

Of the 139 SMRs over 110, 53% are in the two most deprived categories, and only 1% in the most affluent. At 0-64 significant values are fewer, accounting for 25% of sector SMRs, but the pattern is repeated with the association being more pronounced; no low values (<90) are found in the two more deprived categories and no high ones (>110) in the two most affluent.

At 65 and over 21% of sector SMRs differ significantly from 100. The pattern is less pronounced than at 0-64 with the two most affluent categories having only 50% of the low values and the two most deprived only 45% of those of 110 or more compared with 71% and 68% at 0-64. Although weaker the association between deprivation and SMR can nevertheless still be observed. (Appendix tables B4.2/3/4 part (b) show the extended distributions.)

Table 4.11 also shows the very high proportion of affluent sectors with significantly low values, 55% and 27% in DEPCATS 1 and 2 at 0-64, and the more common experience of SMRs over 110 in deprived sectors: 55% and 86% in DEPCATS 6 and 7.

## Health Boards

As well as at postcode sector level the association between deprivation and mortality can be seen at both health board (HB) and local government district (LGD) levels. The gradients in mortality for HBs are not mirrored entirely by their deprivation score (table 4.12) although all boards with positive (deprived) scores have SMRs over 100 and Borders and Grampian have both least deprivation and lowest mortality. Three boards are not consistent with the general trend: Tayside and Lothian where mortality is slightly lower than would be predicted on the basis of their deprivation scores, and Highland where it is much higher.

## Health Board groups: is mortality constant over deprivation categories?

The association between deprivation and mortality is strongest within the Western boards, followed by the Eastern boards and fairly weak in the Rural boards. (Table 4.13) Although the SMRs show as much variation in Rural boards there is much lesser variation in the deprivation scores (table B2.5) as can be seen in the scatter diagrams for groups of health boards (Fig. 4.6 a,b). These show the gradient between deprivation and SMR to be strongest in Western boards, followed by the East and least in the Rural boards.

Mortality ratios by deprivation category for the three groups of health boards show that at all ages mortality is consistently lower in Eastern boards compared with Western boards (table 4.14), at each level of deprivation. Although rates for

Rural boards are below the West they are not much so for some categories, and they are generally slightly higher than Eastern boards except for DEPCAT 5.

The same pattern emerges for 0-64: the higher mortality rates in Western boards are again apparent at all levels of deprivation, with the values for rural boards again being greater than Eastern boards. The differential between West and East coast boards is greater at 0-64 than at all ages - the overall ratio being 1.22 (110/90) compared with 1.13 (107/95).

A similar picture is seen for the SMRs by social class for males 20-64 (table 4.15): with the exception of social class 1 the mortality ratios are always higher in the West than in the East, with Rural boards occupying an intermediate position in the middle of the distribution but with mortality in social classes 1 and 2 being higher in these areas, and in social class 5 just lowest.

Western boards then have higher mortality for equivalent levels of deprivation (and social class) than do Eastern boards; the higher comparative overall ratios of 107 and 110 in the West are in part attributable to this enhanced mortality but in part also to more population and more deaths in Western boards occurring in more deprived areas. Since the correlation between deprivation and mortality is not complete these findings are not surprising; nevertheless, they serve to remind us that deprivation differences do not fully explain differences in mortality and that the East/West divide in Scotland may be equally as relevant as the North/South divide in England is seen to be.

The relationship of SMR with DEP is shown by the b-coefficient which quantifies the slope of the line which may be observed in plots in figures 4.6a and 4.6b. Both at all ages and at age 0-64 these values show greater consistency between the area groups than do the correlation coefficients. At all ages the overall value is 2.98 i.e. the SMR changes by 2.98% for every unit of the DEP score (table 4.16). These values vary only between 2.85 in Western areas and 2.29 in Rural. At age 0-64 this gradient is much steeper, as has been shown (Fig. 4.2), and in this instance around a 5% change in SMR occurs for each unit of DEP with the gradient being slightly stronger in the West than in the East. The % change is slightly steeper in Rural areas although the pattern is not so pronounced as in the other two areas, as can be seen in Fig. 4.6b. At age 65 and over the gradient has been shown to be less steep (Fig. 4.2) and this is reflected in the b-coefficient, 2.04 overall, varying between 1.23 (Rural) and 1.89 (West).

The 95% confidence intervals indicate that there are no significant differences between the three areas in the relationship between mortality and deprivation at any of the age-groups although deprivation explains a very small proportion of the variation in death rates in Rural areas as shown by the $R^2$ values.

## Local government districts

For local government districts the association between DEP and SMR is seen in Figure 4.7. In general there is little deviation from the linear trend but this occurs for a few districts and those with outlying results are listed in table 4.17 in order of degree of deviance.

Positive signs indicate that the district has higher mortality than would be predicted on the basis of the deprivation score and a negative sign that SMR is lower than would be expected. The value gives an indication of the comparative order of difference. One district, Caithness, appears in each of these lists, and heads two of them, with deaths in excess of those expected; Nairn and Kilmarnock appear twice, with excess mortality. Districts with mortality lower than predicted are Dundee (all ages and 0-64) N.E. Fife (all ages and 65 and over), and Berwickshire (all ages and 65 and over).

At all ages and 65 and over districts with excess mortality are distributed in various regions and health boards, but at 0-64 four of the districts are within Highland region, the other two being in Lanarkshire health board (Clydesdale) and Orkney. At all ages and 0-64 districts with lower than expected mortality are found within Tayside and Borders regions, and at 65 and over there is one district from Fife and one from the Borders, but Dumfries and Galloway is represented by two districts with less than expected mortality and one, Wigtown, with mortality higher than expected. There is no obvious link with an urban/rural index since districts with both excess and deficit mortality are found in rural areas but, with the exception of Dundee, Kilmarnock and Cumbernauld, urban districts are notably absent from this list of outliers, i.e. their mortality is more likely to conform to the model.

## Urban and Rural Characteristics

It will be apparent from the SMRs for LGDs that there is a tendency for mortality to be higher in urban districts. The association is seen for PCS grouped into urban/rural bands (as described in chapter 2), in table 4.18: SMRs for each of the three age groups are highest in the most urban band and lowest in the most rural. For 0-64 there is a consistent gradient with SMR values falling from 109 to 89 but the lack of any differentiation between the three middle categories at 65 and over also affects the SMRs for all ages. The SMRs were calculated also for all EDs within a specific U/R category. This distribution has similar characteristics but produces a wider range at 0-64, falling from 115 to 85. While all three SMRs in the most urban band exceed those based on PCS this is not so for the most rural band and the SMRs all ages and 65 and over exceed the PCS-based values. This apparent inconsistency may reflect the fact that PCS with value 5 (i.e. composed entirely of EDs which are all in the most rural band) may lay claim to greater rurality of character than all the EDs with this value, which include a large number which will have been aggregated into the next to most rural band in respect of sectors.

The inter-relationship between mortality, deprivation and the urban/rural factor was explored further by means of a regression analysis using SMR, DEP and the urban/rural score at PCS level. With both DEP and U/R entered simultaneously DEP rather than U/R was shown to have a significant effect in explaining SMR with U/R making virtually no additional contribution, as may be see by the values below:

T-VALUES FOR REGRESSION OF SMR ON DEP AND U/R OVER PCS

| SMR | DEP | U/R |
|---|---|---|
| all ages | 31.05*** | 0.06 N.S. |
| 0-64 | 37.45*** | 0.01 N.S. |
| 65+ | 16.34*** | -0.29 N.S. |

Deprivation, not the urban/rural nature of the area, may thus be regarded as the more powerful determinant of mortality levels.

## Explaining Variations in Mortality

### Health boards and local government districts

Given the strong gradient of mortality rates by deprivation it is not unexpected that boards and other areas with severe deprivation also have high mortality. How far may these variations be explained by differences in deprivation? The rates may be adjusted by standardising for population differences (in the same way as for age and sex) to allow for the contribution of deprivation to these values; adjusted SMRs are calculated using the age/sex mortality rates by deprivation category (see Appendix table B4.1) applied to populations by age, sex and deprivation to give expected deaths. The effect of this procedure is a slight reduction in the range between health boards and local government districts a shown. The main reduction in range occurs for the age group 0-64, which falls from 81-115 to 88-109 for health boards and from 68-124 to 79-122 for local government districts. (Table 4.19)

The general effect is for health boards with high SMRs to show a reduction in values, and for those with low values to show an increase (table 4.20). The reduction for Glasgow health board, with the most severe deprivation is most dramatic, the SMR all ages being adjusted from 107 to 101, and at 0-64 from 115 to 103. A reduction in SMR values also occurs for other West coast boards, but to a minor extent, with all still remaining over 100. The effect of standardising is most striking for boards whose deprivation composition varies most from the Scotland average — thus the effect for Ayr & Arran is small. Boards with low values universally experience increases in SMR values, Grampian and the Borders in particular; although the adjusted SMR 0-64 for Borders is still the lowest in Scotland, that for Grampian moves to a level above that for Tayside and this is the case also for all ages and 65 and over. The adjusted value for Fife (103 at 0-64) puts the area on a level with some West coast boards. The most remarkable result occurs however for Highland, the SMR 0-64 being adjusted to 110, exceeding any other board.

The shifts in values for LGDs gives more detailed information (table 4.21) and show that the increase in SMR value in the Highlands occurs in all districts, since they are all in the more affluent half of the deprivation distribution. The highest adjusted SMR all ages (112) is found in Caithness, as is the SMR 0-64 (122). These findings for Highland districts are in accordance with the greater than expected mortality reported in table 4.17.

It could also be the case that the particular deprivation measure fails to reflect the dimension of affluence/deprivation in rural areas but, against this argument, it may be noted that both the original and adjusted SMRs in the Highland districts exceed those observed in the other rural districts, with the exception of Wigtown. As for health boards, the changes for districts are greater for the more extreme values; within Glasgow Health Board for instance the value for Eastwood is adjusted up from 79 to 92 for all ages and from 68 to 96 for 0-64, while those for Glasgow City fall from 112 to 102 (all ages) and from 124 to 104 (0-64); districts within Glasgow health board therefore become more similar in this outcome measure once their deprivation characteristics are taken into account. In Eastern and Rural districts the pattern is generally of an increase from a low to higher value, the largest adjustments being for the lower values (Gordon from 82-92 all ages, 71-90 at 0-64). Only three districts in the East show a fall in values: West Lothian, Dundee City and the Western Isles, each of these having greater deprivation than other districts in the East or in the Rural areas.

## Deprivation vs Social Class as an explanation

For males aged 20-64 the SMRs for health boards have been standardised by both social class and deprivation as well as by age (using rates based on data in table 4.7) and the adjusted values are seen in table 4.22 and Fig. 4.8. Standardising for social class differences has virtually no effect on the death rates (col. b), while the effect of standardising by deprivation (col. c) is dramatic and causes a major shift in SMRs and in the rank order of health boards: the SMRs for Glasgow is impressively reduced, from 119 to 105, while those for Highland and the Islands increase considerably. As seen in table 4.20, the result of this procedure is to increase the SMRs for all boards which were below 100 originally, (as well as for Highland and the Islands) and to reduce those for the four boards which constitute the Strathclyde region. Adjusting for deprivation reduces the range in the SMRs from 83-119 to 87-113, while adjusting for social class reduces the range only to 84-118.

The dramatic difference in the results of standardising by social class and deprivation is due of course to the population distribution on these two measures; while health boards, and local government districts, vary very considerably in terms of deprivation, Figure 4.9 shows that in comparison health boards are very similar in terms of social class. Although Glasgow has the highest proportion of men aged 20-64 in social class 5, the proportion in social classes 4 and 5 (25%) is exceeded by the Borders (30%) and Dumfries and Galloway (28%), the high proportions in social class 4 (over 20%) in some boards no doubt reflecting employment in agricultural occupations.

At the other end of the scale Glasgow and Lanark have only 20%/21% in social classes 1 and 2 (well below other mainland boards) with Lothian having the highest proportion (29%). Despite these variations it can be seen that the general pattern of the distributions are not dissimilar, with the highest percentage in all cases in class 3 manual. Except for the Borders, Lanark and Orkney the proportion of population in social class 3 manual falls within ±3 of the overall proportion of 37% (i.e. 34%-40%).

The distribution by deprivation category on the other hand is much more varied; the mid-category 4 has 25% of the population overall but within boards (excluding islands) this ranges from 9% (Glasgow) to 36% (Fife). Equally Glasgow has 50% of its population in the two most deprived categories, the range being from zero to

21% (Lanark) in other boards. Deprivation therefore offers a better discriminatory measure of differences in the circumstances of populations and also provides the basis to explain much (although not all) of the variation in death rates between boards.

## England and Wales and Scotland

It has been shown (chapter 3) that mortality in Scotland is higher than in England (and all of its regions) and in Wales, the SMR calculated over the three years 1980-82 providing values for Scotland of 112 at all ages and 125 at 0-64 (England and Wales = 100). Mortality rates for Scottish sectors are also shown to exceed those for wards in the Northern Region, which has the highest mortality (with the North West) of the regions of England and Wales (chapter 3), and more of the population in Scotland is found living at more severe levels of deprivation than in England and Wales (chapter 2). How much of the excess mortality can be explained by this greater deprivation?

To examine this the rates for England and Wales have been standardised using the age/sex/deprivation mortality rates for Scotland (Appendix table B4.1) which have been used in adjusting for the effects of deprivation on mortality within Scotland. The normal procedure would be to standardise the Scotland data using an England and Wales or Great Britain basis but mortality rates by age, sex and deprivation are not available for these populations.

Populations by age, sex and deprivation category were aggregated over the 9,265 wards in England and Wales and expected deaths calculated for each cell and summed to a total. They were then compared with the observed deaths in 1980-82 to give the SMR values. This procedure implies that the gradients in mortality which are observed within Scotland also exist within England and Wales; we believe this assumption to be quite realistic in the light of the data from Townsend [1] who reports a ratio of 2.2 between the wards in the worst and best quintiles for the SMR 0-64, which exactly mirrors the differential seen in our own data in table 4.2. The results are seen in table 4.23.

In part (a) the SMRs are standardised to the basis of Scotland = 100. When standardised by age and sex alone the higher mortality already seen for Scotland (tables 3.7/3.8) results in SMRs for England and Wales which are respectively 11% and 18% below the Scotland level at all ages and 0-64. Standardising for deprivation in addition results in a radical reduction in this differential - to 4% and 5% below the level of Scotland for the respective age groups. These ratios may be converted to the more familiar picture of England and Wales = 100 (part b) when the SMRs fall from 112 to 104 for all ages, and from 122 to 105 at 0-64, when the differing levels of deprivation in the two countries are taken into account. Adjusting for deprivation clearly has more impact at younger ages and this is to be expected in the light of the much steeper mortality gradients below the age of 65. (table 4.5) It appears from these data that a substantial part of the differential in mortality between England and Wales and Scotland may therefore be attributed to the more adverse socio-economic circumstances of the Scottish population. As within Scotland (table 4.22) differences in social class composition do not offer an adequate basis for explaining these differences since the populations of the two countries are not very dissimilar on this basis. [7]

All these data tell us that the association between deprivation and death is strong but they do not tell us anything about the processes involved. It would be unwise to suggest that not having a car, being unemployed, in a low social class or living in overcrowded conditions are by themselves a cause of mortality, or morbidity, though some of these may have direct effects. Factors which may play a more primary role in influencing these associations are explored in a later chapter.

TABLE 4.1   CORRELATION OF SMRs WITH SOCIAL VARIABLES

|  | All ages | 0-64 | 65+ |
|---|---|---|---|
| Deprivation | 0.72 | 0.75 | 0.53 |
| No car | 0.69 | 0.74 | 0.50 |
| Unemployment | 0.70 | 0.71 | 0.51 |
| Low social class | 0.57 | 0.62 | 0.39 |
| Overcrowding | 0.64 | 0.64 | 0.49 |
| One parent households | 0.59 | 0.64 | 0.41 |
| Temporary sick (M) | 0.60 | 0.62 | 0.43 |
| Permanent sick (M & F) | 0.67 | 0.72 | 0.47 |
| With higher qualifications | -0.52 | -0.56 | -0.38 |
| Owner-occupier | -0.54 | -0.55 | -0.41 |
| Born elsewhere UK | -0.44 | -0.47 | -0.34 |
| 1 year migration | -0.15 | -0.l5 | -0.10 |

TABLE 4. 2   GRADIENTS IN MORTALITY BY DEPRIVATION CATEGORY

| | DEPCAT | | | | | | | Rate/1000 =100 |
|---|---|---|---|---|---|---|---|---|
| | Affluent | | | | | Deprived | | |
| | 1 | 2 | 3 | 4 | 5 | 6 | 7 | |
| All ages | 83 | 89 | 95 | 100 | 107 | 113 | 125 | 12.6 |
| 0-64 | 64 | 79 | 91 | 98 | 110 | 125 | 141 | 3.8 |
| 65+ | 90 | 92 | 96 | 101 | 105 | 108 | 118 | 66.7 |

TABLE 4.3   GRADIENTS IN MORTALITY BY DEPRIVATION QUINTILE

| | Affluent | | | | Deprived |
|---|---|---|---|---|---|
| | 1 | 2 | 3 | 4 | 5 |
| All ages | 87 | 95 | 100 | 105 | 117 |
| 0-64 | 74 | 90 | 97 | 108 | 130 |
| 65+ | 80 | 92 | 98 | 107 | 112 |

TABLE 4.4   MORTALITY 0-64 AND DEPRIVATION INDICATORS: SCOTLAND AND NORTHERN REGION

|  | Scotland | North |
|---|---|---|
| Deprivation | 0.75 | 0.62 |
| No car | 0.74 | 0.61 |
| Unemployment | 0.71 | 0.61 |
| Low social class | 0.62 | 0.57 |
| Overcrowding | 0.64 | 0.55 |
| Tenure not owner occupied | 0.54 | 0.39 |

TABLE 4.5   AGE-SEX SPECIFIC DEATH RATIOS 1980-85 FOR DEPRIVATION CATEGORIES
(Overall death rate each age-sex group = 100)

| | | Affluent 1 | 2 | 3 | 4 | 5 | Deprived 6 | 7 | No. of Deaths | Ratio 7:1 |
|---|---|---|---|---|---|---|---|---|---|---|
| 0 - 4 | M | 81 | 88 | 92 | 102 | 108 | 109 | 125 | 2875 | 1.5 |
| | F | 66 | 89 | 92 | 102 | 107 | 113 | 132 | 2131 | 2.0 |
| 5 - 14 | M | 77 | 83 | 105 | 104 | 92 | 99 | 139 | 710 | 1.8 |
| | F | 106 | 109 | 95 | 91 | 115 | 104 | 86 | 442 | 0.8 |
| 15 - 24 | M | 70 | 98 | 109 | 102 | 92 | 91 | 122 | 2317 | 1.7 |
| | F | 96 | 107 | 100 | 93 | 98 | 96 | 119 | 847 | 1.2 |
| 25 - 34 | M | 57 | 80 | 90 | 104 | 109 | 118 | 159 | 2349 | 2.8 |
| | F | 46 | 81 | 84 | 102 | 116 | 122 | 180 | 1222 | 3.9 |
| 35 - 44 | M | 58 | 74 | 87 | 103 | 110 | 133 | 171 | 4401 | 2.9 |
| | F | 68 | 78 | 87 | 100 | 113 | 128 | 158 | 2889 | 2.3 |
| 45 - 54 | M | 62 | 75 | 89 | 98 | 113 | 132 | 146 | 12697 | 2.3 |
| | F | 67 | 76 | 93 | 99 | 109 | 126 | 139 | 8107 | 2.1 |
| 55 - 64 | M | 66 | 81 | 90 | 99 | 110 | 123 | 138 | 33142 | 2.1 |
| | F | 66 | 81 | 92 | 99 | 111 | 124 | 129 | 21341 | 1.9 |
| 65 - 74 | M | 81 | 86 | 94 | 101 | 106 | 114 | 124 | 57956 | 1.5 |
| | F | 77 | 86 | 93 | 101 | 109 | 113 | 127 | 44894 | 1.7 |
| 75+ | M | 93 | 93 | 96 | 102 | 106 | 106 | 110 | 69644 | 1.2 |
| | F | 96 | 95 | 99 | 100 | 104 | 102 | 109 | 110264 | 1.1 |
| 0 - 64 | M | 63 | 80 | 91 | 101 | 111 | 123 | 141 | 58491 | 2.2 |
| | F | 67 | 81 | 92 | 99 | 110 | 123 | 134 | 37159 | 2.0 |
| 65+ | M | 88 | 90 | 95 | 102 | 106 | 110 | 117 | 127600 | 1.3 |
| | F | 91 | 93 | 97 | 100 | 106 | 105 | 115 | 155158 | 1.3 |
| All ages | M | 80 | 87 | 94 | 101 | 108 | 114 | 126 | 186091 | 1.6 |
| | F | 87 | 91 | 96 | 100 | 107 | 109 | 123 | 192317 | 1.4 |

TABLE 4.6   SMRs BY SOCIAL CLASS 1979-83

| | 1 | 2 | Social Class 3a | 3b | 4 | 5 |
|---|---|---|---|---|---|---|
| Men 20-64 | 60 | 73 | 90 | 111 | 107 | 176 |
| Married Women 20-59* | 65 | 77 | 87 | 109 | 116 | 164 |

*classified by husband's occupation
  a   non manual
  b   manual

TABLE 4.7  MORTALITY RATIOS BY AGE, SOCIAL CLASS AND
DEPRIVATION 1980-1982, MALES 20-64. SCOTLAND

| | 20-64† | 20-24 | 25-34 | 35-44 | 45-54 | 55-64 |
|---|---|---|---|---|---|---|
| A    Social Class | | | | | | |
| 1 | 64 | (118) | (66) | (36) | 63 | 65 |
| 2 | 73 | (81) | 60 | 66 | 69 | 76 |
| 3NM | 92 | 74 | 82 | 98 | 90 | 94 |
| 3M | 112 | (93) | 89 | 106 | 110 | 117 |
| 4 | 106 | 100 | 127 | 114 | 103 | 104 |
| 5 | 176 | 171 | 254 | 236 | 192 | 156 |
| Rate*$10^5$ = 100 | 675 | 118 | 114 | 259 | 797 | 2197 |
| B    Deprivation | | | | | | |
| 1 Affluent | 64 | (81) | (53) | (54) | 58 | 69 |
| 2 | 77 | (89) | 76 | 69 | 73 | 80 |
| 3 | 90 | 120 | 85 | 86 | 86 | 91 |
| 4 | 98 | 91 | 104 | 103 | 97 | 98 |
| 5 | 110 | (97) | 111 | 112 | 113 | 109 |
| 6 | 129 | (95) | 128 | 138 | 142 | 124 |
| 7 Deprived | 146 | (118) | 176 | 180 | 150 | 139 |

(deaths fewer than 100)

*includes 661 deaths and 79250 population not classified to social class

†age standardised

TABLE 4.8    SMRS FOR SOCIAL CLASSES WITHIN DEPRIVATION CATEGORIES
1980-82, MALES 20-64

| Deprivation Category | Social Class | | | | | | |
|---|---|---|---|---|---|---|---|
| | 1 | 2 | 3NM | 3M | 4 | 5 | All |
| 1 Affluent | 72 | 74 | 64 | 77 | 114 | (89) | 64 |
| 2 | 85 | 85 | 95 | 82 | 88 | 62 | 77 |
| 3 | 120 | 96 | 97 | 89 | 89 | 80 | 90 |
| 4 | 114 | 106 | 102 | 94 | 94 | 87 | 98 |
| 5 | (116) | 120 | 111 | 108 | 95 | 111 | 110 |
| 6 | (116) | 154 | 117 | 119 | 118 | 125 | 129 |
| 7 Deprived | (321) | 216 | 152 | 132 | 142 | 121 | 146 |
| Rate/$10^5$ = 100 = | 429 | 494 | 623 | 758 | 729 | 1189 | 675 |

(deaths < 100)

TABLE 4.9 POPULATION*: SOCIAL CLASS WITHIN DEPRIVATION CATEGORIES 1981, MALES 20-64, % DISTRIBUTION

| Social Class | Affluent | | | | | Deprived | | All |
|---|---|---|---|---|---|---|---|---|
| | 1 % | 2 % | 3 % | 4 % | 5 % | 6 % | 7 % | % |
| 1 | 18 | 10 | 5 | 4 | 3 | 2 | 1 | 5 |
| 2 | 40 | 30 | 23 | 17 | 13 | 9 | 4 | 19 |
| 3NM | 14 | 12 | 10 | 10 | 9 | 7 | 5 | 10 |
| 3M | 17 | 28 | 35 | 39 | 41 | 42 | 39 | 36 |
| 4 | 6 | 12 | 16 | 19 | 20 | 21 | 22 | 17 |
| 5 | 1 | 3 | 5 | 7 | 6 | 12 | 17 | 7 |
| 100% = | 8065 | 18585 | 29821 | 34859 | 19780 | 15091 | 8864 | 135216 |

*10% census data

TABLE 4.10 SECTOR SMRS: % ALL SECTORS BY DEPCAT

| | Affluent | | | | | Deprived | | ALL |
|---|---|---|---|---|---|---|---|---|
| | 1 | 2 | 3 | 4 | 5 | 6 | 7 | |
| (a) all ages | | | | | | | | |
| <90 | 81 | 53 | 30 | 18 | 5 | 1 | - | 28 |
| 90<110 | 19 | 43 | 62 | 64 | 56 | 36 | 11 | 51 |
| 110+ | - | 4 | 7 | 21 | 39 | 62 | 89 | 21 |
| (b) all ages | | | | | | | | |
| <90 | 97 | 78 | 48 | 32 | 8 | 4 | - | 42 |
| 90<110 | 3 | 17 | 38 | 42 | 42 | 16 | 3 | 30 |
| 110+ | - | 5 | 14 | 26 | 50 | 80 | 97 | 29 |
| (c) 65+ | | | | | | | | |
| <90 | 53 | 41 | 25 | 15 | 5 | 3 | - | 22 |
| 90<110 | 42 | 50 | 61 | 64 | 60 | 48 | 24 | 56 |
| 110+ | 5 | 8 | 14 | 21 | 35 | 49 | 76 | 22 |
| All = 100% | 62 | 135 | 214 | 190 | 97 | 75 | 37 | 810 |

*Sectors with more than 500 population

TABLE 4.11   HIGH/LOW SECTOR SMRs BY DEPRIVATION CATEGORY   (P=<.05)

|  |  | Affluent | | | | | Deprived | |  |
|---|---|---|---|---|---|---|---|---|---|
|  |  | 1 | 2 | 3 | 4 | 5 | 6 | 7 | All |
| A | % in each DEPCAT | | | | | | | | |
| (a) | all ages | | | | | | | | 100% = |
|  | <90 | 27 | 35 | 23 | 13 | 2 | - | - | 120 |
|  | 110+ | - | 1 | 4 | 16 | 25 | 29 | 24 | 139 |
| (b) | 0-64 | | | | | | | | 100% = |
|  | <90 | 35 | 37 | 16 | 11 | 1 | - | - | 98 |
|  | 110+ | - | - | 3 | 10 | 19 | 38 | 30 | 107 |
| (c) | 65+ | | | | | | | | 100% = |
|  | <90 | 16 | 34 | 31 | 16 | 3 | - | - | 74 |
|  | 110+ | 1 | 3 | 7 | 21 | 22 | 21 | 23 | 94 |
| B | % all sectors* | | | | | | | | |
| (a) | all ages | | | | | | | | |
|  | <90 | 52 | 31 | 13 | 8 | 2 | - | - | 15 |
|  | 110+ | - | 1 | 3 | 12 | 36 | 55 | 89 | 17 |
| (b) | 0-64 | | | | | | | | |
|  | <90 | 55 | 27 | 7 | 6 | 1 | - | - | 12 |
|  | 110+ | - | - | 1 | 6 | 21 | 55 | 86 | 13 |
| (c) | 65+ | | | | | | | | |
|  | <90 | 19 | 19 | 11 | 6 | 2 | - | - | 9 |
|  | 110+ | 2 | 2 | 3 | 11 | 22 | 27 | 59 | 12 |
| All = 100% = | | 62 | 135 | 214 | 190 | 97 | 75 | 37 | 810 |

*sectors with more than 500 population; excludes institutional sectors

TABLE 4.12   MORTALITY AND DEPRIVATION: HEALTH BOARDS

|  | DEP score | SMR all ages | SMR 0-64 |
|---|---|---|---|
| Glasgow | 2.50 | 107 | 115 |
| Lanarkshire | 0.87 | 105 | 106 |
| Argyll & Clyde | 0.49 | 107 | 108 |
| Ayr & Arran | 0.05 | 105 | 104 |
| Tayside | -0.55 | 94 | 87 |
| Forth Valley | -0.91 | 98 | 96 |
| Lothian | -0.94 | 94 | 91 |
| Fife | -1.18 | 97 | 97 |
| Dumfries & Galloway | -1.22 | 95 | 96 |
| Islands | -1.26 | 94 | 94 |
| Borders | -1.80 | 93 | 81 |
| Highland | -1.82 | 99 | 100 |
| Grampian | -1.95 | 92 | 83 |

TABLE 4.13   MORTALITY AND DEPRIVATION FOR HEALTH BOARD GROUPS: CORRELATION COEFFICIENTS*

| | Scotland | West | East | Rural |
|---|---|---|---|---|
| All ages | 0.75 | 0.78 | 0.65 | 0.30 |
| 0-64 | 0.78 | 0.81 | 0.70 | 0.44 |
| 65+ | 0.56 | 0.58 | 0.45 | 0.15 |
| No. of sectors | 810 | 338 | 337 | 135 |

*over 810 sectors (excl. PCS<500 & 20 institutional sectors)

TABLE 4.14   SMRs BY DEPRIVATION CATEGORY FOR HEALTH BOARD GROUPS

a - all ages

| | DEPCAT | | | | | | | | No.* |
|---|---|---|---|---|---|---|---|---|---|
| | Affluent | | | | | Deprived | | | |
| AREA | 1 | 2 | 3 | 4 | 5 | 6 | 7 | Total | Sectors |
| West | 85 | 91 | 99 | 104 | 109 | 114 | 127 | 107 | 486 |
| East | 82 | 87 | 92 | 98 | 103 | 107 | 113 | 95 | 450 |
| Rural | (56) | 91 | 95 | 99 | 98 | 113 | (75) | 96 | 219 |
| SCOTLAND | 83 | 89 | 95 | 100 | 107 | 113 | 125 | 100 | 1,155 |

b - 0-64

| | DEPCAT | | | | | | | | No.* |
|---|---|---|---|---|---|---|---|---|---|
| | Affluent | | | | | Deprived | | | |
| AREA | 1 | 2 | 3 | 4 | 5 | 6 | 7 | Total | Sectors |
| West | 68 | 80 | 95 | 104 | 113 | 128 | 144 | 110 | 486 |
| East | 61 | 76 | 89 | 95 | 105 | 111 | 124 | 90 | 450 |
| Rural | (75) | 87 | 90 | 99 | 107 | 150 | (100) | 94 | 219 |
| SCOTLAND | 64 | 79 | 91 | 99 | 110 | 125 | 141 | 100 | 1,155 |

*all sectors except shipping
( <10 deaths)

TABLE 4.15   SMRs BY SOCIAL CLASS FOR HEALTH BOARD GROUPS FOR MALES 20-64

| | Social class | | | | | | |
|---|---|---|---|---|---|---|---|
| AREA | 1 | 2 | 3 NM | 3 M | 4 | 5 | All |
| West | 59 | 77 | 98 | 126 | 117 | 184 | 110 |
| East | 62 | 67 | 86 | 97 | 95 | 141 | 88 |
| Rural | 77 | 80 | 95 | 105 | 98 | 136 | 96 |
| All | 64 | 73 | 92 | 112 | 106 | 176 | 100 |

TABLE 4.16   RELATIONSHIPS OF SMR WITH DEPRIVATION FOR SCOTLAND AND HEALTH BOARD GROUPS

| SMR | Group | B | 95% C.I. | $R^2$ |
|---|---|---|---|---|
| All | SCOTLAND | 2.98 | 2.80-3.16 | 56 |
| | West | 2.85 | 2.61-3.09 | 61 |
| | East | 2.61 | 2.28-2.93 | 42 |
| | Rural | 2.29 | 1.05-3.53 | 9 |
| 0-64 | SCOTLAND | 5.38 | 5.08-5.69 | 60 |
| | West | 5.19 | 4.78-5.60 | 65 |
| | East | 4.97 | 4.42-5.52 | 49 |
| | Rural | 5.78 | 3.77-7.80 | 19 |
| 65+ | SCOTLAND | 2.04 | 1.84-2.25 | 32 |
| | West | 1.89 | 1.60-2.17 | 33 |
| | East | 1.72 | 1.35-2.09 | 20 |
| | Rural | 1.23 | -0.14-2.61 | 2 |

Postcode sectors with Pop < 500 and 20 institutional postcodes excluded

TABLE 4.17   LOCAL GOVERNMENT DISTRICTS WITH OUTLYING SMR VALUES

| all ages | | 0-64 | | 65+ | |
|---|---|---|---|---|---|
| Caithness | +3.0 | Caithness | +3.2 | Annan | -2.6 |
| Nairn | +2.4 | Tweeddale | -2.7 | Nairn | +2.4 |
| Wigtown | +2.1 | Angus | -2.4 | Caithness | +2.3 |
| Annandale | -2.0 | Sutherland | +2.3 | N.E. Fife | -2.2 |
| N.E. Fife | -1.9 | Dundee | -2.3 | Kilmarnock | +2.1 |
| Kilmarnock | +1.8 | Skye & Lochalsh | +2.0 | Cumbernauld | +2.1 |
| Berwickshire | -1.7 | Orkney | +1.9 | Stewartry | -1.8 |
| Clackmannan | +1.7 | Inverness | +1.8 | Cumnock | +1.7 |
| Argyll & Bute | +1.7 | Roxburgh | -1.8 | Berwickshire | -1.6 |

TABLE 4.18   SMRs FOR URBAN AND RURAL AREAS

| U/R Value Range | Mean | Pop. Th. | Av. DEP Score | SMRs: All Ages | 0-64 | 65+ |
|---|---|---|---|---|---|---|
| a Postcode Sectors | | | | | | |
| 1 < 2 | 1.03 | 1611 | 1.31 | 104 | 109 | 102 |
| 2 < 3 | 2.07 | 1063 | 0.26 | 99 | 99 | 99 |
| 3 < 4 | 3.18 | 1224 | -0.39 | 100 | 97 | 101 |
| 4 < 5 | 4.17 | 892 | -1.48 | 97 | 91 | 99 |
| 5 | 5.0 | 242 | -2.45 | 91 | 89 | 92 |

TABLE 4.18   SMRs FOR URBAN AND RURAL AREAS CONTD.

b Enumeration Districts

| SMRs U/R Value | Pop. Th. | SMRs: All Ages | 0-64 | 65+ |
|---|---|---|---|---|
| 1 | 1208 | 109 | 115 | 107 |
| 2 | 1178 | 99 | 97 | 99 |
| 3 | 1171 | 101 | 98 | 103 |
| 4 | 827 | 98 | 95 | 99 |
| 5 | 610 | 93 | 85 | 95 |

TABLE 4.19   RANGE IN SMRs STANDARDISED BY:

| Health Boards | age/sex | age/sex/deprivation |
|---|---|---|
| all ages | 92-107 | 95-106 |
| 0-64 | 81-115 | 88-109 |
| 65+ | 91-106 | 97-105 |
| Local Government Districts | | |
| all ages | 79-112 | 91-112 |
| 0-64 | 68-124 | 79-122 |
| 65+ | 83-109 | 89-112 |

TABLE 4.20   SMRs FOR HEALTH BOARDS ADJUSTED FOR DEPRIVATION

| | DEP score | All ages | | SMR 0-64 | | 65+ | |
|---|---|---|---|---|---|---|---|
| | | a | b | a | b | a | b |
| WEST | | | | | | | |
| Argyll & Clyde | 0.49 | 107 | 106 | 108 | 106 | 106 | 106 |
| Ayr & Arran | 0.05 | 105 | 104 | 104 | 103 | 105 | 105 |
| Glasgow | 2.50 | 107 | 101 | 115 | 103 | 105 | 100 |
| Lanark | 0.87 | 105 | 102 | 106 | 102 | 105 | 103 |
| EAST | | | | | | | |
| Fife | -1.18 | 97 | 100 | 97 | 103 | 97 | 99 |
| Forth Valley | -0.91 | 98 | 100 | 96 | 100 | 98 | 99 |
| Grampian | -1.95 | 92 | 97 | 84 | 93 | 95 | 98 |
| Lothian | -0.94 | 94 | 97 | 91 | 97 | 95 | 97 |
| Tayside | -0.55 | 94 | 95 | 87 | 88 | 96 | 97 |
| RURAL | | | | | | | |
| Borders | -1.80 | 93 | 97 | 82 | 87 | 96 | 100 |
| Dumfries & Galloway | -1.22 | 95 | 98 | 96 | 103 | 94 | 97 |
| Highland | -1.82 | 100 | 104 | 100 | 110 | 99 | 103 |
| Islands | -1.26 | 94 | 97 | 94 | 99 | 94 | 96 |

a - standardised for age and sex
b - standardised for age, sex and deprivation

TABLE 4.21    SMRs FOR LOCAL GOVERNMENT DISTRICTS ADJUSTED FOR DEPRIVATION

| | DEP score | SMR | | | | | |
|---|---|---|---|---|---|---|---|
| | | All ages | | 0-64 | | 65+ | |
| | | a | b | a | b | a | b |
| **WEST** | | | | | | | |
| Argyll & Clyde | | | | | | | |
| Argyll & Bute | -1.38 | 103 | 106 | 100 | 105 | 104 | 106 |
| Dunbarton | -0.22 | 103 | 103 | 99 | 100 | 104 | 104 |
| Inverclyde | 1.95 | 111 | 106 | 123 | 110 | 107 | 104 |
| Renfrew | 0.62 | 108 | 107 | 107 | 116 | 108 | 107 |
| Ayr & Arran | | | | | | | |
| Cumnock & Doon Valley | 1.24 | 110 | 104 | 109 | 100 | 110 | 106 |
| Cunninghame | 0.85 | 105 | 103 | 112 | 106 | 103 | 102 |
| Kilmarnock & Loudoun | 0.00 | 108 | 106 | 103 | 101 | 109 | 108 |
| Kyle & Carrick | -1.35 | 100 | 104 | 93 | 100 | 102 | 105 |
| Glasgow | | | | | | | |
| Bearsden & Milngavie | -5.51 | 80 | 95 | 68 | 100 | 85 | 93 |
| Clydebank | 2.25 | 106 | 98 | 109 | 96 | 105 | 99 |
| Eastwood | -5.65 | 79 | 92 | 68 | 96 | 83 | 91 |
| Glasgow City | 4.08 | 112 | 102 | 124 | 104 | 108 | 101 |
| Strathkelvin | -2.30 | 96 | 102 | 88 | 100 | 99 | 103 |
| Lanarkshire | | | | | | | |
| Clydesdale | -1.36 | 101 | 104 | 103 | 109 | 100 | 102 |
| Cumbernauld | -0.66 | 105 | 105 | 101 | 103 | 108 | 107 |
| East Kilbride | -1.36 | 91 | 96 | 85 | 93 | 94 | 98 |
| Hamilton | 0.52 | 106 | 104 | 106 | 104 | 106 | 105 |
| Monklands | 2.95 | 110 | 101 | 112 | 96 | 109 | 103 |
| Motherwell | 2.34 | 110 | 103 | 117 | 105 | 107 | 102 |
| **EAST** | | | | | | | |
| Fife | | | | | | | |
| Dunfermline | -1.38 | 101 | 104 | 99 | 107 | 101 | 103 |
| Kirkcaldy | -0.39 | 102 | 103 | 102 | 104 | 102 | 102 |
| North East Fife | -2.64 | 84 | 90 | 80 | 92 | 85 | 90 |
| Forth Valley | | | | | | | |
| Clackmannan | -1.05 | 104 | 107 | 103 | 109 | 105 | 106 |
| Falkirk | -0.40 | 96 | 97 | 98 | 99 | 96 | 96 |
| Stirling | -1.79 | 97 | 101 | 89 | 98 | 99 | 103 |
| Grampian | | | | | | | |
| Aberdeen | -1.41 | 96 | 100 | 87 | 94 | 99 | 102 |
| Banff & Buchan | -0.80 | 91 | 94 | 85 | 91 | 93 | 95 |
| Gordon | -4.07 | 82 | 92 | 71 | 90 | 86 | 93 |
| Kincardine & Deeside | -3.81 | 87 | 95 | 73 | 87 | 91 | 97 |
| Moray | -1.84 | 91 | 96 | 87 | 96 | 93 | 96 |
| Lothian | | | | | | | |
| East Lothian | -1.58 | 90 | 93 | 86 | 92 | 91 | 94 |
| Edinburgh | -1.10 | 93 | 97 | 90 | 96 | 94 | 97 |
| Midlothian | -1.51 | 96 | 101 | 85 | 94 | 101 | 104 |
| West Lothian | 0.26 | 101 | 100 | 103 | 102 | 101 | 100 |

TABLE 4.21    SMRs FOR LOCAL GOVERNMENT DISTRICTS ADJUSTED FOR DEPRIVATION
CONTD.

| | DEP score | SMR | | | | | |
|---|---|---|---|---|---|---|---|
| | | All ages | | 0-64 | | 65+ | |
| | | a | b | a | b | a | b |
| Tayside | | | | | | | |
| Angus | -1.46 | 91 | 94 | 76 | 83 | 96 | 98 |
| Dundee | 0.89 | 95 | 93 | 91 | 87 | 96 | 95 |
| Perth & Kinross | -2.05 | 93 | 99 | 85 | 95 | 95 | 100 |
| RURAL | | | | | | | |
| Borders | | | | | | | |
| Berwick | -1.81 | 87 | 91 | 79 | 85 | 89 | 92 |
| Ettrick & Lauderdale | -2.06 | 95 | 99 | 90 | 98 | 96 | 100 |
| Roxburgh | -1.55 | 96 | 100 | 79 | 86 | 101 | 103 |
| Tweeddale | -1.86 | 91 | 96 | 72 | 79 | 96 | 100 |
| Dumfries & Galloway | | | | | | | |
| Annan & Eskdale | -1.59 | 87 | 91 | 90 | 99 | 86 | 89 |
| Nithsdale | -1.02 | 97 | 100 | 100 | 107 | 96 | 98 |
| Stewartry | -1.88 | 88 | 92 | 84 | 92 | 89 | 92 |
| Wigtown | -0.67 | 107 | 108 | 107 | 108 | 107 | 108 |
| Highland | | | | | | | |
| Badenoch & Strathspey | -2.52 | 96 | 104 | 94 | 108 | 97 | 103 |
| Caithness | -1.32 | 109 | 112 | 112 | 122 | 107 | 109 |
| Inverness | -2.08 | 98 | 102 | 98 | 107 | 98 | 101 |
| Lochaber | -0.46 | 103 | 105 | 108 | 110 | 102 | 103 |
| Nairn | -2.42 | 103 | 111 | 93 | 108 | 105 | 112 |
| Ross & Cromarty | -2.30 | 96 | 102 | 93 | 104 | 97 | 102 |
| Skye & Lochalsh | -0.84 | 94 | 96 | 107 | 110 | 93 | 93 |
| Sutherland | -2.11 | 99 | 104 | 101 | 112 | 98 | 102 |
| Islands | | | | | | | |
| Orkney | -2.30 | 92 | 99 | 97 | 114 | 91 | 96 |
| Shetland | -2.46 | 91 | 100 | 77 | 85 | 95 | 99 |
| Western Isles | 0.26 | 97 | 96 | 104 | 101 | 95 | 94 |

a - standardised for age and sex
b - standardised for age, sex, and deprivation

TABLE 4.22   SMRs FOR HEALTH BOARDS FOR MALES 20-64, 1980-1982, SCOTLAND

|                     | (a) | (b) | (c) |
|---------------------|-----|-----|-----|
| Argyll & Clyde      | 111 | 111 | 109 |
| Ayrshire & Arran    | 102 | 103 | 101 |
| Borders             | 81  | 81  | 89  |
| Dumfries & Galloway | 95  | 97  | 103 |
| Fife                | 94  | 93  | 101 |
| Forth Valley        | 93  | 94  | 98  |
| Grampian            | 83  | 84  | 93  |
| Greater Glasgow     | 119 | 118 | 105 |
| Highland            | 102 | 103 | 113 |
| Lanarkshire         | 105 | 103 | 100 |
| Lothian             | 89  | 90  | 94  |
| Tayside             | 85  | 85  | 87  |
| Islands             | 103 | 101 | 111 |

(a) standardised for age
(b) standardised for age and social class
(c) standardised for age and deprivation

TABLE 4.23   STANDARDISED MORTALITY RATIOS, SCOTLAND V ENGLAND
AND WALES 1980-82

|     |                        | by age and sex | | by age and sex and deprivation | |
|-----|------------------------|----------|-------------------|----------|-------------------|
| (a) | Scotland = 100         | Scotland | England & Wales   | Scotland | England & Wales   |
|     | all ages               | 100      | 89                | 100      | 96                |
|     | 0-64                   | 100      | 82                | 100      | 95                |
| (b) | England & Wales = 100  |          |                   |          |                   |
|     | all ages               | 112      | 100               | 104      | 100               |
|     | 0-64                   | 122      | 100               | 105      | 100               |

N.B. these data are computed using the census populations and will differ slightly from published
statistics

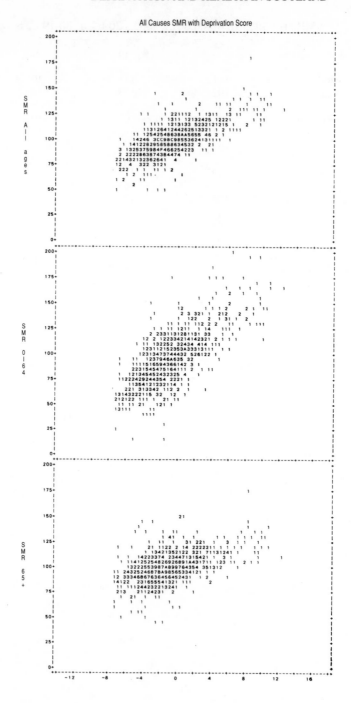

FIGURE 4.1    SCATTER DIAGRAMS: SMRs x DEP score

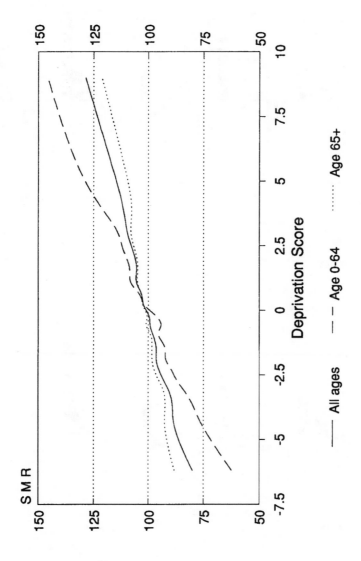

FIGURE 4.2  SMR (ALL CAUSES) VS. DEPRIVATION SCORE SCOTLAND 1980 - 82

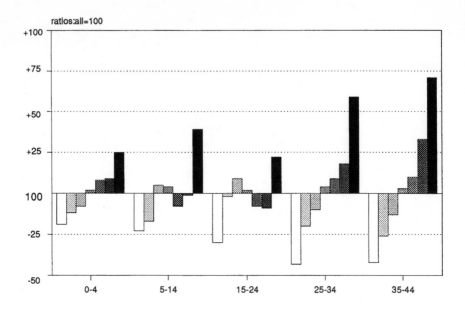

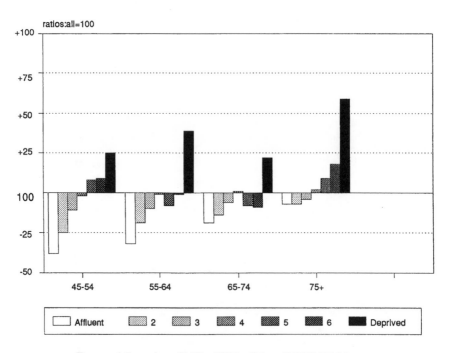

FIGURE 4.3A    AGE SMRs 1980 - 85 BY DEPCAT MALES

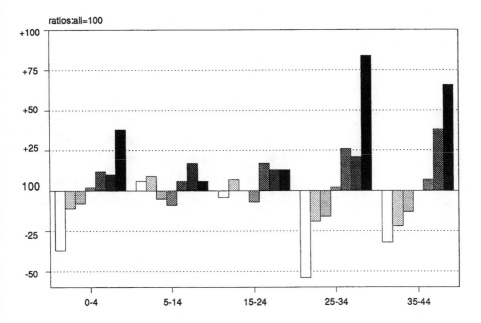

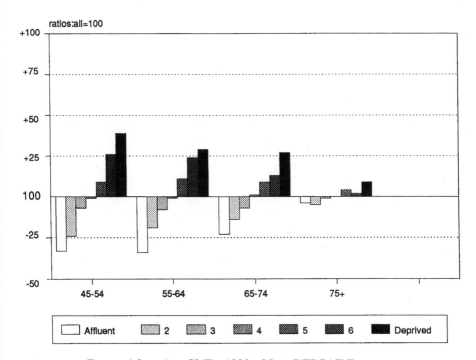

FIGURE 4.3B    AGE SMRS 1980 - 85 BY DEPCAT FEMALES

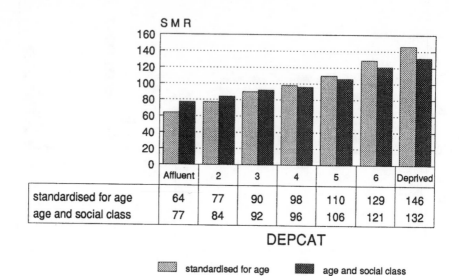

| | Affluent | 2 | 3 | 4 | 5 | 6 | Deprived |
|---|---|---|---|---|---|---|---|
| standardised for age | 64 | 77 | 90 | 98 | 110 | 129 | 146 |
| age and social class | 77 | 84 | 92 | 96 | 106 | 121 | 132 |

DEPCAT

standardised for age          age and social class

FIGURE 4.4    SMRS 1980 - 82 BY DEPRIVATION CATEGORY MALES AGED 20 - 64

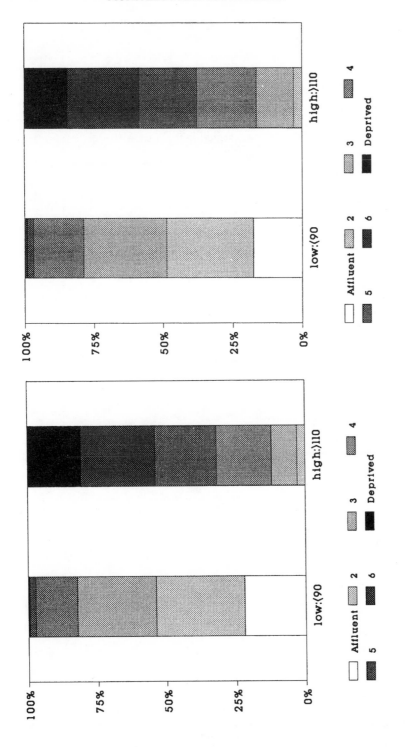

FIGURE 4.5B    HIGH/LOW SMRs 0 - 64* BY DEPCAT

FIGURE 4.5A    HIGH/LOW SMRs ALL AGES* BY DEPCAT

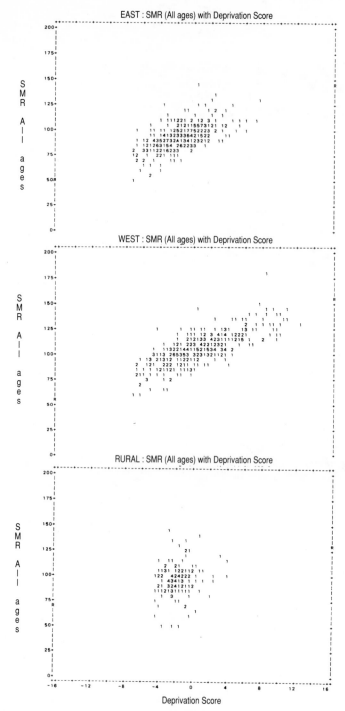

FIGURE 4.6A   SCATTER DIAGRAMS SMR x DEP SCORE FOR EAST, WEST AND RURAL BOARDS
(ALL AGES)

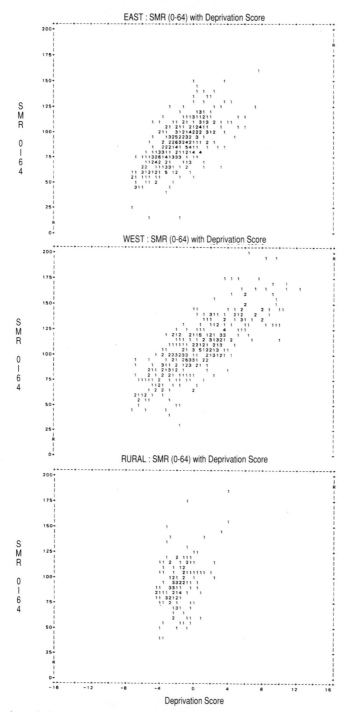

FIGURE 4.6B   SCATTER DIAGRAMS SMR x DEP SCORE FOR EAST, WEST AND RURAL BOARDS
(0 - 64)

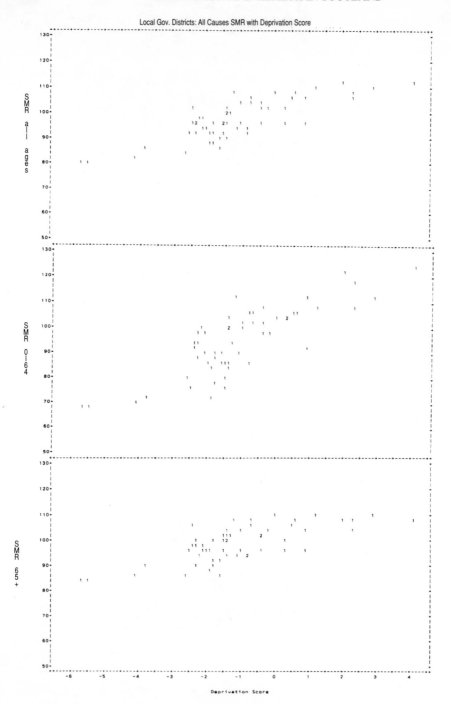

FIGURE 4.7    SCATTER DIAGRAMS SMR x DEP SCORE FOR LOCAL GOVERNMENT
DISTRICTS

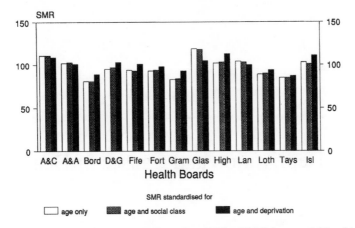

Figure 4.8 SMRs for Health Boards - 1980 - 82 Males aged 20 - 64

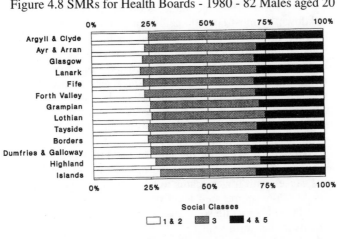

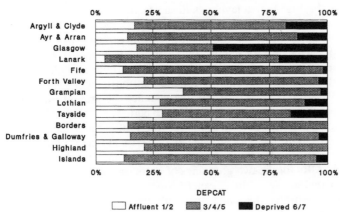

FIGURE 4.9    HEALTH BOARD POPULATION FOR MALES 20 - 64
BY SOCIAL CLASS AND DEPCAT

# CHAPTER 5

# Deprivation and Causes of Death

Over the three years 1980 to 1982 the numbers of deaths (190th.+) is insufficient to permit a breakdown by most specific causes of death at postcode sector level. Analysis is therefore conducted using a data-set for the six years 1980 to 1985 which, with 380th. deaths, provides the opportunity to calculate more reliable rates for a range of causes. The use of the extended data set however also risks introducing lesser reliability into the rates, since these take no account of changes in population characteristics between 1981 and 1985. This problem is likely to be of greater significance at postcode sector level, since small changes could have a big impact on rates, and for this reason the analysis puts more emphasis on data aggregated over PCS to deprivation category to show the gradients in mortality, from affluent to deprived areas, with the ratios in addition being calculated and correlation analysis carried out at local government district (LGD) level. This approach permits causes with fewer deaths to be examined, since the rates will be more reliable at the more aggregated level of LGD of which there are only 56 compared with c.1,000 PCS. While some loss of precision may occur it is unlikely that any changes over the period (in respect of populations or shifts in relative deprivation) at this higher area level would substantially affect the general picture.

The correlations with deprivation, over postcode sectors, for both 1980-82 and 1980-85 are seen in table 5.1 for causes with larger numbers of deaths. The coefficients for each cause for the two time-periods are generally very similar, any differences being mainly in the direction of the correlation being stronger for 1980-85, at all ages; the exception is for the non-traffic accidents for which the coefficient falls, from 0.37 to 0.24. For the younger age group (0-64 or 0-74) the two coefficients show little variation for the two periods.

The level of agreement between the rates for 1980-82 and 1980-85 (over 810 sectors) was very high: r = 0.91 all ages, 0.92 0-64 and 0.83 65 and over and the gradients in mortality on the two bases are essentially similar (table 5.2).

In addition SMRs for the two groupings of years were calculated for deprivation categories for one cause — lung cancer for males; these again show that the gradients are essentially the same on both year bases (table 5.3) despite the stronger correlation with DEP for 1980-85 than for 1980-82 at all ages (table 5.1). The correlation between the two year bases in this case was somewhat less — 0.82 for all ages and 0.81 for 0-64 (table 5.3b). At local government district level the correlation coefficients are seen to be much stronger than at postcode sector level (table 5.4).

These stronger correlations result from the lesser variation in the data over LGDs than PCSs, but since there are only 56 LGDs the correlations are less likely to be statistically significant. In general with only 56 events the coefficients will be significant at the five percent level only at or above plus or minus 0.26 at which level only about seven percent of the variation is explained by the variation in deprivation. At the one percent level the results will be significant with a coefficient of 0.34 and at 0.1% level of 0.43.

## *Correlation by cause*

Correlations between DEP and cause are shown in table 5.5 according to the degree of association. The strongest associations are found for all cancers (malignant neoplasms), cancer of the lung and chronic respiratory disorders (chronic bronchitis, emphysema and asthma) and slightly lower coefficients for diseases of the digestive system and liver disease and cirrhosis. More moderate associations occur in respect of infectious diseases and chronic rheumatic heart disease (both with low numbers), for ischaemic heart disease (all ages) and cerebrovascular disease 0-64, also for pneumonia, stomach ulcers and suicide and undetermined causes.

As with the all causes data, where numbers are sufficient to calculate the values for the younger age group these exhibit stronger associations with deprivation than do deaths at all ages. The enhanced association is particularly notable for cerebrovascular disease at 0.65 for 0-64, although it is effectively non-existent for all ages. This lack of agreement between the younger and older age groups could reflect differences in aetiology, in cause or in certification. In those aged under 65, 38% of these deaths are attributable to intracranial haemorrhage compared with only 7% in the older age group, and a smaller proportion to acute or other but ill-defined disease: 47% compared to 83%. The most important risk factor in CVD is hypertension but differences in environmental temperature, in the intake of fruit and vegetables and in smoking may all play a part, some of these causal factors having underlying long-term consequences while others may play a more precipitating role [1], and the influence of these respective factors may be more dominant at one age than another. Certification of cause of death is also likely to be fairly accurate in younger age groups but multiple pathology may lead to some lack of precision in the elderly.

Differences in aetiology may equally play a part in the stronger association seen for ischaemic heart disease at 0-64 (0.75) than at all ages (0.55) with the implication that the gradients are much weaker at age 65 and over. For chronic respiratory disorders the correlation is somewhat lower at 0-64, although the smallish number of events may partly explain this result. For all malignant neoplasms, cancer of the lung and bronchitis (causes with the highest correlations) the associations differ very little between 0-64 and all ages at LGD level.

A number of causes show low positive correlations with deprivation. Of these only cancer of the cervix, hypertensive disease and pulmonary heart disease reach the five percent level of significance (above 0.26); all have rather low numbers of events, as is the case also for musculo-skeletal disorders, the only cause for which the coefficient is negative and statistically significant.

In addition to this examination of some of the ICD chapter headings and more specific causes, deaths were also combined for a number of diseases to give a group of 'avoidable' and 'smoking-related' deaths.

The avoidable deaths include those selected from a more extensive list as being causes for which deaths should not occur given appropriate medical intervention; that is, the state of medical knowledge is sufficiently advanced that deaths should be avoidable except in the very young and very old.[2] Potentially, rather than totally, avoidable might be a better descriptive label however since many factors outside the control of health services may have an influence on the occurrence or outcome for a disease, and even good medical care may not always prove effective. The disease categories included in this list are given in Figure 5.1 together with the age groups which are all below age 65. Since cerebrovascular disease constitutes such a large proportion of the total, deaths from this cause have been analysed separately. Excluding these, deaths over six years from 'avoidable' causes are fairly low in number.

Since the basic proposition is that these diseases are considered to be avoidable given the application of appropriate medical knowledge then the correlation coefficient of 0.54 with DEP could lead to conclusions that the quality or level of medical care is differentially delivered to various sections of the community, that the effectiveness of health care varies within the population, or that the association seen reflects a differential in the development of disease which is transmitted through to the fact of death. This last possibility will be examined in chapter 6. Similar processes must be considered also in respect of deaths from cerebrovascular and hypertensive diseases (age 35-64) for which the correlation is high at 0.74; in view of the rather large number of deaths from these causes however (6,655 in the age group) their identification as 'avoidable' seems somewhat questionable and it would appear more realistic to regard them rather as causes which offer the potential for a reduction in the number of deaths — particularly in view of the higher levels of mortality in Scotland compared with other countries of the United Kingdom — SMRs of 125 for men and 117 for women in 1985[3] - and of the European Community.[4]

## Smoking-related deaths

Smoking-related causes of illness and death have been the subject of intensive investigation and the risks have been quantified in relation to a number of causes of illness and death, cancer of the lung being the disease most directly implicated with 90% of the incidence regarded as attributable to smoking in men.[5] Of the other diseases of the respiratory system, chronic obstructive lung disease (chronic bronchitis) hardly ever occurs in non-smokers; while it occurs in only about one fifth of cigarette smokers the risks are increased 20 to 30 fold when smoking is regular and heavy.[5]

The well-known study of British doctors[6] has quantified the risks ratios for current smokers relative to non-smokers and light smokers for various diseases of the circulatory system also, as detailed below:

|                              | Ex-smokers | All smokers | 25 or more/day |
|------------------------------|-----------|-------------|----------------|
| Pulmonary heart disease      | 3.3       | 3.8         | 9.5            |
| Aortic aneurysm              | 2.0       | 4.3         | 5.7            |
| Myocardial degeneration      | 1.3       | 1.9         | 2.7            |
| Ischaemic heart disease      | 1.2       | 1.6         | 1.8            |
| Cerebrovascular disease      | 1.1       | 1.5         | 1.7            |
| Other cardiovascular disease | 0.9       | 1.2         | 1.4            |

A number of studies have shown that the risks from smoking in relation to coronary heart disease are much higher at younger ages - 35-44 and 45-54.[6]

The list of smoking-related diseases (see Fig. 5.1) is taken from the report of the Surgeon-General of the United States[7] which has quantified the attributable risks for males and females for ten selected causes of death, from cigarette smoking. We have calculated the attributable risk for men and women combined:

|  | | % deaths due to smoking | |
|  | M+F | M | F |
| --- | --- | --- | --- |
| Cancer of oesophagus | 77 | 78 | 75 |
| Cancer of trachea, bronchus and lung | 87 | 90 | 79 |
| Cancer of pancreas | 32 | 29 | 34 |
| Ischaemic heart disease    < 65 | 44 | 45 | 41 |
| 65 + | 16 | 21 | 12 |
| Cerebrovascular disease   < 65 | 53 | 51 | 55 |
| 65 + | 13 | 24 | 6 |
| Chronic obstructive pulmonary disease | 82 | 84 | 79 |

This list does not include four causes also identified in the Surgeon General's list, as they were not separately available in the database: cancer of lip, larynx, bladder and kidney account for only small numbers of deaths and would augment those identified in the list above by only 4%. The group of chronic respiratory disorders (chronic obstructive pulmonary disease) on the other hand includes a few causes which have not been identified as smoking-related, i.e. ICD 493, 494 and 495 — asthma, bronchiectasis and extrinsic allergic alveolitis. These could not be excluded from the group of ICD 490-496 held in the database but they account for only about 7.5% of the deaths in that group, and just over 1% of all deaths identified as smoking-related.

The smoking-related deaths identified on this basis amount to 18% of all deaths and may be estimated at around 24% of those in the age group 0-64. Although a much smaller proportion of deaths from heart disease than from lung cancer is attributed to smoking these nevertheless make the biggest contribution, 33%, lung cancer accounting for 31%, cerebrovascular disease for 14% and the chronic respiratory disorders for 17%. Cancers of the oesophagus and pancreas contribute together only about 5%.

This group of diseases produces the highest correlation with deprivation of any of the causes considered (0.91). The known pattern of smoking — lower consumption in upper social classes and greater in lower social classes[8] — suggests a reasonable expectation that there would be a similar trend in relation to deprivation. Information on smoking behaviour is not available for all of Scotland but the levels of smoking in the age group 40-59 for 22 of the LGDs in Scotland have recently been reported from a sample survey carried out in 1986[9] and are seen in relation to DEP in table 5.6. Although the level of smoking is not always similar for men and women in the same district (and in some districts is higher in women) the correspondence between DEP and smoking is apparent, with the most affluent district, Eastwood, having the smallest proportions of smokers, and the most deprived, Motherwell and Glasgow having the highest proportions. Data for more extended age groups, available for Edinburgh and North Glasgow show that smoking is more common at 35-44 and 45-54 than in the younger or older age groups; is much lower in Edinburgh than in North Glasgow, in each of four age and sex groups; and is higher in women than men at the two younger age groups in North Glasgow, reaching a level of 59% for women aged 35-44.[10]

Within the 11 LGDs in the more affluent half of the distribution only four of the proportions (male or female) reach values of 40%-41%, while in the 11 more deprived LGDs 15 values are in a range from 41% up to 52% and only in one district — Dumbarton — does the proportion fall below 35% compared with ten values below this level in the more affluent districts. The correlation between DEP and smoking level is 0.90 both for men and women. This analysis does not seek to establish the relationship between smoking and mortality from specific causes since this has been amply demonstrated, but this relationship may be observed (in table 5.6) for smoking-related causes which tend to be below 100 in districts with smoking levels above 40%, with Monklands and Glasgow City having both the highest levels of smoking and the highest mortality. The correlation between % smoking and deaths from these causes (SMR all ages M + F) is extremely high, 0.88 for men and 0.87 for women, but somewhat less for deaths from lung cancer at 0.77 for men and 0.71 for women.

For a number of causes of death the correlations are shown for the specific components of the deprivation measure as well as DEP (table 5.7). These are generally highest with unemployment and no car, followed by overcrowding and lowest for low social class. The exceptions are the causes in the lower half of the table for which the correlations with DEP are low but with social class are equal to or higher than other variables, notably so for the road traffic accidents. Coefficients at this level are not statistically significant however.

These four variables also emerged as strongly correlated (across the 56 local government districts) with mortality from coronary heart disease in the age group 35-64 in the period 1979-83, with unemployment producing the strongest correlation of 0.74.[11] Small differences in the database (age range, period) and in the methods used (rank correlation) no doubt account for the lack of total agreement with the results in table 5.7.

## *Gradients in Mortality*

The gradients in mortality by cause seen in table 5.8, which also shows the correlation coefficients and numbers of deaths, are steepest for the following causes:

|  | SMRs | | |
|---|---|---|---|
|  | Most Affluent | Most Deprived | Ratio |
| ca. lung | 67 | 176 | 2.6 |
| 0-64 | 58 | 179 | 3.1 |
| ca. cervix | (44) | 163 | 3.7 |
| pneumonia | | | |
| 0-64 | (53) | 168 | 3.2 |
| chronic respiratory disorders | 63 | 203 | 3.2 |
| 0-64 | (38) | 213 | 5.6 |
| liver disease/cirrhosis | 66 | 172 | 2.6 |

(<100 deaths)

The gradient is particularly strong for chronic respiratory disorders, being at a level over 200 in the most deprived category, and with the ratio between most affluent and most deprived being greatest, at 3.2 all ages and 5.6 at 0-64. In the most deprived category the next highest SMRs are for cancer of the lung (170+), liver disease and cirrhosis (172) and pneumonia (168), with the ratio being over 2.5 for all of these as also for cancer of the cervix (for which the correlation coefficient was only 0.32) although the low SMR of 44 in the most affluent category should be regarded with some caution. Gradients in registrations for cancer will be seen in the next chapter to present a very similar picture for the specific sites. Consistent increases from the most affluent to the most deprived category are also seen for a number of other causes listed below:

| | Most affluent | Most deprived | Ratio |
| --- | --- | --- | --- |
| all cancers | 84 | 129 | 1.5 |
| 0-64 | 78 | 129 | 1.7 |
| ca. stomach | 74 | 134 | 1.8 |
| endocrine disorders | 54 | 121 | 2.2 |
| cerebrovascular 0-64 | 58 | 128 | 2.2 |
| digestive system | 82 | 134 | 1.6 |
| avoidable (various) | (52) | 147 | 2.8 |
| avoidable (cvd) | 62 | 130 | 2.1 |
| smoking-related | 73 | 148 | 2.0 |

Most of these causes show strong to moderate associations with DEP, the exception being the endocrine disorders with a coefficient of 0.23 only. The restricted gradient for smoking-related disorders is somewhat unexpected in view of its high coefficient, but the stronger trends observed for cancer of the lung and chronic respiratory disorders are moderated by the lesser gradients in the other disease categories.

For a number of other causes while there is strong evidence of a gradient the SMRs do not necessarily increase consistently with each step in the dimension of deprivation:

| | Most affluent | Most deprived | Ratio |
| --- | --- | --- | --- |
| all infectious diseases | 77 | 166 | 2.4 |
| ca. oesophagus | 82 | 129 | 1.6 |
| chronic rheumatic heart disease | 90 | 150 | 1.7 |
| ischaemic heart disease | 82 | 110 | 1.3 |
| 0-64 | 63 | 123 | 2.0 |
| pulmonary heart disease | 92 | 130 | 1.4 |
| stomach ulcers | 88 | 122 | 1.4 |
| non-road traffic accidents | 70 | 131 | 1.9 |
| suicide/undetermined | 62 | 157 | 2.5 |

Differences in the SMRs from most affluent to most deprived categories are seen for a range of causes in Figure 5.2.

A few causes show no evidence of association (positive or negative) with deprivation - cancer of the large bowel, cancer of the breast, disease of the nervous system, diseases of the arteries. Although none of the causes examined shows strong evidence of a trend in the reverse direction there is a slight suggestion of this pattern for cancers of the lymphatic tissue and for leukaemia. For some categories of disease the low number of deaths means that it has been possible to include these only at the rather non-specific level of chapter headings of the classification of diseases. Within these of course there may lie hidden more specific causes which would further illuminate this examination of differentials in mortality but in most cases the number of deaths involved would be too few to provide a really reliable result.

The causes of death examined in table 5.7 account for around 90% of total deaths and while not all causes are shown to be linked to the dimension of affluence/deprivation a very substantial proportion, including the major causes of death and accounting for approximately 70% of total deaths, do show this link.

Similar relative mortality to that reported here was found in the Whitehall study of civil servants [12] the differentials being greatest (table 5.9) for chronic bronchitis (7.3 in 'other' grades relative to professional/executive since there were no deaths among administrators), followed by lung cancer (3.6) and then by other respiratory and genito-urinary disorders (ratios of 3.1). With the exception of the genito-urinary and gastro-intestinal disorders the relative ratios seen are generally similar.

Cerebrovascular disease would assume a more prominent ranking in the Scottish data, but in the Whitehall study ratios between the two extremes are not reported since the number of deaths among administrators was very low for all causes. Those which emerge from the present analysis may be viewed with some confidence being based, for most causes, on substantial numbers of events. (table 5.9)

## Deprivation and Social Class

Comparison of these cause data with differentials by social class encounters the limitation that social class data are most reliable for males 20-64 but restriction to this sex and age range results in small numbers of deaths for some causes at least for social class 1, with consequent doubt about reliability of the SMR values. For those causes with sufficient numbers the range between social class 1 and social class 5 (for men 20-64) is compared with the range from DEPCAT 1 to 7, these values being for men and women combined, and for age 0-64 for the causes which have been calculated on that basis, but otherwise for all ages. For all causes shown except cancer of the lung the range is greater by social class than by deprivation (table 5.10). For cancer of the lung the range by DEPCAT calculated for men aged 0-64, (table 5.3) shows little difference to the combined values for males plus females so that a discrepancy between the gradients for the sexes does not explain the higher value for DEPCAT 7 compared with social class 5.

Both of the classifications indicate the greatest range occurring for chronic respiratory disorders. By social class this is followed by stomach ulcers, the wider range compared with the all ages range by DEPCAT suggesting that social factors may influence mortality more at younger ages, as may also be the case for suicide. Similarly, the greater range for motor vehicle accidents and pneumonia by social class suggests that the gradients may be more extreme in men than in women.

With some exceptions in the direction of more extreme values in social class 5 these two sets of data are in general agreement. In the age group 20-64 only 8% of men are not allocated to a social class and only 3% of deaths so that problems of non-allocation are not likely to affect the rates other than to a minor extent, but bias due to the numerator/denominator problem may be present (see chapter 4 p. 68) and influence some of the extreme values seen in social class 5. [13]

# Cause by Area

## Health boards

Table 5.11 shows the SMRs and rank order of health boards from the 44 causes (see Fig. 5.3 for key to causes). As would be expected Western boards figure more prominently in the lower rankings, i.e. with greater mortality, with Greater Glasgow exhibiting the highest values seen in the table with SMRs above 130 for cancer of the lung (all ages and 0-64), chronic rheumatic heart disease and hypertensive disease, pneumonia, bronchitis (all ages and 0-64) and liver disease and cirrhosis. Apart from the symptoms category other high values are seen for: infectious and parasitic diseases (137) in the Islands, road traffic accidents (134 in Grampian and 163 in Highland), pulmonary heart disease (139) in Borders, and suicide deaths (136) in Highland, endocrine disorders (141) and musculo-skeletal disorders (177) in the Islands.

## Local government districts

Cause SMRs and rankings for LGDs in table 5.12 show Glasgow City ranking as first or second highest on nine of the 44 causes and with 23 causes in the highest quintile (i.e. ranks 1-11). Bearsden in contrast is ranked in the lowest quintile (46-56) in 23 cases and is in the last two (ranks 55/56) for seven causes. A brief summary is given for 16 specific causes with more than 6,000 deaths in the period in table 5.13 with LGDs listed which fall into the highest or lowest quintile of SMR values. Selected causes are also mapped in Figure 5.4.

For those causes highly correlated with deprivation LGDs with high SMRs are those which rank more severely on deprivation — in the fourth or fifth quintiles in general, although there are some exceptions — Edinburgh with an SMR above the mean for ca. lung all ages, Badenoch & Strathspey with an SMR of 123 for stomach cancer, (not significant) Sutherland (SMR 106) for all cancer sites, Caithness (SMR 115) for digestive disorders: Strathkelvin (in quintile 1 for DEP) has high SMRs for pneumonia and bronchitis, and LGDs in DEP quintiles 2 and 3 are sparsely interspersed in cerebrovascular (at 0-64) and respiratory diseases.

In the bottom quintile for mortality for these causes LGDs come overwhelmingly from the two more affluent quintiles of deprivation although those in the middle (third) quintile also appear; LGDs in the two most deprived quintiles do not appear among the low SMRs with a few exceptions, Skye & Lochalsh and Banff appearing on a number of the cause lists.

The picture for causes with low association with deprivation is of course quite different although not reversed, and districts from each quintile of deprivation are found in both the top and bottom quintiles for mortality although it is noticeable that the more urban deprived districts in the West are not well represented at either end of this spectrum.

Not all of the SMRs seen in this table are statistically significant (significance may be seen in table 5.12a). Reaching a significantly high or low value depends to some extent on the size of population and for districts with small population size SMRs will need to be more extreme to obtain a significant result. Two small districts tend to find themselves at either end of the distribution, i.e. in the top or bottom quintile of the cause SMRs, although the results are not significant. These include Lochaber which has seven SMRs within the upper quintile, and only three in the lower, and Skye & Lochalsh which has ten SMR values in the lowest quintile and only one in the upper. These two districts both have very similar scores on deprivation — slightly more deprived than the mean — and other (unknown) factors are clearly moderating the association with deprivation. We have already noted the tendency for mortality to be higher than would be expected on the basis of deprivation in a number of LGDs (table 4.17) and it is not surprising to find some of these — Caithness, Sutherland, Inverness — with low deprivation nevertheless appearing in the top quintile for some causes of mortality. The level of significant events depends to some extent on the variability in the data; if mortality rates were uniform for a cause there would be no variability and no significant variation from 100. The degree of variation may be readily seen in the standard deviations (table 5.14) which (apart from all causes) are lowest for all cancer, cerebrovascular disease, ischaemic heart disease and smoking-related causes (all with substantial numbers) and greatest for ca. cervix, musculoskeletal, and symptoms — all with smaller numbers of deaths.

The greatest variability is seen for symptoms with some authorities, mostly rural, exhibiting very high SMR values. This phenomenon will of course be accompanied by a lack of certification to specific causes and may have influenced some of the low SMRs which are reported.

These rankings for local government districts largely mirror those reported by the Registrar general for the period 1974-1984 which listed the ten highest and lowest SMRs for all causes and five main causes of death. [14] Lack of agreement between the two lists is generally in respect of areas with smaller populations, for which the SMRs would be less stable.

## *Urban/Rural Factors*

Deprivation was found to be a predominantly more important factor than the urban/rural measure in relation to all causes mortality. For specific causes there are however a number of instances where the urban/rural (U/R) character of the district makes a significant contribution to the explanation of the variance as shown in table 5.14 for a range of causes. The correlations with DEP and U/R independently are given and the % of variation explained by DEP alone. DEP and U/R are jointly regressed on the mortality rates and $R^2$ shows the percent explained by the two variables together and the additional contribution by U/R over and above the percent explained by DEP alone.

The way in which the urban or rural character of the district is related to cause of death is shown by the correlation coefficient (U/R only) with negative coefficients implying that the rates are higher in more urban districts and positive coefficients a tendency to be higher in rural districts. The strongest negative associations are for cancer of the lung, (-0.83), chronic rheumatic heart disease (-0.82), bronchitis (-0.77) and liver disease and cirrhosis (-0.77). Causes with a tendency to be higher in rural areas are less common, and only cerebrovascular diseases (all ages, not 0-64), diseases of the arteries, musculoskeletal disorders and road traffic accidents, have coefficients which exceed the level of 0.26 which indicates a result that is statistically significant at the 5% level. Many causes do not reach that level, as is also the case for association with DEP.

Multiple regression using the two variables of DEP and U/R shows that DEP rather than U/R explains most of the variation. Where the correlation with DEP is strong the U/R additional contribution is generally low: for lung cancer 0-64 for instance U/R adds only 4.7% to the variance explained and this % is low also for bronchitis, for ischaemic heart disease 0-64 and for smoking-related diseases. For lung cancer all ages, chronic rheumatic heart disease, liver disease and cirrhosis, the U/R factor enhances an already fairly high correlation with DEP, the result suggesting that deprivation does not explain all of the influence exerted by the urban environment. The contribution of U/R is strong also, with the rural influence predominating, for endocrine disorders, cerebrovascular disease (all ages), arterial disease and road traffic accidents, all causes with which the link with deprivation is weak.

TABLE 5.1    CORRELATIONS: CAUSE SMRs WITH DEPRIVATION SCORE 1980-82 AND 1980-85 (OVER PCS)

|  | All ages | | 0-64/74* | |
|  | 80-82 | 80-85 | 80-82 | 80-85 |
|---|---|---|---|---|
| All causes | 0.72 | 0.73 | 0.74 | 0.79 |
| Chronic Respiratory | 0.64 | 0.72 | 0.69* | 0.60 |
| Ca. Lung | 0.58 | 0.70 | 0.65 | 0.65 |
| Ischaemic Heart Disease | 0.45 | 0.49 | 0.59 | 0.59 |
| All Cancers | N/A | 0.61 | 0.55 | 0.54 |
| Hypertension and Stroke | 0.18 | 0.20 | - | - |
| Ca. Cervix | 0.25 | 0.25 | - | - |
| Non-traffic Accidents | 0.37 | 0.24 | - | - |
| Ca. Stomach | 0.39 | 0.39 | - | - |
| Ca. Breast | -0.04 | -0.06 | -0.06* | - |
| Road Traffic Accidents | 0.04 | 0.04 | - | - |

*causes with small numbers of deaths at 0-64 are shown for 0-74

TABLE 5.2    GRADIENTS IN MORTALITY 1980-82 AND 1980-85

|  | DEPCAT | | | | | | |
|  | Affluent | | | | | Deprived | |
|  | 1 | 2 | 3 | 4 | 5 | 6 | 7 |
|---|---|---|---|---|---|---|---|
| 0-64 | | | | | | | |
| 1980-82 | 64 | 79 | 91 | 98 | 110 | 125 | 141 |
| 1980-85 | 66 | 80 | 91 | 99 | 110 | 123 | 139 |
| 65+ | | | | | | | |
| 1980-82 | 90 | 92 | 96 | 101 | 105 | 108 | 118 |
| 1980-85 | 90 | 92 | 96 | 101 | 106 | 108 | 116 |
| All ages | | | | | | | |
| 1980-82 | 83 | 89 | 95 | 100 | 107 | 113 | 125 |
| 1980-85 | 84 | 89 | 95 | 101 | 107 | 112 | 113 |

TABLE 5.3   CANCER OF THE LUNG (MALES) 1980-82 AND 1980-85

(a) SMRs by Deprivation Category:

| All ages | Affluent 1 | 2 | 3 | 4 | 5 | Deprived 6 | 7 | Rate/ =100 | n = |
|---|---|---|---|---|---|---|---|---|---|
| 1980-82 | 66 | 80 | 78 | 102 | 113 | 126 | 177 | 12.1 | 8842 |
| 1980-85 | 65 | 78 | 81 | 100 | 116 | 129 | 171 | 12.2 | 17716 |
| 0-64 | | | | | | | | | |
| 1980-82 | (55) | 72 | 75 | 104 | 111 | 132 | 181 | 4.6 | 2984 |
| 1980-85 | 54 | 70 | 79 | 99 | 117 | 134 | 178 | 4.6 | 5936 |

(<100 deaths)

(b) correlation matrix for SMRs (over 1010 sectors)

| Year | SMR | 1980-82 All | 1980-85 All | 1980-82 0-64 |
|---|---|---|---|---|
| 1980-82 | (all) | | | |
| 1980-85 | (all) | 0.816 | | |
| 1980-82 | (0-64) | 0.696 | 0.554 | |
| 1980-85 | (0-64) | 0.670 | 0.736 | 0.810 |

TABLE 5.4   ALL CAUSES MORTALITY: CORRELATIONS WITH DEP OVER PCS AND LGDS

| | PCS 1980-82 | PCS 1980-85 | LGD 1980-85 |
|---|---|---|---|
| All ages | 0.72 | 0.73 | 0.85 |
| 0-64 | 0.75 | 0.79 | 0.92 |
| 65+ | 0.52 | 0.51 | 0.73 |

TABLE 5.5   CORRELATIONS OF DEPRIVATION WITH CAUSES OF DEATH

| cause* | r | n = |
|---|---|---|
| **High Association** | | |
| all malignant neoplasms | 0.82 | 84224 |
| 0-64 | 0.86 | 27891 |
| ca. stomach | 0.72 | 6195 |
| ca. lung | 0.81 | 24784 |
| 0-64 | 0.87 | 8576 |

| ischaemic heart disease | | |
|---|---|---|
| 0-64 | 0.75 | 26492 |
| chronic respiratory | 0.87 | 15121 |
| 0-64 | 0.82 | 3416 |
| digestive system | 0.76 | 12447 |
| liver disease & cirrhosis | 0.76 | 2540 |

*Moderate Association*

| infectious diseases | 0.59 | 1661 |
|---|---|---|
| chronic rheumatic heart disease | 0.69 | 1808 |
| ischaemic heart disease | 0.55 | 108753 |
| cerebrovascular disease | | |
| 0-64 | 0.65 | 52448 |
| pneumonia | 0.53 | 23478 |
| 0-64 | 0.57 | 2006 |
| stomach ulcers | 0.62 | 2870 |
| suicide/undetermined | 0.52 | 4242 |

*Low Association*

| ca. oesophagus | 0.25 | 3245 |
|---|---|---|
| ca. pancreas | 0.17 | 3681 |
| ca. cervix | 0.32 | 1246 |
| endocrine disorders | 0.23 | 4599 |
| hypertensive disease | 0.42 | 2703 |
| pulmonary heart disease | 0.34 | 1801 |
| genitourinary | 0.24 | 5189 |
| congenital anomalies | 0.17 | 1760 |
| non RTAs | 0.18 | 8204 |

*Negative Low Association*

| ca. lymphatic tissue | -0.13 | 4827 |
|---|---|---|
| leukaemia | -0.23 | 1847 |
| musculo-skeletal | -0.26 | 1494 |
| symptoms | -0.16 | 1560 |
| road traffic accidents | -0.14 | 3841 |

*Association Lacking*

| ca. large bowel | 0.03 | 10286 |
|---|---|---|
| 0-64 | -0.07 | 2532 |
| ca. breast | 0.02 | 7315 |
| nervous system | -0.03 | 4525 |
| cerebrovascular disease | | |
| (all ages) | 0.04 | 52448 |
| diseases of arteries | -0.09 | 8843 |

*Combination Causes*

| avoidable causes: | | |
|---|---|---|
| - various | 0.54 | 1566 |
| - cerebrovascular | 0.74 | 6655 |
| 35-64 | | |
| smoking related all ages | 0.91 | 71786 |

*ICD order, see Figure 5.3 for ICD codes

TABLE 5.6    DEPRIVATION SCORE AND SMOKING FOR LOCAL GOVERNMENT DISTRICTS

| | Percent Smokes Cigarettes: | | DEP score | SMR Smoking causes# |
| | M* % | F* % | | |
|---|---|---|---|---|
| Eastwood | 29 | 24 | -5.65 | 73 |
| Inverness | 38 | 30 | -2.08 | 88 |
| Perth & Kinross | 32 | 35 | -2.05 | 84 |
| Stirling | 35 | 34 | -1.79 | 93 |
| East Lothian | 38 | 40 | -1.58 | 89 |
| Roxburgh | 33 | 35 | -1.55 | 86 |
| Aberdeen | 32 | 30 | -1.41 | 94 |
| Dunfermline | 41 | 40 | -1.38 | 100 |
| Kyle & Carrick | 33 | 37 | -1.35 | 95 |
| Edinburgh | 35 | 33 | -1.10 | 95 |
| Nithsdale | 39 | 41 | -1.02 | 96 |
| Banff & Buchan | 39 | 39 | -0.80 | 84 |
| Falkirk | 46 | 37 | -0.40 | 97 |
| Kirkcaldy | 45 | 41 | -0.39 | 103 |
| Dumbarton | 30 | 34 | -0.22 | 96 |
| Hamilton | 39 | 43 | 0.52 | 104 |
| Renfrew | 43 | 42 | 0.62 | 112 |
| Cunninghame | 42 | 41 | 0.85 | 106 |
| Dundee | 41 | 38 | 0.89 | 100 |
| Monklands | 51 | 49 | 2.95 | 113 |
| North Glasgow | 52 | 51 ⎫ | 4.08 | 123 |
| South Glasgow | 51 | 45 ⎭ | | |

*ages 40-59
#all ages


TABLE 5.7    CAUSE SMRs SCOTLAND 1980-85 AND SOCIAL/ECONOMIC FACTORS

| | | Male Unemployment | Low Social Class | No Car | Over-crowding | DEP |
|---|---|---|---|---|---|---|
| All causes | (0-64) | 0.72 | 0.61 | 0.74 | 0.62 | 0.76 |
| Chronic respiratory | (0-74) | 0.67 | 0.52 | 0.69 | 0.61 | 0.69 |
| Ca. lung | (0-64) | 0.61 | 0.50 | 0.66 | 0.57 | 0.65 |
| Heart disease | (0-64) | 0.56 | 0.50 | 0.54 | 0.55 | 0.59 |
| All cancers | (0-64) | 0.52 | 0.44 | 0.55 | 0.47 | 0.55 |
| Hypertension/stroke | (0-64) | 0.41 | 0.34 | 0.41 | 0.37 | 0.42 |
| Acute respiratory | (0-74) | 0.42 | 0.31 | 0.39 | 0.38 | 0.41 |
| Ca. stomach | | 0.36 | 0.30 | 0.38 | 0.37 | 0.39 |
| Ca. cervix | | 0.23 | 0.22 | 0.22 | 0.22 | 0.25 |
| Non-traffic accidents | | 0.22 | 0.23 | 0.23 | 0.19 | 0.24 |
| Ca. breast | (0-74) | -0.06 | -0.06 | -0.05 | -0.04 | -0.06 |
| Road traffic accidents | | 0.02 | 0.12 | -0.04 | 0.04 | 0.04 |
| Ca. colon/rectum | (0-74) | 0.01 | 0.03 | 0.01 | -0.01 | 0.01 |

TABLE 5.8    1980-1985 CAUSE SMRs BY DEPRIVATION CATEGORY

| ICD Chpt | Cause | DEPCAT Affluent 1 | 2 | 3 | 4 | 5 | Deprived 6 | 7 | r* | No. of Deaths |
|---|---|---|---|---|---|---|---|---|---|---|
| | All Causes | 84 | 89 | 95 | 101 | 107 | 112 | 123 | 0.85 | 378,355 |
| | All Causes 0-64 | 66 | 80 | 91 | 99 | 110 | 123 | 138 | 0.92 | 95,484 |
| | All Causes 65+ | 90 | 92 | 96 | 101 | 106 | 108 | 116 | 0.73 | 282,871 |
| I | Infectious & Parasitic | (77) | 89 | 88 | 91 | 104 | 131 | 166 | 0.59 | 1,661 |
| II | Malignant Neoplasms | 84 | 89 | 93 | 100 | 106 | 115 | 129 | 0.82 | 84,224 |
| | Malignant Neoplasms 0-64 | 78 | 87 | 92 | 99 | 106 | 119 | 129 | 0.86 | 27,891 |
| | Ca. Oesophagus | 82 | 94 | 102 | 96 | 96 | 112 | 129 | 0.25 | 3,245 |
| | Ca. Stomach | 74 | 76 | 87 | 102 | 118 | 128 | 134 | 0.72 | 6,195 |
| | Ca. Large Bowel | 93 | 99 | 102 | 98 | 99 | 103 | 102 | 0.03 | 10,286 |
| | Ca. Large Bowel 0-64 | 106 | 105 | 99 | 98 | 94 | 107 | 96 | -0.07 | 2,532 |
| | Ca. Pancreas | 96 | 94 | 98 | 99 | 102 | 111 | 108 | 0.17 | 3,681 |
| | Ca. Lung | 67 | 78 | 82 | 98 | 113 | 130 | 176 | 0.81 | 24,784 |
| | Ca. Lung 0-64 | 58 | 70 | 79 | 97 | 114 | 138 | 179 | 0.87 | 8,576 |
| | Ca. Breast | 98 | 99 | 102 | 101 | 100 | 102 | 87 | 0.02 | 7,315 |
| | Ca. Cervix | (44) | 77 | 88 | 102 | 113 | 121 | 163 | 0.32 | 1,246 |
| | Ca. Lymphatic Tissue | 103 | 100 | 96 | 101 | 97 | 103 | 87 | -0.13 | 4,827 |
| | Leukaemia | 114 | 111 | 96 | 102 | 93 | 100 | (81) | -0.23 | 1,847 |
| III | Endocrine | 54 | 90 | 99 | 100 | 109 | 117 | 121 | 0.23 | 4,599 |
| VI | Nervous System | 84 | 103 | 97 | 101 | 104 | 99 | 108 | -0.03 | 4,529 |
| VII | Circulatory System: | | | | | | | | | |
| | Chronic Rheumatic HD | (90) | 72 | 84 | 106 | 106 | 127 | 150 | 0.69 | 1,808 |
| | Hypertensive HD | 119 | 79 | 96 | 92 | 104 | 115 | 156 | 0.42 | 2,703 |
| | Ischaemic HD | 82 | 89 | 96 | 102 | 110 | 110 | 110 | 0.55 | 108,753 |
| | Ischaemic HD 0-64 | 63 | 75 | 93 | 101 | 116 | 124 | 123 | 0.75 | 26,492 |
| | Pulmonary HD | 92 | 95 | 76 | 108 | 103 | 123 | 130 | 0.34 | 1,801 |
| | Cerebrovascular Disease | 89 | 91 | 100 | 104 | 104 | 103 | 105 | 0.04 | 52,448 |
| | CVD 0-64 | 58 | 79 | 93 | 102 | 110 | 126 | 128 | 0.65 | 6,405 |
| | Arteries | 90 | 96 | 108 | 102 | 101 | 94 | 86 | -0.09 | 8,843 |
| VIII | Respiratory System: | | | | | | | | | |
| | Pneumonia | 92 | 94 | 91 | 96 | 108 | 117 | 134 | 0.53 | 23,478 |
| | Pneumonia 0-64 | (53) | 68 | 90 | 96 | 112 | 135 | 168 | 0.57 | 2,006 |
| | Bronchitis | 63 | 72 | 79 | 97 | 116 | 138 | 203 | 0.87 | 15,121 |
| | Bronchitis 0-64 | (38) | 57 | 74 | 94 | 125 | 143 | 213 | 0.82 | 3,416 |
| IX | Digestive System | 82 | 86 | 89 | 98 | 110 | 125 | 134 | 0.76 | 12,447 |
| | Stomach&Duodenal Ulcer | 88 | 86 | 89 | 96 | 116 | 129 | 122 | 0.62 | 2,870 |
| | Liver Dis&Cirrhosis | 66 | 75 | 79 | 92 | 108 | 146 | 172 | 0.76 | 2,540 |
| X | Genitourinary | 91 | 93 | 102 | 102 | 97 | 99 | 123 | 0.24 | 5,189 |
| XIII | Musculoskeletal | (94) | 117 | 92 | 99 | 96 | 98 | (107) | -0.26 | 1,494 |
| XIV | Congenital Abnormalities | (87) | 93 | 104 | 96 | 107 | 103 | 106 | 0.17 | 1,760 |
| XVI | Symptoms | (53) | 104 | 110 | 103 | 72 | 83 | 156 | -0.16 | 1,560 |
| | Road Traffic Accidents | 80 | 99 | 106 | 99 | 97 | 95 | 116 | -0.14 | 3,841 |
| | Non-RTAs | 70 | 96 | 96 | 102 | 101 | 109 | 131 | 0.18 | 8,204 |
| | Suicide&Undetermined | 62 | 90 | 90 | 102 | 97 | 113 | 157 | 0.52 | 4,242 |
| | Avoidable - Various | (52) | 76 | 91 | 97 | 112 | 135 | 147 | 0.54 | 1,566 |
| | Avoidable - CVD & Hyper | 65 | 83 | 98 | 105 | 118 | 135 | 138 | 0.74 | 6,655 |
| | Smoking Related | 73 | 82 | 89 | 100 | 111 | 122 | 148 | 0.91 | 71,786 |

*Correlation with DEP over 56 local government districts
(<100 deaths)

TABLE 5.9    RELATIVE MORTALITY: LOWEST TO HIGHEST SOCIAL CATEGORY,
WHITEHALL STUDY AND SCOTLAND

|                        | Whitehall [a] | Scotland [b] |
|------------------------|---------------|--------------|
| chronic respiratory    | 7.3           | 5.6          |
| lung cancer            | 3.6           | 3.1          |
| other respiratory      | 3.1           |              |
| pneumonia              |               | 3.2          |
| genito-urinary         | 3.1           | 1.3          |
| gastro-intestinal      | 2.8           | 1.6          |
| suicide                | 1.9           | 2.5          |
| IHD/CHD                | 1.7           | 2.0          |
| accidents & violence   | 1.5           |              |
| RTAs                   |               | 1.5          |
| other accidents        |               | 1.9          |
| all cancer             | 1.4           | 1.7          |
| cerebrovascular        | 1.2           | 2.2          |

(a) 10-year mortality in 17,000 civil servants aged 45-60 on recruitment to the study in 1967-69
(b) 0-64


TABLE 5.10    RANGE IN CAUSE SMR VALUES BY DEPCAT AND SOCIAL CLASS

|                         | DEPCAT 1980-85 M + F all ages, or 0-64* | SOCIAL CLASS [#] 1979-83 M20-64 |
|-------------------------|------------------------------------------|----------------------------------|
| All neoplasms           | 78 - 129*                                | 69 - 157                         |
| Ca. stomach             | 74 - 134                                 | (42) - 147                       |
| Ca. lung                | 58 - 179*                                | 53 - 173                         |
| Ischaemic heart disease | 63 - 123*                                | 66 - 158                         |
| Cerebrovascular disease | 58 - 128*                                | 52 - 184                         |
| Pneumonia               | [53] - 168*                              | (21) - 202                       |
| Bronchitis/asthma       | [38] - 213*                              | (36) - 225                       |
| Stomach ulcers          | 88 - 122                                 | (45) - 224                       |
| Liver disease/cirrhosis | 66 - 172                                 | 64 - 176                         |
| Motor vehicle accidents | 80 - 116                                 | 55 - 158                         |
| Suicide                 | 62 - 157                                 | 93 - 224                         |

(<20 deaths)
[<100 deaths]

#source Table SD28 Scottish tables, ref 12

TABLE 5.11A    1980-1985 CAUSES SMRs FOR HEALTH BOARDS

| | 1 | 2 | 3 | 4 | 5 | 6 | 7 | 8 | 9 | 10 | 11 | 12 | 13 | 14 | 15 | 16 | 17 | 18 | 19 | 20 | 21 | 22 |
|---|---|---|---|---|---|---|---|---|---|---|---|---|---|---|---|---|---|---|---|---|---|---|
| Ayr & Arran | 104* | 102 | 105* | 75* | 97* | 98 | 93 | 107 | 105 | 102 | 101 | 90* | 90* | 101 | 103 | 103 | 115 | 106 | 91 | 82* | 126* | 108* |
| Argyll & Clyde | 105* | 108* | 104* | 119* | 102 | 104 | 96 | 111* | 97 | 96 | 111 | 103 | 102 | 111* | 100 | 89* | 85 | 103 | 97 | 97 | 93 | 108* |
| Greater Glasgow | 106* | 113* | 104* | 123* | 113* | 113* | 103 | 111* | 104 | 106 | 98 | 134* | 135* | 100 | 100 | 97 | 95 | 97 | 98 | 140* | 136* | 100 |
| Lanarkshire | 106* | 105* | 106* | 102 | 101 | 104* | 98 | 119* | 93* | 96 | 90 | 99 | 103 | 103 | 110 | 102 | 92 | 107 | 87* | 109 | 93 | 113* |
| Fife | 98* | 95* | 99 | 76* | 94* | 96 | 97 | 92 | 92* | 98 | 95 | 88* | 90* | 96 | 141* | 109 | 117 | 99 | 72* | 75* | 70* | 102 |
| Forth Valley | 99 | 97* | 100 | 103 | 98 | 96 | 106 | 100 | 99 | 96 | 94 | 96 | 95 | 113* | 102 | 93 | 97 | 92 | 115* | 81 | 67* | 98 |
| Grampian | 93* | 88* | 95* | 83* | 93* | 90* | 104 | 86* | 107* | 106 | 93 | 81* | 78* | 89* | 85 | 97 | 110 | 84* | 121* | 89 | 50* | 93* |
| Lothian | 95* | 92* | 96* | 96 | 100 | 96* | 99 | 89* | 93* | 92 | 106 | 102 | 95 | 94* | 92 | 106 | 111 | 104 | 100 | 113* | 112* | 92* |
| Tayside | 94* | 88* | 96* | 88 | 96* | 92* | 96 | 102 | 107* | 96 | 107 | 90* | 83* | 98 | 82 | 91 | 78* | 90 | 104 | 80* | 73* | 96* |
| Borders | 93* | 85* | 95* | 96 | 88* | 86* | 100 | 65* | 98 | 91 | 110 | 80* | 83* | 103 | 64 | 96 | 95 | 104 | 112 | 55* | 92 | 92* |
| Dumfries & Galloway | 96* | 94* | 97* | 75 | 87* | 91* | 98 | 81* | 96 | 116 | 91 | 74* | 76* | 95 | 99 | 91 | 92 | 100 | 111 | 56* | 113 | 105* |
| Highland | 100 | 102 | 99 | 106 | 95* | 98 | 122* | 92 | 108 | 114 | 109 | 75* | 82* | 109 | 94 | 107 | 113 | 111 | 113 | 69* | 108 | 98 |
| The Islands | 93* | 92* | 93* | 137 | 79* | 90 | 81 | 79* | 84* | 81 | 80 | 55* | 72* | 107 | 100 | 100 | 141* | 107 | 107 | 69 | 121 | 94* |

| | 23 | 24 | 25 | 26 | 27 | 28 | 29 | 30 | 31 | 32 | 33 | 34 | 35 | 36 | 37 | 38 | 39 | 40 | 41 | 42 | 43 | 44 |
|---|---|---|---|---|---|---|---|---|---|---|---|---|---|---|---|---|---|---|---|---|---|---|
| Ayr & Arran | 110 | 113 | 116* | 114* | 116* | 83* | 81* | 100 | 105 | 105 | 110 | 91 | 110 | 96 | 104 | 91 | 105 | 92 | 90 | 116 | 120* | 102 |
| Argyll & Clyde | 113* | 78* | 112* | 110* | 125* | 96 | 123* | 102 | 101 | 122* | 111 | 131* | 111* | 79* | 92 | 92 | 82* | 112* | 88* | 107 | 114* | 106 |
| Greater Glasgow | 107* | 111* | 94* | 104 | 86* | 118* | 132* | 138* | 143* | 115* | 122* | 141* | 101 | 84* | 105 | 81* | 99 | 98 | 121* | 108 | 117* | 117* |
| Lanarkshire | 120* | 89 | 98 | 111* | 126* | 115* | 120* | 100 | 97 | 102 | 107 | 97 | 103 | 90 | 99 | 48* | 79* | 100 | 80* | 110 | 113* | 105* |
| Fife | 102 | 78* | 114* | 111* | 105 | 91* | 77* | 90* | 82* | 85* | 79* | 78* | 100 | 94 | 87 | 122* | 99 | 96 | 97 | 109 | 114* | 97* |
| Forth Valley | 94* | 75* | 101 | 102 | 124* | 116* | 163* | 96 | 98 | 105 | 121* | 92 | 89 | 80 | 93 | 41* | 93 | 93 | 82* | 114 | 105 | 97 |
| Grampian | 80* | 120* | 95* | 88* | 89* | 97 | 78* | 77* | 69* | 81* | 77* | 61* | 91* | 116 | 95 | 129* | 134* | 112* | 103 | 77* | 86* | 86* |
| Lothian | 87* | 120* | 93* | 85* | 80* | 89* | 72* | 101 | 97 | 97 | 97 | 95 | 90* | 102 | 117* | 95 | 85* | 86* | 91* | 86* | 93 | 96* |
| Tayside | 88* | 92 | 90* | 89* | 80* | 111* | 67* | 85* | 73* | 88* | 85* | 68* | 100 | 125* | 76* | 47* | 106 | 104 | 104 | 89 | 95 | 91* |
| Borders | 82* | 139* | 101 | 104 | 113 | 76* | 60* | 73* | 77 | 87* | 80 | 68* | 120* | 99 | 95 | 238* | 106 | 80 | 80 | 85 | 107 | 86* |
| Dumfries & Galloway | 101 | 73 | 106* | 91 | 117* | 81* | 78 | 75* | 82 | 96 | 73* | 102 | 114 | 99 | 114 | 112 | 104 | 92 | 94 | 77 | 91 | 89* |
| Highland | 96 | 62* | 109* | 88 | 115* | 75* | 79 | 70* | 70* | 82* | 72* | 82 | 94 | 150* | 119 | 296* | 163* | 130* | 136* | 93 | 98 | 88* |
| The Islands | 92 | 49* | 104 | 92 | 124* | 76* | 74 | 55* | 51* | 78* | 59* | 64* | 124* | 177* | 73 | 229* | 103 | 128* | 97 | 109 | 101 | 75* |

see Figure 5.3 p137 for list of causes

TABLE 5.11B    1980 - 1985 CAUSES SMRs FOR HEALTH BOARDS RANKING

| HB | 1 | 2 | 3 | 4 | 5 | 6 | 7 | 8 | 9 | 10 | 11 | 12 | 13 | 14 | 15 | 16 | 17 | 18 | 19 | 20 | 21 | 22 |
|---|---|---|---|---|---|---|---|---|---|---|---|---|---|---|---|---|---|---|---|---|---|---|
| Ayr and Arran | 4 | 4 | 2 | 13 | 6 | 4 | 12 | 4 | 4 | 5 | 6 | 6 | 7 | 7 | 3 | 4 | 2 | 4 | 11 | 6 | 2 | 3 |
| Argyll and Clyde | 3 | 2 | 3 | 3 | 2 | 3 | 10 | 2 | 8 | 9 | 1 | 2 | 3 | 8 | 5 | 13 | 12 | 7 | 10 | 4 | 7 | 2 |
| Greater Glasgow | 1 | 1 | 4 | 2 | 1 | 1 | 4 | 3 | 5 | 4 | 7 | 1 | 1 | 8 | 6 | 8 | 9 | 10 | 9 | 1 | 1 | 6 |
| Lanarkshire | 2 | 3 | 1 | 6 | 3 | 2 | 7 | 1 | 11 | 10 | 12 | 4 | 2 | 5 | 2 | 5 | 10 | 3 | 12 | 3 | 8 | 1 |
| Fife | 7 | 7 | 7 | 11 | 9 | 6 | 9 | 7 | 12 | 6 | 8 | 8 | 6 | 10 | 1 | 1 | 1 | 9 | 13 | 9 | 11 | 5 |
| Forth Valley | 6 | 6 | 5 | 5 | 5 | 7 | 2 | 6 | 6 | 8 | 9 | 5 | 5 | 1 | 4 | 10 | 7 | 11 | 2 | 7 | 12 | 7 |
| Grampian | 11 | 12 | 11 | 10 | 10 | 11 | 3 | 10 | 2 | 3 | 10 | 9 | 11 | 13 | 11 | 7 | 5 | 13 | 1 | 5 | 13 | 11 |
| Lothian | 9 | 10 | 10 | 7 | 4 | 8 | 6 | 9 | 10 | 11 | 5 | 3 | 4 | 12 | 10 | 3 | 4 | 5 | 8 | 2 | 5 | 13 |
| Tayside | 10 | 11 | 9 | 9 | 7 | 9 | 11 | 5 | 3 | 7 | 4 | 7 | 8 | 9 | 12 | 11 | 13 | 12 | 7 | 8 | 10 | 9 |
| Borders | 12 | 13 | 12 | 8 | 11 | 13 | 5 | 13 | 7 | 12 | 2 | 10 | 9 | 6 | 13 | 9 | 8 | 6 | 4 | 13 | 9 | 12 |
| Dumfries & Galloway | 8 | 8 | 8 | 12 | 12 | 10 | 8 | 11 | 9 | 1 | 11 | 12 | 12 | 11 | 8 | 12 | 11 | 8 | 5 | 12 | 4 | 4 |
| Highland | 5 | 5 | 6 | 4 | 8 | 5 | 1 | 8 | 1 | 2 | 3 | 11 | 10 | 3 | 9 | 2 | 3 | 2 | 3 | 11 | 6 | 8 |
| The Islands | 13 | 9 | 13 | 1 | 13 | 12 | 13 | 12 | 13 | 13 | 13 | 13 | 13 | 4 | 7 | 6 | 6 | 1 | 6 | 10 | 3 | 10 |

| HB | 23 | 24 | 25 | 26 | 27 | 28 | 29 | 30 | 31 | 32 | 33 | 34 | 35 | 36 | 37 | 38 | 39 | 40 | 41 | 42 | 43 | 44 |
|---|---|---|---|---|---|---|---|---|---|---|---|---|---|---|---|---|---|---|---|---|---|---|
| Ayr and Arran | 3 | 4 | 1 | 1 | 6 | 9 | 5 | 5 | 2 | 4 | 4 | 6 | 4 | 8 | 5 | 9 | 5 | 10 | 9 | 1 | 1 | 4 |
| Argyll and Clyde | 2 | 8 | 3 | 4 | 2 | 6 | 3 | 2 | 3 | 1 | 3 | 2 | 3 | 13 | 10 | 8 | 12 | 4 | 10 | 7 | 4 | 2 |
| Greater Glasgow | 4 | 5 | 11 | 5 | 11 | 1 | 2 | 1 | 1 | 2 | 1 | 1 | 7 | 11 | 4 | 10 | 8 | 7 | 2 | 6 | 2 | 1 |
| Lanarkshire | 1 | 7 | 9 | 2 | 1 | 3 | 4 | 4 | 5 | 5 | 5 | 3 | 5 | 10 | 6 | 11 | 13 | 6 | 13 | 3 | 5 | 3 |
| Fife | 5 | 9 | 2 | 3 | 9 | 7 | 9 | 7 | 7 | 10 | 10 | 8 | 8 | 9 | 11 | 5 | 9 | 8 | 6 | 4 | 3 | 6 |
| Forth Valley | 8 | 10 | 8 | 7 | 4 | 2 | 1 | 6 | 4 | 3 | 2 | 5 | 8 | 12 | 9 | 13 | 10 | 9 | 11 | 2 | 7 | 5 |
| Grampian | 13 | 3 | 10 | 12 | 10 | 5 | 8 | 9 | 12 | 12 | 11 | 13 | 13 | 4 | 8 | 4 | 2 | 3 | 4 | 13 | 13 | 12 |
| Lothian | 11 | 2 | 12 | 13 | 13 | 8 | 11 | 3 | 6 | 6 | 6 | 4 | 11 | 6 | 2 | 7 | 11 | 13 | 8 | 10 | 11 | 7 |
| Tayside | 10 | 6 | 13 | 10 | 12 | 4 | 12 | 8 | 10 | 7 | 8 | 10 | 9 | 3 | 12 | 12 | 4 | 5 | 3 | 9 | 10 | 8 |
| Borders | 12 | 1 | 7 | 6 | 8 | 11 | 13 | 11 | 8 | 8 | 9 | 11 | 6 | 7 | 7 | 12 | 3 | 12 | 12 | 11 | 6 | 11 |
| Dumfries & Galloway | 6 | 11 | 5 | 9 | 5 | 10 | 7 | 10 | 8 | 9 | 7 | 9 | 6 | 5 | 3 | 6 | 6 | 11 | 7 | 12 | 6 | 9 |
| Highland | 7 | 12 | 4 | 11 | 7 | 13 | 6 | 12 | 11 | 11 | 12 | 7 | 10 | 2 | 1 | 1 | 7 | 1 | 1 | 8 | 9 | 10 |
| The Islands | 9 | 13 | 6 | 8 | 3 | 12 | 10 | 13 | 13 | 13 | 13 | 12 | 1 | 1 | 13 | 3 | 7 | 2 | 5 | 5 | 8 | 13 |

TABLE 5.11c  1980 - 1985 CAUSES NOS FOR HEALTH BOARDS

| | 1 | 2 | 3 | 4 | 5 | 6 | 7 | 8 | 9 | 10 | 11 | 12 | 13 | 14 | 15 | 16 | 17 | 18 | 19 | 20 | 21 | 22 |
|---|---|---|---|---|---|---|---|---|---|---|---|---|---|---|---|---|---|---|---|---|---|---|
| Ayr & Arran | 28,660 | 7,265 | 21,395 | 91 | 6,019 | 2,041 | 220 | 487 | 790 | 193 | 273 | 1,654 | 573 | 544 | 96 | 369 | 156 | 356 | 301 | 109 | 247 | 8,547 |
| Argyll & Clyde | 33,145 | 9,047 | 24,098 | 167 | 7,189 | 2,533 | 261 | 575 | 834 | 212 | 341 | 2,124 | 761 | 693 | 108 | 366 | 133 | 396 | 369 | 149 | 209 | 9,765 |
| Greater Glasgow | 80,894 | 21,911 | 58,983 | 409 | 19,256 | 6415 | 673 | 1,388 | 2167 | 551 | 733 | 6,676 | 2,380 | 1,515 | 257 | 948 | 350 | 906 | 891 | 519 | 748 | 21,983 |
| Lanarkshire | 35,913 | 11,005 | 24,908 | 162 | 7,800 | 3,135 | 289 | 663 | 851 | 260 | 300 | 2,273 | 942 | 721 | 137 | 470 | 162 | 448 | 370 | 185 | 219 | 10,999 |
| Fife | 24,258 | 5,853 | 18,405 | 83 | 5,205 | 1,724 | 207 | 373 | 621 | 159 | 229 | 1,448 | 497 | 450 | 114 | 348 | 141 | 298 | 214 | 88 | 123 | 7,291 |
| Forth Valley | 18,585 | 4,918 | 13,667 | 87 | 4,174 | 1,425 | 172 | 309 | 507 | 129 | 172 | 1,222 | 431 | 409 | 65 | 229 | 91 | 210 | 262 | 73 | 89 | 5,338 |
| Grampian | 33,463 | 7,467 | 25,996 | 130 | 7,325 | 2,233 | 317 | 499 | 1,040 | 237 | 321 | 1,875 | 589 | 589 | 97 | 442 | 192 | 364 | 518 | 146 | 127 | 9,506 |
| Lothian | 52,746 | 12,498 | 40,248 | 232 | 12,272 | 3,828 | 472 | 808 | 1,409 | 335 | 575 | 3,661 | 1,170 | 1,015 | 171 | 761 | 300 | 709 | 665 | 299 | 450 | 14,663 |
| Tayside | 30,789 | 6,550 | 24,239 | 122 | 6,858 | 2,012 | 266 | 545 | 952 | 192 | 338 | 1,879 | 560 | 601 | 86 | 374 | 121 | 357 | 396 | 122 | 171 | 9,043 |
| Borders | 8,593 | 1,617 | 6,976 | 37 | 1,779 | 483 | 78 | 98 | 249 | 47 | 98 | 474 | 145 | 172 | 18 | 110 | 41 | 116 | 119 | 23 | 62 | 2,449 |
| Dumfries & Galloway | 11,301 | 2,657 | 8,644 | 38 | 2,292 | 759 | 99 | 157 | 309 | 88 | 104 | 578 | 197 | 207 | 37 | 136 | 52 | 142 | 153 | 31 | 95 | 3,565 |
| Highland | 14,117 | 3,512 | 10,605 | 66 | 2,969 | 971 | 148 | 212 | 413 | 102 | 149 | 698 | 249 | 284 | 42 | 195 | 78 | 190 | 192 | 45 | 108 | 3,982 |
| The Islands | 5,891 | 1,184 | 4,707 | 37 | 1,086 | 332 | 43 | 81 | 144 | 27 | 48 | 222 | 82 | 115 | 18 | 79 | 30 | 107 | 79 | 19 | 55 | 1,712 |

| | 23 | 24 | 25 | 26 | 27 | 28 | 29 | 30 | 31 | 32 | 33 | 34 | 35 | 36 | 37 | 38 | 39 | 40 | 41 | 42 | 43 | 44 |
|---|---|---|---|---|---|---|---|---|---|---|---|---|---|---|---|---|---|---|---|---|---|---|
| Ayr & Arran | 2,162 | 148 | 4,359 | 542 | 735 | 1,400 | 121 | 1,110 | 267 | 948 | 228 | 175 | 410 | 103 | 137 | 106 | 297 | 546 | 284 | 137 | 562 | 5,357 |
| Argyll & Clyde | 2,619 | 117 | 4,831 | 616 | 899 | 1,845 | 217 | 1,268 | 301 | 1,266 | 263 | 290 | 474 | 98 | 147 | 127 | 276 | 770 | 330 | 148 | 625 | 6,362 |
| Greater Glasgow | 5,784 | 404 | 10,003 | 1,367 | 1,525 | 5,581 | 537 | 4,145 | 1,008 | 2,905 | 704 | 734 | 1,059 | 257 | 350 | 247 | 756 | 1,615 | 1,021 | 335 | 1,504 | 16,916 |
| Lanarkshire | 3,396 | 143 | 4,374 | 765 | 929 | 2,250 | 262 | 1356 | 356 | 1,153 | 270 | 254 | 455 | 117 | 212 | 81 | 333 | 759 | 369 | 193 | 759 | 6,986 |
| Fife | 1,735 | 92 | 3,885 | 456 | 606 | 1,395 | 99 | 899 | 181 | 691 | 149 | 130 | 341 | 91 | 102 | 127 | 245 | 509 | 268 | 110 | 460 | 4,565 |
| Forth Valley | 1,318 | 67 | 2,556 | 347 | 527 | 1,316 | 174 | 733 | 177 | 651 | 171 | 123 | 225 | 58 | 88 | 33 | 188 | 377 | 187 | 96 | 350 | 3,542 |
| Grampian | 1,870 | 205 | 4,789 | 498 | 765 | 2,217 | 139 | 1,115 | 208 | 952 | 210 | 143 | 454 | 164 | 157 | 194 | 478 | 876 | 407 | 109 | 474 | 5,754 |
| Lothian | 3,291 | 321 | 7,319 | 780 | 1,060 | 3,114 | 206 | 2,213 | 476 | 1,792 | 413 | 353 | 693 | 228 | 281 | 211 | 471 | 1,047 | 568 | 194 | 841 | 10,070 |
| Tayside | 1,834 | 144 | 4,168 | 448 | 632 | 2,316 | 104 | 1,099 | 196 | 950 | 212 | 142 | 458 | 163 | 97 | 59 | 313 | 727 | 347 | 107 | 469 | 5,526 |
| Borders | 445 | 62 | 1,343 | 135 | 258 | 463 | 24 | 271 | 54 | 264 | 57 | 38 | 159 | 37 | 30 | 78 | 81 | 176 | 69 | 26 | 137 | 1,470 |
| Dumfries & Galloway | 804 | 41 | 1,735 | 173 | 326 | 597 | 46 | 362 | 84 | 334 | 86 | 57 | 165 | 52 | 54 | 50 | 114 | 227 | 117 | 35 | 172 | 1,998 |
| Highland | 909 | 42 | 2,142 | 200 | 384 | 663 | 57 | 406 | 85 | 380 | 78 | 77 | 183 | 82 | 85 | 187 | 231 | 400 | 215 | 53 | 218 | 2,350 |
| The Islands | 325 | 15 | 944 | 78 | 197 | 321 | 20 | 144 | 23 | 161 | 29 | 24 | 113 | 44 | 20 | 60 | 58 | 175 | 60 | 23 | 84 | 878 |

TABLE 5.12A     1980 - 1985 CAUSES SMRs FOR LOCAL GOVERNMENT DISTRICTS

| | 1 | 2 | 3 | 4 | 5 | 6 | 7 | 8 | 9 | 10 | 11 | 12 | 13 | 14 | 15 | 16 | 17 | 18 | 19 | 20 | 21 | 22 |
|---|---|---|---|---|---|---|---|---|---|---|---|---|---|---|---|---|---|---|---|---|---|---|
| Argyll & Bute | 100 | 99 | 101 | 114 | 94* | 99 | 98 | 94 | 107 | 118 | 85 | 80* | 79* | 120* | 102 | 94 | 88 | 108 | 90 | 57 | 94 | 92* |
| Dumbarton | 102 | 100 | 103 | 112 | 100 | 107 | 88 | 103 | 87 | 68 | 92 | 100 | 105 | 104 | 95 | 100 | 89 | 119 | 101 | 104 | 120 | 99 |
| Inverclyde | 108* | 118* | 104* | 133 | 105* | 104 | 103 | 114 | 98 | 102 | 112 | 111* | 104 | 119* | 102 | 76* | 86 | 130* | 118 | 112 | 107 | 110* |
| Renfrew | 108* | 108* | 107* | 117 | 105* | 104 | 95 | 120* | 96 | 96 | 128* | 109* | 107 | 106 | 99 | 90 | 83 | 81* | 87 | 103 | 75* | 118* |
| Cumnock & Doon V | 110* | 107* | 111* | 125 | 94 | 101 | 109 | 110 | 93 | 92 | 64 | 81* | 75* | 95 | 193* | 140* | 158* | 160* | 93 | 81 | 135 | 125* |
| Cunninghame | 106* | 107* | 105* | 73 | 101 | 107 | 116 | 114 | 107 | 114 | 93 | 99 | 109 | 98 | 93 | 101 | 134* | 94 | 83 | 91 | 96 | 106* |
| Kilmarnock & Loudoun | 106* | 104 | 106* | 93 | 94* | 93 | 84 | 110 | 109 | 116 | 123 | 88* | 86 | 95 | 85 | 91 | 84 | 108 | 83 | 92 | 164* | 109* |
| Kyle & Carrick | 100 | 94* | 102 | 47* | 96 | 91* | 69* | 99 | 104 | 83 | 109 | 86* | 78* | 110 | 94 | 100 | 101 | 101 | 104 | 67* | 131* | 103 |
| Bears. & Milngavie | 78* | 68* | 82* | 66 | 92 | 89 | 65 | 78 | 112 | 138 | 96 | 82* | 72 | 112 | 21 | 105 | 135 | 64 | 67 | 99 | 78 | 75* |
| Clydebank | 105* | 107* | 104* | 81 | 109* | 101 | 92 | 99 | 117 | 148* | 115 | 116* | 99 | 100 | 78 | 76 | 67 | 145* | 83 | 165* | 148 | 107* |
| Eastwood | 81* | 66* | 86* | 74 | 87* | 79* | 88 | 66* | 100 | 112 | 62* | 76* | 53 | 97 | 66 | 91 | 87 | 68* | 71 | 95 | 111 | 78* |
| Glasgow City | 110* | 121* | 106* | 137* | 117* | 119* | 107 | 117* | 103 | 102 | 110 | 144* | 150 | 99 | 109 | 97 | 95 | 99 | 102 | 146* | 139* | 102* |
| Strathkelvin | 98 | 93 | 101 | 56 | 98 | 94 | 90 | 99 | 97 | 96 | 97 | 102 | 97 | 113 | 77 | 102 | 102 | 85 | 106 | 99 | 148* | 95 |
| Cumbernauld | 108* | 106 | 110 | 147 | 115* | 118* | 91 | 142* | 103 | 87 | 73 | 132* | 136* | 101 | 82 | 108 | 73 | 95 | 121 | 108 | 56 | 113* |
| E. Kilbride | 93* | 84* | 97 | 67 | 92* | 91 | 90 | 84 | 79* | 82 | 75 | 101 | 91 | 88 | 70 | 95 | 104 | 75 | 73 | 111 | 74 | 100 |
| Hamilton | 108* | 105* | 110* | 132 | 100 | 103 | 89 | 97 | 96 | 107 | 90 | 100 | 100 | 101 | 109 | 122* | 122 | 126* | 77 | 114 | 110 | 115* |
| Clydesdale | 100 | 97 | 101 | 96 | 88* | 95 | 109 | 107 | 95 | 107 | 78 | 69* | 81 | 84 | 105 | 101 | 82 | 108 | 98 | 98 | 118 | 106* |
| Monklands | 109* | 111* | 109* | 116 | 107* | 107 | 110 | 136 | 88 | 85 | 98 | 107 | 106 | 114 | 123 | 97 | 69 | 116 | 96 | 114 | 96 | 124* |
| Motherwell | 110* | 116* | 107* | 79 | 101 | 109* | 97 | 134* | 95 | 102 | 101 | 95 | 102 | 113 | 133* | 95 | 93 | 107 | 79* | 108 | 86 | 114* |
| Dunfermline | 101 | 97 | 102 | 70 | 98 | 96 | 97 | 104 | 88 | 75 | 97 | 92 | 94 | 94 | 146* | 112 | 109 | 102 | 73* | 83 | 40* | 104 |
| Kirkcaldy | 102* | 101 | 103* | 79 | 96 | 100 | 98 | 95 | 91 | 102 | 110 | 93 | 93 | 86 | 148* | 103 | 115 | 101 | 85 | 75 | 86 | 109* |
| N. E. Fife | 87* | 80* | 88* | 82 | 86* | 89* | 97 | 68* | 101 | 131 | 65* | 75* | 76* | 118 | 119 | 116 | 132 | 93 | 49* | 64 | 82 | 88* |
| Clackmannan | 105* | 98 | 107* | 87 | 108* | 102 | 129 | 104 | 123* | 113 | 115 | 107 | 108 | 148* | 93 | 92 | 98 | 92 | 96 | 47 | 90 | 103 |
| Falkirk | 99 | 98 | 99 | 102 | 96 | 95 | 87 | 104 | 92 | 96 | 92 | 97 | 95 | 98 | 103 | 91 | 93 | 99 | 114 | 95 | 63* | 98 |
| Stirling | 96* | 93* | 97 | 115 | 96 | 96 | 127 | 89 | 98 | 86 | 85 | 89* | 87 | 119 | 106 | 98 | 104 | 80 | 127* | 74 | 62* | 97 |
| Aberdeen City | 96* | 89* | 99 | 83 | 102 | 96 | 97 | 92 | 111* | 96 | 107 | 102 | 92 | 84* | 77 | 103 | 124* | 78* | 132* | 119 | 40* | 95* |
| Banff & Buchan | 94* | 93* | 94* | 80 | 86* | 81 | 118 | 88 | 95 | 87 | 98 | 65* | 67* | 85 | 43* | 92 | 102 | 78 | 98 | 84 | 52* | 97 |
| Gordon | 84* | 76* | 86* | 97 | 79* | 79* | 96 | 54* | 92 | 114 | 85 | 60* | 49* | 97 | 120 | 89 | 78 | 88 | 122 | 21 | 59* | 83* |
| Kincar. & Deeside | 88* | 79* | 91* | 100 | 86* | 85* | 100 | 94* | 102 | 107 | 95 | 64* | 57* | 101 | 92 | 118 | 128 | 78 | 136* | 64 | 22 | 88* |

TABLE 5.12A    1980 - 1985 CAUSES SMRs FOR LOCAL GOVERNMENT DISTRICTS CONTD.

| | 1 | 2 | 3 | 4 | 5 | 6 | 7 | 8 | 9 | 10 | 11 | 12 | 13 | 14 | 15 | 16 | 17 | 18 | 19 | 20 | 21 | 22 |
|---|---|---|---|---|---|---|---|---|---|---|---|---|---|---|---|---|---|---|---|---|---|---|
| Moray | 94* | 92* | 95* | 68* | 91* | 95 | 118 | 101 | 123* | 149* | 57* | 68* | 79* | 93 | 120 | 78 | 98 | 107 | 107 | 68 | 81 | 90* |
| E. Lothian | 91* | 87* | 92* | 82 | 96 | 92 | 106 | 88 | 93 | 110 | 100 | 91 | 74* | 100 | 48 | 94 | 90 | 127* | 100 | 121 | 67* | 93* |
| Edinburgh City | 93* | 90* | 94* | 100 | 100 | 97 | 99 | 90* | 92* | 91 | 109 | 104* | 98 | 94 | 95 | 105 | 114 | 97 | 103 | 113 | 133* | 88* |
| Midlothian | 98 | 88* | 103 | 70 | 98 | 89* | 84 | 89 | 90 | 106 | 98 | 97 | 83 | 83 | 91 | 109 | 111 | 109 | 90 | 103 | 80 | 99 |
| W. Lothian | 102 | 102 | 102 | 104 | 102 | 98 | 105 | 82 | 95 | 76 | 104 | 106 | 107 | 96 | 114 | 122* | 117 | 120 | 94 | 113 | 61* | 102 |
| Angus | 91* | 79* | 95* | 67 | 92* | 82* | 95 | 111 | 123* | 94 | 89 | 71* | 62* | 104 | 78 | 104 | 82 | 103 | 128* | 56* | 76 | 98 |
| Dundee City | 97* | 95* | 98* | 93 | 102 | 99 | 99 | 113 | 100 | 92 | 104 | 110* | 102 | 89 | 83 | 86 | 65* | 84* | 111 | 116 | 74* | 98 |
| Perth & Kinross | 93* | 86* | 95* | 95 | 89* | 90* | 92 | 82* | 105 | 105 | 125* | 77* | 69* | 105 | 84 | 88 | 94 | 90 | 76* | 46* | 68* | 93* |
| Berwickshire | 85* | 75* | 87* | 139 | 80* | 80 | 61 | 57* | 94 | 52 | 102 | 72* | 88 | 109 | 20 | 113 | 100 | 107 | 112 | 51 | 81 | 91* |
| Ett. & Lauderdale | 96* | 92* | 97 | 115 | 95 | 88 | 97 | 86 | 118 | 115 | 106 | 87 | 72 | 100 | 68 | 116 | 155* | 108 | 117 | 68 | 66 | 100 |
| Roxburgh | 96* | 88* | 98 | 44 | 85* | 88 | 106 | 59* | 79 | 98 | 109 | 74* | 84 | 105 | 81 | 77 | 46 | 97 | 113 | 61 | 123 | 86* |
| Tweeddale | 90* | 77* | 93* | 122 | 92 | 83 | 138 | 45* | 108 | 72 | 128 | 91 | 94 | 97 | 73 | 77 | 78 | 108 | 101 | 16 | 89 | 90* |
| Ann. & Eskdale | 89* | 86* | 90* | 40 | 79* | 87 | 88 | 90 | 92 | 122 | 106 | 65* | 68 | 77 | 98 | 73 | 58 | 83 | 132 | 37 | 87 | 100 |
| Nithsdale | 99 | 101 | 99 | 106 | 90* | 95 | 99 | 87 | 94 | 138* | 95 | 81* | 83 | 107 | 106 | 81 | 90 | 84 | 113 | 78 | 77 | 110* |
| Stewartry | 91* | 89* | 92* | 45 | 89* | 98 | 115 | 66 | 96 | 122 | 63 | 67* | 72 | 107 | 111 | 102 | 91 | 83 | 70 | 52 | 79 | 90* |
| Wigtown | 103 | 98 | 105* | 86 | 90* | 86 | 92 | 73 | 104 | 64 | 90 | 76* | 77 | 85 | 79 | 120 | 138 | 166* | 116 | 45 | 240* | 114* |
| Badenoch & Strathspey | 95 | 92 | 96 | 88 | 93 | 84 | 163 | 123 | 148* | 104 | 92 | 69* | 68 | 63 | 0 | 100 | 106 | 116 | 86 | 111 | 106 | 87 |
| Caithness | 108* | 111* | 107* | 151 | 92 | 102 | 84 | 88 | 94 | 99 | 128 | 78* | 101 | 87 | 97 | 135 | 136 | 107 | 99 | 55 | 155* | 107 |
| Inverness | 98 | 100 | 97 | 109 | 96 | 93 | 123 | 103 | 114 | 117 | 98 | 70* | 68* | 124* | 84 | 102 | 124 | 118 | 123 | 59 | 93 | 98 |
| Lochaber | 104 | 113* | 100 | 102 | 116* | 124* | 125 | 122 | 117 | 124 | 111 | 108 | 120 | 109 | 162 | 135 | 138 | 95 | 126 | 49 | 66 | 97 |
| Nairn | 97 | 88 | 100 | 112 | 91 | 89 | 156 | 88 | 119 | 174 | 138 | 71 | 71 | 87 | 39 | 86 | 76 | 90 | 123 | 106 | 101 | 90 |
| Ross & Cromarty | 99 | 98 | 100 | 78 | 98 | 100 | 135 | 77 | 107 | 89 | 117 | 76* | 82 | 130* | 81 | 101 | 96 | 120 | 92 | 70 | 83 | 97 |
| Skye & Lochalsh | 93* | 99 | 91* | 120 | 70* | 67* | 95 | 49 | 88 | 99 | 63 | 49* | 58 | 78 | 36 | 107 | 108 | 135 | 123 | 47 | 111 | 101 |
| Sutherland | 99 | 106 | 97 | 93 | 88* | 106 | 120 | 81 | 83 | 161 | 122 | 74 | 82 | 114 | 219* | 83 | 84 | 86 | 151 | 107 | 185* | 93 |
| Orkney | 92* | 90 | 92* | 174 | 84* | 102 | 73 | 72 | 64* | 55 | 84 | 61* | 84 | 83 | 190* | 129 | 130 | 135 | 75 | 28 | 131 | 100 |
| Shetland | 90* | 80* | 93* | 173* | 75* | 74* | 63 | 69 | 107 | 95 | 62 | 46* | 60* | 121 | 78 | 111 | 84 | 141 | 107 | 161 | 74 | 87* |
| Western Isles | 94* | 101 | 93* | 95 | 79* | 93 | 95 | 87 | 81 | 87 | 87 | 56* | 72 | 112 | 61 | 78 | 92 | 144* | 124 | 39 | 141 | 94 |

TABLE 5.12A　1980 - 1985 CAUSES SMRs FOR LOCAL GOVERNMENT DISTRICTS CONTD.

| | 23 | 24 | 25 | 26 | 27 | 28 | 29 | 30 | 31 | 32 | 33 | 34 | 35 | 36 | 37 | 38 | 39 | 40 | 41 | 42 | 43 | 44 |
|---|---|---|---|---|---|---|---|---|---|---|---|---|---|---|---|---|---|---|---|---|---|---|
| Argyll & Bute | 95 | 67 | 114* | 98 | 178* | 85* | 121 | 69* | 54* | 104 | 88 | 106 | 94 | 76 | 71 | 160* | 68* | 118* | 108 | 119 | 101 | 87* |
| Dumbarton | 97 | 78 | 101 | 93 | 164* | 104 | 136 | 85* | 75 | 120* | 142* | 102 | 112 | 59 | 54* | 105 | 90 | 126* | 82 | 106 | 97 | 96 |
| Inverclyde | 123* | 71 | 108* | 132* | 118* | 95 | 107 | 127* | 149* | 139* | 103 | 177* | 120 | 75 | 96 | 79 | 62* | 122* | 93 | 103 | 136* | 115* |
| Renfrew | 120* | 87 | 118* | 109 | 86* | 99 | 128* | 109* | 101 | 121* | 113 | 127* | 114 | 90 | 112 | 68* | 94 | 98 | 82* | 105 | 113* | 113* |
| Cumnock & Doon V | 123* | 134 | 113* | 122 | 125* | 96 | 64 | 106 | 108 | 111 | 130 | 79 | 105 | 54 | 84 | 77 | 104 | 107 | 85 | 195* | 125 | 105 |
| Cunninghame | 109* | 118 | 124* | 123* | 107 | 97 | 89 | 105 | 116 | 111 | 113 | 89 | 108 | 87 | 117 | 77 | 105 | 101 | 101 | 125 | 127* | 106* |
| Kilmarnock & Loudoun | 120* | 131 | 106 | 94 | 130* | 81* | 104 | 109 | 114 | 111 | 115 | 97 | 134* | 120 | 90 | 100 | 105 | 101 | 81 | 93 | 106 | 102 |
| Kyle & Carrick | 98 | 90 | 114* | 113 | 115* | 68* | 62* | 88* | 86 | 97 | 97 | 95 | 98 | 103 | 108 | 76 | 96 | 86 | 84 | 91 | 120* | 95* |
| Bears. & Milngavie | 62* | 71 | 84* | 72 | 71* | 81* | 38 | 54* | 30* | 80 | 79 | 80 | 74 | 94 | 79 | 66 | 66 | 82* | 51* | 54 | 79 | 73* |
| Clydebank | 119* | 89 | 102 | 102 | 79 | 127* | 131 | 96 | 91 | 110 | 154* | 134 | 77 | 59 | 85 | 34 | 102 | 92 | 71 | 113 | 120 | 108* |
| Eastwood | 62* | 73 | 82* | 53* | 86 | 83* | 66 | 69* | 42* | 90 | 82 | 77 | 102 | 56 | 111 | 52 | 66 | 59* | 63* | 75 | 57* | 74* |
| Glasgow City | 112* | 117* | 95* | 112* | 86* | 120* | 137* | 150* | 163* | 121* | 126* | 154* | 103 | 86* | 109 | 92 | 103 | 103 | 137* | 117* | 124* | 124* |
| Strathkelvin | 94 | 96 | 89* | 82 | 91 | 141* | 174* | 110 | 101 | 85 | 103 | 86 | 107 | 97 | 99 | 42* | 95 | 94 | 79 | 74 | 96 | 99 |
| Cumbernauld | 119* | 122 | 102 | 100 | 72 | 135* | 117 | 115 | 127 | 109 | 115 | 129 | 76 | 142 | 94 | 77 | 103 | 85 | 79 | 78 | 99 | 117* |
| E. Kilbride | 88* | 80* | 85* | 87 | 91 | 117* | 62 | 84 | 74 | 79* | 89 | 86 | 112 | 110 | 99 | 18 | 70* | 99 | 72* | 69 | 87 | 94 |
| Hamilton | 126* | 68 | 92* | 98 | 182* | 107 | 124 | 96 | 99 | 97 | 116 | 103 | 96 | 64 | 86 | 31* | 78 | 105 | 86 | 125 | 106 | 104 |
| Clydesdale | 104 | 64 | 109* | 103 | 158* | 82* | 101 | 82* | 107 | 88 | 101 | 51* | 103 | 111 | 105 | 34* | 85 | 102 | 59* | 102 | 100 | 90* |
| Monklands | 132* | 139* | 98 | 107 | 70* | 135* | 126 | 109 | 71* | 116* | 99 | 119 | 106 | 106 | 89 | 57* | 83 | 83 | 90 | 119 | 111 | 113* |
| Motherwell | 129* | 102 | 102 | 142* | 139* | 115* | 151* | 108 | 114 | 112* | 116 | 92 | 108 | 67 | 118 | 62* | 71* | 112 | 81* | 129* | 141* | 108* |
| Dunfermline | 105 | 95 | 121* | 126* | 95 | 94 | 77 | 95 | 92 | 92 | 67* | 73 | 91 | 95 | 94 | 158* | 113 | 98 | 79* | 98 | 129* | 101 |
| Kirkcaldy | 110* | 71 | 120* | 108 | 111 | 88* | 78 | 102 | 88 | 84* | 99 | 88 | 115 | 104 | 93 | 119 | 91 | 94 | 111 | 131* | 111 | 103 |
| N. E. Fife | 78* | 71 | 94 | 90 | 105 | 91 | 74 | 60* | 50* | 77* | 61* | 66 | 87 | 76 | 86 | 68 | 88 | 95 | 99 | 80 | 92 | 79* |
| Clackmannan | 100 | 84 | 103 | 100 | 258* | 108 | 195* | 107 | 110 | 110 | 116 | 107 | 93 | 60 | 98 | 49 | 108 | 84 | 61* | 102 | 99 | 105 |
| Falkirk | 96 | 75 | 103 | 111 | 85* | 126* | 142* | 94 | 92 | 101 | 103 | 92 | 95 | 96 | 103 | 35* | 74* | 101 | 89 | 108 | 115* | 97 |
| Stirling | 85* | 70 | 96 | 87 | 123* | 103 | 185* | 94 | 101 | 110 | 155* | 82 | 77 | 63 | 71 | 46* | 118 | 82 | 83 | 133 | 92 | 93* |
| Aberdeen City | 81* | 156* | 88* | 84* | 81* | 110* | 87 | 93 | 81* | 85* | 83 | 77* | 95 | 127* | 94 | 125* | 96 | 123* | 102 | 69* | 80* | 94* |
| Banff & Buchan | 91 | 99 | 119* | 112 | 104 | 66* | 98 | 66* | 59* | 68* | 60* | 33* | 88 | 101 | 75 | 97 | 188* | 120* | 104 | 74 | 111 | 84* |
| Gordon | 67* | 92 | 90* | 78 | 89 | 102 | 75 | 59* | 53* | 80* | 81 | 47* | 86 | 113 | 91 | 125 | 147* | 100 | 70 | 88 | 77 | 71* |
| Kincar. & Deeside | 62* | 78 | 85* | 67* | 74* | 107 | 20 | 59* | 52* | 68* | 81 | 74 | 114 | 88 | 69 | 167* | 173* | 97 | 121 | 73 | 63* | 73* |

TABLE 5.12A    1980 - 1985 CAUSES SMRs FOR LOCAL GOVERNMENT DISTRICTS  CONTD.

| | 23 | 24 | 25 | 26 | 27 | 28 | 29 | 30 | 31 | 32 | 33 | 34 | 35 | 36 | 37 | 38 | 39 | 40 | 41 | 42 | 43 | 44 |
|---|---|---|---|---|---|---|---|---|---|---|---|---|---|---|---|---|---|---|---|---|---|---|
| Moray | 83* | 87 | 103 | 92 | 105 | 86* | 65 | 72* | 68* | 89 | 71 | 50* | 75* | 119 | 134 | 150* | 148* | 93 | 118 | 95 | 93 | 81* |
| E. Lothian | 89* | 113 | 84 | 78* | 72* | 98* | 69 | 80* | 89 | 91 | 112 | 58* | 88 | 87 | 114 | 69 | 92 | 66* | 98 | 63 | 85 | 89* |
| Edinburgh City | 80* | 119* | 92* | 81 | 79* | 81* | 73* | 100 | 89 | 96 | 90 | 109 | 86* | 97 | 123* | 97 | 77* | 91* | 98 | 84 | 92 | 95* |
| Midlothian | 90* | 109 | 100 | 96 | 83 | 108 | 53* | 106 | 88 | 97 | 78 | 73 | 111 | 121 | 89 | 100 | 94 | 84 | 62* | 89 | 103 | 98 |
| W. Lothian | 108* | 138* | 106 | 95 | 92 | 112* | 83 | 115* | 141* | 107 | 135* | 78 | 97 | 129 | 119 | 100 | 100 | 79* | 83 | 106 | 100 | 106* |
| Angus | 80* | 63* | 92* | 79* | 64* | 86* | 52* | 71* | 60* | 73* | 77 | 53* | 104 | 115 | 74 | 49* | 121 | 96 | 99 | 74 | 84 | 82* |
| Dundee City | 96 | 129* | 82* | 95 | 75* | 128* | 63* | 103 | 81* | 94 | 93 | 81 | 98 | 127* | 70* | 27* | 96 | 109 | 103 | 91 | 101 | 100 |
| Perth & Kinross | 82* | 62* | 100 | 88 | 99 | 106 | 83 | 69* | 70* | 93 | 80 | 60* | 100 | 128 | 87 | 78 | 108 | 104 | 110 | 97 | 94 | 84* |
| Berwickshire | 74* | 97 | 91 | 87 | 117 | 42* | 40 | 56* | 69 | 81 | 61 | 86 | 95 | 45 | 84 | 83 | 128 | 79 | 63 | 53 | 88 | 76* |
| Ett. & Lauderdale | 92 | 114 | 92 | 108 | 90 | 92 | 93 | 78* | 115 | 90 | 89 | 79 | 142*ʼ | 111 | 80 | 213* | 124 | 98 | 73 | 92 | 112 | 91* |
| Roxburgh | 85 | 161* | 119* | 108 | 135* | 78* | 63 | 80* | 72 | 101 | 72 | 66 | 91 | 145 | 108 | 347* | 70 | 90 | 92 | 102 | 116 | 86* |
| Tweeddale | 62* | 194* | 90 | 109 | 102 | 80 | 0 | 65* | 11 | 57* | 102 | 25 | 173* | 35 | 111 | 226* | 129 | 88 | 90 | 71 | 99 | 86* |
| Ann. & Eskdale | 99 | 72 | 76 | 102 | 92 | 93 | 88 | 68* | 78 | 90 | 104 | 62 | 80 | 161* | 120 | 64 | 82 | 91 | 68 | 90 | 70 | 82* |
| Nithsdale | 104 | 87 | 115* | 97 | 92 | 80* | 84 | 88 | 92 | 80* | 124 | 68 | 97 | 94 | 134 | 99 | 100 | 94 | 96 | 74 | 99 | 96 |
| Stewartry | 84 | 59 | 105 | 91 | 137* | 72* | 63 | 60* | 36* | 93 | 61 | 98 | 118 | 98 | 57 | 56 | 141 | 76 | 110 | 113 | 102 | 79* |
| Wigtown | 112 | 61 | 111* | 97 | 164* | 77* | 65 | 75* | 104 | 89 | 66 | 75 | 121 | 108 | 109 | 236* | 110 | 103 | 109 | 43 | 95 | 93 |
| Badenoch & Strathspey | 66* | 79 | 108 | 107 | 68 | 72 | 80 | 67 | 31 | 85 | 82 | 138 | 125 | 356* | 190 | 462* | 151 | 148* | 170* | 34 | 126 | 82* |
| Caithness | 104 | 77 | 122* | 97 | 97 | 114 | 114 | 67* | 62 | 115 | 69 | 89 | 126 | 82 | 130 | 245* | 154* | 115 | 157* | 73 | 123 | 92 |
| Inverness | 103 | 70 | 100 | 79 | 120 | 72* | 57 | 86 | 84 | 80* | 81 | 82 | 110 | 110 | 135 | 171* | 147* | 126* | 112 | 71 | 89 | 88* |
| Lochaber | 106 | 81 | 111 | 76 | 108 | 46* | 97 | 88 | 118 | 84 | 123 | 88 | 57 | 161 | 107 | 432* | 91 | 123 | 172* | 157 | 82 | 102 |
| Nairn | 79 | 75 | 111 | 43 | 157* | 54* | 82 | 85 | 46 | 62 | 47 | 78 | 59 | 336* | 112 | 147 | 176* | 102 | 157 | 34 | 44 | 86 |
| Ross & Cromarty | 87 | 54 | 125* | 101 | 98 | 71* | 84 | 61* | 59 | 74* | 64 | 62 | 80 | 118 | 89 | 170* | 191* | 135* | 130 | 134 | 106 | 88* |
| Skye & Lochalsh | 103 | 42 | 99 | 102 | 91 | 101 | 50 | 32* | 15 | 59* | 26 | 35 | 90 | 101 | 161 | 262* | 280* | 196* | 80 | 33 | 88 | 71* |
| Sutherland | 91 | 16 | 87 | 88 | 189* | 56* | 75 | 58* | 87 | 82 | 71 | 118 | 71 | 221* | 88 | 1152* | 156 | 125 | 163* | 124 | 124 | 81* |
| Orkney | 84 | 13 | 81* | 61 | 167* | 95 | 55 | 45* | 41 | 84 | 73 | 80 | 119 | 210* | 75 | 143 | 119 | 145* | 118 | 176 | 62 | 72* |
| Shetland | 80 | 49 | 102 | 100 | 141* | 72* | 25 | 55* | 32 | 74 | 54 | 76 | 132 | 135 | 84 | 278* | 80 | 160* | 100 | 77 | 112 | 69* |
| Western Isles | 104 | 69 | 116* | 106 | 94 | 69* | 117 | 61* | 69 | 77* | 55 | 47 | 122 | 183* | 61 | 241* | 110 | 101 | 83 | 89 | 119 | 80* |

TABLE 5.12B · 1980 - 1985 CAUSES SMRs FOR LOCAL GOVERNMENT DISTRICTS  RANKING

| | 1 | 2 | 3 | 4 | 5 | 6 | 7 | 8 | 9 | 10 | 11 | 12 | 13 | 14 | 15 | 16 | 17 | 18 | 19 | 20 | 21 | 22 |
|---|---|---|---|---|---|---|---|---|---|---|---|---|---|---|---|---|---|---|---|---|---|---|
| Argyll & Bute | 20 | 21 | 23 | 16 | 30 | 19 | 27 | 26 | 17 | 11 | 43 | 32 | 35 | 5 | 21 | 37 | 39 | 21 | 39 | 42 | 24 | 42 |
| Dunbarton | 17 | 19 | 17 | 18 | 14 | 6 | 45 | 18 | 51 | 53 | 37 | 15 | 10 | 23 | 26 | 28 | 38 | 13 | 29 | 18 | 14 | 27 |
| Inverclyde | 8 | 2 | 14 | 7 | 7 | 10 | 21 | 8 | 28 | 28 | 11 | 4 | 11 | 6 | 20 | 54 | 41 | 8 | 14 | 11 | 19 | 9 |
| Renfrew | 9 | 7 | 7 | 12 | 8 | 9 | 35 | 6 | 31 | 36 | 3 | 6 | 7 | 20 | 22 | 43 | 45 | 49 | 41 | 20 | 40 | 3 |
| Cumnock & Doon V | 1 | 10 | 1 | 9 | 29 | 15 | 15 | 13 | 40 | 39 | 51 | 31 | 39 | 38 | 2 | 1 | 45 | 2 | 37 | 30 | 9 | 1 |
| Cunninghame | 10 | 9 | 12 | 45 | 12 | 7 | 12 | 9 | 14 | 16 | 35 | 17 | 4 | 32 | 28 | 25 | 7 | 37 | 45 | 26 | 23 | 15 |
| Kilmarnock & Loudoun | 11 | 14 | 9 | 32 | 28 | 33 | 51 | 12 | 12 | 13 | 6 | 26 | 26 | 39 | 32 | 42 | 44 | 22 | 46 | 25 | 3 | 10 |
| Kyle & Carrick | 21 | 30 | 18 | 53 | 25 | 36 | 53 | 23 | 19 | 48 | 16 | 28 | 36 | 14 | 27 | 29 | 25 | 29 | 25 | 37 | 11 | 17 |
| Bears. & Milngavie | 56 | 55 | 56 | 51 | 34 | 39 | 54 | 43 | 10 | 6 | 32 | 29 | 42 | 15 | 54 | 17 | 6 | 56 | 55 | 22 | 37 | 56 |
| Clydebank | 12 | 8 | 13 | 39 | 4 | 16 | 39 | 22 | 7 | 3 | 9 | 3 | 15 | 29 | 40 | 55 | 53 | 3 | 44 | 1 | 6 | 13 |
| Eastwood | 55 | 56 | 55 | 44 | 45 | 54 | 46 | 49 | 25 | 18 | 55 | 37 | 55 | 35 | 48 | 40 | 40 | 55 | 53 | 23 | 16 | 55 |
| Glasgow City | 3 | 1 | 10 | 6 | 1 | 2 | 17 | 7 | 21 | 27 | 25 | 1 | 1 | 31 | 15 | 31 | 30 | 31 | 27 | 3 | 8 | 19 |
| Strathkelvin | 28 | 33 | 21 | 52 | 18 | 31 | 42 | 21 | 29 | 33 | 31 | 12 | 17 | 11 | 43 | 23 | 24 | 44 | 24 | 21 | 5 | 37 |
| Cumbernauld | 5 | 11 | 4 | 4 | 3 | 3 | 41 | 1 | 22 | 43 | 49 | 2 | 2 | 26 | 36 | 15 | 51 | 35 | 13 | 14 | 52 | 7 |
| E. Kilbride | 43 | 47 | 34 | 49 | 33 | 37 | 43 | 39 | 54 | 49 | 4H | 14 | 23 | 44 | 46 | 35 | 21 | 54 | 51 | 13 | 41 | 23 |
| Hamilton | 6 | 13 | 3 | 8 | 16 | 11 | 44 | 24 | 32 | 22 | 40 | 16 | 6 | 25 | 14 | 6 | 13 | 10 | 48 | 7 | 18 | 4 |
| Clydesdale | 22 | 28 | 22 | 27 | 43 | 27 | 16 | 14 | 34 | 22 | 47 | 46 | 3 | 51 | 18 | 27 | 13 | 19 | 32 | 27 | 15 | 14 |
| Monklands | 4 | 6 | 4 | 13 | 6 | 5 | 14 | 2 | 49 | 47 | 27 | 9 | 9 | 10 | 8 | 32 | 52 | 15 | 35 | 8 | 22 | 2 |
| Motherwell | 2 | 3 | 6 | 41 | 13 | 4 | 31 | 3 | 36 | 29 | 23 | 20 | 13 | 12 | 7 | 34 | 33 | 25 | 47 | 15 | 29 | 5 |
| Dunfermline | 19 | 27 | 19 | 47 | 20 | 25 | 30 | 16 | 50 | 51 | 30 | 22 | 20 | 40 | 6 | 12 | 18 | 28 | 52 | 29 | 55 | 16 |
| Kirkcaldy | 16 | 17 | 16 | 42 | 23 | 17 | 26 | 25 | 46 | 26 | 13 | 21 | 21 | 47 | 5 | 21 | 15 | 30 | 43 | 32 | 30 | 11 |
| N. E. Fife | 52 | 49 | 52 | 38 | 46 | 40 | 32 | 48 | 24 | 7 | 50 | 38 | 38 | 8 | 11 | 1o | 8 | 38 | 56 | 38 | 32 | 50 |
| Clackmannan | 13 | 23 | 5 | 34 | 5 | 12 | 5 | 15 | 2 | 17 | 10 | 8 | 5 | 1 | 29 | 39 | 27 | 39 | 34 | 48 | 26 | 18 |
| Falkirk | 25 | 24 | 28 | 23 | 29 | 26 | 48 | 17 | 42 | 35 | 36 | 19 | 18 | 33 | 19 | 41 | 32 | 32 | 17 | 24 | 48 | 30 |
| Stirling | 33 | 31 | 32 | 14 | 22 | 26 | 6 | 31 | 27 | 46 | 45 | 25 | 25 | 7 | 16 | 33 | 22 | 50 | 6 | 33 | 49 | 33 |
| Aberdeen City | 32 | 39 | 27 | 36 | 10 | 24 | 28 | 27 | 11 | 34 | 17 | 13 | 22 | 50 | 44 | 20 | 12 | 51 | 4 | 5 | 54 | 36 |
| Banff & Buchan | 39 | 32 | 41 | 40 | 48 | 51 | 11 | 34 | 44 | 29 | 29 | 50 | 50 | 49 | 51 | 38 | 23 | 52 | 33 | 28 | 53 | 35 |
| Gordon | 54 | 53 | 54 | 26 | 53 | 53 | 33 | 54 | 45 | 15 | 44 | 53 | 56 | 36 | 10 | 44 | 48 | 42 | 12 | 55 | 51 | 54 |
| Kincar. & Deeside | 51 | 51 | 50 | 25 | 47 | 47 | 22 | 51 | 23 | 21 | 33 | 51 | 54 | 27 | 30 | 8 | 10 | 53 | 2 | 39 | 56 | 49 |

TABLE 5.12B   1980 - 1985 Causes SMRs for local government districts  RANKING  Contd.

| | 1 | 2 | 3 | 4 | 5 | 6 | 7 | 8 | 9 | 10 | 11 | 12 | 13 | 14 | 15 | 16 | 17 | 18 | 19 | 20 | 21 | 22 |
|---|---|---|---|---|---|---|---|---|---|---|---|---|---|---|---|---|---|---|---|---|---|---|
| Moray | 38 | 35 | 38 | 48 | 37 | 30 | 10 | 20 | 3 | 4 | 56 | 47 | 34 | 42 | 9 | 51 | 28 | 26 | 22 | 35 | 33 | 45 |
| E.Lothian | 47 | 44 | 46 | 37 | 21 | 35 | 19 | 33 | 41 | 19 | 24 | 23 | 40 | 28 | 50 | 36 | 37 | 9 | 30 | 4 | 45 | 40 |
| Edinburgh City | 40 | 37 | 42 | 24 | 15 | 23 | 23 | 28 | 44 | 41 | 15 | 11 | 16 | 41 | 25 | 18 | 16 | 34 | 26 | 10 | 10 | 48 |
| Midlothian | 27 | 42 | 15 | 46 | 19 | 42 | 49 | 30 | 47 | 23 | 26 | 18 | 30 | 53 | 31 | 14 | 17 | 17 | 40 | 19 | 35 | 26 |
| W.Lothian | 18 | 15 | 20 | 21 | 11 | 22 | 20 | 40 | 33 | 50 | 20 | 10 | 8 | 37 | 12 | 5 | 14 | 11 | 36 | 9 | 50 | 20 |
| Angus | 46 | 50 | 40 | 50 | 35 | 50 | 34 | 11 | 4 | 38 | 41 | 43 | 51 | 24 | 41 | 19 | 46 | 27 | 5 | 43 | 39 | 29 |
| Dundee City | 31 | 29 | 31 | 31 | 9 | 20 | 25 | 10 | 26 | 40 | 21 | 5 | 12 | 43 | 35 | 46 | 54 | 45 | 21 | 6 | 43 | 31 |
| Perth & Kinross | 41 | 46 | 39 | 28 | 41 | 38 | 38 | 41 | 18 | 24 | 5 | 34 | 46 | 21 | 33 | 45 | 31 | 40 | 49 | 50 | 44 | 39 |
| Berwickshire | 53 | 54 | 53 | 5 | 51 | 52 | 56 | 53 | 39 | 56 | 22 | 41 | 24 | 17 | 55 | 11 | 26 | 24 | 20 | 46 | 34 | 43 |
| Ett. & Lauderdale | 35 | 36 | 30 | 15 | 27 | 43 | 29 | 38 | 6 | 14 | 18 | 27 | 41 | 30 | 47 | 9 | 2 | 18 | 15 | 36 | 46 | 22 |
| Roxburgh | 34 | 43 | 30 | 55 | 49 | 44 | 18 | 52 | 55 | 32 | 14 | 40 | 27 | 22 | 38 | 52 | 56 | 33 | 18 | 40 | 13 | 53 |
| Tweeddale | 48 | 52 | 44 | 10 | 36 | 49 | 3 | 56 | 13 | 52 | 4 | 24 | 19 | 34 | 45 | 53 | 49 | 20 | 28 | 56 | 27 | 47 |
| Annan Eskdale | 50 | 45 | 51 | 56 | 52 | 45 | 47 | 29 | 43 | 10 | 19 | 49 | 49 | 55 | 23 | 56 | 55 | 47 | 3 | 53 | 28 | 24 |
| Nithsdale | 24 | 18 | 29 | 20 | 40 | 28 | 24 | 37 | 37 | 5 | 34 | 30 | 29 | 19 | 17 | 49 | 36 | 46 | 19 | 31 | 38 | 8 |
| Stewartry | 45 | 40 | 48 | 54 | 42 | 21 | 13 | 50 | 30 | 9 | 52 | 48 | 43 | 18 | 13 | 24 | 35 | 48 | 54 | 45 | 36 | 44 |
| Wigtown | 15 | 25 | 11 | 35 | 39 | 46 | 40 | 4 | 1 | 54 | 39 | 36 | 37 | 48 | 39 | 7 | 4 | 1 | 16 | 51 | 1 | 6 |
| Badenoch & Strathspey | 36 | 34 | 37 | 33 | 31 | 48 | 1 | 35 | 38 | 25 | 38 | 45 | 47 | 56 | 56 | 30 | 20 | 16 | 42 | 12 | 20 | 51 |
| Caithness | 7 | 5 | 8 | 3 | 32 | 14 | 50 | 4 | 9 | 30 | 2 | 33 | 14 | 46 | 24 | 2 | 5 | 23 | 31 | 44 | 4 | 12 |
| Inverness | 29 | 20 | 33 | 19 | 26 | 32 | 8 | 19 | 9 | 12 | 28 | 44 | 48 | 3 | 34 | 22 | 11 | 14 | 11 | 41 | 25 | 28 |
| Lochaber | 14 | 4 | 24 | 22 | 2 | 1 | 7 | 5 | 8 | 8 | 12 | 7 | 3 | 16 | 4 | 3 | 3 | 36 | 7 | 47 | 47 | 34 |
| Nairn | 30 | 41 | 26 | 17 | 38 | 41 | 2 | 32 | 5 | 8 | 1 | 42 | 45 | 45 | 52 | 47 | 50 | 41 | 10 | 17 | 21 | 46 |
| Ross & Cromarty | 23 | 26 | 25 | 43 | 17 | 18 | 4 | 44 | 15 | 42 | 8 | 35 | 32 | 2 | 37 | 26 | 29 | 12 | 38 | 34 | 31 | 32 |
| Skye & Lochalsh | 42 | 22 | 49 | 11 | 56 | 36 | 36 | 55 | 48 | 31 | 53 | 55 | 53 | 54 | 53 | 16 | 19 | 7 | 9 | 49 | 17 | 21 |
| Sutherland | 26 | 12 | 35 | 30 | 44 | 8 | 9 | 42 | 52 | 2 | 7 | 39 | 31 | 9 | 1 | 48 | 43 | 43 | 1 | 16 | 2 | 41 |
| Orkney | 44 | 38 | 47 | 1 | 50 | 13 | 52 | 46 | 56 | 55 | 46 | 52 | 28 | 52 | 3 | 4 | 9 | 6 | 50 | 54 | 12 | 25 |
| Shetland | 49 | 48 | 45 | 2 | 55 | 55 | 55 | 47 | 16 | 37 | 54 | 56 | 52 | 4 | 42 | 13 | 42 | 5 | 23 | 2 | 42 | 52 |
| Western Isles | 37 | 16 | 43 | 29 | 54 | 34 | 37 | 36 | 53 | 45 | 42 | 54 | 44 | 13 | 49 | 50 | 34 | 4 | 8 | 52 | 7 | 38 |

TABLE 5.12B   1980 - 1985 CAUSES SMRs FOR LOCAL GOVERNMENT DISTRICTS   RANKING  CONTD.

| | 23 | 24 | 25 | 26 | 27 | 28 | 29 | 30 | 31 | 32 | 33 | 34 | 35 | 36 | 37 | 38 | 39 | 40 | 41 | 42 | 43 | 44 |
|---|----|----|----|----|----|----|----|----|----|----|----|----|----|----|----|----|----|----|----|----|----|----|
| Argyll & Bute | 29 | 45 | 12 | 25 | 4 | 35 | 12 | 38 | 44 | 15 | 30 | 11 | 37 | 44 | 50 | 15 | 53 | 13 | 16 | 12 | 26 | 35 |
| Dunbarton | 26 | 32 | 30 | 34 | 6 | 18 | 7 | 28 | 32 | 4 | 3 | 13 | 15 | 51 | 56 | 23 | 41 | 6 | 38 | 17 | 34 | 22 |
| Inverclyde | 5 | 38 | 19 | 2 | 18 | 26 | 16 | 2 | 2 | 1 | 18 | 1 | 9 | 46 | 27 | 33 | 56 | 11 | 27 | 20 | 2 | 3 |
| Renfrew | 6 | 24 | 8 | 10 | 42 | 22 | 9 | 6 | 16 | 3 | 14 | 6 | 14 | 38 | 13 | 39 | 36 | 29 | 39 | 19 | 14 | 5 |
| Cumnock & Doon V | 4 | 6 | 13 | 5 | 15 | 25 | 41 | 12 | 11 | 9 | 5 | 31 | 23 | 54 | 43 | 39 | 36 | 17 | 33 | 1 | 6 | 10 |
| Cunninghame | 13 | 11 | 2 | 4 | 23 | 24 | 22 | 13 | 6 | 8 | 15 | 20 | 20 | 41 | 11 | 24 | 25 | 25 | 20 | 8 | 4 | 8 |
| Kilmarnock & Loudoun | 7 | 7 | 20 | 33 | 14 | 40 | 17 | 8 | 9 | 16 | 13 | 15 | 3 | 16 | 33 | 25 | 17 | 44 | 40 | 27 | 23 | 14 |
| Kyle & Carrich | 25 | 21 | 11 | 6 | 20 | 51 | 45 | 23 | 27 | 21 | 25 | 16 | 29 | 28 | 19 | 37 | 33 | 50 | 34 | 30 | 10 | 24 |
| Bears. & Milngavie | 56 | 40 | 52 | 52 | 53 | 38 | 53 | 54 | 54 | 44 | 38 | 29 | 53 | 37 | 45 | 41 | 54 | 54 | 56 | 51 | 50 | 52 |
| Clydebank | 9 | 22 | 27 | 19 | 48 | 5 | 8 | 17 | 21 | 11 | 2 | 4 | 49 | 52 | 40 | 52 | 29 | 39 | 48 | 15 | 9 | 6 |
| Eastwood | 55 | 36 | 55 | 55 | 43 | 36 | 38 | 39 | 49 | 29 | 33 | 36 | 27 | 53 | 16 | 46 | 55 | 56 | 51 | 39 | 55 | 50 |
| Glasgow City | 10 | 12 | 37 | 8 | 41 | 7 | 6 | 1 | 1 | 2 | 6 | 2 | 25 | 42 | 18 | 31 | 27 | 20 | 6 | 13 | 7 | 1 |
| Strathkelvin | 30 | 18 | 47 | 44 | 37 | 1 | 3 | 5 | 15 | 35 | 22 | 25 | 21 | 33 | 24 | 50 | 35 | 36 | 45 | 40 | 35 | 18 |
| Cumbernauld | 8 | 9 | 28 | 22 | 51 | 3 | 14 | 3 | 4 | 13 | 12 | 5 | 51 | 9 | 30 | 36 | 28 | 45 | 44 | 37 | 30 | 2 |
| E. Kilbride | 36 | 28 | 50 | 40 | 38 | 8 | 46 | 29 | 33 | 46 | 28 | 23 | 16 | 24 | 25 | 56 | 51 | 28 | 47 | 48 | 45 | 26 |
| Hamilton | 3 | 44 | 39 | 26 | 3 | 15 | 11 | 18 | 17 | 19 | 9 | 12 | 33 | 48 | 39 | 54 | 47 | 18 | 32 | 9 | 22 | 12 |
| Clydesdale | 18 | 47 | 17 | 18 | 8 | 37 | 18 | 30 | 12 | 33 | 21 | 50 | 26 | 21 | 22 | 53 | 43 | 23 | 55 | 21 | 29 | 31 |
| Monklands | 1 | 4 | 35 | 16 | 54 | 2 | 10 | 7 | 35 | 5 | 24 | 50 | 22 | 26 | 34 | 44 | 44 | 48 | 29 | 11 | 18 | 4 |
| Motherwell | 2 | 31 | 29 | 1 | 11 | 9 | 4 | 9 | R | 7 | 11 | 18 | 19 | 47 | 10 | 43 | 50 | 15 | 41 | 7 | 1 | 7 |
| Dunfermline | 16 | 19 | 4 | 3 | 32 | 28 | 32 | 19 | 20 | 26 | 46 | 41 | 40 | 35 | 28 | 16 | 20 | 30 | 43 | 24 | 3 | 16 |
| Kirkcaldy | 12 | 39 | 5 | 14 | 21 | 32 | 31 | 15 | 24 | 39 | 23 | 21 | 12 | 27 | 31 | 22 | 40 | 35 | 12 | 6 | 17 | 13 |
| N. E. Fife | 49 | 46 | 38 | 37 | 24 | 31 | 35 | 48 | 47 | 48 | 50 | 43 | 44 | 45 | 55 | 40 | 42 | 34 | 23 | 36 | 40 | 48 |
| Clackmannan | 23 | 26 | 23 | 23 | 1 | 13 | 1 | 10 | 10 | 10 | 10 | 10 | 38 | 50 | 26 | 47 | 24 | 46 | 54 | 22 | 33 | 11 |
| Falkirk | 27 | 34 | 25 | 9 | 44 | 6 | 5 | 20 | 18 | 17 | 19 | 17 | 34 | 34 | 23 | 51 | 49 | 24 | 31 | 16 | 13 | 20 |
| Stirling | 39 | 41 | 36 | 42 | 16 | 19 | 2 | 21 | 14 | 12 | 1 | 26 | 50 | 49 | 49 | 49 | 19 | 49 | 37 | 5 | 41 | 27 |
| Aberdeen City | 44 | 3 | 48 | 43 | 46 | 12 | 24 | 22 | 30 | 34 | 31 | 35 | 36 | 13 | 29 | 20 | 34 | 9 | 19 | 49 | 49 | 25 |
| Banff & Buchan | 32 | 16 | 6 | 7 | 26 | 52 | 19 | 43 | 43 | 52 | 52 | 55 | 43 | 30 | 47 | 29 | 3 | 12 | 17 | 43 | 19 | 39 |
| Gordon | 51 | 20 | 45 | 49 | 40 | 20 | 34 | 50 | 45 | 45 | 35 | 53 | 46 | 20 | 32 | 21 | 10 | 27 | 49 | 34 | 51 | 55 |
| Kincar. & Deeside | 54 | 30 | 51 | 53 | 16 | 16 | 55 | 49 | 46 | 53 | 34 | 39 | 13 | 39 | 52 | 14 | 5 | 32 | 8 | 45 | 53 | 51 |

TABLE 5.12B  1980 - 1985 CAUSES SMRs FOR LOCAL GOVERNMENT DISTRICTS RANKING CONTD.

| | 23 | 24 | 25 | 26 | 27 | 28 | 29 | 30 | 31 | 32 | 33 | 34 | 35 | 36 | 37 | 38 | 39 | 40 | 41 | 42 | 43 | 44 |
|---|---|---|---|---|---|---|---|---|---|---|---|---|---|---|---|---|---|---|---|---|---|---|
| Moray | 42 | 25 | 24 | 35 | 25 | 33 | 40 | 35 | 39 | 32 | 43 | 51 | 52 | 17 | 4 | 17 | 9 | 38 | 10 | 26 | 38 | 45 |
| E. Lothian | 35 | 14 | 53 | 48 | 52 | 23 | 37 | 31 | 23 | 27 | 16 | 48 | 42 | 40 | 12 | 38 | 38 | 55 | 24 | 50 | 46 | 32 |
| Edinburgh City | 45 | 10 | 41 | 45 | 47 | 39 | 36 | 16 | 22 | 22 | 27 | 9 | 45 | 32 | 7 | 30 | 48 | 40 | 25 | 35 | 39 | 23 |
| Midlothian | 34 | 15 | 31 | 30 | 45 | 36 | 49 | 11 | 25 | 20 | 39 | 40 | 17 | 15 | 36 | 27 | 37 | 47 | 53 | 32 | 24 | 19 |
| W. Lothian | 14 | 5 | 21 | 32 | 34 | 11 | 28 | 4 | 3 | 14 | 4 | 33 | 32 | 11 | 9 | 26 | 30 | 51 | 35 | 18 | 28 | 9 |
| Angus | 46 | 48 | 40 | 47 | 56 | 34 | 50 | 36 | 41 | 51 | 40 | 49 | 24 | 19 | 48 | 48 | 16 | 33 | 22 | 42 | 47 | 41 |
| Dundee City | 28 | 8 | 54 | 31 | 49 | 4 | 43 | 14 | 29 | 23 | 26 | 28 | 30 | 14 | 51 | 55 | 32 | 16 | 18 | 29 | 27 | 17 |
| Perth & Kinross | 43 | 49 | 32 | 39 | 29 | 17 | 27 | 37 | 36 | 25 | 37 | 47 | 28 | 12 | 38 | 34 | 23 | 19 | 13 | 25 | 37 | 40 |
| Berwickshire | 50 | 17 | 43 | 41 | 19 | 56 | 52 | 52 | 37 | 41 | 51 | 24 | 35 | 55 | 41 | 32 | 14 | 52 | 52 | 52 | 43 | 49 |
| Ett. & Lauderdale | 31 | 13 | 42 | 13 | 39 | 30 | 21 | 33 | 7 | 28 | 29 | 32 | 2 | 22 | 44 | 11 | 15 | 31 | 46 | 28 | 16 | 30 |
| Roxburgh | 38 | 2 | 7 | 12 | 13 | 43 | 44 | 32 | 34 | 18 | 42 | 44 | 39 | 8 | 20 | 4 | 52 | 42 | 28 | 23 | 12 | 36 |
| Tweeddale | 53 | 1 | 44 | 11 | 27 | 41 | 56 | 44 | 56 | 56 | 20 | 56 | 1 | 56 | 15 | 10 | 13 | 43 | 30 | 47 | 31 | 38 |
| Ann. & Eskdale | 24 | 37 | 46 | 51 | 28 | 29 | 23 | 40 | 31 | 30 | 17 | 45 | 47 | 6 | 8 | 42 | 45 | 41 | 50 | 31 | 52 | 42 |
| Nithsdale | 20 | 23 | 10 | 27 | 35 | 42 | 26 | 25 | 19 | 43 | 7 | 42 | 31 | 36 | 5 | 28 | 31 | 37 | 26 | 41 | 32 | 21 |
| Stewartry | 40 | 51 | 22 | 36 | 12 | 48 | 42 | 47 | 51 | 24 | 49 | 14 | 11 | 31 | 54 | 45 | 12 | 53 | 14 | 14 | 25 | 47 |
| Wigtown | 11 | 50 | 14 | 29 | 7 | 44 | 39 | 34 | 13 | 31 | 47 | 38 | 8 | 25 | 17 | 9 | 22 | 21 | 15 | 53 | 36 | 28 |
| Badenoch & Strathspey | 52 | 29 | 18 | 15 | 55 | 45 | 30 | 41 | 53 | 36 | 32 | 3 | 6 | 1 | 1 | 2 | 8 | 3 | 2 | 55 | 5 | 43 |
| Caithness | 17 | 33 | 3 | 28 | 31 | 47 | 15 | 42 | 40 | 6 | 45 | 19 | 5 | 43 | 6 | 7 | 7 | 14 | 5 | 44 | 8 | 29 |
| Inverness | 21 | 42 | 33 | 46 | 17 | 47 | 47 | 26 | 28 | 42 | 36 | 27 | 18 | 23 | 3 | 12 | 11 | 7 | 11 | 46 | 42 | 33 |
| Lochaber | 15 | 27 | 15 | 50 | 22 | 55 | 20 | 24 | 5 | 37 | 8 | 22 | 56 | 7 | 21 | 3 | 39 | 10 | 1 | 3 | 48 | 15 |
| Nairn | 48 | 35 | 16 | 56 | 9 | 54 | 29 | 27 | 48 | 54 | 55 | 34 | 55 | 2 | 14 | 18 | 4 | 22 | 4 | 54 | 56 | 37 |
| Ross & Cromarty | 37 | 52 | 1 | 21 | 30 | 49 | 25 | 45 | 42 | 49 | 48 | 46 | 48 | 18 | 35 | 13 | 2 | 5 | 7 | 4 | 21 | 34 |
| Skye & Lochalsh | 22 | 54 | 34 | 20 | 36 | 21 | 51 | 56 | 55 | 55 | 56 | 54 | 41 | 29 | 2 | 6 | 1 | 1 | 42 | 56 | 44 | 54 |
| Sutherland | 33 | 55 | 49 | 38 | 2 | 53 | 33 | 51 | 26 | 40 | 44 | 8 | 54 | 3 | 37 | 1 | 6 | 8 | 3 | 10 | 20 | 44 |
| Orkney | 41 | 56 | 56 | 54 | 5 | 27 | 48 | 55 | 50 | 38 | 41 | 30 | 10 | 4 | 46 | 19 | 18 | 4 | 9 | 2 | 54 | 53 |
| Shetland | 47 | 53 | 26 | 24 | 10 | 46 | 54 | 53 | 52 | 50 | 54 | 37 | 4 | 10 | 42 | 5 | 46 | 2 | 21 | 38 | 15 | 56 |
| Western Isles | 19 | 43 | 9 | 17 | 33 | 50 | 13 | 46 | 38 | 47 | 53 | 52 | 7 | 5 | 53 | 8 | 21 | 26 | 36 | 33 | 11 | 46 |

TABLE 5.12C　　1980 - 1985 CAUSES NOS FOR LOCAL GOVERNMENT DISTRICTS

| | 1 | 2 | 3 | 4 | 5 | 6 | 7 | 8 | 9 | 10 | 11 | 12 | 13 | 14 | 15 | 16 | 17 | 18 | 19 | 20 | 21 | 22 |
|---|---|---|---|---|---|---|---|---|---|---|---|---|---|---|---|---|---|---|---|---|---|---|
| Argyll & Bute | 5875 | 1168 | 4707 | 28 | 1184 | 342 | 48 | 89 | 171 | 37 | 48 | 294 | 84 | 127 | 18 | 68 | 24 | 76 | 61 | 15 | 40 | 1553 |
| Dunbarton | 5265 | 1409 | 3856 | 26 | 1154 | 431 | 39 | 87 | 122 | 25 | 46 | 338 | 129 | 107 | 17 | 68 | 23 | 75 | 64 | 26 | 44 | 1452 |
| Inverclyde | 7603 | 2274 | 5329 | 42 | 1671 | 584 | 63 | 133 | 189 | 52 | 78 | 519 | 180 | 168 | 25 | 70 | 30 | 112 | 101 | 39 | 54 | 2227 |
| Renfrew | 14402 | 4196 | 10206 | 71 | 3180 | 1176 | 111 | 266 | 352 | 98 | 169 | 973 | 368 | 291 | 48 | 160 | 56 | 133 | 143 | 69 | 71 | 4533 |
| Cunnock & Doon V | 3285 | 956 | 2329 | 17 | 652 | 265 | 29 | 55 | 76 | 22 | 19 | 172 | 61 | 56 | 20 | 56 | 24 | 58 | 34 | 12 | 28 | 1090 |
| Cunninghame | 9952 | 2624 | 7328 | 31 | 2138 | 754 | 94 | 176 | 275 | 73 | 85 | 615 | 234 | 181 | 30 | 125 | 63 | 108 | 95 | 41 | 64 | 2860 |
| Kilmarnock & Loudoun | 6096 | 1611 | 4485 | 24 | 1236 | 422 | 42 | 105 | 173 | 48 | 70 | 343 | 120 | 109 | 17 | 69 | 24 | 76 | 58 | 26 | 67 | 1823 |
| Kyle & Carrick | 9327 | 2074 | 7253 | 19 | 1993 | 600 | 55 | 151 | 266 | 50 | 99 | 524 | 158 | 198 | 29 | 119 | 45 | 114 | 114 | 30 | 88 | 2774 |
| Bears. & Milngavie | 2091 | 519 | 1572 | 8 | 554 | 201 | 15 | 34 | 82 | 28 | 25 | 142 | 49 | 61 | 2 | 37 | 18 | 21 | 22 | 13 | 15 | 577 |
| Clydebank | 3747 | 1124 | 2623 | 13 | 902 | 314 | 29 | 59 | 115 | 42 | 41 | 290 | 95 | 73 | 10 | 36 | 12 | 63 | 36 | 30 | 37 | 1105 |
| Eastwood | 3255 | 669 | 2586 | 13 | 772 | 233 | 30 | 43 | 109 | 30 | 24 | 194 | 48 | 76 | 9 | 47 | 17 | 33 | 34 | 18 | 32 | 898 |
| Glasgow City | 67014 | 18163 | 48851 | 362 | 15938 | 5253 | 561 | 1173 | 1734 | 413 | 597 | 5715 | 2060 | 1191 | 222 | 760 | 277 | 738 | 733 | 434 | 614 | 17995 |
| Strathkelvin | 4787 | 1436 | 3351 | 13 | 1090 | 414 | 38 | 79 | 127 | 38 | 46 | 335 | 128 | 114 | 14 | 68 | 26 | 51 | 66 | 24 | 50 | 1318 |
| Cumbernauld | 2889 | 1049 | 1840 | 20 | 714 | 324 | 21 | 62 | 73 | 21 | 19 | 241 | 109 | 59 | 9 | 42 | 11 | 32 | 44 | 15 | 10 | 850 |
| E. Kilbride | 3969 | 1314 | 2655 | 14 | 924 | 410 | 34 | 60 | 92 | 33 | 32 | 298 | 124 | 84 | 12 | 57 | 24 | 40 | 41 | 25 | 22 | 1227 |
| Hamilton | 7042 | 2073 | 4969 | 40 | 1482 | 582 | 50 | 104 | 170 | 55 | 57 | 439 | 185 | 135 | 26 | 107 | 41 | 101 | 63 | 37 | 50 | 2133 |
| Clydesdale | 3930 | 1006 | 2924 | 17 | 780 | 286 | 37 | 69 | 102 | 29 | 30 | 179 | 74 | 64 | 14 | 52 | 16 | 52 | 47 | 17 | 33 | 1198 |
| Monklands | 7034 | 2212 | 4822 | 35 | 1576 | 615 | 62 | 144 | 154 | 44 | 62 | 468 | 185 | 151 | 29 | 85 | 23 | 92 | 78 | 37 | 43 | 2282 |
| Motherwell | 11049 | 3351 | 7698 | 36 | 2324 | 918 | 85 | 224 | 260 | 78 | 100 | 648 | 265 | 228 | 47 | 127 | 47 | 131 | 97 | 54 | 61 | 3309 |
| Dunfermline | 8242 | 2223 | 6019 | 26 | 1814 | 633 | 69 | 141 | 195 | 45 | 78 | 512 | 191 | 150 | 41 | 122 | 45 | 102 | 73 | 33 | 23 | 2455 |
| Kirkcaldy | 10910 | 2714 | 8196 | 37 | 2299 | 788 | 90 | 167 | 264 | 73 | 114 | 658 | 226 | 175 | 52 | 142 | 60 | 130 | 108 | 38 | 65 | 3338 |
| N. E. Fife | 5106 | 916 | 4190 | 20 | 1092 | 303 | 48 | 65 | 162 | 41 | 37 | 278 | 80 | 125 | 21 | 84 | 36 | 66 | 33 | 17 | 35 | 1498 |
| Clackmannan | 3155 | 863 | 2292 | 12 | 745 | 260 | 34 | 52 | 101 | 26 | 34 | 219 | 84 | 90 | 10 | 37 | 15 | 34 | 36 | 7 | 19 | 890 |
| Falkirk | 9945 | 2710 | 7235 | 46 | 2203 | 761 | 76 | 174 | 254 | 70 | 91 | 667 | 235 | 190 | 35 | 121 | 47 | 121 | 139 | 46 | 45 | 2854 |
| Stirling | 5485 | 1345 | 4140 | 29 | 1226 | 404 | 62 | 83 | 152 | 33 | 47 | 336 | 112 | 129 | 20 | 71 | 29 | 55 | 87 | 20 | 25 | 1594 |
| Aberdeen City | 15620 | 3414 | 12206 | 58 | 3628 | 1091 | 134 | 242 | 490 | 99 | 168 | 1049 | 322 | 264 | 41 | 212 | 96 | 154 | 253 | 91 | 47 | 4433 |
| Banff & Buchan | 5597 | 1357 | 4240 | 21 | 1134 | 340 | 60 | 86 | 153 | 33 | 56 | 258 | 86 | 92 | 8 | 71 | 30 | 56 | 70 | 23 | 22 | 1659 |
| Gordon | 3678 | 774 | 2904 | 19 | 748 | 226 | 35 | 38 | 107 | 29 | 35 | 168 | 42 | 73 | 16 | 50 | 17 | 46 | 65 | 4 | 18 | 1031 |
| Kincar. & Deeside | 2834 | 576 | 2258 | 14 | 598 | 176 | 27 | 33 | 88 | 20 | 29 | 131 | 36 | 57 | 9 | 48 | 20 | 30 | 52 | 9 | 5 | 811 |

TABLE 5.12c   1980 - 1985 CAUSES NOS FOR LOCAL GOVERNMENT DISTRICTS CONTD.

| | 1 | 2 | 3 | 4 | 5 | 6 | 7 | 8 | 9 | 10 | 11 | 12 | 13 | 14 | 15 | 16 | 17 | 18 | 19 | 20 | 21 | 22 |
|---|---|---|---|---|---|---|---|---|---|---|---|---|---|---|---|---|---|---|---|---|---|---|
| Moray | 5734 | 1346 | 4388 | 18 | 1217 | 400 | 61 | 100 | 202 | 56 | 33 | 269 | 103 | 103 | 23 | 61 | 29 | 78 | 78 | 19 | 35 | 1572 |
| E. Lothian | 5888 | 1370 | 4518 | 23 | 1392 | 429 | 59 | 94 | 164 | 47 | 63 | 391 | 108 | 122 | 10 | 78 | 28 | 99 | 77 | 37 | 31 | 1745 |
| Edinburgh City | 34522 | 7438 | 27084 | 156 | 8061 | 2373 | 310 | 542 | 936 | 202 | 390 | 2410 | 743 | 669 | 114 | 486 | 198 | 435 | 443 | 196 | 361 | 9388 |
| Midlothian | 4782 | 1336 | 3446 | 16 | 1102 | 389 | 36 | 72 | 119 | 42 | 47 | 330 | 111 | 81 | 16 | 72 | 28 | 65 | 55 | 25 | 27 | 1387 |
| W. Lothian | 7554 | 2354 | 5200 | 37 | 1717 | 637 | 67 | 100 | 190 | 44 | 75 | 530 | 208 | 143 | 31 | 125 | 46 | 110 | 90 | 41 | 31 | 2143 |
| Angus | 6977 | 1363 | 5614 | 22 | 1549 | 412 | 62 | 139 | 256 | 43 | 66 | 348 | 96 | 148 | 31 | 100 | 30 | 95 | 115 | 20 | 42 | 2153 |
| Dundee City | 14094 | 3275 | 10819 | 58 | 3264 | 1005 | 122 | 266 | 396 | 85 | 146 | 1010 | 321 | 253 | 40 | 159 | 45 | 149 | 189 | BO | 78 | 4068 |
| Perth & Kinross | 9718 | 1912 | 7806 | 42 | 2045 | 595 | 82 | 140 | 300 | 64 | 126 | 521 | 143 | 200 | 27 | 115 | 46 | 113 | 92 | 22 | 51 | 2822 |
| Berwickshire | 1455 | 266 | 1189 | 10 | 302 | 84 | 9 | 16 | 44 | 5 | 17 | 81 | 29 | 33 | 1 | 24 | 8 | 22 | 22 | 4 | 10 | 451 |
| Ett. & Lauderdale | 2789 | 559 | 2230 | 14 | 603 | 160 | 24 | 41 | 94 | 19 | 30 | 163 | 41 | 53 | 6 | 42 | 21 | 38 | 39 | 9 | -14 | 843 |
| Roxburgh | 3100 | 594 | 2506 | 6 | 600 | 176 | 29 | 31 | 70 | 18 | 34 | 152 | 53 | 62 | B | 31 | 7 | 38 | 42 | 9 | 29 | 798 |
| Tweeddale | 1249 | 198 | 1051 | 7 | 274 | 63 | 16 | 10 | 41 | 5 | 17 | 78 | 22 | 24 | 3 | 13 | 5 | 18 | 16 | 1 | 9 | 357 |
| Ann.& Eskdale | 2578 | 601 | 1977 | 5 | 514 | 179 | 22 | 43 | 73 | 23 | 30 | 127 | 44 | 41 | 9 | 27 | B | 29 | 45 | 5 | 18 | 840 |
| Nithsdale | 4304 | 1087 | 3217 | 20 | 874 | 302 | 37 | 62 | 112 | 40 | 40 | 234 | 82 | 88 | 15 | 45 | 19 | 44 | 58 | 16 | 24 | 1377 |
| Stewartry | 1934 | 398 | 1536 | 4 | 419 | 131 | 21 | 23 | 56 | 15 | 13 | 95 | 30 | 40 | 7 | 27 | 9 | 21 | 17 | 5 | 12 | 557 |
| Wigtown | 2485 | 571 | 1914 | 9 | 485 | 147 | 19 | 29 | 68 | 10 | 21 | 122 | 41 | 38 | 6 | 37 | 16 | 48 | 33 | 5 | 41 | 791 |
| Badenoch & Strathspey | 753 | 165 | 588 | 3 | 163 | 44 | 11 | 16 | 32 | 5 | 7 | 36 | 11 | 9 | 0 | 10 | 4 | 11 | 8 | 4 | 6 | 200 |
| Caithness | 2081 | 562 | 1519 | 13 | 399 | 148 | 14 | 28 | 49 | 13 | 24 | 101 | 45 | 31 | 6 | 34 | 13 | 25 | 23 | 5 | 21 | 596 |
| Inverness | 3834 | 1011 | 2823 | 19 | 830 | 272 | 41 | 66 | 121 | 31 | 37 | 178 | 61 | 93 | 11 | 52 | 24 | 56 | 58 | 11 | 26 | 1101 |
| Lochaber | 1346 | 389 | 957 | 6 | 337 | 122 | 14 | 26 | 41 | 11 | 11 | 94 | 36 | 27 | 7 | 23 | 9 | 15 | 20 | 4 | 6 | 363 |
| Nairn | 811 | 154 | 657 | 4 | 165 | 45 | 11 | 12 | 27 | 8 | 11 | 38 | 11 | 13 | 1 | 9 | 3 | 9 | 12 | 4 | 6 | 216 |
| Ross & Cromarty | 3105 | 777 | 2328 | 11 | 681 | 224 | 36 | 39 | 90 | 18 | 35 | 158 | 56 | 73 | B | 41 | 15 | 45 | 35 | 10 | 18 | 871 |
| Skye & Lochalsh | 925 | 187 | 738 | 5 | 150 | 37 | B | 8 | 24 | 5 | 6 | 31 | 10 | 13 | 1 | 13 | 5 | 16 | 14 | 2 | B | 290 |
| Sutherland | 1262 | 267 | 995 | 5 | 244 | 79 | 13 | 17 | 29 | 11 | 15 | 62 | 19 | 25 | B | 13 | 5 | 13 | 22 | 6 | 17 | 345 |
| Orkney | 1478 | 308 | 1170 | 12 | 298 | 102 | 10 | 19 | 28 | 5 | 13 | 65 | 26 | 23 | 9 | 26 | 10 | 26 | 14 | 2 | 15 | 466 |
| Shetland | 1537 | 302 | 1235 | 13 | 275 | 78 | 9 | 19 | 49 | 9 | 10 | 49 | 19 | 36 | 4 | 24 | 7 | 29 | 22 | 12 | 9 | 421 |
| Western Isles | 2876 | 574 | 2302 | 12 | 513 | 152 | 24 | 43 | 67 | 13 | 25 | 108 | 37 | 56 | 5 | 29 | 13 | 52 | 43 | 5 | 31 | 825 |

TABLE 5.12c    1980 - 1985 CAUSES NOS FOR LOCAL GOVERNMENT DISTRICTS CONTD.

| | 23 | 24 | 25 | 26 | 27 | 28 | 29 | 30 | 31 | 32 | 33 | 34 | 35 | 36 | 37 | 38 | 39 | 40 | 41 | 42 | 43 | 44 |
|---|---|---|---|---|---|---|---|---|---|---|---|---|---|---|---|---|---|---|---|---|---|---|
| Argyll & Bute | 312 | 19 | 962 | 78 | 259 | 330 | 30 | 162 | 23 | 199 | 40 | 37 | 79 | 18 | 16 | 36 | 33 | 147 | 59 | 23 | 79 | 932 |
| Dunbarton | 369 | 19 | 713 | 86 | 194 | 327 | 40 | 172 | 37 | 205 | 55 | 37 | 78 | 12 | 16 | 26 | 52 | 145 | 52 | 25 | 88 | 942 |
| Inverclyde | 654 | 24 | 1037 | 170 | 189 | 406 | 43 | 357 | 103 | 325 | 55 | 89 | 114 | 21 | 34 | 24 | 47 | 187 | 78 | 32 | 172 | 1558 |
| Renfrew | 1284 | 55 | 2119 | 282 | 257 | 782 | 104 | 577 | 138 | 537 | 113 | 127 | 203 | 47 | 81 | 41 | 144 | 291 | 141 | 68 | 286 | 2929 |
| Cumnoch & Doon V | 310 | 19 | 444 | 73 | 81 | 165 | 12 | 131 | 35 | 109 | 29 | 18 | 41 | 6 | 13 | 10 | 35 | 68 | 32 | 28 | 74 | 633 |
| Cunninghame | 727 | 53 | 1597 | 200 | 231 | 559 | 46 | 396 | 100 | 345 | 80 | 58 | 138 | 32 | 58 | 44 | 107 | 209 | 113 | 52 | 202 | 1906 |
| Kilmarnock & Loudoun | 515 | 36 | 835 | 98 | 170 | 279 | 34 | 253 | 63 | 197 | 50 | 40 | 104 | 27 | 26 | 25 | 73 | 107 | 56 | 24 | 108 | 1143 |
| Kyle & Carrick | 610 | 40 | 1483 | 171 | 253 | 397 | 29 | 330 | 69 | 297 | 69 | 59 | 127 | 38 | 40 | 27 | 82 | 162 | 83 | 33 | 178 | 1675 |
| Bears.& Milngavie | 131 | 9 | 311 | 37 | 44 | 133 | 6 | 56 | 8 | 72 | 16 | 16 | 27 | 10 | 11 | 8 | 19 | 40 | 17 | 7 | 40 | 373 |
| Clydebank | 350 | 15 | 481 | 73 | 61 | 260 | 29 | 141 | 35 | 129 | 41 | 36 | 36 | 8 | 15 | 5 | 40 | 69 | 31 | 19 | 85 | 769 |
| Eastwood | 173 | 14 | 458 | 36 | 82 | 212 | 14 | 109 | 15 | 120 | 25 | 21 | 57 | 9 | 21 | 9 | 26 | 52 | 29 | 13 | 38 | 555 |
| Glasgow City | 4739 | 344 | 8184 | 1139 | 1242 | 4580 | 432 | 3628 | 897 | 2445 | 586 | 628 | 871 | 212 | 270 | 214 | 611 | 1349 | 888 | 276 | 1247 | 14284 |
| Strathkelvin | 391 | 22 | 569 | 82 | 96 | 396 | 56 | 211 | 53 | 139 | 36 | 33 | 68 | 18 | 33 | 11 | 60 | 105 | 56 | 20 | 94 | 935 |
| Cumbernauld | 303 | 15 | 335 | 62 | 38 | 190 | 24 | 119 | 41 | 97 | 22 | 30 | 25 | 14 | 24 | 14 | 45 | 55 | 37 | 14 | 59 | 618 |
| E.Kilbride | 376 | 16 | 465 | 89 | 80 | 275 | 20 | 140 | 40 | 114 | 28 | 32 | 60 | 18 | 29 | 4 | 43 | 99 | 49 | 18 | 87 | 807 |
| Hamilton | 671 | 21 | 793 | 127 | 259 | 405 | 51 | 250 | 68 | 210 | 56 | 51 | 82 | 16 | 35 | 10 | 62 | 153 | 76 | 42 | 134 | 1325 |
| Clydesdale | 294 | 12 | 585 | 71 | 143 | 198 | 22 | 130 | 39 | 115 | 30 | 14 | 55 | 17 | 22 | 6 | 36 | 88 | 28 | 18 | 67 | 678 |
| Monklands | 715 | 42 | 825 | 141 | 97 | 500 | 53 | 280 | 50 | 246 | 47 | 59 | 89 | 26 | 38 | 19 | 68 | 120 | 79 | 40 | 143 | 1432 |
| Motherwell | 1037 | 37 | 1371 | 275 | 312 | 682 | 92 | 437 | 118 | 371 | 87 | 68 | 144 | 26 | 64 | 28 | 79 | 244 | 100 | 61 | 269 | 2125 |
| Dunfermline | 661 | 37 | 1325 | 191 | 175 | 459 | 37 | 314 | 75 | 249 | 41 | 43 | 99 | 30 | 43 | 59 | 104 | 175 | 81 | 37 | 192 | 1606 |
| Kirkcaldy | 821 | 36 | 1756 | 194 | 276 | 579 | 44 | 443 | 85 | 294 | 80 | 64 | 168 | 43 | 48 | 54 | 99 | 216 | 134 | 58 | 197 | 2109 |
| N.E.Fife | 253 | 19 | 804 | 71 | 155 | 357 | 18 | 142 | 21 | 148 | 28 | 23 | 74 | 18 | 11 | 14 | 42 | 118 | 53 | 15 | 71 | 850 |
| Clackmannan | 240 | 12 | 414 | 58 | 171 | 190 | 36 | 128 | 34 | 110 | 26 | 24 | 37 | 7 | 17 | 7 | 38 | 56 | 24 | 15 | 56 | 619 |
| Falkirk | 740 | 36 | 1393 | 205 | 193 | 762 | 82 | 388 | 91 | 335 | 78 | 67 | 128 | 37 | 52 | 15 | 81 | 220 | 109 | 49 | 207 | 1911 |
| Stirling | 338 | 19 | 749 | 84 | 163 | 364 | 56 | 217 | 5Z | 206 | 67 | 32 | 60 | 14 | 19 | 11 | 69 | 101 | 54 | 32 | 87 | 1013 |
| Aberdeen City | 870 | 121 | 2012 | 218 | 315 | 1130 | 70 | 592 | 112 | 458 | 103 | 82 | 214 | 83 | 60 | 77 | 149 | 433 | 179 | 43 | 205 | 2854 |
| Banff & Buchan | 363 | 28 | 974 | 108 | 146 | 245 | 30 | 161 | 30 | 133 | 27 | 13 | 72 | 23 | 23 | 26 | 115 | 154 | 70 | 18 | 104 | 956 |
| Gordon | 179 | 19 | 551 | 51 | 95 | 289 | 16 | 105 | 18 | 114 | 27 | 13 | 53 | 19 | 24 | 28 | 68 | 98 | 36 | 16 | 48 | 577 |
| Kincar.& Deeside | 123 | 12 | 385 | 32 | 58 | 223 | 3 | 78 | 13 | 71 | 20 | 15 | 52 | 11 | 11 | 24 | 54 | 68 | 42 | 9 | 29 | 435 |

TABLE 5.12c   1980 - 1985 CAUSES NOS FOR LOCAL GOVERNMENT DISTRICTS CONTD.

| | 23 | 24 | 25 | 26 | 27 | 28 | 29 | 30 | 31 | 32 | 33 | 34 | 35 | 36 | 37 | 38 | 39 | 40 | 41 | 42 | 43 | 44 |
|---|---|---|---|---|---|---|---|---|---|---|---|---|---|---|---|---|---|---|---|---|---|---|
| Moray | 335 | 25 | 867 | 89 | 151 | 330 | 20 | 179 | 35 | 176 | 33 | 20 | 63 | 28 | 39 | 39 | 92 | 123 | 80 | 23 | 88 | 931 |
| E.Lothian | 399 | 35 | 755 | 84 | 109 | 393 | 23 | 211 | 51 | 194 | 55 | 25 | 78 | 22 | 30 | 17 | 56 | 90 | 68 | 16 | 90 | 1101 |
| Edinburgh City | 1859 | 213 | 4908 | 458 | 716 | 1945 | 126 | 1452 | 268 | 1179 | 256 | 255 | 452 | 148 | 159 | 128 | 259 | 732 | 368 | 112 | 507 | 6490 |
| Midlothian | 374 | 25 | 633 | 97 | 87 | 298 | 17 | 210 | 47 | 156 | 28 | 28 | 70 | 22 | 27 | 24 | 56 | 90 | 42 | 23 | 101 | 949 |
| W.Lothian | 659 | 48 | 1023 | 141 | 148 | 478 | 40 | 340 | 110 | 263 | 74 | 45 | 93 | 36 | 65 | 42 | 100 | 135 | 90 | 43 | 143 | 1531 |
| Angus | 382 | 23 | 1002 | 91 | 118 | 422 | 19 | 218 | 37 | 183 | 45 | 26 | 112 | 35 | 24 | 15 | 85 | 157 | 78 | 21 | 96 | 1168 |
| Dundee City | 932 | 90 | 1679 | 223 | 261 | 1181 | 46 | 585 | 102 | 450 | 103 | 77 | 198 | 75 | 41 | 15 | 132 | 343 | 158 | 51 | 232 | 2716 |
| Perth & Kinross | 520 | 31 | 1487 | 134 | 253 | 713 | 39 | 296 | 57 | 317 | 64 | 39 | 148 | 53 | 32 | 29 | 96 | 227 | 111 | 35 | 141 | 1642 |
| Berwickshire | 75 | 8 | 221 | 21 | 49 | 47 | 3 | 40 | 9 | 45 | 8 | 9 | 23 | 3 | 5 | 5 | 18 | 28 | 10 | 3 | 21 | 246 |
| Ett. & Lauderdale | 160 | 16 | 384 | 45 | 65 | 176 | 12 | 92 | 26 | 86 | 20 | 14 | 59 | 13 | 8 | 22 | 30 | 60 | 20 | 9 | 46 | 492 |
| Roxburgh | 165 | 25 | 554 | 50 | 108 | 165 | 9 | 103 | 18 | 107 | 18 | 13 | 42 | 19 | 12 | 40 | 19 | 62 | 28 | 11 | 53 | 515 |
| Tweeddale | 45 | 13 | 184 | 19 | 36 | 75 | 0 | 36 | 1 | 26 | 11 | 2 | 35 | 2 | 5 | 11 | 14 | 26 | 11 | 3 | 17 | 216 |
| Ann. & Eskdale | 197 | 10 | 358 | 36 | 69 | 168 | 13 | 81 | 20 | 85 | 23 | 12 | 32 | 18 | 14 | 7 | 22 | 55 | 21 | 10 | 33 | 454 |
| Nithsdale | 315 | 18 | 694 | 71 | 94 | 216 | 19 | 154 | 36 | 115 | 41 | 20 | 58 | 16 | 25 | 17 | 42 | 87 | 46 | 13 | 71 | 798 |
| Stewartry | 108 | 6 | 313 | 28 | 70 | 97 | 6 | 53 | 6 | 64 | 10 | 13 | 35 | 8 | 4 | 4 | 25 | 33 | 22 | 8 | 31 | 317 |
| Wigtown | 184 | 7 | 370 | 38 | 93 | 116 | 8 | 74 | 22 | 70 | 12 | 12 | 40 | 10 | 11 | 22 | 25 | 52 | 28 | 4 | 37 | 429 |
| Badenoch & Strathspey | 33 | 3 | 121 | 13 | 13 | 37 | 3 | 22 | 2 | 22 | 5 | 7 | 14 | 11 | 6 | 14 | 11 | 25 | 14 | 1 | 15 | 122 |
| Caithness | 146 | 7 | 320 | 32 | 43 | 134 | 12 | 53 | 11 | 73 | 10 | 12 | 33 | 6 | 13 | 21 | 32 | 48 | 36 | 6 | 40 | 340 |
| Inverness | 287 | 13 | 541 | 53 | 110 | 175 | 12 | 134 | 30 | 104 | 24 | 22 | 59 | 17 | 27 | 30 | 60 | 108 | 51 | 12 | 58 | 656 |
| Lochaber | 99 | 5 | 195 | 17 | 32 | 36 | 7 | 46 | 14 | 36 | 12 | 8 | 10 | 8 | 8 | 27 | 13 | 35 | 27 | 9 | 18 | 253 |
| Nairn | 38 | 3 | 131 | 5 | 32 | 29 | 3 | 29 | 3 | 17 | 3 | 4 | 7 | 11 | 4 | 5 | 13 | 18 | 13 | 1 | 5 | 133 |
| Ross & Cromarty | 186 | 8 | 531 | 52 | 71 | 137 | 14 | 78 | 16 | 75 | 15 | 13 | 34 | 14 | 17 | 27 | 64 | 92 | 48 | 18 | 53 | 521 |
| Skye & Lochalsh | 55 | 2 | 143 | 13 | 23 | 68 | 2 | 13 | 1 | 19 | 2 | 2 | 13 | 4 | 6 | 10 | 22 | 41 | 7 | 1 | 11 | 131 |
| Sutherland | 65 | 1 | 160 | 15 | 60 | 47 | 4 | 31 | 8 | 34 | 7 | 9 | 13 | 11 | 4 | 53 | 16 | 33 | 19 | 5 | 18 | 194 |
| Orkney | 80 | 1 | 183 | 14 | 65 | 98 | 4 | 30 | 5 | 44 | 9 | 8 | 27 | 13 | 5 | 9 | 17 | 49 | 19 | 10 | 14 | 219 |
| Shetland | 79 | 4 | 248 | 24 | 59 | 81 | 2 | 38 | 4 | 41 | 7 | 8 | 32 | 9 | 8 | 23 | 14 | 61 | 19 | 5 | 26 | 215 |
| Western Isles | 166 | 10 | 513 | 40 | 73 | 142 | 14 | 76 | 14 | 76 | 13 | 8 | 54 | 22 | 7 | 28 | 27 | 65 | 22 | 8 | 44 | 444 |

TABLE 5.13   LOCAL GOVERNMENT DISTRICTS IN TOP AND BOTTOM QUINTILE OF
SMRS FOR SELECTED CAUSES* 1980-85

| Smoking-related all ages r=0.9l | | Cancer All sites all ages r=0.82 | | Cancer All sites 0-64 r=0.86 | |
|---|---|---|---|---|---|

TOP QUINTILE SMR

| DEP+ | | | DEP | | | DEP | | |
|---|---|---|---|---|---|---|---|---|
| 5 | Glasgow | 124 | 5 | Glasgow | 117 | 4 | Lochaber | 124 |
| 4 | Cumbernauld | 117 | 4 | Lochaber | 116 | 4 | Cumbernauld | 119 |
| 5 | Inverclyde | 115 | 4 | Cumbernauld | 115 | 5 | Glasgow | 119 |
| 4 | Monklands | 113 | 5 | Clydebank | 109 | 5 | Motherwell | 109 |
| 5 | Renfrew | 113 | 4 | Clackmannan | 108 | 4 | Dumbarton | 107 |
| 5 | Motherwell | 108 | 5 | Monklands | 107 | 5 | Monklands | 107 |
| 5 | Clydebank | 108 | 5 | Inverclyde | 105 | 5 | Cunninghame | 107 |
| 5 | Cunninghame | 106 | 5 | Renfrew | 105 | 2 | Sutherland | 106 |
| 5 | W. Lothian | 106 | 3 | Aberdeen | 102 | 5 | Renfrew | 104 |
| 5 | Cumnock | 105 | 5 | Dundee | 102 | 5 | Inverclyde | 104 |
| 5 | Hamilton | 104 | 5 | West Lothian | 102 | 5 | Hamilton | 103 |

BOTTOM QUINTILE SMR

| DEP+ | | | DEP | | | DEP | | |
|---|---|---|---|---|---|---|---|---|
| 1 | Shetland | 69 | 4 | Skye & Lochalsh | 70 | 4 | Skye | 67 |
| 1 | Gordon | 71 | 1 | Shetland | 75 | 1 | Shetland | 74 |
| 4 | Skye & Lochalsh | 71 | 5 | Western Isles | 79 | 1 | Eastwood | 79 |
| 1 | Bearsden | 73 | 1 | Gordon | 79 | 1 | Gordon | 79 |
| 1 | Orkney | 72 | 2 | Annan | 79 | 4 | Banff | 81 |
| 1 | Eastwood | 74 | 2 | Berwick | 80 | 2 | Berwick | 81 |
| 1 | Kincardine | 73 | 1 | Orkney | 84 | 3 | Angus | 82 |
| 2 | Berwick | 76 | 3 | Roxburgh | 85 | 2 | Tweeddale | 83 |
| 1 | N.E. Fife | 78 | 4 | Banff | 86 | 1 | Badenoch | 84 |
| 2 | Stewartry | 79 | 1 | Kincardine | 86 | 1 | Kincardine | 85 |
| 1 | Badenoch | 82 | 1 | N.E. Fife | 85 | 4 | Wigtown | 86 |

*over 6,000 deaths
+DEP quintile

TABLE 5.13   LOCAL GOVERNMENT DISTRICTS IN TOP AND BOTTOM QUINTILE OF SMRs FOR SELECTED CAUSES* 1980-85 CONTD.

| Ca. Lung all ages r=0.81 | | Ca. Lung 0-64 r=0.81 | | Ca. Stomach all ages r=0.72 | |
|---|---|---|---|---|---|

**TOP QUINTILE SMR**

| DEP | | | DEP | | | DEP | | |
|---|---|---|---|---|---|---|---|---|
| 5 | Glasgow | 144 | 5 | Glasgow | 150 | 4 | Cumbernauld | 142 |
| 4 | Cumbernauld | 132 | 4 | Cumbernauld | 136 | 5 | Monklands | 137 |
| 5 | Clydebank | 116 | 4 | Lochaber | 120 | 5 | Motherwell | 134 |
| 5 | Inverclyde | 111 | 5 | Cunninghame | 109 | 1 | Badenoch | 123 |
| 5 | Dundee | 110 | 4 | Clachmannan | 108 | 4 | Lochaber | 122 |
| 5 | Renfrew | 109 | 5 | Hamilton | 108 | 5 | Renfrew | 120 |
| 4 | Lochaber | 108 | 5 | Renfrew | 107 | 5 | Glasgow | 117 |
| 5 | Monklands | 107 | 5 | West Lothian | 107 | 5 | Inverclyde | 114 |
| 4 | Clackmannan | 107 | 5 | Monklands | 106 | 5 | Cunninghame | 114 |
| 5 | West Lothian | 106 | 5 | Dundee | 105 | 5 | Dundee | 113 |
| 3 | Edinburgh | 104 | 5 | Inverclyde | 104 | 5 | Cumnock | 112 |

**BOTTOM QUINTILE SMR**

| DEP | | | DEP | | | DEP | | |
|---|---|---|---|---|---|---|---|---|
| 1 | Shetland | 46 | 1 | Gordon | 49 | 2 | Tweeddale | 45 |
| 4 | Skye | 49 | 1 | Eastwood | 53 | 4 | Skye | 49 |
| 5 | Western Isles | 56 | 1 | Kincardine | 57 | 1 | Gordon | 54 |
| 1 | Gordon | 60 | 4 | Skye | 58 | 2 | Berwick | 57 |
| 1 | Orkney | 61 | 1 | Shetland | 60 | 3 | Roxburgh | 59 |
| 1 | Kincardine | 64 | 3 | Angus | 62 | 1 | Eastwood | 60 |
| 4 | Banff | 65 | 4 | Banff | 67 | 1 | Kincardine | 64 |
| 2 | Annan | 65 | 2 | Inverness | 68 | 2 | Stewartry | 66 |
| 2 | Stewartry | 67 | 2 | Annan | 68 | 1 | N.E. Fife | 68 |
| 2 | Moray | 68 | 1 | Badenoch | 68 | 1 | Shetland | 69 |
| 3 | Clydesdale | 69 | 2 | Perth & Kinross | 69 | 1 | Orkney | 72 |

TABLE 5.13   LOCAL GOVERNMENT DISTRICTS IN TOP AND BOTTOM QUINTILE OF SMRS FOR SELECTED CAUSES* 1980-85 CONTD.

| Digestive r=0.76 | | Ischaemic heart disease all ages r=0.55 | | 0-64 r=0.76 | |
|---|---|---|---|---|---|

**TOP QUINTILE SMR**

| DEP | | | DEP | | | DEP | | |
|---|---|---|---|---|---|---|---|---|
| 5 | Inverclyde | 139 | 5 | Cumnock | 125 | 5 | Monklands | 133 |
| 5 | Glasgow | 121 | 5 | Monklands | 124 | 5 | Motherwell | 129 |
| 5 | Renfrew | 121 | 5 | Renfrew | 118 | 5 | Hamilton | 126 |
| 4 | Dunbarton | 120 | 5 | Hamilton | 115 | 5 | Cumnock | 123 |
| 5 | Monklands | 116 | 5 | Motherwell | 114 | 5 | Inverclyde | 123 |
| 3 | Caithness | 115 | 4 | Wigtown | 114 | 5 | Renfrew | 120 |
| 5 | Motherwell | 112 | 4 | Cumbernauld | 114 | 4 | Kilmarnock | 120 |
| 5 | Cumnock | 111 | 4 | Nithsdale | 110 | 4 | Cumbernauld | 119 |
| 5 | Cunninghame | 111 | 5 | Inverclyde | 110 | 5 | Clydebank | 119 |
| 4 | Clackmannan | 110 | 4 | Kilmarnock | 109 | 5 | Glasgow | 112 |
| 5 | Clydebank | 110 | 4 | Kirkcaldy | 109 | 4 | Wigtown | 112 |

**BOTTOM QUINTILE SMR**

| DEP | | | DEP | | | DEP | | |
|---|---|---|---|---|---|---|---|---|
| 2 | Tweeddale | 57 | 1 | Bearsden | 75 | 1 | Bearsden | 62 |
| 4 | Skye | 59 | 1 | Eastwood | 78 | 1 | Eastwood | 62 |
| 1 | Nairn | 62 | 1 | Gordon | 83 | 1 | Kincardine | 62 |
| 4 | Banff | 68 | 1 | Kincardine | 83 | 2 | Tweeddale | 62 |
| 1 | Kincardine | 68 | 3 | Roxburgh | 86 | 1 | Badenoch | 66 |
| 3 | Angus | 73 | 1 | Shetland | 87 | 1 | Gordon | 67 |
| 1 | Ross & Cromarty | 74 | 1 | Badenoch | 87 | 2 | Berwick | 74 |
| 1 | Shetland | 74 | 1 | N.E. Fife | 88 | 1 | N.E. Fife | 78 |
| 5 | Western Isles | 77 | 3 | Edinburgh | 88 | 1 | Nairn | 79 |
| 1 | N.E. Fife | 77 | 2 | Tweeddale | 90 | 1 | Shetland | 80 |
| 3 | East Kilbride | 79 | 1 | Nairn | 90 | 3 | Angus | 80 |

TABLE 5.13    LOCAL GOVERNMENT DISTRICTS IN TOP AND BOTTOM QUINTILE OF
SMRs FOR SELECTED CAUSES* 1980-85  CONTD.

| Cerebrovascular disease 0-64 r=0.65 | | Pneumonia r=0.53 | | Bronchitis r=0.57 | |
|---|---|---|---|---|---|

### TOP QUINTILE SMR

| DEP | | | DEP | | | DEP | | |
|---|---|---|---|---|---|---|---|---|
| 5 | Motherwell | 142 | 1 | Strathkelvin | 141 | 5 | Glasgow | 150 |
| 5 | Inverclyde | 132 | 4 | Cumkernauld | 135 | 5 | Inverclyde | 127 |
| 3 | Dunfermline | 126 | 5 | Monklands | 135 | 4 | Cumkernauld | 115 |
| 5 | Cunninghame | 123 | 5 | Dundee | 128 | 5 | West Lothian | 115 |
| 5 | Cumnock | 122 | 5 | Clydebank | 127 | 1 | Strathkelvin | 110 |
| 3 | Kyle & Carrick | 113 | 4 | Falkirk | 126 | 5 | Renfrew | 109 |
| 4 | Banff | 112 | 3 | East Kilbride | 117 | 4 | Kilmarnock | 109 |
| 5 | Glasgow | 112 | 5 | Motherwell | 115 | 5 | Monklands | 109 |
| 4 | Falkirk | 111 | 3 | Caithness | 114 | 5 | Motherwell | 108 |
| 5 | Renfrew | 109 | 5 | West Lothian | 112 | 4 | Clackmannan | 107 |
| 2 | Tweeddale | 109 | 3 | Aberdeen | 110 | 3 | Midlothian | 106 |

### BOTTOM QUINTILE SMR

| DEP | | | DEP | | | DEP | | |
|---|---|---|---|---|---|---|---|---|
| 1 | Nairn | 43 | 2 | Berwick | 42 | 4 | Skye | 32 |
| 1 | Eastwood | 53 | 4 | Lochaber | 46 | 1 | Orkney | 45 |
| 1 | Orkney | 61 | 1 | Nairn | 54 | 1 | Bearsden | 54 |
| 1 | Kincardine | 67 | 2 | Sutherland | 56 | 1 | Shetland | 55 |
| 1 | Bearsden | 72 | 4 | Banff | 66 | 2 | Berwick | 56 |
| 2 | Annan | 76 | 3 | Kyle & Carrick | 68 | 1 | Gordon | 59 |
| 4 | Lochaber | 76 | 5 | Western Isles | 69 | 1 | Kincardine | 59 |
| 1 | Gordon | 78 | 1 | Ross & Cromarty | 71 | 2 | Stewartry | 60 |
| 3 | East Lothian | 78 | 2 | Stewartry | 72 | 1 | N.E. Fife | 60 |
| 3 | Angus | 79 | 1 | Badenoch | 72 | 1 | Ross & Cromarty | 61 |
| 2 | Inverness | 79 | 2 | Inverness | 72 | 5 | Western Isles | 61 |

TABLE 5.13    LOCAL GOVERNMENT DISTRICTS IN TOP AND BOTTOM QUINTILE OF SMRs FOR SELECTED CAUSES* 1980-85 CONTD.

| Ca. Breast all ages r=0.02 | | | Cerebrovascular disease all ages r=0.04 | | | Arterial disease all ages r=0.09 | |
|---|---|---|---|---|---|---|---|

**TOP QUINTILE SMR**

| DEP | | | DEP | | | DEP | | |
|---|---|---|---|---|---|---|---|---|
| 4 | Clackmannan | 148 | 1 | Ross & Cromarty | 125 | 4 | Clackmannan | 258 |
| 1 | Ross & Cromarty | 130 | 5 | Cunninghame | 118 | 2 | Sutherland | 189 |
| 2 | Inverness | 124 | 3 | Caithness | 122 | 5 | Hamilton | 182 |
| 1 | Shetland | 121 | 3 | Dunfermline | 120 | 3 | Argyll & Bute | 178 |
| 3 | Argyll & Bute | 120 | 4 | Kirkcaldy | 120 | 4 | Dumbarton | 164 |
| 5 | Inverclyde | 119 | 3 | Roxburgh | 119 | 3 | Clydesdale | 158 |
| 2 | Stirling | 119 | 4 | Banff | 119 | 4 | Wigtown | 164 |
| 1 | N.E. Fife | 118 | 5 | Renfrew | 118 | 1 | Nairn | 157 |
| 2 | Sutherland | 114 | 5 | Western Isles | 116 | 1 | Orkney | 167 |
| 5 | Monklands | 114 | 4 | Nithsdale | 115 | 1 | Shetland | 141 |
| 1 | Strathkelvin | 113 | 3 | Kyle | 114 | 5 | Motherwell | 139 |

**BOTTOM QUINTILE**

| DEP | | | DEP | | | DEP | | |
|---|---|---|---|---|---|---|---|---|
| 1 | Badenoch | 63 | 1 | Orkney | 81 | 3 | Angus | 64 |
| 2 | Annan | 77 | 1 | Eastwood | 82 | 1 | Badenoch | 68 |
| 4 | Skye | 78 | 5 | Dundee | 82 | 5 | Monklands | 70 |
| 3 | Midlothian | 83 | 2 | East Lothian | 84 | 1 | Bearsden | 71 |
| 1 | Orkney | 83 | 1 | Bearsden | 84 | 4 | Cumbernauld | 72 |
| 3 | Aberdeen | 84 | 1 | Kincardine | 85 | 2 | East Lothian | 72 |
| 3 | Clydesdale | 84 | 3 | East Kilbride | 85 | 1 | Kincardine | 74 |
| 4 | Banff | 85 | 2 | Sutherland | 87 | 5 | Dundee | 75 |
| 4 | Wigtown | 85 | 3 | Aberdeen | 88 | 5 | Clydebank | 79 |
| 4 | Kirkcaldy | 86 | 1 | Strathkelvin | 89 | 3 | Edinburgh | 79 |
| 3 | Caithness | 87 | 2 | Annan | 90 | 3 | Aberdeen | 81 |

TABLE 5.14    DEPRIVATION AND URBAN/RURAL CHARACTERISTICS IN RELATION TO SELECTED CAUSES OF DEATH AND STANDARD DEVIATIONS

| | Correlation | | | | Regression standard deviations | | |
|---|---|---|---|---|---|---|---|
| | DEP only only | | U/R | | DEP + U/R | | |
| | r | $R^2$ (%) | r | $R^2$ (%) | | $R^2$ change (%) # | S.D. |
| All causes | 0.851 | 72.4 | -0.480 | 73.6 | | 1.2 | 7.5 |
| Malignant cancer | 0.817 | 66.8 | -0.800 | 78.6 | | 11.8* | 9.8 |
| ca. lung | 0.811 | 65.8 | -0.831 | 81.1 | | 15.3* | 23.4 |

TABLE 5.14   CONTD.

| | | | | | | |
|---|---|---|---|---|---|---|
| ca. lung 0-64 | 0.867 | 75.3 | -0.739 | 80.0 | 4.7* | 25.8 |
| ca. cervix | 0.324 | 10.5 | -0.037 | 16.1 | 5.6 | 26.3 |
| Endocrine | 0.234 | 5.5 | 0.186 | 16.3 | 20.8* | 17.2 |
| Chronic rheumatic HD | 0.691 | 47.7 | -0.819 | 70.9 | 23.2* | 31.3 |
| Ischaemic heart | | | | | | |
| disease 0-64 | 0.750 | 56.3 | -0.349 | 59.2 | 4.2 | 17.2 |
| Cerebrovascular | 0.045 | 0.2 | 0.317 | 21.6 | 21.4* | 11.6 |
| CVD - 0-64 | 0.645 | 41.7 | -0.220 | 49.4 | 7.7* | 17.0 |
| Arteries | -0.086 | 0.7 | 0.374 | 18.7 | 18.0* | 30.9 |
| Pneumonia | 0.526 | 27.7 | -0.526 | 33.3 | 5.6* | 19.7 |
| Bronchitis | 0.867 | 75.3 | -0.765 | 81.7 | 6.4* | 26.6 |
| Liver disease & cirrhosis | 0.759 | 57.7 | -0.767 | 70.1 | 12.4* | 33.8 |
| Musculoskeletal | 0.261 | 6.8 | 0.322 | 10.8 | 4.0 | 28.9 |
| Symptoms | -0.159 | 2.5 | 0.327 | 11.3 | 8.8* | 77.4 |
| R.T.As. | -0.136 | 1.8 | 0.422 | 21.5 | 19.7* | 26.2 |
| Avoidable various | 0.541 | 29.3 | -0.183 | 34.9 | 5.6* | 23.4 |
| Avoidable - CVD 35-64 | 0.736 | 54.2 | -0.342 | 58.0 | 3.8* | 17.9 |
| Smoking related | 0.907 | 82.3 | -0.728 | 85.2 | 2.9* | 14.2 |

#shows % of variation explained by urban/rural measure in addition to DEP
*sig. at least at 0.05 level

FIGURE 5.1   AGGREGATE CAUSES

(a) 'Avoidable' causes of death

| ICD No. | | age |
|---|---|---|
| 010-018 | Tuberculosis | 5-64 |
| 180 | Ca. cervix | 15-64 |
| 201 | Hodgkin's disease | 5-64 |
| 393-398 | Chronic rheumatic heart disease | 5-44 |
| 460-519 | Respiratory diseases | 1-14 |
| 493 | Asthma | 5-44 |
| 540-543 | Appendicitis | 5-64 |
| 550-553 | Hernia | 5-64 |
| 574-575 | Cholelithiasis and other disorders of gall bladder | 5-64 |
| 630-676 | Maternal deaths | any |
| 401-405) 430-438) | Hypertensive and cerebrovascular disease | 35-64 |

(b) Smoking-related causes of death

| 140 | Ca. lip/oral cavity & pharynx | |
|---|---|---|
| 150 | Ca. oesophagus | |
| 162 | Ca. lung | all |
| 410-414 | Ischaemic heart disease | ages |
| 430-438 | Cerebrovascular disease | |
| 490-496 | Chronic respiratory disease | |

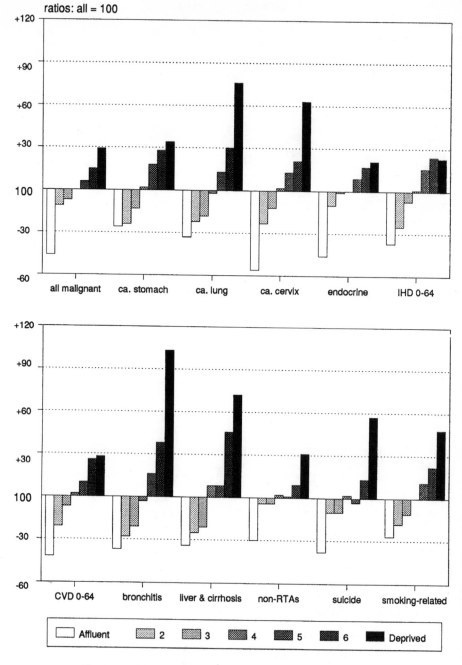

FIGURE 5.2 CAUSE SMRs (M&F) 1980 - 85 BY DEPCAT

FIGURE 5.3 KEY: 1980 - 1985 CAUSE DATA, ICD9 CODES AND AGE GROUPS

|  | Cause | ICD | Age |
|---|---|---|---|
| 1. | All Causes | All | All |
| 2. | All Causes | All | 0-64 |
| 3. | All Causes | All | 65+ |
| 4. | Infectious & Parasitic | 1-139 | All |
| 5. | Malignant Neoplasms | 140-208 | All |
| 6. | Malignant Neoplasms | 140-208 | 0-64 |
| 7. | Ca. Oesophagus | 150 | All |
| 8. | Ca. Stomach | 151 | All |
| 9. | Ca. Large Bowel | 153,154 | All |
| 10. | Ca. Large Bowel | 153,154 | 0-64 |
| 11. | Ca. Pancreas | 157 | All |
| 12. | Ca. Lung | 162 | All |
| 13. | Ca. Lung | 162 | 0-64 |
| 14. | Ca. Breast | 174 | All |
| 15. | Ca. cervix | 180 | All |
| 16. | Ca. Lymphatic Tissue | 200-208 | All |
| 17. | Leukemia | 204-208 | All |
| 18. | Endocrine | 240-279 | All |
| 19. | Nervous System | 320-389 | All |
| 20. | Chronic Rheumatic HD | 393-398 | All |
| 21. | Hypertensive HD | 401-405 | All |
| 22. | Ischaemic HD | 410-414 | All |
| 23. | Ischaemic HD | 410-414 | 0-64 |
| 24. | Pulmonary HD | 415-417 | All |
| 25. | Cerebrovascular Disease | 430-438 | All |
| 26. | Cerebrovascular Disease | 430-438 | 0-64 |
| 27. | Arteries | 440-448 | All |
| 28. | Pneumonia | 480-486 | All |
| 29. | Pneumonia | 480-486 | 0-64 |
| 30. | Bronchitis | 490-496 | All |
| 31. | Bronchitis | 490-496 | 0-64 |
| 32. | Digestive System | 520-579 | All |
| 33. | Stomach & Duodenal Ulcer | 531-533 | All |
| 34. | Liver Dis & Cirrhosis | 571 | All |
| 35. | Genitourinary | 580-629 | All |
| 36. | Musculoskeletal | 710-739 | All |
| 37. | Congenital Abnormalities | 740-759 | All |
| 38. | Symptoms | 760-779 | All |
| 39. | Road Traffic Accidents | 810-825 | All |
| 40. | Non-RTAs | 860-929 | All |
| 41. | Suicide & Undetermined | 950-959,980-989 | All |
| 42. | Avoidable - Various | See Figure 5.1 | |
| 43. | Avoidable - CVD & Hyper | See Figure 5.1 | |
| 44. | Smoking Related | See Figure 5.1 | |

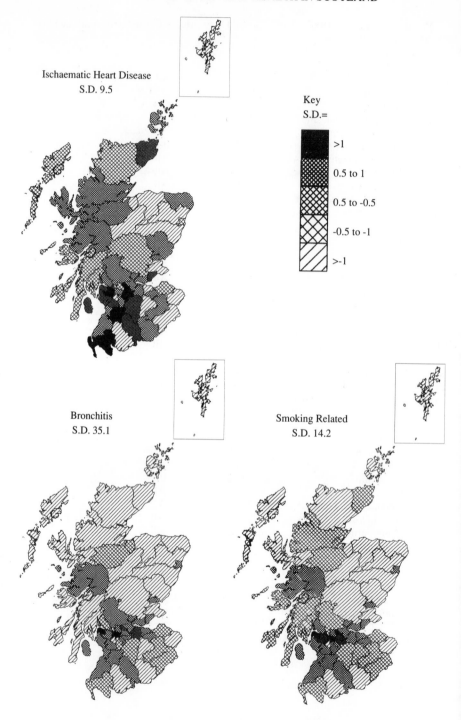

FIGURE 5.4A   SMRs FOR SELECTED CAUSES 1980 - 85
ALL AGES, FOR LOCAL GOVERNMENT DISTRICTS

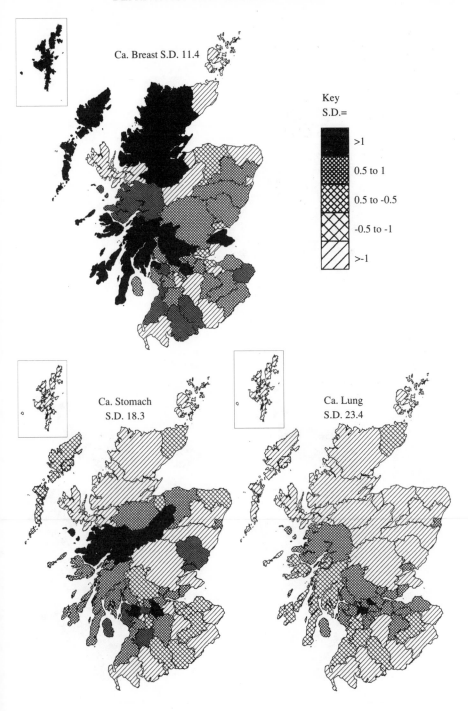

FIGURE 5.4B    SMRs FOR SELECTED CAUSES 1980 - 85
ALL AGES, FOR LOCAL GOVERNMENT DISTRICTS

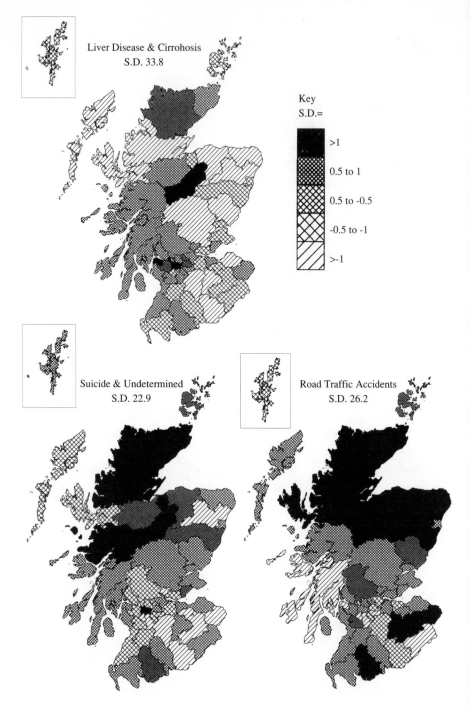

FIGURE 5.4C    SMRS FOR SELECTED CAUSES 1980 - 85
ALL AGES, FOR LOCAL GOVERNMENT DISTRICTS

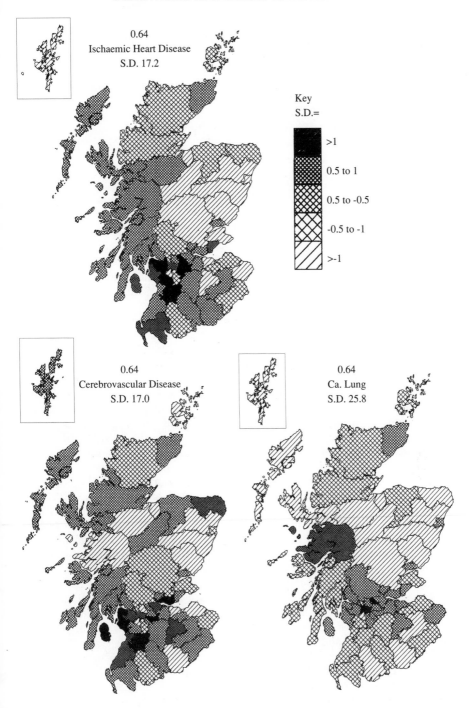

Key
S.D.=

>1
0.5 to 1
0.5 to -0.5
-0.5 to -1
>-1

0.64
Ischaemic Heart Disease
S.D. 17.2

0.64
Cerebrovascular Disease
S.D. 17.0

0.64
Ca. Lung
S.D. 25.8

FIGURE 5.4D    SMRs 0.64FOR SELECTED CAUSES 1980 - 85
FOR LOCAL GOVERNMENT DISTRICTS

CHAPTER 6

# Morbidity

This chapter deals with a number of aspects of morbidity in the population considering events related to birth, general measures of sickness from the census, cancer registrations and admissions to mental hospitals.

Morbidity measures describe the distribution of illness in the population; unlike death the occurrence of illness is not so readily discerned and problems of perception, of definition and severity affect the identification of illness in a population. Information in illness which is readily available and on a comprehensive basis for the most part comes from contact with the health service. While the General Household Survey[1] supplies information which is not dependent on this contact this is limited to a small sample of the population which does not permit any regional analysis within Scotland. Constraints of sample size also apply to data collected on the first level of contact with the health service, that is with general practitioners, which documents contacts at that level in relation to cause of consultation.[2] Morbidity statistics in general practice are collected at approximately 10-yearly intervals and in 1981 the sample included around 100 practices; data for Scotland are not separately available from this source. The increasing use of computers in general practice may well result in morbidity data becoming available at some future date but at present the opportunity to analyse data which covers the total population, and permits analysis at postcode sector level, is virtually restricted to hospital contacts, and to admissions,since no individual statistical record is created for outpatient attendances. Admission to hospital of course relates to the more serious end of the spectrum of disease and fails to encompass many aspects of both acute and chronic sickness in the population. While it is thus lacking in comprehensiveness the fact of admission to hospital confers a degree of recognition of illness which establishes the authenticity of the event in an way which is not true for contacts at other levels of service since the individual's decision to consult his general practitioner and the doctor's decisions to refer for an outpatient consultation will vary and influence contacts at these levels. The authenticity or integrity of hospital admission is not perfect however since alternative modes of treatment — by the general practitioner, or as an outpatient — will be appropriate in relation to some episodes of illness, and some patients may fail to be admitted even when this is necessary, as a consequence of long waiting lists or other resource constraints. The trend towards use of private medical facilities, in more recent years, would also detract from the completeness of the picture of morbidity in the population since these episodes are not included in the database but this factor is unlikely to have been influential in 1981. Decisions to refer, to admit or to discharge from hospital may also be based on social factors with the single and widowed for instance having both higher admission rates and longer lengths of stay than those who are married. Admission to hospital as recorded in the statistical database also has other limitations since a record is completed when a patient is transferred to another hospital, or to another speciality in the same hospital, and some patients may also experience multiple admissions to hospital for an episode of illness while others have only one, so that counts of these events in relation to population could prove misleading.

While hospital data are useful in respect of resources used (bed-days) they have therefore only limited value in respect of the levels of disease in the population.

One of the routine hospital schemes nevertheless may be restricted to the analysis of unique and complete events, namely the records relating to discharges from maternity units; although like other hospital records these capture all admissions (in respect of maternity care) they can nevertheless be reduced to information relating to individual events by considering only the delivery episode — the occasion on which a birth takes place. Other information relating to admissions prior to delivery may also be amalgamated with these events, giving some indication of needs for hospital care in the ante-natal period.

Admissions to mental hospitals also carry some of the features of morbidity; as with other hospital schemes multiple admissions occur, but first admissions (to any mental hospital) may be separately analysed.

One national scheme not confined to the fact of hospital admission is the cancer register which includes all persons identified as having the disease; although a very high proportion of these individuals will experience spells as inpatients, people treated on an outpatient basis are also registered as are those deaths attributed to the disease which were not registered earlier, due in the main to the rapid development of terminal illness in elderly patients where a decision is made to care for them at home. Cancer register data provide a very valuable set of data on morbidity differences albeit restricted to a subset of the total range of sickness in the population.

Two additional items of information on health status are in contrast very general; they cover the population of working age and come from the census question that seeks to determine the working status of the population; individuals may cite either short-term or long-term sickness as reasons for not being in a job. No information on cause of illness is available for these responses.

All of these four sources allow the examination of differences in various aspects of morbidity in the population, and we consider them separately, starting with the birth-related hospital events, and including here also the infant-related deaths, from the mortality statistics.

## Maternity Events

Maternity events are captured by the SMR (2) scheme which creates a record for all patients admitted to maternity beds in maternity units or in general hospitals. These admissions include both ante-natal and post-natal admissions as well as some abortions (mainly spontaneous) and of course the deliveries, for which stage information is recorded for both mother and infant. For the three years 1980-1982 there were 205,427 total births reported by the Registrar General of which 1096 (0.5%) were at home. Of the remaining live and still births 98.7% were recorded by the SMR (2) system as a delivery event. Some discrepancy between these two figures is to be expected since the RG's data are by year of registration and the maternity record by year of event; it is likely also that a few events fail to be recorded, and a few births that take place in private hospitals are not captured by the scheme.

Some measures examined, e.g. birthweight may be affected by whether the birth is a single or multiple event and for these analysis is restricted to singleton births, around 176000, 95% of eligible single births. As with other hospital data all records for Fife residents are excluded due to the lack of specific postcodes (see Appendix A1 for further details).

The data for the delivery events show a moderate association between birth rate and deprivation of 0.35 (table 6.1), the birth rate tending to be higher in more deprived areas. Other population characteristics indicate a variation in height of mother with shorter mothers being found in deprived and taller mothers in affluent sectors. A similar positive association is found with age with more younger mothers (under 18) in deprived areas, and more older mothers (over 35) in affluent areas. Single marital state is also positively associated with deprivation.

The deprivation score is associated also (0.49) with having three or more previous admissions ( in this pregnancy) or any previous admission (0.29) and a very small but positive association (0.15) with having a pre-delivery stay of three or more days also occurs. Mothers in deprived areas are also more likely to have had more previous pregnancies. Outcome measures available include the Apgar score and birthweight, with the coefficient of correlation with deprivation of having an Apgar score of less than or equal to five being positive but weak, at 0.18. The Apgar score is a measure of well-being in the infant based on heart rate, respiration, muscle tone, reflexes and colour, each being allocated a score from 0 (bad) to 2 (good). Scores at the lower end of the range thus indicate an infant in poorer condition compared with those with higher scores, and low scores tend to be more common in deprived sectors. Low birthweight (less than 2500 grams) produces a fairly strong association of 0.59 (singleton births only). Length of stay measures produce only a very weak association with deprivation.

Aggregated over postcode sectors the percent of low birthweight births was four percent in the most affluent areas, rising to 8.5% in the most deprived i.e. a 2-fold difference (table 6.2, fig. 6.1). These gradients do not exhibit strong variations by health board group: particularly for the first four deprivation categories (more affluent) the ratios for East and West are very similar (table 6.2) and for the last three there is no consistency, since category 6 has a higher ratio in the East, and categories 5 and 7 are higher in the West, but only slightly so for the most deprived category. The ratios are generally lower in Rural boards except for the affluent areas.

The overall ratio is clearly much higher in Western boards (108) and lowest in Rural boards (83) with the East falling in between (94), the differences between East and West being explained by the higher proportion of births in the West which occur in the more deprived areas — 62% in categories 5, 6 or 7 compared with 28% in Eastern boards. The lower overall rate in Rural areas is partly explained by the same phenomenon (eight percent in categories 5, 6 or 7) but also by the lower ratios found at equivalent levels of deprivation. There does not therefore appear to be an East/West differential in low birthweight which is not explained by deprivation (Table 6.2a).

Both biological and behavioural factors have been shown to influence low birthweight, older, taller, higher parity mothers having babies which are heavier. After adjustment for biological factors a recent report found smoking to be the most important factor in low birthweight, the effects of socio-economic and stress factors becoming non-significant after smoking was controlled for. The incidence of low birthweight increased in those who both smoked and drank although no evidence appeared for an alcohol effect in non-smokers.[3]

Our data do not allow exploration of the likely causal factors in detail but they do show that mothers in deprived areas are both shorter and younger than in affluent areas but are on the other hand likely to have higher parity (more previous pregnancies).

Information on smoking for the 22 local government districts (see table 5.6) also shows that levels of smoking are higher in deprived areas in women, so that both types of factor, biological and behavioural, are likely to make a contribution to the gradients seen (Table 6.2b).

The proportion of mothers who declared themselves single is seen to vary very considerably with a ratio of 32 in the most affluent areas and 241 in the most deprived, i.e. nearly 19% of births in DEPCAT 7. (Table 6.2b) Since the proportion of 7.7% shown as single is somewhat below the level in the birth registrations (12.5% 1980-82) some under-reporting in the maternity records must occur, which may affect the gradients seen. The proportion of illegitimate births has risen continuously since 1977, the numbers having more than doubled to 1985[4] when births to unmarried parents accounted for nearly 19% of births, and further to 1987 when such births accounted for almost a quarter of the total. Social habits are clearly changing with more mothers choosing to remain unmarried and 'illegitimacy' having very different connotations in the present than in the past, with many such babies being born into stable partnerships. The Registrar General for Scotland has shown that joint registration of these births increased, from 1974 to 1984, from 43% to 63%, with parents with the same address comprising 69% of joint registrations in 1984 (i.e. 43% of illegitimate births). Nevertheless joint registrations and those with the same address tend to be to mothers in older age groups and although joint registrations have increased in the age group under 20 in 1984 they accounted for only 52% of those births compared with 70-80% in age groups over 25.[5] Younger mothers are more common in deprived areas and it seems probable that young unsupported single mothers will also constitute a higher proportion of total births in deprived than affluent areas.

Despite the low correlation a modest gradient is seen in the total stay per delivery. This stay includes both ante-natal and post-natal admissions with all of the trend being accounted for by ante-natal stay (which takes into account both the fact of admission and the length of stay) with a two-fold difference between deprived and affluent areas. No gradient appears either for stay at the time of delivery or for post-natal admissions.

## Perinatal and Infant Mortality

The stillbirth and infant deaths are analysed over the six years 1980-1985 to give an enhanced number of events for analysis. Even so the largest count (4524 perinatal deaths) is insufficient to provide reliable data at sector level. Accordingly ratios have been calculated for deprivation categories and correlation analysis carried out at local government district level (56 districts).

Relatively low correlations with the deprivation score are found for these measures, the highest being for perinatal deaths (0.36) followed by post-neonatal deaths (0.17). The correlation between perinatal, neonatal and infant deaths is high as might be expected since the rates are not independent of one another, but both the perinatal and neonatal rates show a negative although low association with post-neonatal mortality (table 6.3), suggesting perhaps that some of these deaths may have been deferred from the earlier period.

For the standardised ratios by deprivation category the trend (table 6.4 and fig. 6.1) is such that the values are always less than 100 for categories 1, 2 and 3 (and lowest of all for the most affluent areas) and are generally (but not without exception) above 100 for categories 4 to 7, both perinatal and neonatal ratios being higher in category 5 than in the more deprived categories 6 and 7, although for post-neonatal events the gradient increases from categories 5 to 7, the ratio of 159 in the most deprived category far exceeding any of the other values.

Unlike general mortality rates therefore there is no continuing increase in infant mortality measures with deprivation although there is certainly a dichotomy, with the population in the three more affluent categories (with 40% of births) having a more favourable experience than those in the remaining (more deprived) areas.

The influences on these various events are likely to differ with birthweight having been shown to be the most powerful determinant of inter-area variations in perinatal mortality in an analysis at (English) health authority level, but with the birthweight distribution being influenced by social indices of economic disadvantage [6] as in our own findings. This study also found nevertheless that at each birthweight perinatal mortality was higher in disadvantaged than better endowed areas, an analysis we have not been able to replicate.

Neonatal mortality, in the first month of life, is mainly attributable to factors present at birth, including congenital anomalies and immaturity, with low birthweight being a feature of such deaths. Congenital anomalies still account for some post-neonatal deaths (occurring 1 to 11 months after birth) although the proportion is much reduced and the majority of deaths do not result from conditions present at birth, but are more likely to be influenced by environmental and social factors, although it should be noted that, in 1988, 52% of deaths in the year were attributed to sudden infant death syndrome for which the causes still remain obscure. The weak correlation of these deaths with deprivation (0.17) is unreliable due to the low number of events and the ratios by DEPCAT provide a more realistic picture of the influence of deprivation.

For infant deaths data are also available by social class from published sources. [7] Averaged over the same three years they exhibit a somewhat stronger differential with the rate in social class 5 being twice as high (15.5/1000) as in social class 1 (7.9) compared with 50% higher in DEPCAT 7 than in DEPCAT 1.

These rates do not suffer from the numerator/denominator problem which affects the analysis of adult deaths by social class as denominators are supplied by births in the same period, but do suffer from the problem of incomplete allocation with around 25% of deaths not being classified to a social class, and the omission of these may well have some influence on the gradients observed.

# *Temporary and Permanent Sickness*

Some limited measures of health status come from the responses made to a question on work activity in the week before the census return is completed. Among the options for response are:

- prevented by temporary sickness from seeking work, and
- permanently sick or disabled.

Although individuals may endorse more than one option most of those over working age will be classified as retired in preference to one of the two options above.

Since these responses are self-selected some element of subjective perception is likely to affect the response chosen, i.e. whether a respondent describes themselves as seeking work (unemployed) or as prevented from doing so by temporary sickness or whether a woman describes herself as a housewife rather than as permanently sick or disabled; in cases where both options are chosen she would be classified as permanently sick if of working age. It should be noted that temporary sickness does not include people who were sick in the previous week if they had a job and may well fail to include some people absent from the household due to being in hospital on census day, and it is therefore an incomplete count of acute illness. Nevertheless the broad picture of morbidity is likely to have reasonable validity and this is supported by data from the Longitudinal Study (table 6.5) which has shown mortality rates for the period 1971 to 1983 as highest in those describing themselves as permanently sick in the 1971 census (SMR M393, F502) or not in a job because of temporary sickness (SMR M323, F432). These ratios vastly exceeded those for all other economic positions, including the retired, and the unemployed for whom mortality was elevated, for men, compared with the employed.

In 1981 the proportion of population declaring themselves to be temporarily sick was lower (15.5 per 1,000) than those declaring permanent sickness (41.4 per 1,000). The gradients seen for temporary sickness are particularly steep — from 36 to 216 overall (table 6.6 and fig. 6.2) — i.e. a ratio of six between affluent and deprived areas although slightly less for women than men.

The measure of permanent sickness, which is likely to be more reliable, shows a three-fold difference overall between the most deprived and most affluent areas and again the gradient is steeper for men — in this case a ratio of 4.4. Despite the consistent increase in the ratio for each step in deprivation the correlation coefficient with DEP is low — only 0.22 for males and females combined. This result may reflect the fact that the permanently sick include persons in long-term institutional care, if they are of working age; about 22% of the permanently sick are not in private households, and this circumstance is likely to confuse the picture for some postcode sectors, those for instance with mental illness or mental handicap hospitals, and the large standard deviation (48.7) compared with that for the temporarily sick (11.6) is probably a reflection of this phenomenon. The next measure, of males plus females permanently sick in private households shows the effect of the exclusion of persons in institutions in the rate of 32.3 per 1,000 economically active population compared with 41.4 for all those classified as permanently sick. For this measure the correlation with DEP is high at 0.77, (just below the level of 0.84 found by Townsend in the Northern region) and the gradient is more extreme than for the overall measure, the ratio rising from 41 in

the most affluent to 183 in the most deprived categories (fig. 6.2). Comparable data
are not available for the Northern region since gradients are shown by health
quintiles and not by a scale for deprivation. [9] While there is some possibility of
people describing themselves as sick rather than unemployed when the prospects
of re-employment seem poor — particularly perhaps in older age groups — it is
also the case that the ratios in (male) unemployment rise from 32 in the most
affluent to 245 in the most deprived categories (table 2.2) and the concordance in
these two measures does not suggest that trade-off between these economic
activity states provides an explanation of the differentials observed.

# Cancer Registrations

Cancer registration involves the recording of all diagnoses of malignant tumours in
a population. This recording of a unique event, not dependent on hospital
admission, thus avoids the problems of interpretation inherent in hospital data,
which may record any numbers of admissions for an individual for an episode of
illness, and is not necessarily complete for any disorder unless treatment requires
admission to hospital. The cancer register thus provides one of the few routine data
sources to present a comprehensive picture of the pattern for a group of diseases in
the population although the validity of this picture depends on registration being
carried out to a high standard. The quality of recording in Scotland has not been
formally assessed but publication of the Cancer Atlas for Scotland [10] and inclusion
of Scottish data in Cancer in Five Continents [11], both published by the International
Agency for Research in Cancer of the World Health Organisation, suggests that
confidence exists in the standard of recording.

The cancer registrations examined are for the four-year period 1979-1982, with
a total of over 93 thousand events.

The age-sex specific rates for all sites combined and those with more than 5000
cases show overall rates (table 6.7) which are similar for men and women although
under age 55 the rates are higher for women, and for men in the three older age
groups. For four sites the age-specific rates tend to be higher for men, lung cancer
showing a rapid increase with age which is not apparent in women.

Other differences occur between the sexes, with lung cancer accounting for over
28% of the registrations for men (table 6.8) but for only 10% for women, in whom
breast cancer is the commonest site accounting for 19.6% followed by lung and
skin cancers each at 10% and then by cancer of the colon with 8.5% of
registrations. Skin cancers account for a similar proportion in men (11%), followed
by prostate (8%) and then by stomach, colon and bladder cancers, all just over six
percent. As well as cancers of the lung those for the stomach and bladder are
relatively more numerous in men while cancers of the colon are more numerous in
women. Cases not specified by site in this table, amounting to 21-23% of the total,
are spread in small numbers between numerous other specific and non-specific
sites including carcinoma in situ and certain benign neoplasms.

Correlation analysis was carried out over postcode sectors (PCS) for all sites
and, as with the mortality analysis by cause, using the rates and DEP scores for the
56 local government districts. For sites with relatively low numbers of events (see
table 6.10) the results over PCS must be viewed with caution.

The correlation of cancer registration rates (CRRs) with deprivation over PCS is
seen (table 6.9) to be only moderate for all sites at 0.36 for all ages and somewhat

lower at 0-64 (0.27) and 65 and over (0.30) but to be stronger at 0-64 only over LGDs. For specific sites the correlations are strongest for lung cancer (0.74 at all ages, 0.81 at 0-64) over LGDs, for cancer of the stomach (0.64), cancer of the cervix (0.49), oesophagus (0.45) and bladder (0.28). For a few sites the correlations are negative: melanoma (-0.41), skin (-0.35), breast (-0.24), uterus (-0.32) and prostate (-0.39) while for all other sites they are very low, whether positive or negative. All sites except the rectum exhibit positive or negative association with deprivation at both sector and local government district level although for many sites the number of events (table 6.10) is insufficient for reliable analysis at sector level, and the enhanced coefficients seen for districts reflect the more robust data at this level.

The relationship with deprivation will be seen also in the gradients by DEPCAT which are examined later.

The correlation between deaths for some cancer sites and deprivation are of the same order as for the registrations although somewhat stronger for all sites (both age groups), as also for cancers of the stomach and lung than is the case for registrations and with the negative association for leukaemia being more strongly observed (table 6.9). This is no doubt due to the differing composition of deaths than of registrations in terms of cause since for some sites, such as melanoma, skin, breast and cervix, case fatality will be low while for others — oesophagus, stomach, pancreas and lung — it will be high. [12] Lung cancer for instance accounts for 19% of registrations but 29% of cancer deaths while skin cancers comprise 11% of registrations and 6% of cancer deaths.

The correlations of CRRs (1979-82) with SMRs from cancer causes (1980-85) are also shown in table 6.9 and are all positive, varying from 0.37 for cancer of the breast to 0.84 for lung cancer with an overall value of 0.64 at all ages over PCS. For most specific sites the correlations are enhanced at LGD level: from 0.84 to 0.96 for cancer of the lung (all ages) and from 0.47 to 0.76 for cancer of the stomach. The coefficient is also moderately strong for most other sites shown varying from 0.51 for leukaemia to 0.76 for stomach, but being at a lower level of 0.20 for breast cancer. These coefficients will also of course reflect survival probabilities, which vary considerably, and the likelihood of death from a cause other than cancer. No correlation is shown for instance between registrations for 'other' skin cancers and deaths from this cause, since the latter number around 100 a year in comparison with around 1600 registrations.

The lower correlation observed between registrations and deaths for the age group 0-64 (over both PCS and LGDs) compared with all ages will be affected in addition by the likelihood that many of the deaths for persons registered in this age-group will occur after the age of 64. Since death may occur many years after registration the association between registration and mortality may also be influenced by the possibility of people changing their place of residence (i.e. postcode sector) between these two events.

More substantial agreement between registration and mortality rates was shown for a number of sites in an earlier analysis, 0.90 for cancer of the breast for instance [13], these correlations being calculated over 14-18 countries and for the mid-1960s. It seems possible that survival probabilities may have changed since that time which could account for some of the weaker association observed in table 6.9 but another likely explanation would relate to the area basis for analysis, most registrations and deaths being contained within the same area at country level, but probably not in all cases at sector or district level.

The gradients in the cancer registrations in the main reflect the coefficients, the variation from most affluent to most deprived categories being strongest for cancer of the lung at age 0-64 with a three-fold difference in the ratios, from 58 to 185 (table 6.10, fig. 6.3). This is followed by cancer of the cervix, with a ratio in the most deprived category two and a half times that in the most affluent (67-166). Cancers of the oesophagus, stomach and bladder also exhibit consistent gradients although with a lesser differential between affluent and deprived sectors.

The cancer type with the strongest reverse trend is melanoma with the rate in the most affluent category almost exactly three times that in the most deprived, although with no variation in the three middle categories. For other sites with negative coefficients there is no consistent decline with each step in deprivation although for cancers of the colon, breast, uterus, prostate and 'other' skin a tendency for rates to be higher in affluent and lower in deprived areas is discernible.

For the remaining causes a link with deprivation, either positive or negative, is not apparent.

Those causes for which the incidence of cancer shows a strong positive link with deprivation account for 35% of the total registrations for malignant tumours (cancers of the lung accounting for half of this group) and those which are inversely related for almost exactly the same proportion (table 6.11).

These data are substantially in agreement with those from the Longitudinal Study which calculated cancer registration rates for a number of social factors, as recorded at the 1971 census: housing tenure, car ownership, housing amenities, education and social class. The range in values between upper and lower social class groupings for the sites analysed above are shown in table 6.12.

The data are reported for social classes combined into two categories, non-manual and manual, since the number of events was low (zero in some sites for women) in individual social classes. Where these were adequate the range was usually somewhat wider across the distribution from social class 1 to 5. These results are consistent with those from our own analysis although the differentials shown above are limited by the need to combine the social classes and the range in the Scottish data is wider. Even the extended distribution for cancer of the lung in the LS for instance exhibits a much lesser differential (S.C.1,63; S.C.5,123) than the range from 69 to 183 by deprivation category in Scotland. Both approaches provide evidence of strong gradients by the two respective social factors for cancers of the stomach, lung, and bladder for men and for cancer of the cervix for women. Both data sets also show reverse gradients in cancers of the breast and the prostate. The results are similar despite that fact that the LS data are based on much smaller numbers compared with our own e.g. 1,241 registrations for lung cancer (male) compared with 13,261, and 949 for breast cancer compared with 9,377. In the LS also a higher proportion of cases could not be allocated to a social class. 10% male lung cancer, seven percent breast cancer, for married women classified to husband's occupation, and 60% when based on a woman's own occupation: these deficits compare with three percent and two percent respectively not allocated to a deprivation category.

All of the gradients in mortality from cancer are consistent with those for registrations, as seen in table 6.13. These two measures of cancer registrations and deaths show very similar patterns although for all sites for both age groups the range in SMRs slightly exceeds that for the CRRs, carrying with it the implication that there may exist deprivation-linked differentials in survival; this phenomenon is not apparent however in any of the specific sites seen in the table.

# Cancer rates in health boards and local government districts

Cancer registrations for health boards show ratios (CRRs) which are highest in Glasgow and Lothian at all ages and at 0-64 and also at 0-64 in Fife with Grampian and Tayside also having values above 100 (table 6.14).

These overall rates mask differences in the pattern by cause with Glasgow's higher overall rate being repeated in all those sites which have a strong association with deprivation and being particularly high for lung cancer, while for skin and breast cancers — with low negative association — the values are low. In Lothian on the other hand the CRRs for deprivation-linked causes are at a lower level than in Glasgow, but those for breast and skin cancer are higher.

The highest CRRs seen are for melanoma in Borders (154), skin and uterus (140, 156) in Highland, followed by cancer of the lung in Glasgow (136,139). In general the values for health boards reflect the association of the specific sites with deprivation although this link is not sustained throughout the data.

More specific data are provided by the rates for local government districts (table 6.15) which indicates that at all ages the highest ratios of 110 or more are found in the four cities, followed by Clydebank, East Mid and West Lothian, Ettrick & Lauderdale, Tweeddale, Nithsdale and Lochaber all with ratios of 104 or more. The lowest ratios — below 80 — occur in rural areas: the Islands, Skye, Sutherland and Caithness, with the Western Isles also having a significantly low value at 0-64. CRRs are low at all three age groups in Eastwood but not in the other of the two most affluent districts — Bearsden & Milngavie — for which they are all at or above 100.

At age 0-64 significantly high values are found in a number of rural areas: Angus, Ettrick and Lauderdale, Annan and Eskdale, Nithsdale, Stewartry, Wigtown, as well as in Edinburgh and Dundee cities. Low values are found in some urban areas, Inverclyde, Renfrew for instance, as well as in rural. Despite the statistical significance, these results should be evaluated in terms of the number of cases which are often low.

For cancer of the lung which has a strong correlation with deprivation high SMRs tend to occur, as would be expected, in deprived districts: Inverclyde, Clydebank and Monklands with the CRRs for Glasgow City (148 all ages, 155 0-64) exceeding others; Cumnock and Motherwell (also in the fifth quintile on deprivation) both have SMRs below 100 however.

Stomach cancer is also seen to be high in many of the more deprived districts: highest in Motherwell (134), Dundee City (133), Dunfermline (120) and Glasgow (115), and low in rural and affluent areas.

Melanomas, cancers of the skin, breast, uterus and prostate are all negatively associated with deprivation and the general picture is for districts with low deprivation to have higher ratios — Bearsden and Milngavie for instance has high CRRs for four of these sites, uterus being the exception, although Eastwood maintains its low position except for melanomas; N.E. Fife, Tweeddale & Nithsdale also exhibit a similar pattern of higher rates for these causes as does the deprived rural district of Lochaber. Districts with greater deprivation tend to show lower values, Glasgow for instance having all five CRRs below 100, although it is more common for one of the CRRs to exceed 100, with Motherwell having a CRR for breast cancer of 103, (although not statistically significant).

Cigarette smoking is known as the most overwhelming risk factor for lung cancer, and to be implicated in respect of other cancer sites, oesophagus, bladder and pancreas among others[13], all of these sites showing increases in incidence with greater deprivation. The percentage of population currently smoking in 22 local government districts in Scotland in the age group 35-64 has been shown to be highly associated with the DEP score for these LGDs both for men and women and with deaths from smoking-related diseases and from lung cancer (see chapter 5). It also correlates moderately strongly with the lung cancer registration rate all ages at 0.68 for males and 0.67 for females. Smoking behaviour may thus act as a causal factor in many of the gradients seen. Of the other sites which show strong gradients with deprivation the main aetiological factors which may be influential in stomach cancer have not been elucidated as yet, with studies focusing on nutritional aspects, and more recently, on a possible bacterial cause[16] while cervical cancer is associated in the main with sexual activity being highest among prostitutes and not occurring in nuns, and with smoking probably also making a contribution.

# Mental Hospital Admissions

Data for mental illness and mental handicap hospitals are restricted to admissions. While it would have been desirable also to examine the differentials for patients actually residing in hospital at a particular point in time this did not prove feasible; although data are available on residents, accurate information on previous residence at postcode sector level is not available for a high proportion of patients who were admitted before the postcoding system came into operation. The data for admissions to mental illness hospitals relates to 95% of admissions in the years 1980 to 1982 excluding Fife residents; as with other hospital analyses Fife residents are nor included due to the lack of specific postcodes.

Admissions to mental handicap hospitals numbered almost 6000 over the three years but among these over 50% were holiday admissions and only 673 were first admissions. The correlations with deprivation are low and there are no consistent gradients. These data are also of very limited value in relation to demand for hospital care since the pattern for individuals who are resident outwith hospital and being admitted for brief spells of holiday relief is likely to differ considerably from those who are resident in hospital. These data are not therefore examined further.

The data for mental illness admissions, which covers the years 1980 to 1982, comprises around 68,000 total admissions and 26,000 first admissions. Admission rates by age and sex for both categories (table 6.16) show these as higher for the elderly, and next highest at 35-44, with first admission rates tending to be similar for both sexes under age 65, but higher for women in the elderly; and all admissions being higher in women over the age of 55.

Over the postcode sectors the correlations of all illness admissions with deprivation are only modest, being highest for the age-group 0-64 at 0.53 (table 6.17) and these coefficients do not increase when computed over local government districts. Analysis at this level provides the opportunity nevertheless to examine some of the more common causes of admission and also to show the slightly stronger association with DEP for first admissions than for all admissions, 0.47 compared with 0.42 at all ages. For specific causes the strongest association is seen for schizophrenia (0-64) followed by alcoholism (0-64) and for both of these causes the coefficients for first admissions slightly exceeded those for all admissions. For other psychoses and depressions the coefficients are weaker and for senile conditions no association is seen.

The gradients over deprivation categories (table 6.18) show that the ratios for all causes of admission in general increase from DEPCAT 1 to 7, although the pattern is not consistent for categories 2 and 3, which are influenced by a reversal in the trend at age 65 and over, and with little difference seen between these two categories at 0-64. As with other health measures the gradients are steeper at 0-64 than at 65 and over being nearly three times higher in the younger age group in DEPCAT 7 than in DEPCAT 1 compared with only 40% greater for the age group 65 and over. The gradients are also much steeper for males than for females ranging from 48 to 199 (i.e. x 4) for all admissions at 0-64 compared with from 76 to 165 (x2.2) for women. For first admissions (i.e. patients with no previous admission to any mental hospital) which comprise 39% of the total, the gradients vary very little from those for all admissions.

In relation to cause of admission the strongest gradients seen are for alcoholic causes (fig. 6.5) being steeper for men than women, rising from around 40 to 240, with no marked variation as between all and first admissions. They are nevertheless steep for women, being three times higher in the most deprived than in the most affluent sectors. Both the incidence of alcoholism and choices for treatment may affect these gradients. Alcoholic causes account for 17% of first and seven percent of all admissions

The gradient is also fairly strong for admissions for schizophrenia, which accounted for 11.5% of all admissions but only 4.7% of first admissions, nearly all falling into the age group under 65. For this cause the gradients for first admissions are less marked (75 to 145 at 0-64) than for all admissions (55 to 175) implying a difference in readmission as between more affluent and more deprived areas.

For the other psychoses there are no consistent trends in the admission rates although these tend to be lower in more affluent and higher in more deprived areas. Admissions for depression show a greater differentiation, ranging from 63 to 175 at 0-64, with the gradient being slightly weaker for first admissions (75 to 148), but with little variation in the middle categories for either all or first admissions.

The remaining diagnostic category — senile conditions — shows no distinct pattern although there is a tendency for rates to be slightly higher in more deprived categories.

These data then exhibit the characteristics seen in other measures of hospital use, with steeper gradients for the younger age group and with many, but not all, causes, displaying higher admission rates in more deprived areas. Neither all admissions nor first admissions are of great value in identifying differences in the incidence of disease within the population, since treatment for mental illness is not confined to hospital and inpatient care; various options for treatment exist both within and outside the health service and may be differentially used, with one estimate suggesting that only one in eight or so of those with significant morbidity is referred to the psychiatric service. [17]

The probability is however that the schizophrenia will result in inpatient treatment within the NHS and the gradient seen for the first admissions, with a two-fold difference between affluent and deprived categories, is likely to reflect the pattern of disease. Schizophrenics have been found to be downwardly mobile in terms of social class compared with their fathers but not individuals with other mental illnesses of anxiety, depression, psychopathy and organic psychoses. [18]

Thus the pattern by deprivation for this cause, as also for alcoholism, may well be affected by the phenomenon of social drift, some individuals with mental problems and lack of family support tending to gravitate to inner city deprived areas where social support and lodging house accommodation tend to be located.

In chapter 1 it was noted that Jarman UPA scores had been used in England and Wales in analysis of hospital admission and discharge rates. UPA scores are also featured in a report by the Royal College of Psychiatrists[19] which gives information from three separate small-scale exercises, all of which showed positive correlations with the UPA scores, ranging from 0.41 for discharges from 20 hospitals and 0.80 for 0.64 admissions for 15 districts of the North West Thames Region. These coefficients tend to be somewhat higher than those reported here for Scotland which is not surprising since they relate to a different patient demand, i.e. acute adult discharges staying less than one year in hospital. With fewer beds to population available in England and Wales compared with Scotland admission policies are likely to differ considerably, but these findings serve to confirm the general relationship with a measure of deprivation although none of the studies reported on specific causes of admission.

## Conclusion

The measures of morbidity reported in this chapter provide overwhelming evidence of differences in the illness experience of the population according to the socio-economic characteristics of the area in which they live. Data on infant morbidity and cancer provide particularly strong and objective evidence. Those for mental illness hospitals may be influenced by factors other than true morbidity (e.g. decisions to seek treatment, choice of treatment and admission policies). While it seems unlikely that the major differences seen between affluent and deprived areas could be explained by these factors clearly the gradients seen for this measure cannot be attributed solely to morbidity differences. Despite the subjective nature of the measures of temporary and permanent sickness these are not confused by issues about the availability of health facilities or choice of treatment and the eventual greater mortality in these two groups provides some confidence in the validity of the two measures. The results from this examination of morbidity provide reasonable support for the hypothesis that differential sickness experience will underlie much of the variation seen in mortality,a conclusion supported particularly by the cancer data which exhibit very similar gradients for registrations and deaths and very high correlations between the two measures for those sites in which case-fatality is high.

TABLE 6.1 CORRELATION OF DELIVERY EVENTS WITH DEPRIVATION SCORE

|  | r with DEP | Rate |
|---|---|---|
| Birth rate/1000 F15-44 (annual average) | 0.35 | 64.7 |
|  |  | Percent in population |
| Height of mother <155 cm | 0.47 | 16.9 |
| >160 cm | -0.68 | 52.0 |
| Age of mother <18 years | 0.77 | 2.9 |
| <19 years | 0.81 | 6.0 |
| >35 years | -0.31 | 5.7 |
| Marital state single | 0.68 | 7.7 |
| Had previous admission (ante-natal) | 0.29 | 23.7 |
| Had 3+ previous admissions | 0.49 | 2.0 |
| Pre-delivery stay 3+ days (singleton births) | 0.15 | 13.8 |
| 3+ previous pregnancies | 0.46 | 13.2 |
| Apgar Score <5 (singleton births) | 0.18 | 2.4 |
| Birthweight <2500g. (singleton births) | 0.59 | 6.4 |
|  |  | Days |
| Mean stay (delivery event) | 0.15 | 7.0 |
| Mean total stay per delivery | 0.15 | 9.6 |
| Ante-natal stay per delivery | 0.30 | 1.7 |

TABLE 6.2A GRADIENTS IN LOW BIRTH WEIGHT* BY DEPRIVATION CATEGORY AND HEALTH BOARD GROUP

|  | DEPCAT Affluent | | | | | Deprived | | All | r with DEP | No. of sectors |
|---|---|---|---|---|---|---|---|---|---|---|
|  | 1 | 2 | 3 | 4 | 5 | 6 | 7 |  |  |  |
| Scotland | 67 | 77 | 82 | 100 | 110 | 125 | 141 | 100 =6.3% | 0.59 | 957 |
| West | 66 | 78 | 84 | 99 | 115 | 125 | 142 | 108 | 0.63 | 420 |
| East | 67 | 75 | 85 | 102 | 102 | 133 | 138 | 94 | 0.53 | 352 |
| Rural | 81 | | 75 | 95 | 93 | | - | 83 | 0.23 | 185 |

*singleton births <2500 gms. excl. Fife

TABLE 6.2B   GRADIENTS IN SINGLE MARITAL STATE AND LENGTH OF STAY

| | DEPCAT | | | | | | | All= |
| | Affluent | | | | | Deprived | | |
| | 1 | 2 | 3 | 4 | 5 | 6 | 7 | 100% |
|---|---|---|---|---|---|---|---|---|
| Single m.s. | 32 | 48 | 61 | 88 | 112 | 152 | 241 | 7.7% |
| Total stay per delivery | 91 | 93 | 99 | 99 | 103 | 104 | 111 | 9.6 days |
| Ante-natal stay per delivery | 70 | 75 | 87 | 96 | 114 | 119 | 145 | 1.7 days |

TABLE 6.3   CORRELATION MATRIX FOR PERINATAL AND INFANT DEATHS

| | Perinatal | Infant | Neo-natal |
|---|---|---|---|
| Perinatal | | | |
| Infant | 0.64 | | |
| Neonatal | 0.75 | 0.83 | |
| Postneonatal | -0.04 | 0.46 | -0.10 |

TABLE 6.4   PERINATAL AND INFANT DEATHS: RATIOS BY DEPRIVATION CATEGORY

| | DEPCAT | | | | | | | All* | | r |
| | Affluent | | | | | Deprived | | = | | with |
| | 1 | 2 | 3 | 4 | 5 | 6 | 7 | 100 | n= | DEP |
|---|---|---|---|---|---|---|---|---|---|---|
| Perinatal | 73 | 92 | 92 | 105 | 112 | 105 | 110 | 11.3 | 4524 | 0.36 |
| Infant | 82 | 91 | 92 | 103 | 106 | 104 | 122 | 10.7 | 4261 | 0.16 |
| Neonatal | 81 | 91 | 93 | 106 | 112 | 106 | 98 | 6.6 | 2625 | 0.07 |
| Post-neonatal | [85] | 91 | 90 | 98 | 96 | 102 | 159 | 4.1 | 1636 | 0.17 |

[<100 events]
*per 1000 total or live births

TABLE 6.5   MORTALITY 1971-1983 BY ECONOMIC ACTIVITY AT 1971 CENSUS

| | SMR all causes | |
| Economic position | M 15-64 | F 15-59 |
|---|---|---|
| employed | 86 | 81 |
| temporarily sick | 323 | 432 |
| unemployed | 130 | 80 |
| retired | 153 | 141 |
| permanently sick or disabled | 393 | 502 |
| students/others | 95 | 114 |

Source:   ref 8

TABLE 6.6   TEMPORARILY AND PERMANENTLY SICK BY DEPRIVATION CATEGORY

| | Affluent | | | | | Deprived | | All*<br>=100 | S.D. | r#<br>with<br>DEP |
|---|---|---|---|---|---|---|---|---|---|---|
| | 1 | 2 | 3 | 4 | 5 | 6 | 7 | | | |
| Temporarily sick | | | | | | | | | | |
| M & F | 36 | 46 | 63 | 93 | 126 | 184 | 216 | 15.5 | 11.6 | 0.72 |
| Male | 31 | 44 | 62 | 95 | 126 | 184 | 224 | 16.7 | 12.6 | 0.74 |
| Female | 46 | 50 | 63 | 90 | 128 | 185 | 202 | 13.6 | 11.2 | 0.62 |
| Permanently sick | | | | | | | | | | |
| M & F | 51 | 73 | 84 | 95 | 113 | 134 | 148 | 41.4 | 48.7 | 0.22 |
| Male | 38 | 64 | 79 | 94 | 117 | 145 | 167 | 39.9 | 47.5 | 0.28 |
| Female | 68 | 85 | 90 | 95 | 106 | 118 | 122 | 43.8 | 55.5 | 0.11 |
| Permanently sick | | | | | | | | | | |
| M & F<br>in private<br>h'holds | 41 | 64 | 77 | 97 | 121 | 151 | 182 | 32.3 | 15.4 | 0.77@ |

#over 1,010 sectors
*rate per 1,000 economically active population, age/sex standardised except permanently sick in private households
@value differs from table 7.10 due to no. of sectors

TABLE 6.7   CANCER REGISTRATION RATES 1979-82
PER 100,000 POPULATION, MAJOR SITES

| All Sites | M | F | Stomach | M | F |
|---|---|---|---|---|---|
| 0 - 34 | 21 | 43 | 0 - 34 | - | - |
| 35 - 44 | 91 | 223 | 35 - 44 | 4 | 2 |
| 45 - 54 | 287 | 408 | 45 - 54 | 20 | 7 |
| 55 - 64 | 904 | 767 | 55 - 64 | 60 | 23 |
| 65 - 74 | 2079 | 1227 | 65 - 74 | 137 | 61 |
| 75 + | 4527 | 2286 | 75 + | 293 | 168 |
| All ages | 468 | 458 | All ages | 30 | 21 |
| n = 93199 | | | n = 5134 | | |

| Colon & Rectum | M | F | Lung | M | F |
|---|---|---|---|---|---|
| 0 - 34 | 1 | 1 | 0 - 34 | - | - |
| 35 - 44 | 6 | 9 | 35 - 44 | 10 | 5 |
| 45 - 54 | 29 | 27 | 45 - 54 | 71 | 33 |
| 55 - 64 | 89 | 75 | 55 - 64 | 199 | 111 |
| 65 - 74 | 216 | 159 | 65 - 74 | 669 | 175 |
| 75 + | 536 | 388 | 75 + | 1177 | 183 |
| All ages | 49 | 55 | All ages | 133 | 47 |
| n = 10533 | | | n = 17824 | | |

TABLE 6.7  CANCER REGISTRATION RATES 1979-82
PER 100,000 POPULATION, MAJOR SITES  CONTD.

| Skin | M | F | Breast | M | F |
|------|---|---|--------|---|---|
| 0 - 34 | 1 | 1 | 0 - 34 | - | 1 |
| 35 - 44 | 12 | 11 | 35 - 44 | - | 67 |
| 45 - 54 | 37 | 30 | 45 - 54 | - | 150 |
| 55 - 64 | 99 | 61 | 55 - 64 | - | 182 |
| 65 - 74 | 226 | 128 | 65 - 74 | - | 215 |
| 75 + | 512 | 310 | 75 + | - | 325 |
| All ages | 62 | 46 | All ages | - | 90 |
| n = 9861 | | | n = 9377 | | |

TABLE 6.8  CANCER REGISTRATIONS BY SITE BY SEX 1979-1982

| | Male % | Female % |
|---|---|---|
| Oesophagus | 2.5 | 2.0 |
| Stomach | 6.3 | 4.6 |
| Colon | 6.4 | 8.5 |
| Rectum | 4.0 | 3.6 |
| Pancreas | 2.6 | 2.8 |
| Trachea, bronchus & lung | 28.4 | 10.1 |
| Melanoma | 0.8 | 1.4 |
| Skin | 11.1 | 10.1 |
| Breast | - | 19.6 |
| Cervix | - | 3.4 |
| Uterus | - | 2.5 |
| Ovary | - | 3.8 |
| Prostate | 8.0 | - |
| Bladder | 6.4 | 2.8 |
| Leukaemia | 2.0 | 1.6 |
| Other* | 21.5 | 23.2 |
| TOTAL* = 100% | = 46,714 | = 49,218 |

*includes benign neoplasms (n=3670)

TABLE 6.9   CANCER REGISTRATIONS 1979-82 AND CANCER DEATHS 198-85

| | Correlations with DEP | | | | Correlation of registrations with deaths | |
| | Registrations | | Deaths | | | |
| | (a) | (b) | (a) | (b) | (a) | (b) |
|---|---|---|---|---|---|---|
| All sites (d) | 0.36 | 0.33 | 0.61 | 0.82 | 0.64 | 0.58 |
| 0-64 | 0.27 | 0.37 | 0.54 | 0.86 | 0.49 | 0.44 |
| 65+ | 0.30 | 0.28 | 0.47 | | | |
| Oesophagus | 0.21 | 0.45 | 0.13 | 0.25 | 0.25 | 0.53 |
| Stomach | 0.33 | 0.64 | 0.39 | 0.72 | 0.47 | 0.76 |
| Colon | -0.07 | -0.16 | | | | 0.54(c) |
| Rectum | 0.02 | -0.02 | | | | 0.46(c) |
| Colon & rectum | -0.03 | | 0.01 | 0.03 | 0.38 | |
| Pancreas | 0.05 | 0.02 | 0.07 | 0.17 | | 0.61 |
| Lung | 0.66 | 0.74 | 0.70 | 0.81 | 0.84 | 0.96 |
| 0-64 | 0.60 | 0.81 | 0.65 | 0.87 | | 0.94 |
| Melanoma | -0.21 | -0.41 | | | | |
| Skin | -0.14 | -0.35 | | | | |
| Breast | -0.16 | -0.24 | -0.06 | 0.02 | 0.37 | 0.20 |
| Cervix | 0.29 | 0.49 | 0.25 | 0.32 | | 0.57 |
| Uterus | -0.09 | -0.32 | | | | |
| Ovary | -0.04 | -0.13 | | | | |
| Prostate | -0.09 | -0.39 | | | | |
| Bladder | 0.08 | 0.28 | | | | |
| Leukaemia | -0.02 | -0.06 | -0.10 | -0.23 | 0.51 | |

(a) over 1,010 PCS
(b) over 56 LGDs
(c) with deaths from colon and rectum
(d) malignant only

TABLE 6.10   CANCER REGISTRATIONS: GRADIENTS BY DEPCAT

| | DEPCAT | | | | | | | |
| | Affluent | | | | | Deprived | | N = |
| | 1 | 2 | 3 | 4 | 5 | 6 | 7 | |
|---|---|---|---|---|---|---|---|---|
| All sites* | 95 | 96 | 94 | 100 | 101 | 107 | 122 | 89505 |
| 0-64 | 95 | 96 | 95 | 99 | 101 | 107 | 117 | 35042 |
| 65+ | 94 | 96 | 94 | 101 | 101 | 106 | 126 | 54103 |
| Oesophagus | (78) | 86 | 101 | 92 | 104 | 118 | 148 | 2116 |
| Stomach | 79 | 80 | 86 | 103 | 109 | 128 | 138 | 5134 |
| Colon | 104 | 106 | 99 | 99 | 98 | 97 | 96 | 6957 |
| Rectum | 100 | 98 | 102 | 98 | 98 | 100 | 109 | 3576 |
| Pancreas | 104 | 93 | 96 | 101 | 99 | 112 | 107 | 2530 |
| Lung | 69 | 77 | 80 | 100 | 110 | 128 | 183 | 17824 |
| Lung 0-64 | 58 | 68 | 77 | 101 | 112 | 135 | 185 | 6871 |
| Melanoma | (164) | 115 | 101 | 101 | 101 | (65) | [54] | 1003 |
| Skin | 108 | 111 | 103 | 101 | 89 | 90 | 98 | 9861 |
| Breast | 114 | 109 | 99 | 100 | 96 | 95 | 89 | 9377 |
| Cervix | (67) | 72 | 91 | 94 | 120 | 124 | 166 | 1634 |

TABLE 6.10    CANCER REGISTRATIONS: GRADIENTS BY DEPCAT CONTD.

|          | DEPCAT |    |    |    |    |    |    | N = |
|          | Affluent | | | | | Deprived | | |
|          | 1 | 2 | 3 | 4 | 5 | 6 | 7 | |
|----------|------|-----|-----|-----|-----|-----|------|------|
| Uterus   | (92) | 112 | 104 | 108 | 91  | 83  | (79) | 1189 |
| Ovary    | 94   | 105 | 99  | 105 | 95  | 95  | (93) | 1817 |
| Prostate | 115  | 106 | 99  | 103 | 96  | 90  | 92   | 3593 |
| Bladder  | 92   | 93  | 95  | 100 | 105 | 106 | 120  | 4177 |
| Leukaemia| 107  | 107 | 96  | 102 | 89  | 104 | (100)| 1608 |

*malignant neoplasms, For ICD codes see table ...

(   ) less than 100 cases
[   ] less than 50 cases

TABLE 6.11    RATIO FOR CRRS IN MOST AFFLUENT AND MOST DEPRIVED CATEGORIES

|          |       | Most affluent | Most deprived | ratio | % of total* |
|----------|-------|---------------|---------------|-------|-------------|
| (a) positive association | | | | | |
| lung     | 0-64  | 58  | 185 | 3.2 | 7.7  |
|          | all   | 69  | 183 | 2.7 | 19.9 |
| cervix   |       | 67  | 166 | 2.5 | 1.8  |
| oesophagus |     | 78  | 148 | 1.9 | 2.4  |
| stomach  |       | 79  | 138 | 1.7 | 5.7  |
| bladder  |       | 92  | 120 | 1.3 | 4.7  |
| (b) negative association | | | | | |
| melanoma |       | 164 | 54  | 0.3 | 1.1  |
| breast   |       | 114 | 89  | 0.8 | 10.5 |
| prostate |       | 115 | 92  | 0.8 | 4.0  |
| other skin |     | 108 | 98  | 0.9 | 11.0 |
| colon    |       | 104 | 96  | 0.9 | 7.8  |
| uterus   |       | 92  | 79  | 0.9 | 1.3  |

*all malignant neoplasms

TABLE 6.12 RANGE IN STANDARDISED CANCER REGISTRATION RATIOS: HIGH TO LOW
SOCIAL CLASS + (LONGITUDINAL STUDY)

|           | M      | F*      | F[#]    |
|-----------|--------|---------|---------|
| all sites | 85-114 | 50-96   | 91-99   |
| stomach   | 78-110 | 69-138  | 66-125  |
| colon     | 114-91 | 95-97   | 98-103  |
| rectum    | 84-102 | 109-97  | 103-96  |
| pancreas  | 92-96  | 102-62  | 91-104  |
| lung      | 80-110 | 101-111 | 86-105  |

TABLE 6.12 CONTD

|  | M | F* | F# |
|---|---|---|---|
| other skin | 107- 98 | 90- 96 | 106- 87 |
| breast | | 109-98 | 110-99 |
| cervix | | 67-131 | 51-114 |
| uterus | | 95-99 | 118-87 |
| ovary | | 90-92 | 114-97 |
| prostate | 108-94 | | |
| bladder | 82-105 | | |

source:    ref.14
*own occupation        #husband's occupation

TABLE 6.13    RANGE IN STANDARDISED RATIOS FOR CANCER FROM
DEPCAT 1-7 FOR REGISTRATIONS AND DEATHS

|  | CRRs | SMRs |
|---|---|---|
| all sites | 95-122 | 84-129 |
| 0-64 | 95-117 | 78-129 |
| oesophagus | 78-148 | 82-129 |
| stomach | 79-138 | 74-134 |
| colon | 104-96 | |
| rectum | l00-109 | |
| colon & rectum | 108-105 | 93-102 |
| pancreas | 104-107 | 96-108 |
| lung | 69-183 | 67-176 |
| 0-64 | 58-185 | 58-179 |
| breast | 114-89 | 98-87 |
| cervix | 67-166 | 44-163 |

TABLE 6.14A   1979-1982 CAUSE CRRs FOR HEALTH BOARDS

| | * | 1 | 2 | 3 | 4 | 5 | 6 | 7 | 8 | 9 | 10 | 11 | 12 | 13 | 14 | 15 | 16 | 17 | 18 | 19 | 20 | 21 |
|---|---|---|---|---|---|---|---|---|---|---|---|---|---|---|---|---|---|---|---|---|---|---|
| Ayrshire & Arran | | 89* | 81* | 89* | 91* | 88* | 91 | 101 | 96 | 96 | 102 | 81* | 76* | 110 | 66* | 93 | 98 | 102 | 95 | 94 | 99 | 99 |
| Argyll & Clyde | | 91* | 49* | 92* | 90* | 94* | 108 | 102 | 88* | 85* | 113 | 99 | 92 | 81 | 75* | 95 | 100 | 78* | 99 | 84* | 95 | 96 |
| Greater Glasgow | | 107* | 99 | 108* | 106* | 180* | 111* | 110* | 103 | 105 | 99 | 136* | 139* | 87 | 87* | 99 | 107 | 81* | 92 | 89* | 109* | 104 |
| Lanarkshire | | 91* | 58* | 92* | 94* | 90* | 105 | 114* | 89* | 91 | 82* | 95* | 102 | 99 | 78* | 95 | 100 | 70* | 98 | 81* | 96 | 88 |
| Fife | | 103* | 108 | 102 | 106* | 100 | 80* | 96 | 91 | 98 | 96 | 93* | 97 | 100 | 127* | 98 | 118 | 131* | 117 | 114* | 120* | 101 |
| Forth Valley | | 93* | 124* | 92* | 93* | 91* | 97 | 95 | 91 | 95 | 89 | 96 | 94 | 84 | 56* | 103 | 89 | 81 | 103 | 122* | 115* | 112 |
| Grampian | | 102 | 82* | 103* | 99 | 106* | 89 | 89* | 119* | 122* | 96 | 85* | 83* | 98 | 125* | 95 | 80* | 119* | 117* | 111* | 102 | 113 |
| Lothian | | 109* | 113* | 109* | 108* | 110* | 96 | 100 | 99 | 98 | 116* | 109* | 101 | 112 | 118* | 115* | 95 | 119* | 105 | 118* | 107 | 101 |
| Tayside | | 105* | 163* | 102 | 101 | 103* | 117* | 109 | 104 | 102 | 113 | 88* | 86* | 106 | 126* | 97 | 119* | 101 | 89 | 109 | 90 | 85 |
| Borders | | 97 | 115 | 97 | 99 | 95 | 95 | 84 | 98 | 116 | 98 | 82* | 75* | 154* | 126* | 102 | 91 | 113 | 107 | 91 | 71* | 87 |
| Dumfries & Galloway | | 101 | 253* | 95* | 97 | 94* | 99 | 82* | 106 | 101 | 97 | 77* | 85* | 115 | 118* | 103 | 112 | 116 | 102 | 103 | 75* | 96 |
| Highland | | 93* | 88 | 93* | 101 | 88* | 97 | 72* | 120* | 90 | 76* | 61* | 64* | 121 | 140* | 106 | 74 | 156* | 98 | 87 | 73* | 118 |
| The Islands | | 75* | 46* | 76* | 86* | 71* | 55* | 66* | 90 | 86 | 65* | 42* | 58* | 103 | 94 | 92 | 94 | 124 | 62 | 79 | 58* | 81 |

* see Fig 6.4, p 172 for key to causes.

TABLE 6.14B 1979 - 1982 CRRs No. Cases for Health Boards

| | 1 | 2 | 3 | 4 | 5 | 6 | 7 | 8 | 9 | 10 | 11 | 12 | 13 | 14 | 15 | 16 | 17 | 18 | 19 | 20 | 21 |
|---|---|---|---|---|---|---|---|---|---|---|---|---|---|---|---|---|---|---|---|---|---|
| Ayrshire & Arran | 6,055 | 221 | 5,834 | 2,338 | 3,496 | 141 | 378 | 485 | 250 | 188 | 1,066 | 384 | 81 | 474 | 641 | 119 | 89 | 127 | 246 | 302 | 117 |
| Argyll & Clyde | 7078 | 154 | 6,924 | 2,746 | 4,177 | 190 | 433 | 509 | 253 | 239 | 1,464 | 544 | 69 | 620 | 762 | 141 | 79 | 154 | 243 | 330 | 130 |
| Greater Glasgow | 20,052 | 708 | 19,344 | 7,475 | 11,865 | 473 | 1,131 | 1,451 | 761 | 506 | 4847 | 1,922 | 173 | 1,720 | 1,891 | 348 | 199 | 344 | 622 | 908 | 331 |
| Lanarkshire | 7,950 | 227 | 7,723 | 3,559 | 4,164 | 203 | 529 | 560 | 299 | 186 | 1,574 | 737 | 100 | 712 | 871 | 169 | 80 | 175 | 255 | 369 | 136 |
| Fife | 6,218 | 257 | 5,961 | 2,346 | 3,613 | 110 | 322 | 412 | 228 | 159 | 1,091 | 420 | 64 | 813 | 587 | 123 | 99 | 136 | 275 | 330 | 106 |
| Forth Valley | 4,382 | 239 | 4,143 | 1,704 | 2,439 | 103 | 244 | 313 | 170 | 112 | 876 | 336 | 43 | 277 | 483 | 75 | 48 | 94 | 224 | 244 | 91 |
| Grampian | 8,825 | 279 | 8,546 | 3,040 | 5,495 | 175 | 424 | 772 | 1,405 | 226 | 1405 | 495 | 90 | 1,148 | 803 | 118 | 127 | 191 | 388 | 395 | 170 |
| Lothian | 14,776 | 612 | 14,164 | 5,361 | 8,800 | 298 | 746 | 1,015 | 512 | 430 | 2783 | 981 | 162 | 1,690 | 1,573 | 227 | 207 | 279 | 606 | 643 | 236 |
| Tayside | 8,140 | 470 | 7,670 | 2,721 | 4,948 | 210 | 476 | 619 | 310 | 245 | 1310 | 459 | 85 | 1,051 | 752 | 155 | 100 | 134 | 336 | 316 | 113 |
| Borders | 2,103 | 87 | 2,016 | 685 | 1,331 | 48 | 103 | 164 | 99 | 60 | 342 | 103 | 33 | 295 | 212 | 31 | 30 | 43 | 82 | 71 | 32 |
| Dumfries & Galloway | 2,893 | 265 | 2628 | 996 | 1,632 | 65 | 131 | 227 | 112 | 76 | 430 | 172 | 34 | 360 | 286 | 53 | 41 | 55 | 122 | 99 | 47 |
| Highland | 3,199 | 119 | 3,080 | 254 | 1,825 | 76 | 138 | 308 | 119 | 71 | 402 | 153 | 44 | 511 | 350 | 43 | 65 | 63 | 123 | 114 | 71 |
| The Islands | 1,097 | 24 | 1,073 | 395 | 678 | 19 | 55 | 101 | 50 | 27 | 121 | 52 | 15 | 149 | 123 | 21 | 21 | 16 | 52 | 40 | 21 |

TABLE 6.15A  1979-1982 CAUSE CRRs FOR LOCAL GOVERNMENT DISTRICTS

| | 1 | 2 | 3 | 4 | 5 | 6 | 7 | 8 | 9 | 10 | 11 | 12 | 13 | 14 | 15 | 16 | 17 | 18 | 19 | 20 | 21 |
|---|---|---|---|---|---|---|---|---|---|---|---|---|---|---|---|---|---|---|---|---|---|
| Argyll & Bute | 89* | 89 | 89* | 94 | 87* | 91 | 81 | 84 | 91 | 88 | 74* | 72* | 96 | 82* | 108 | 125 | 77 | 110 | 90 | 69* | 107 |
| Dumbarton | 91* | 50* | 93* | 91* | 94 | 125 | 88 | 68* | 74 | 90 | 104 | 94 | 84 | 82* | 95 | 118 | 78 | 129 | 85 | 94 | 97 |
| Inverclyde | 101 | 39* | 103 | 102 | 104 | 120 | 117 | 97 | 86 | 137* | 107 | 98 | 120 | 85* | 121* | 108 | 73 | 77 | 97 | 116 | 125 |
| Renfrew | 86* | 39* | 88* | 84* | 91* | 101 | 107 | 92 | 86 | 121* | 103 | 95 | 55* | 65* | 77* | 81 | 80 | 95 | 73* | 95 | 76 |
| Cumnock & Doon Valley | 84* | 90 | 84* | 88* | 81* | 92 | 110 | 74 | 92 | 79 | 67* | 61* | 35 | 55* | 88 | 159* | 144 | 67 | 76 | 100 | 136 |
| Cunninghame | 91* | 86 | 91* | 97 | 87* | 110 | 100 | 96 | 107 | 76 | 90* | 95 | 129 | 62* | 87 | 97 | 124 | 111 | 91 | 90 | 107 |
| Kilmarnock & Loudoun | 88* | 66* | 89* | 84* | 92* | 89 | 119 | 108 | 92 | 141* | 80* | 72* | 114 | 47* | 103 | 84 | 72 | 87 | 109 | 99 | 76 |
| Kyle & Carrick | 89* | 83 | 89* | 89* | 89* | 73 | 87 | 95 | 88 | 110 | 78* | 66* | 114 | 86* | 94 | 88 | 93 | 93 | 92 | 107 | 94 |
| Bears. & Milngavie | 100 | 109 | 100 | 101 | 99 | 27 | 72 | 113 | 126 | 73 | 82 | 65* | 183* | 113 | 134* | 16 | 56 | 123 | 131 | 68 | 120 |
| Clydebank | 104 | 69 | 106 | 103 | 108 | 82 | 99 | 124* | 109 | 103 | 111 | 109 | 109 | 88 | 110 | 113 | 107 | 92 | 107 | 99 | 102 |
| Eastwood | 82* | 37* | 84* | 78* | 88* | 109 | 84 | 103 | 96 | 98 | 73* | 59* | 113 | 44* | 99 | 57 | 56 | 57 | 88 | 83 | 65 |
| Glasgow City | 110* | 106 | 110* | 110* | 111* | 118* | 115* | 101 | 106 | 98 | 148* | 155* | 79* | 87* | 96 | 119* | 80* | 95 | 86* | 112* | 104 |
| Strathkelvin | 97 | 97 | 97 | 95 | 98 | 91 | 87 | 102 | 90 | 121 | 89 | 87 | 86 | 97 | 104 | 63 | 98 | 70 | 94 | 115 | 124 |
| Cumbernauld & Kilsyth | 95 | 78 | 96 | 91 | 101 | 79 | 101 | 97 | 108 | 90 | 111 | 118 | 53 | 80 | 78 | 73 | 63 | 84 | 99 | 137* | 80 |
| East Kilbride | 90* | 71* | 91* | 93 | 87* | 77 | 81 | 92 | 81 | 83 | 94 | 89 | 141 | 80* | 106 | 62 | 64 | 110 | 68 | 107 | 69 |
| Hamilton | 89* | 64* | 90* | 94 | 88* | 81 | 114 | 84 | 86 | 92 | 94 | 105 | 119 | 84* | 88 | 89 | 119 | 132 | 59* | 96 | 115 |
| Lanark (Clydesdale) | 89* | 66 | 93* | 94 | 87* | 168* | 99 | 83 | 113 | 53* | 70* | 86 | 139 | 93 | 78* | 90 | 97 | 73 | 109 | 85 | 111 |
| Monklands | 91* | 47* | 93* | 94 | 91* | 112 | 119 | 89 | 71* | 81 | 105 | 107 | 58 | 61* | 99 | 112 | 55 | 91 | 104 | 75* | 61 |
| Motherwell | 92* | 45* | 94* | 97 | 91* | 112 | 134* | 92 | 100 | 84 | 93 | 99 | 92 | 79* | 103 | 131* | 42* | 89 | 71* | 97 | 90 |
| Dunfermline | 104 | 101 | 104 | 103 | 105 | 73 | 120* | 92 | 80 | 117 | 99 | 99 | 62 | 123* | 105 | 120 | 127 | 107 | 108 | 119 | 103 |
| Kirkcaldy | 104* | 120* | 104* | 110* | 100 | 67* | 94 | 89 | 105 | 91 | 100 | 105 | 100 | 121* | 89 | 121 | 131 | 119 | 106 | 131* | 110 |
| North East Fife | 97 | 95 | 97 | 102 | 95 | 112 | 65* | 94 | 109 | 77 | 72* | 74* | 164* | 143* | 107 | 108 | 137 | 130 | 135* | 104 | 82 |
| Clackmannan | 99 | 180* | 95 | 95 | 95 | 140 | 89 | 77 | 110 | 98 | 109 | 113 | 104 | 72* | 101 | 97 | 30 | 78 | 140* | 117 | 119 |
| Falkirk | 91* | 113 | 90* | 92* | 89* | 82 | 97 | 100 | 89 | 81 | 91 | 84* | 62 | 50* | 104 | 84 | 79 | 113 | 116 | 119* | 112 |
| Stirling | 93* | 111 | 92* | 91* | 92* | 101 | 94 | 82 | 97 | 98 | 99 | 101 | 113 | 57* | 100 | 93 | 114 | 100 | 123 | 106 | 107 |
| Aberdeen City | 111* | 82* | 113* | 105 | 117* | 79 | 103 | 131* | 128* | 108 | 110* | 104 | 104 | 123* | 98 | 70* | 121 | 141* | 108 | 118* | 114 |
| Banff & Buchan | 97 | 81 | 98 | 95 | 99 | 121 | 72* | 110 | 120 | 102 | 69* | 70* | 124 | 126* | 91 | 86 | 154* | 104 | 110 | 96 | 109 |
| Gordon | 91* | 56* | 93* | 88* | 95 | 72 | 44* | 110 | 106 | 78 | 61* | 57* | 89 | 130* | 102 | 67 | 93 | 108 | 104 | 66* | 137 |
| Kincardine & Deeside | 96 | 95 | 96 | 95 | 97 | 80 | 75 | 114 | 116 | 105 | 62* | 44* | 100 | 123* | 99 | 119 | 78 | 116 | 122 | 104 | 104 |

TABLE 6.15A    1979-1982 CAUSE CRRs FOR LOCAL GOVERNMENT DISTRICTS  CONTD.

| | 1 | 2 | 3 | 4 | 5 | 6 | 7 | 8 | 9 | 10 | 11 | 12 | 13 | 14 | 15 | 16 | 17 | 18 | 19 | 20 | 21 |
|---|---|---|---|---|---|---|---|---|---|---|---|---|---|---|---|---|---|---|---|---|---|
| Moray | 95 | 96 | 95 | 94 | 96 | 99 | 106 | 107 | 120 | 65* | 68* | 77* | 65 | 129* | 85 | 93 | 118 | 70 | 120 | 88 | 101 |
| East Lothian | 107* | 116 | 106* | 106 | 106 | 102 | 107 | 95 | 105 | 106 | 95 | 88 | 104 | 135* | 104 | 94 | 147* | 113 | 107 | 106 | 93 |
| Edinburgh City | 111* | 117* | 111* | 111* | 111* | 101 | 96 | 105 | 98 | 118* | 115* | 106 | 112 | 112* | 123* | 99 | 119* | 102 | 123* | 107 | 106 |
| Midlothian | 104 | 105 | 104 | 97 | 110* | 61 | 119 | 87 | 110 | 101 | 93 | 86 | 143 | 138* | 93 | 86 | 87 | 92 | 102 | 99 | 90 |
| West Lothian | 105* | 101 | 105* | 105 | 105 | 93 | 100 | 86 | 85 | 126 | 103 | 104 | 96 | 116* | 100 | 89 | 116 | 120 | 117 | 110 | 97 |
| Angus | 101 | 183* | 97 | 85* | 104 | 116 | 108 | 125* | 103 | 118 | 73* | 67* | 101 | 118* | 89 | 108 | 66 | 106 | 102 | 89 | 98 |
| Dundee City | 113* | 200* | 110* | 108* | 111* | 126* | 133* | 95 | 107 | 116 | 106 | 107 | 90 | 139* | 95 | 105 | 110 | 85 | 117 | 98 | 67* |
| Perth & Kinross | 95* | 91 | 95* | 102 | 92* | 104 | 76* | 102 | 95 | 105 | 75* | 69* | 133 | 114* | 108 | 149* | 115 | 82 | 104 | 79* | 100 |
| Berwickshire | 91 | 124 | 90 | 89 | 91 | 63 | 74 | 74 | 125 | 53 | 74* | 70 | 101 | 105 | 85 | 48 | 102 | 41 | 114 | 74 | 102 |
| Ettrick & Lauderdale | 105 | 141* | 104 | 110 | 101 | 81 | 111 | 112 | 107 | 103 | 88 | 70 | 176* | 156* | 117 | 92 | 118 | 157* | 78 | 61 | 129 |
| Roxburgh | 89* | 90 | 89* | 92 | 87* | 130 | 79 | 97 | 111 | 98 | 77* | 81 | 145 | 93 | 85 | 117 | 106 | 91 | 84 | 78 | 54 |
| Tweeddale | 109 | 109 | 109 | 108 | 109 | 80 | 49 | 100 | 135 | 143 | 93 | 76 | 194 | 168* | 136* | 82 | 129 | 120 | 103 | 76 | 55 |
| Annandale & Eskdale | 96 | 256* | 90* | 92 | 89* | 92 | 81 | 112 | 109 | 119 | 72* | 79 | 96 | 98 | 84 | 78 | 58 | 106 | 86 | 108 | 92 |
| Nithsdale | 105 | 239* | 100 | 104 | 97 | 115 | 93 | 116 | 95 | 97 | 81* | 84 | 134 | 113 | 119 | 143 | 172* | 83 | 102 | 64* | 105 |
| Stewartry | 100 | 317* | 92 | 95 | 91 | 76 | 66 | 96 | 80 | 56 | 67* | 70 | 61 | 138* | 106 | 103 | 99 | 87 | 135 | 63 | 59 |
| Wigtown | 102 | 224* | 97 | 93 | 99 | 97 | 77 | 89 | 119 | 106 | 84 | 105 | 148 | 133* | 95 | 103 | 97 | 145 | 98 | 67 | 120 |
| Badenoch & Strathspey | 95 | 126 | 94 | 100 | 90 | 114 | 85 | 112 | 108 | 76 | 49* | 47 | 51 | 133 | 95 | 32 | 174 | 57 | 135 | 80 | 92 |
| Caithness | 77* | 48 | 78* | 93 | 68* | 93 | 69 | 94 | 71 | 62 | 60* | 85 | 137 | 85 | 106 | 49 | 104 | 79 | 47 | 41* | 168* |
| Inverness | 99 | 83 | 99 | 106 | 95 | 101 | 85 | 146* | 93 | 69 | 68* | 62* | 86 | 144* | 128* | 88 | 149 | 139 | 76 | 56* | 101 |
| Lochaber | 109 | 138 | 108 | 109 | 107 | 82 | 79 | 139 | 81 | 81 | 71* | 80 | 142 | 165* | 106 | 106 | 175 | 65 | 126 | 117 | 193* |
| Nairn | 92 | 27 | 94 | 95 | 94 | 153 | 81 | 93 | 91 | 109 | 71 | 74 | 201 | 132 | 80 | 63 | 168 | - | 130 | 77 | 146 |
| Ross & Cromarty | 100 | 111 | 100 | 108 | 95 | 122 | 55* | 127* | 99 | 88 | 51* | 50* | 110 | 155* | 105 | 84 | 199* | 86 | 116 | 83 | 124 |
| Skye & Lochalsh | 74* | 93 | 74* | 80 | 71* | 19 | 61 | 96 | 121 | 31 | 45* | 51 | 275* | 161* | 68 | 30 | 113 | 151 | 29 | 93 | 76 |
| Sutherland | 79* | 61 | 80* | 92 | 74* | 57 | 70 | 87 | 59 | 95 | 63* | 61 | 104 | 143* | 77 | 68 | 143 | 114 | 59 | 79 | 20 |
| Orkney | 81* | 50 | 82* | 87 | 79* | 67 | 74 | 62 | 80 | 75 | 53* | 58 | 13 | 173 | 74 | 185* | 90 | 59 | 128 | 95 | 60 |
| Shetland | 78* | 37 | 80* | 74* | 83* | 55 | 72 | 126 | 71 | 64 | 38* | 40* | 47 | 108 | 109 | 30 | 172 | 97 | 76 | 39* | 110 |
| Western Isles | 70* | 49* | 70* | 94 | 60* | 49 | 58* | 84 | 98 | 61 | 39* | 69 | 123 | 97 | 92 | 82 | 115 | 42 | 54* | 49* | 75 |

TABLE 6.15B    1979-1982 CRRs No. CASES FOR LOCAL GOVERNMENT DISTRICTS

| | 1 | 2 | 3 | 4 | 5 | 6 | 7 | 8 | 9 | 10 | 11 | 12 | 13 | 14 | 15 | 16 | 17 | 18 | 19 | 20 | 21 |
|---|---|---|---|---|---|---|---|---|---|---|---|---|---|---|---|---|---|---|---|---|---|
| Argyll & Bute | 1,215 | 43 | 1,172 | 400 | 771 | 29 | 63 | 89 | 49 | 34 | 191 | 60 | 13 | 121 | 142 | 27 | 13 | 28 | 51 | 43 | 25 |
| Dumbarton | 1,168 | 27 | 1,141 | 457 | 684 | 36 | 61 | 64 | 36 | 31 | 251 | 91 | 12 | 110 | 126 | 28 | 13 | 33 | 40 | 53 | 22 |
| Inverclyde | 1,773 | 27 | 1,746 | 710 | 1,036 | 48 | 113 | 127 | 58 | 65 | 359 | 133 | 23 | 158 | 219 | 34 | 17 | 27 | 63 | 91 | 38 |
| Renfrew | 2,922 | 57 | 2,865 | 1,179 | 1,686 | 77 | 196 | 229 | 110 | 109 | 663 | 260 | 21 | 231 | 275 | 52 | 36 | 66 | 89 | 143 | 45 |
| Cumnock & Doon Valley | 649 | 28 | 621 | 283 | 338 | 16 | 46 | 41 | 27 | 16 | 103 | 39 | 3 | 44 | 68 | 22 | 14 | 10 | 23 | 35 | 18 |
| Cunninghame | 2,120 | 84 | 2,036 | 860 | 1,176 | 58 | 128 | 166 | 95 | 48 | 400 | 160 | 33 | 152 | 206 | 41 | 37 | 51 | 82 | 94 | 44 |
| Kilmarnock & Loudoun | 1,280 | 39 | 1,241 | 474 | 767 | 29 | 94 | 116 | 51 | 55 | 224 | 79 | 18 | 71 | 152 | 22 | 17 | 25 | 60 | 64 | 19 |
| Kyle & Carrick | 2,006 | 70 | 1936 | 721 | 1,215 | 38 | 110 | 162 | 77 | 69 | 339 | 106 | 27 | 207 | 215 | 34 | 21 | 41 | 81 | 109 | 36 |
| Bears. & Milngavie | 673 | 31 | 642 | 285 | 357 | 4 | 26 | 56 | 32 | 13 | 103 | 35 | 14 | 80 | 97 | 2 | 5 | 17 | 31 | 20 | 14 |
| Clydebank | 963 | 25 | 938 | 395 | 543 | 17 | 49 | 83 | 38 | 25 | 200 | 82 | 11 | 84 | 104 | 19 | 13 | 17 | 37 | 41 | 16 |
| Eastwood | 802 | 15 | 787 | 288 | 499 | 24 | 45 | 75 | 36 | 26 | 134 | 42 | 12 | 45 | 100 | 10 | 7 | 11 | 33 | 36 | 11 |
| Glasgow City | 16,388 | 578 | 15,810 | 5,975 | 9,831 | 403 | 953 | 1,145 | 613 | 403 | 4,199 | 1,672 | 123 | 1,385 | 1,450 | 301 | 158 | 281 | 479 | 748 | 262 |
| Strathkelvin | 1,226 | 59 | 1,167 | 532 | 635 | 25 | 58 | 92 | 42 | 39 | 211 | 91 | 13 | 126 | 140 | 16 | 16 | 18 | 42 | 63 | 28 |
| Cumbernauld & Kilsyth | 695 | 32 | 663 | 321 | 342 | 12 | 37 | 48 | 28 | 16 | 148 | 76 | 5 | 59 | 63 | 12 | 6 | 13 | 23 | 42 | 11 |
| East Kilbride | 1,037 | 39 | 998 | 529 | 469 | 19 | 48 | 74 | 34 | 24 | 203 | 97 | 20 | 94 | 136 | 15 | 10 | 27 | 25 | 53 | 14 |
| Hamilton | 1,498 | 48 | 1,450 | 667 | 783 | 30 | 101 | 101 | 54 | 40 | 299 | 143 | 23 | 146 | 155 | 29 | 26 | 45 | 36 | 71 | 34 |
| Lanark (Clydesdale) | 868 | 27 | 841 | 353 | 488 | 37 | 53 | 60 | 42 | 14 | 130 | 62 | 15 | 96 | 77 | 16 | 12 | 14 | 41 | 37 | 19 |
| Monklands | 1,510 | 34 | 1,476 | 679 | 797 | 41 | 105 | 106 | 44 | 35 | 334 | 147 | 11 | 105 | 172 | 36 | 12 | 31 | 62 | 55 | 18 |
| Motherwell | 2,342 | 47 | 2,295 | 1,010 | 1,285 | 64 | 185 | 171 | 97 | 57 | 460 | 212 | 26 | 212 | 268 | 61 | 14 | 45 | 68 | 111 | 40 |
| Dunfermline | 2,155 | 87 | 2,068 | 850 | 1,218 | 34 | 135 | 139 | 63 | 64 | 395 | 159 | 14 | 265 | 218 | 45 | 33 | 43 | 86 | 110 | 37 |
| Kirkcaldy | 2,737 | 125 | 2,612 | 1,067 | 1,543 | 40 | 136 | 173 | 106 | 65 | 508 | 200 | 28 | 336 | 230 | 55 | 43 | 60 | 111 | 155 | 50 |
| North East Fife | 1,326 | 45 | 1,281 | 429 | 852 | 36 | 51 | 100 | 59 | 30 | 188 | 61 | 22 | 212 | 139 | 23 | 23 | 33 | 78 | 65 | 19 |
| Clackmannan | 764 | 60 | 704 | 302 | 402 | 24 | 37 | 43 | 32 | 20 | 160 | 69 | 9 | 58 | 80 | 14 | 3 | 12 | 39 | 40 | 16 |
| Falkirk | 2,319 | 117 | 2,202 | 921 | 1,281 | 47 | 135 | 185 | 86 | 55 | 448 | 164 | 17 | 134 | 263 | 38 | 25 | 55 | 116 | 137 | 49 |
| Stirling | 1,299 | 62 | 1,237 | 481 | 756 | 32 | 72 | 85 | 52 | 37 | 268 | 103 | 17 | 85 | 140 | 23 | 20 | 27 | 69 | 67 | 26 |
| Aberdeen City | 4,340 | 123 | 4,217 | 1,479 | 2,734 | 71 | 223 | 387 | 194 | 116 | 806 | 284 | 43 | 511 | 387 | 47 | 61 | 108 | 161 | 205 | 76 |
| Banff & Buchan | 1,411 | 46 | 1,365 | 498 | 864 | 40 | 58 | 118 | 67 | 40 | 194 | 71 | 19 | 194 | 126 | 21 | 27 | 28 | 67 | 64 | 28 |
| Gordon | 946 | 26 | 920 | 318 | 602 | 17 | 25 | 85 | 42 | 22 | 121 | 39 | 10 | 143 | 99 | 12 | 11 | 20 | 47 | 31 | 26 |
| Kincardine & Deeside | 733 | 29 | 704 | 249 | 454 | 14 | 32 | 65 | 34 | 22 | 91 | 22 | 8 | 100 | 71 | 15 | 7 | 16 | 40 | 36 | 14 |

TABLE 6.15A  1979-1982 CRRs No. CASES FOR LOCAL GOVERNMENT DISTRICTS  CONTD.

| | 1 | 2 | 3 | 4 | 5 | 6 | 7 | 8 | 9 | 10 | 11 | 12 | 13 | 14 | 15 | 16 | 17 | 18 | 19 | 20 | 21 |
|---|---|---|---|---|---|---|---|---|---|---|---|---|---|---|---|---|---|---|---|---|---|
| Moray | 1,395 | 55 | 1,340 | 496 | 841 | 33 | 86 | 117 | 68 | 26 | 193 | 79 | 10 | 200 | 120 | 23 | 21 | 19 | 73 | 59 | 26 |
| East Lothian | 1,679 | 69 | 1,610 | 608 | 1,002 | 37 | 94 | 112 | 64 | 46 | 291 | 100 | 17 | 227 | 160 | 25 | 29 | 34 | 68 | 76 | 25 |
| Edinburgh City | 9,748 | 387 | 9,361 | 3,350 | 6,009 | 205 | 471 | 708 | 336 | 289 | 1,890 | 630 | 102 | 1,052 | 1,093 | 147 | 136 | 176 | 408 | 418 | 157 |
| Midlothian | 1,328 | 61 | 1,267 | 536 | 730 | 17 | 80 | 78 | 52 | 33 | 229 | 91 | 21 | 181 | 121 | 21 | 14 | 23 | 48 | 56 | 20 |
| West Lothian | 2,021 | 95 | 1,926 | 867 | 1,059 | 39 | 101 | 117 | 60 | 62 | 373 | 160 | 22 | 230 | 199 | 34 | 28 | 46 | 82 | 93 | 34 |
| Angus | 1,835 | 126 | 1,709 | 533 | 1,176 | 49 | 110 | 174 | 73 | 60 | 254 | 81 | 19 | 231 | 159 | 33 | 15 | 37 | 75 | 74 | 31 |
| Dundee City | 3,951 | 264 | 3,687 | 1,354 | 2,332 | 101 | 259 | 252 | 145 | 112 | 696 | 266 | 33 | 516 | 337 | 63 | 50 | 59 | 152 | 152 | 40 |
| Perth & Kinross | 2,354 | 80 | 2,274 | 834 | 1,440 | 60 | 107 | 193 | 92 | 73 | 360 | 112 | 33 | 304 | 256 | 59 | 35 | 38 | 109 | 90 | 42 |
| Berwickshire | 369 | 17 | 352 | 114 | 238 | 6 | 17 | 23 | 20 | 6 | 59 | 18 | 4 | 46 | 32 | 3 | 5 | 20 | 20 | 14 | 7 |
| Ettrick & Lauderdale | 718 | 34 | 684 | 244 | 440 | 13 | 43 | 59 | 29 | 20 | 116 | 31 | 12 | 115 | 77 | 10 | 10 | 13 | 22 | 19 | 15 |
| Roxburgh | 672 | 24 | 648 | 226 | 422 | 23 | 34 | 57 | 33 | 21 | 111 | 40 | 11 | 76 | 62 | 14 | 10 | 7 | 26 | 27 | 7 |
| Tweeddale | 344 | 12 | 332 | 101 | 231 | 6 | 9 | 25 | 17 | 13 | 56 | 14 | 6 | 58 | 41 | 4 | 5 | 14 | 14 | 11 | 3 |
| Annandale & Eskdale | 678 | 66 | 612 | 234 | 378 | 15 | 32 | 59 | 30 | 23 | 100 | 40 | 7 | 74 | 57 | 9 | 5 | 17 | 25 | 35 | 11 |
| Nithsdale | 1,115 | 97 | 1,018 | 408 | 610 | 28 | 55 | 92 | 39 | 28 | 167 | 65 | 15 | 128 | 125 | 26 | 23 | 8 | 43 | 31 | 19 |
| Stewartry | 504 | 54 | 450 | 156 | 294 | 9 | 19 | 37 | 16 | 8 | 67 | 23 | 3 | 75 | 50 | 8 | 6 | 16 | 30 | 15 | 5 |
| Wigtown | 596 | 48 | 548 | 198 | 350 | 13 | 25 | 39 | 27 | 17 | 96 | 44 | 9 | 83 | 54 | 10 | 7 | 2 | 24 | 18 | 12 |
| Badenoch & Strathspey | 180 | 9 | 171 | 65 | 106 | 5 | 9 | 16 | 8 | 4 | 18 | 6 | 1 | 27 | 17 | 1 | 4 | 7 | 11 | 7 | 3 |
| Caithness | 368 | 9 | 359 | 169 | 189 | 10 | 18 | 33 | 13 | 8 | 56 | 30 | 7 | 43 | 49 | 4 | 6 | 26 | 9 | 9 | 14 |
| Inverness | 949 | 33 | 916 | 385 | 531 | 22 | 45 | 104 | 34 | 18 | 125 | 44 | 9 | 146 | 124 | 15 | 18 | 4 | 28 | 24 | 17 |
| Lochaber | 352 | 18 | 334 | 134 | 200 | 6 | 14 | 33 | 10 | 7 | 44 | 19 | 5 | 56 | 34 | 6 | 7 | - | 16 | 17 | 11 |
| Nairn | 181 | 2 | 179 | 60 | 119 | 7 | 9 | 14 | 7 | 6 | 27 | 9 | 4 | 28 | 15 | 2 | 4 | 12 | 11 | 7 | 5 |
| Ross & Cromarty | 765 | 35 | 730 | 303 | 427 | 21 | 23 | 71 | 29 | 18 | 75 | 27 | 9 | 125 | 76 | 11 | 18 | 6 | 37 | 29 | 17 |
| Skye & Lochalsh | 169 | 7 | 162 | 54 | 108 | 1 | 8 | 17 | 11 | 2 | 20 | 7 | 6 | 40 | 14 | 1 | 3 | 6 | 3 | 10 | 3 |
| Sutherland | 235 | 6 | 229 | 84 | 145 | 4 | 12 | 20 | 7 | 8 | 37 | 11 | 3 | 46 | 21 | 3 | 5 | 4 | 8 | 11 | 1 |
| Orkney | 308 | 7 | 301 | 108 | 193 | 6 | 16 | 18 | 12 | 8 | 40 | 14 | 5 | 30 | 26 | 11 | 4 | 7 | 22 | 17 | 4 |
| Shetland | 311 | 6 | 305 | 98 | 207 | 5 | 16 | 38 | 11 | 7 | 29 | 10 | 2 | 46 | 41 | 2 | 8 | 5 | 13 | 7 | 8 |
| Western Isles | 478 | 11 | 467 | 189 | 278 | 8 | 23 | 45 | 27 | 12 | 52 | 28 | 8 | 73 | 56 | 8 | 9 | 17 | 17 | 16 | 9 |

TABLE 6.16   MENTAL ILLNESS HOSPITAL ADMISSION RATES 1980-82
BY AGE AND SEX

| Age | First admission rates* | | All admission rates* | |
|---|---|---|---|---|
| | Male | Female | Male | Female |
| 0 - | 0.1 | . . | 0.2 | 0.1 |
| 5 - | 0.3 | 0.2 | 0.5 | 0.3 |
| 15 - | 1.3 | 1.3 | 2.7 | 3.0 |
| 25 - | 2.0 | 2.0 | 5.8 | 5.7 |
| 35 - | 2.4 | 2.2 | 7.2 | 7.0 |
| 45 - | 2.0 | 1.9 | 6.2 | 6.8 |
| 55 - | 1.8 | 1.8 | 4.9 | 6.5 |
| 65 - | 2.3 | 2.7 | 5.4 | 7.5 |
| 75+ | 7.2 | 8.0 | 10.9 | 13.8 |

*annual average per 1,000 population

TABLE 6.17   ADMISSIONS TO MENTAL ILLNESS HOSPITALS 1980-82
CORRELATIONS WITH DEPRIVATION SCORE

| Cause# | | P.C.S. | L.G.Ds.* | |
|---|---|---|---|---|
| | | All admissions | All admissions | First admissions |
| | | | r | r |
| All causes | - all | 0.50 | 0.42 | 0.47 |
| | - 0-64 | 0.53 | 0.50 | 0.56 |
| | - 65+ | 0.17 | 0.08 | 0.10 |
| Alcoholism | - 0-64 | | 0.43 | 0.50 |
| | - male | | 0.43 | 0.47 |
| | - female | | 0.39 | 0.54 |
| Schizophrenia 0-64 | | | 0.59 | 0.61 |
| Other psychoses 0.64 | | | 0.33 | 0.29 |
| Depression 0-64 | | | 0.32 | 0.31 |
| Senile conditions 65+ | | | 0.03 | 0.01 |

*53 LGDs excluding Fife
#see table 6.18 for ICD codes

TABLE 6.18   MENTAL HOSPITAL ADMISSIONS: GRADIENTS BY DEPCAT

| Type | Group | Affluent 1 | 2 | 3 | 4 | 5 | Deprived 6 | 7 | Cases | Rate =60 | r |
|------|-------|---|---|---|---|---|---|---|-------|------|---|
| All | All | 70 | 87 | 84 | 97 | 103 | 126 | 169 | 67,807 | 480 | 0.42 |
|  | First | 76 | 89 | 86 | 97 | 102 | 120 | 165 | 26,277 | 186 | 0.47 |
| 0-64 | All | 63 | 81 | 82 | 94 | 104 | 132 | 181 | 49,310 | 406 | 0.50 |
|  | First | 69 | 83 | 84 | 94 | 102 | 124 | 180 | 17,344 | 143 | 0.56 |
| 65+ | All | 89 | 103 | 86 | 102 | 100 | 110 | 127 | 18,497 | 929 | 0.08 |
|  | First | 90 | 100 | 88 | 101 | 101 | 112 | 128 | 8933 | 448 | 0.10 |
| All male | All | 55 | 80 | 82 | 95 | 105 | 135 | 189 | 29,240 | 400 | 0.51 |
|  | First | 60 | 83 | 83 | 98 | 102 | 126 | 182 | 11,624 | 171 | 0.54 |
| 0-64 | All | 48 | 74 | 80 | 94 | 105 | 141 | 199 | 23,592 | 390 | 0.56 |
|  | First | 53 | 76 | 82 | 98 | 102 | 130 | 194 | 8,710 | 144 | 0.58 |
| 65+ | All | 87 | 104 | 87 | 98 | 103 | 107 | 140 | 5,288 | 693 | 0.06 |
|  | First | 83 | 100 | 87 | 99 | 105 | 114 | 137 | 2,914 | 382 | 0.10 |
| All female | All | 81 | 93 | 85 | 98 | 102 | 120 | 152 | 38,567 | 527 | 0.31 |
|  | First | 89 | 94 | 88 | 95 | 102 | 116 | 151 | 14,653 | 200 | 0.35 |
| 0-64 | All | 76 | 87 | 84 | 95 | 104 | 124 | 165 | 25,718 | 422 | 0.39 |
|  | First | 85 | 89 | 87 | 91 | 103 | 119 | 167 | 8,634 | 142 | 0.47 |
| 65+ | All | 90 | 103 | 86 | 104 | 98 | 111 | 121 | 12,849 | 1045 | 0.08 |
|  | First | 93 | 100 | 88 | 102 | 99 | 111 | 123 | 6,019 | 490 | 0.10 |
| Alcohol | All | 45 | 68 | 82 | 85 | 104 | 154 | 231 | 11,416 | 94 | 0.43 |
| 0-64 | First | 50 | 64 | 80 | 89 | 109 | 151 | 228 | 4,539 | 37 | 0.50 |
| Male | All | 38 | 68 | 80 | 85 | 100 | 160 | 239 | 8,350 | 138 | 0.43 |
|  | First | 42 | 63 | 80 | 91 | 101 | 150 | 240 | 3,371 | 56 | 0.47 |
| Female | All | 63 | 69 | 86 | 84 | 116 | 135 | 207 | 3,066 | 50 | 0.39 |
|  | First | 74 | 69 | 80 | 81 | 116 | 154 | 194 | 1,168 | 19 | 0.54 |
| Schizo- | All | 54 | 76 | 79 | 96 | 111 | 141 | 175 | 7,803 | 55 | 0.56 |
| phrenia | First | 80 | 74 | 86 | 92 | 115 | 137 | 145 | 1,229 | 9 | 0.63 |
| 0-64 | All | 55 | 76 | 78 | 96 | 111 | 144 | 175 | 7,319 | 60 | 0.59 |
|  | First | 75 | 78 | 87 | 92 | 114 | 133 | 145 | 1,163 | 10 | 0.60 |
| Other | All | 93 | 96 | 87 | 95 | 105 | 120 | 128 | 15,825 | 112 | 0.30 |
| psychoses | First | 94 | 91 | 90 | 99 | 108 | 117 | 135 | 5,101 | 36 | 0.36 |
| 0-64 | All | 91 | 92 | 86 | 93 | 104 | 127 | 137 | 10,681 | 88 | 0.33 |
|  | First | 100 | 95 | 88 | 97 | 106 | 118 | 143 | 3,112 | 26 | 0.29 |
| Depres- | All | 65 | 84 | 102 | 89 | 102 | 111 | 175 | 2,286 | 16 | 0.31 |
| sion | First | 78 | 84 | 98 | 92 | 104 | 118 | 147 | 1,043 | 7 | 0.30 |
| 0-64 | All | 63 | 83 | 104 | 87 | 104 | 110 | 175 | 1,048 | 17 | 0.32 |
|  | First | 75 | 85 | 101 | 89 | 106 | 115 | 148 | 965 | 8 | 0.31 |
| Senile | All | 87 | 111 | 84 | 101 | 97 | 113 | 126 | 8,103 | 407 | 0.03 |
| Condi-tions 65+ | First | 91 | 109 | 87 | 98 | 96 | 113 | 125 | 4,841 | 243 | 0.01 |

*Notes*

Data excludes all cases in Fife
First           =   First admissions only (SMR4 previous psychiatric care code = 3)
Rates are annual per 100,000 population
r               =   population wighted correlations over Local Authority Districts (N=53)
Senile          =   ICD code 290
Alcohol         =   ICD codes 291 and 303
Schizophrenia   =   ICD code 295
Other psychoses =   ICD codes 293, 294, 296, 297 and 298
Depression      =   ICD code 300 excluding 300.4

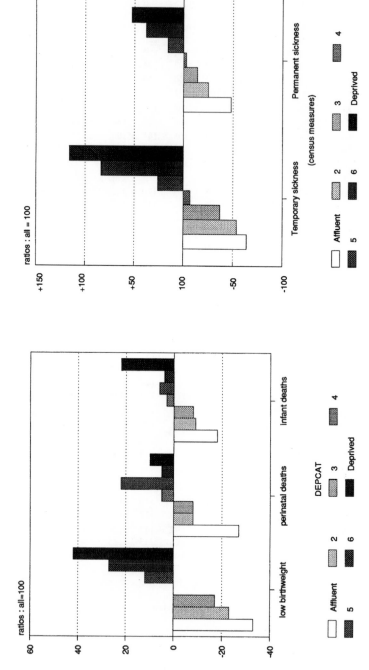

FIGURE 6.2    SICKNESS IN ADULTS BY DEPCAT

FIGURE 6.1    INFANT MEASURES BY DEPCAT

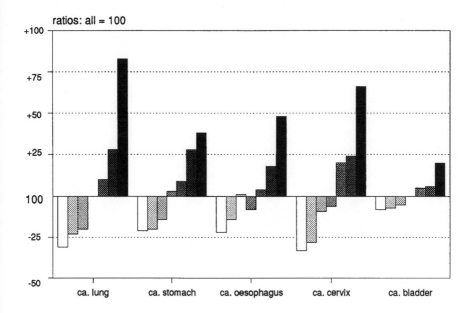

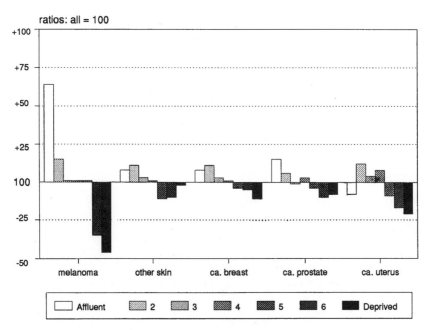

FIGURE 6.3 CANCER REGISTRATIONS 1979 - 82 BY DEPCAT

Neoplasm Site & ICD9 Code

1.  All                  140-208,230-239

2.  Non-Malignant        230-239

3.  Malignant (All )      140-208

4.  Malignant (0-64)      140-208

5.  Malignant (65+)       140-208

6.  Oesophagus            150

7.  Stomach               151

8.  Colon                 153

9.  Rectum                154

10. Pancreas              157

11. Lung (All)            162

12. Lung ( 0-64 )         162

13. Melanoma              172

14. Skin                  173

15. Breast ( F)           174

16. Cervix ( F)           180

17. Uterus ( F)           182

18. Ovary (F)             183

19. Prostate (M)          185

20. Bladder               188

21. Leukemia              2 04-2 08

FIGURE 6.4    1979 - 82 CANCER REGISTRATION: KEY TO CAUSES

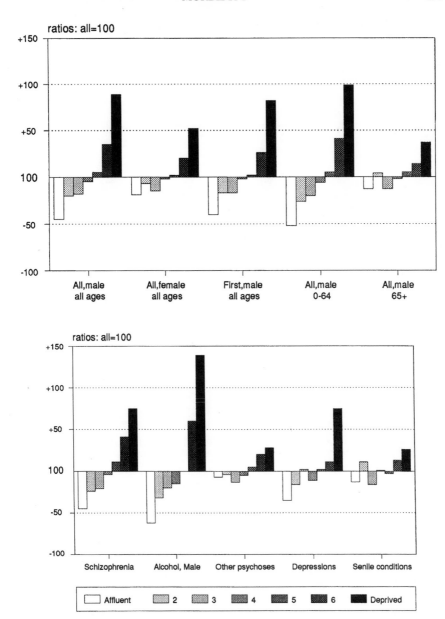

FIGURE 6.5   MENTAL ILLNESS HOSPITAL ADMISSIONS 1980 - 82 BY DEPCAT

CHAPTER 7

# Use of Beds in General Hospitals

This chapter examines the association of hospital beduse with both deprivation and mortality. The influence of supply factors (available beds) and distance to services are also taken into account and the variation in bed use rates is then examined in relation to these four factors jointly by means of regression analysis which provides equations which predict bed-days. The implication of the findings in relation to resource allocation in the health service are considered in the next chapter.

## *Hospital Use and Deprivation*

The database consists of all discharges (including day cases) from general (non-psychiatric/non obstetric) hospitals for one year, 1981. For this and other hospital data sets Fife health board residents are excluded since the board was not supplying full postcodes for its own residents in 1981. The local government district of Annan & Eskdale is also excluded since some patients cross the border into Carlisle for treatment although cross-border flow into England from other areas is negligible. These exclusions reduce the number of postcode sectors in the analysis to 928. For this reason some of the correlation coefficients with mortality seen in this chapter will differ slightly from those which appear in tables in chapter 4, which relates to all sectors.

Table 7.1 shows the data for general hospitals which provides the basis for the analysis. Mental illness, mental handicap and maternity beds are not included and have been examined in chapter 6. Discharges from acute beds comprise 97% of the total with only three percent coming from long-stay beds which comprise geriatric assessment and geriatric long-stay, general practitioner long-stay beds and those for the young chronic sick. All other beds, comprising a wide range of medical or surgical specialties, are termed acute. Bed-days (beduse) presents a very different picture with 61% occurring in acute beds and 39% in long-stay. Overall the elderly (65 and over) account for only 29% of discharges but 63% of all beds used. Of course the older age group contributes the majority of discharges and beduse in long-stay beds; although only 10% of elderly discharges are from long-stay beds more than half of the beds used by them are long-stay. Fewer than one percent of younger discharges are from long-stay beds but these account for 14% of the beduse by this age group due to the long mean stay of this group comprising the 'young' chronic sick. Although many elderly also experience long spells in hospital patients who die within a relatively short period after admission influence the mean stay for this group. In the acute beds length of stay for the age group 65 and over is almost three times that of the younger group, hence they occupy almost half of the bed-days although comprising only 27% of discharges. Discharge and bed-day rates by age and sex for the different categories of bed are given in table 7.2.

The correlation of hospital measures with deprivation, mortality and the permanently sick (census measure) is strongest for the younger age group on all three measures: discharges, bed-days and mean stay. In all cases the correlation coefficient is low, for age 65 and over and for long-stay beds (table 7.3). Since these two groups contribute more to bed-days than to discharges (table 7.1) they have more influence on the correlations for all beds and all acute bed for these two measures than on discharges which contains a higher proportion in the 0-64 age group. Mean stay for the elderly and long-stay beds shows no association with any of the variables and those for 0-64 are lower than for discharges or bed-days. For these two measures the correlation with DEP is somewhat stronger than with the other variables. Both discharges and bed-days (acute) 0-64 correlate more strongly with SMR0-64 than with all ages whereas for 65 and over and long-stay the correlation is stronger with the SMR65 and over, although at a low level. The association of discharges and bed-days (0-64) with the population permanently sick is also strong. There are some problems in the analysis of discharges and mean-stay due to the inclusion of day cases which were not consistently recorded in 1981 with the result that the pattern for these two measures may be impaired. Discharges also suffer as a measure from problems associated with recording conventions, which can result in one episode of care having more than one admission, and also from any variations in local practice in terms of repeat admissions. For these reasons the remainder of the analysis of these hospital data concentrates on the more robust measure of bed-days which measures the actual use of resources for inpatients. Day cases are not allocated any length of stay and this demand on hospital resources is therefore excluded. Even allocated one day of stay they would nevertheless contribute only around one percent of total bed-days so this is not a major loss. The outpatient demand on services is also excluded since no individual record is completed for this patient type for statistical purposes, and thus no address basis exists for allocation to an area of residence. The development of computerised systems for the administration of patient records should make these records more accessible for analysis in the future, at least at health board level, although the large number of events could operate against analysis at national level. Although new outpatients at consultative clinics number two million and total attendances over five million[1] the major resource cost nevertheless attaches to inpatients, who account for over eight million occupied bed-days (Appendix A1) and also for more than half of the attendances at ancillary departments such as radiology, physiotherapy and occupational therapy.[1]

As with other data bed-days are aggregated to provide values for deprivation categories; for all beds these show a gradient rising from 80 in affluent to 127 in the most deprived category (table 7.4). For the acute beds and the age group 0-64 the gradient is somewhat steeper, from 73 to 142, but there is no marked trend for the elderly. These two age groups influence the gradient for all acute beds which displays lesser values for categories 1 and 2, and higher for 6 and 7, with little variation in the three middle categories. Despite the lower correlation a less steep but nevertheless distinct gradient also appears for the long-stay beds (see fig. 7.1).

The ratios in bed-days by age and sex (table 7.5) show that these by no means increase consistently in line with deprivation. These gradients are consistent however in displaying ratios which are always highest in DEPCAT 7, followed (nearly always) by DEPCAT 6, and with ratios in DEPCATS 1 and 2 tending to be lower than the other categories.

## *Bed Supply and Distance*

The level of local bed supply (i.e. available beds) would of course be expected to have some influence on the level of use since in areas with more beds in relation to population admission and beduse rates would be expected to be higher than in those with a low level of bed supply. Distance to hospital services in addition may also affect beduse, large distances and the inconvenience of travel acting as disincentives to hospital admission where other medical care offers a feasible alternative. Measures for both of these factors were therefore devised and are described in detail in Appendix A9 and 10.

The bed supply measure for a postcode sector is calculated as described briefly below.

1.    For all beds, acute beds and long-stay beds catchment populations were calculated for each of the 34 health districts which existed in 1981 (but have since been abolished) using data on district of treatment and area of residence. The catchment population base takes account of the cross-boundary flow of patients and the demand from patients resident in other districts. The cross-border flow table at health board level (table 7.6) shows for instance that, of the 5910 beds used in Glasgow, 4875 (82%) were used by the resident population, and patients from all other boards used some beds in Glasgow; 5% of the beduse by Glasgow residents was in other health boards.

2.    Beds available in 1981 divided by catchment population provide the bed supply ratios in a health district.
      Table 7.7 shows the available bed ratios for health boards and health districts for both all beds and acute beds on a resident and catchment basis, the difference between the two ratios reflecting cross-border flow: for Borders and South Lothian for instance the differing ratios reflect the use of beds in South Lothian by patients from the Borders in 1981. In general high resident bed ratios are diminished by taking into account the population using beds in an area and low bed ratios are increased and the variance in catchment-based ratios is less than in those which are resident-based.

3.    The bed supply for a postcode sector is calculated by adding the proportion of all discharges/bed-days treated in any district weighted by the bed supply ratio in that district. For instance, for postcode sector XX:

      | District of treatment | discharges | | acute bed supply ratio | |
      |---|---|---|---|---|
      | District A | .33 | x | 5.4 | = 1.78 |
      | District B | 25 | x | 4.6 | = 1.15 |
      | District C | .42 | x | 4.2 | = 1.76 |
      | Total = | 1.00 | | | = 4.69 |

      Thus sector XX would have a bed-supply ratio of 4.69 per 1000 population, calculated from the three districts in which patients were treated.

In respect of distance it was not feasible to construct any complex measures using travel routes, times and modes of travel and the measures of distance are based on crow-fly distance using the grid reference of the centroid of the postcode sector from the census, and of a hospital using the central postcode directory to provide a grid reference for the unit postcode. The distance between these two reference points is then derived, in miles. Two measures were constructed: in respect of DGH-type (with a range of acute specialties) and for any acute beds (generally small local hospitals with facilities in at least general medicine and general surgery). In some cases of course the two facilities are provided at the same hospital but for more remote populations a DGH-type facility will be at a greater distance. The distance to general practitioner and long-stay beds was not considered relevant since these provide only a small proportion of hospital care and the entry into most long-stay services is generally through geriatric assessment services which tend to be located together with the acute specialties (see Methods Appendix A9 for more detail).

Distance to services (table 7.8) shows a very small proportion of the population not close to any acute service (only 5.5% more than 20 miles) and only 11.5% at the same distance to a wider range of services. The bulk of the population lives within five miles of both types of service: nearly 70% to any acute service and 62% to DGH-type facilities. Given this ready access to services distance factors cannot be expected to have a major influence on use of services for the major part of the population.

## *Correlation of Supply and Distance with Beduse*

The relationship between these two measures and beduse, mortality and deprivation is seen in the correlation matrix (table 7.9). The most important feature emerging from this table is the lack of association of bed supply with deprivation, two of the three coefficients being negative and all very low; this implies that the association found between beduse and deprivation is not merely reflecting levels of supply.

Since bed-supply ratios vary between health boards however the association between bed supply and deprivation for sectors within health boards was also calculated to see whether there was any deviation from that trend. For all beds there was one positive association, in Highland, with the coefficients being negative in all other boards and ranging from -0.01 in Borders to -0.47 in Lanarkshire. For acute beds all coefficients were negative and ranged from -0.01 in Grampian to -0.34 in Ayr & Arran. Many of these coefficients would not be statistically significant. Bed supply and SMR also display only weak correlations; although slightly stronger than for deprivation these are all negative, i.e. the level of beds available is inversely related to mortality.

Since deprived sectors exhibit more mortality and morbidity it might be expected that more beds would be available to populations in these areas if hospital planning responded to the needs of the population. The results of this analysis do not show this relationship but seem to make sense on the basis that large hospitals will serve communities which are geographically widespread and the bed supply will be available to sectors which are widely diverse in terms of deprivation.

The association between bed supply and beduse is also seen to be low but, in contrast to other findings, slightly stronger at 65 and over than at 0-64 for the acute beds, suggesting that bed supply may have more influence on levels of acute beduse by the older than younger age group.

It may appear somewhat illogical to suggest that bed supply and bed use are not strongly correlated and at a larger area level this is certainly the case, as can be seen for health boards in table 7.10, the populations in boards with more available beds in general making more use of hospital beds - mostly of course in their own board of residence.

The use of the smaller area base allows these relationships to be examined more specifically and the matrix (table 7.9) shows that beduse at sector level is more highly associated with deprivation and mortality than it is with the beds available. This matrix also includes the measure of the permanently sick (in private households) and a moderately strong coefficient (0.55) is seen here with the use of acute beds by the age group 0-64, so that at least one general measure of morbidity is fairly associated with beduse.

Distance measures are negatively associated with deprivation, i.e. distance to services reduces as deprivation increases, although the association is very weak. Only for the age group 0-64 is distance negatively associated with beduse, that is beduse reduces as distance increases. All of the coefficients are low however and the influence of distance weak.

## The Determination of Bed-Days

The relationships may be examined over all variables using methods of regression analysis to establish the influence of the four factors — mortality, deprivation, supply and distance — in determining the variations in hospital beduse. The results from this analysis are seen for various kinds of beds and for SMRs for different age groups, in table 7.11. Deprivation is of course calculated on a constant, i.e. all ages, basis for a sector. The bed supply measure used is that appropriate to the particular analysis, i.e. type of bed, as is the distance measure. Since the association between deprivation and beduse by the elderly, for acute and long-stay beds, has been shown to be very low these are not considered further and the regression analyses are confined to all beds, acute beds and acute 0-64. Regression analysis builds on the correlation analysis which has quantified the degree of association between any two variables, e.g. bed-days and mortality, bed-days and deprivation (table 7.9) and determines the combined association of one variable (in this case bed-days) with a number of others taking into account the fact that these are also inter-correlated with one another.

In these analyses mortality is entered first into the equation and deprivation last. The reasons for this approach are based in the objective of examining aspects of the resource allocation formula which follows in the next chapter, in which mortality differentials (at 0-64) provide one element in the determination of needs for hospital care. The separate and additional contributions of deprivation are also examined. Since the review of the resource allocation formula in England[2] has recommended use of the SMR0-74 this measure is also included. Table 7.11 examines the variation in three different types of bed, using three different SMRs.

The tables show first the simple correlation (Sr) of each variables with the particular beds examined, followed by multiple r which shows the total correlation achieved as each factor is added in. The $R^2$ % shows the percent added to the explanation of variance by each of the variables in turn, and these values may be summed to give the total percent explained. The final column gives the value of the b-coefficient for the SMR, i.e. the way in which SMR changes for each unit of bed-days. The results for all beds show the simple r to be very similar for both SMR (0.294) and DEP (0.283) with SUP making a minor contribution to the explanation but DIS very little. Of the three SMRs considered, SMRall functions just better than the other two, with the regression on this basis nevertheless explaining only 12.3% of the variation in beduse.

For acute beds, the regressions based on all three SMRs explain just over 31% of the variance. This level improves for the acute beds 0-64 with SMR0-64 making a stronger contribution than the other two to the explanation and with this regression in total accounting for 47.6% of the variance..

For acute beds and acute 0-64 the simple correlation of DEP with bed-days tends to be higher than SMR (e.g. 0.604 and 0.564 for SMR0-64), but the inclusion of distance and supply enhances the multiple correlation in each case, for the SMR0-64 to a level of 0.641.

Distance measures have little influence on these equations but the supply measure makes a definite contribution for all acute beds in particular, although of lesser importance for acute 0-64. DEP is seen to make little contribution in addition to SMR to the explanation of all bed-days and to be strongest for acute 0-64, although for these beds more of the contribution of DEP is accounted for by the SMR0-64 than SMRall

The relationship of SMR to bed-days is shown by the b-coefficient. For all beds and SMRall the value of 0.63 indicates that for each unit of SMR bed-days changes by 0.63%. This value increases with the addition of distance and supply, to 0.69% When deprivation is also entered into the regression however the change in bed-days for one unit of SMR falls to 0.47%

The b-coefficient of SMR is always steeper for the SMRall than for the other two SMRs. For all equations the value of this b-coefficient falls considerably when DEP is also entered into the equation, due to DEP and SMR being highly correlated, and the resulting value for acute 0-64 beds is very similar for SMRall (0.28) and for SMR0-64 (0.29).

The regression analyses supply the equations which are the best determinants of bed-days. For all beds this is given by:

$$\text{Bed-days (all)} = \text{SMR* x 0.47 + DEP x 0.015 (DIS/SUP)}$$

For acute beds 0-64 the slope of the line (i.e. change in bed-days with SMR) is somewhat less, the b-coefficient of 0.54 rising to 0.57 when supply is also taken into account, and falling to 0.29 when DEP is also entered, the regression equation in this case being:

$$\text{Bed-days (acute 0-64)} = \text{SMR64* x 0.29 + DEP x 0.029 (DIS/SUP)}$$

*SMR± 100

The relationship between SMR and acute 0-64 beds is of course much stronger than for all beds, as may be seen in the scatter diagrams for these two types of bed at figure 7.2; figure 7.3 shows the slopes of the various lines considered.

In these two models DEP has been allowed to take its full share in the explanation of variance and the relationship between SMR and bed-days is modified by DEP. To examine the contribution DEP would make over and above that explained by SMR it is necessary to adopt a two-stage model. This is done for acute beds 0-64 and takes the regression through the first three stages: SMR, DIS and SUP, at which stage 40.9% of the variance in beduse is explained and the relationship of SMR with bed-days is shown by the b-coefficient of 0.57. Expected values are then calculated for bed-days for each sector using the regression equation for SMR, DIS and SUP, which procedure effectively adjusts the expected bed-days in respect of the values of these three variables in each postcode sector.

The adjusted bed-days are compared with observed bed-days to provide a new ratio which is the residual variation - SMR, DIS and SUP having been taken into account. This adjusted ratio when regressed on DEP shows the additional contribution of deprivation, in this case independent of its link with mortality. Much of the variation which is explained by DEP has already been accounted for by SMR and this is reflected in the low coefficient for DEP seen in the regression equation:

$$\text{Bed-days} = \text{SMR}^* \times 0.57 + \text{DEP} \times 0.011$$
$$\text{(acute 0-64)} \quad \text{(DIS/SUP}$$

A model on a similar basis to this can also be computed, giving precedence to DEP instead of SMR, and supplying the equation:

$$\text{Bed-days} = \text{DEP} \times 0.046 + \text{SMR}^* \times 0.11$$
$$\text{(acute 0-64)}$$

$$^* \text{SMR} \pm 100$$

and with this model explaining 45.8% of the variance.

The explanatory power of the two factors — mortality and deprivation — singly and in combination are summarised in table 7.12 which shows the proportion of variance in acute 0-64 beduse which is explained by the measures. This is highest for the simple regression model at 47.6%, followed by the two-stage models, with DEP first in explaining 45.8% of the variance and SMR first in 44.1%, with the simple model therefore best explaining the variation. DEP alone explains more of the variance (36.5%) than SMR alone (31.7%); when distance and supply are taken into account the power of SMR is enhanced to 40.9% and that of DEP to 43.6% although there is only minor change in the b-coefficients for both variables from 0.54 to 0.57 for SMR and from 0.45 to 0.46 for DEP.

Comparison of the results for Scotland with those from the analysis for England in relation to RAWP has been made elsewhere (3) but it may be noted that the model selected in the RAWP analysis using all beds and SMR0-74,[2] would explain only 11.7% of the variation in bed-days in Scotland (table 7.11) although in the analysis over wards in six English regions it was found, in association with Jarman UPA scores, to account for 41% of the variance (in discharges). The b-coefficient of 0.44 for SMR0-74 (bed availability taken into account) is somewhat lower than the value of 0.51 seen in the Scottish data for the same (all) beds.

## *Results for Health Board Groups*

The stronger correlation with deprivation of acute beds and acute 0-64 compared with all beds (table 7.11) can also be seen for health boards grouped into areas (table 7.13). The correlation is always strongest in Western boards usually followed by those in the East and very weak in Rural areas (it was noted earlier that this may result from the smaller number of sectors and the low variability in deprivation scores in rural boards). Except for all beds the slope of the line (b-coefficient) is similar for the West and East groups; for the acute beds 0-64 the slope is also closer for Rural boards, and the 95% confidence intervals show that the slopes of the line are within the same range for all area groups for these particular beds — i.e. the relationship between DEP and bed-days may be considered as reasonably uniform throughout Scotland. These relationships would be slightly enhanced by the inclusion of DIS and SUP, as for SMR.

For mortality the correlation with bed-days has already been shown to be strongest (as with DEP) for acute beds 0-64 and, as with deprivation, the association is strongest in the West for all three categories of bed, and weakest in Rural boards (table 7.14). For the acute beds 0-64 the correlation is fairly strong in both West and East. For all beds and all acute beds the slope of the line is steeper in the West than East but for acute beds 0-64 is very similar. The confidence limits show that the relationship between SMR and bed-days does not differ significantly between West and East. The wide confidence limits for Rural areas also places these within the same range for all beds and all acute beds, but for acute 0-64 beds the upper limit (0.47) does not quite creep into the same range as the other two area groups. Given the limitations on the analysis for Rural boards this result is not significant. The correlation of SMR with bed-days is slightly stronger (DIS/SUP taken into account) than with DEP at Scotland level, and this can be seen also for health board groups, the stronger association being most apparent for Rural areas, and for the acute beds.

The relationships between bed-days and the four variables of mortality, distance, supply and deprivation which have been clarified in this chapter provide the basis for consideration of resources implications in the next.

TABLE 7.1   HOSPITAL USE MEASURES

|  |  | Discharges | | Bed-days | | Mean stay |
|  |  | Rates* | Percent | Rates* | Percent | [days] |
|---|---|---|---|---|---|---|
| All beds |  | 130 | 100 | 1733 | 100 | 13.3 |
|  | - 0-64 | 110 | 71.0 | 738 | 36.6 | 6.7 |
|  | - 65+ | 256 | 29.0 | 7794 | 63.4 | 30.5 |
| Acute | - all | 126 | 96.8 | 1055 | 60.9 | 8.3 |
|  | - 0-64 | 110 | 70.9 | 635 | 31.5 | 5.8 |
|  | - 65+ | 228 | 25.9 | 3626 | 29.4 | 15.9 |
| Long-stay | - all | 4.2 | 3.2 | 678 | 39.5 | 162 |
|  | - 0-64 | 0.3 | 0.2 | 103 | 5.1 | 412 |
|  | - 65+ | 27.8 | 3.0 | 4186 | 34.0 | 150 |

*per 1,000 population. all ages, 0-64. 65+ as appropriate

TABLE 7.2   DISCHARGE AND BED-DAYS RATES BY SEX AND AGE 1981
PER 1,000 POPULATION

|  | All specialities | | Acute | | Long-stay | |
|  | Male | Female | Male | Female | Male | Female |
|---|---|---|---|---|---|---|
| A - Discharge rates* | | | | | | |
| 0 - 4 | 160 | 112 | 160 | 112 | 0 | 0 |
| 5 - 14 | 82 | 59 | B2 | 59 | 0 | 0 |
| 15 - 24 | 79 | 92 | 79 | 92 | 0 | 0 |
| 25 - 34 | 85 | 126 | 85 | 126 | 0.1 | 0 |
| 35 - 44 | 95 | 131 | 94 | 131 | 0.2 | 0.2 |
| 45 - 54 | 124 | 130 | 124 | 130 | 0.4 | 0.3 |
| 55 - 64 | 181 | 136 | 179 | 135 | 1.5 | 1.2 |
| 65 - 74 | 270 | 193 | 259 | 183 | 11.1 | 9.5 |
| 75 + | 401 | 311 | 346 | 252 | 55.3 | 59.2 |
| B - Bed Day rates* | | | | | | |
| 0 - 4 | 791 | 659 | 791 | 659 | 0 | 0 |
| 5 - 14 | 347 | 253 | 347 | Z53 | 0 | 0 |
| 15 - 24 | 386 | 344 | 386 | 337 | 0 | 0 |
| 25 - 34 | 451 | 503 | 387 | 484 | 64 | 19 |
| 35 - 44 | 608 | 789 | 548 | ~684 | 61 | 105 |
| 45 - 54 | 1165 | 1075 | 922 | 884 | 244 | 191 |
| 55 - 64 | 2112 | 1752 | 1643 | 1324 | 469 | 428 |
| 65 - 74 | 4383 | 4187 | 2934 | 2461 | 1449 | 1726 |
| 75 + | 11173 | 14804 | 5281 | 5181 | 5892 | 9622 |

*excludes Fife

TABLE 7.3    CORRELATION OF HOSPITAL MEASURES, WITH DEPRIVATION, MORTALITY
AND PERMANENTLY SICK

|  | DEP | SMR all | 0-64 | 65+ | PERM SICK |
|---|---|---|---|---|---|
| Discharges |  |  |  |  |  |
| all | 0.46 | 0.30 | 0.32 | 0.21 | 0.36 |
| acute | 0.45 | 0.29 | 0.31 | 0.19 | 0.35 |
| 0-64 | 0.49 | 0.32 | 0.36 | 0.20 | 0.40 |
| 65+ | 0.16 | 0.10 | 0.06 | 0.14 | 0.07 |
| long-stay | 0.18 | 0.19 | 0.15 | 0.17 | 0.19 |
| Bed-days |  |  |  |  |  |
| all | 0.25 | 0.25 | 0.22 | 0.20 | 0.23 |
| acute | 0.41 | 0.33 | 0.35 | 0.22 | 0.34 |
| 0-64 | 0.60 | 0.48 | 0.56 | 0.31 | 0.55 |
| 65+ | 0.10 | 0.09 | 0.07 | 0.09 | 0.05 |
| long-stay | 0.10 | 0.16 | 0.12 | 0.15 | 0.14 |
| Mean stay |  |  |  |  |  |
| all | 0.01 | 0.08 | 0.04 | 0.09 | 0.04 |
| acute | 0.04 | 0.09 | 0.11 | 0.05 | 0.05 |
| 0-64 | 0.21 | 0.24 | 0.30 | 0.14 | 0.24 |
| 65+ | -0.01 | 0.01 | 0.03 | -0.01 | 0.01 |
| long-stay | -0.04 | 0.00 | -0.04 | 0.01 | -0.02 |

correlation over 928 sectors
(excludes Fife, Annandale/Eskdale and institutional sectors)

TABLE 7.4    HOSPITAL BED-DAYS BY DEPRIVATION CATEGORY
RATIOS PER 1,000 POPULATION

|  | Rate* All=100 | DEPCAT | | | | | | |
|---|---|---|---|---|---|---|---|---|
|  |  | Affluent 1 | 2 | 3 | 4 | 5 | Deprived 6 | 7 |
| All beds | 1733 | 80 | 92 | 97 | 99 | 102 | 110 | 127 |
| Acute beds | 1,055 | 79 | 91 | 97 | 99 | 100 | 111 | 132 |
| - 0-64 | 635 | 73 | 86 | 93 | 99 | 104 | 119 | 142 |
| - 65+ | 4,186 | 89 | 97 | 102 | 99 | 96 | 101 | 118 |
| Long-stay | 678 | 83 | 94 | 96 | 97 | 105 | 110 | 116 |

*per 1,000 population all ages, 0-64, 65+ as appropriate

TABLE 7.5 BED-DAYS RATIOS BY AGE, SEX AND DEPCAT

| | | DEPCAT | | | | | | | |
|---|---|---|---|---|---|---|---|---|---|
| | | Affluent 1 | 2 | 3 | 4 | 5 | 6 | Deprived 7 | ALL=* 100 |
| 0 - 4 | M | 81 | 86 | 82 | 95 | 100 | 123 | 165 | 791 |
| | F | 107 | 78 | 72 | 101 | 95 | 122 | 176 | 658 |
| 5 - 14 | M | 81 | 80 | 91 | 101 | 107 | 116 | 131 | 347 |
| | F | 85 | 81 | B9 | 94 | 9B | 119 | 160 | 253 |
| 15 - 24 | M | 79 | 102 | 100 | 102 | 96 | 101 | 111 | 387 |
| | F | 86 | 90 | 91 | 96 | 97 | 121 | 126 | 344 |
| 25 - 34 | M | 85 | 81 | 84 | 121 | 87 | 124 | 136 | 451 |
| | F | 70 | 81 | 92 | 106 | 101 | 116 | 150 | 503 |
| 35 - 44 | M | 61 | B8 | 86 | 95 | 107 | 118 | 193 | 608 |
| | F | 73 | 84 | 114 | 92 | 94 | 122 | 129 | 788 |
| 45- 54M | 58 | 99 | 75 | 97 | 114 | 130 | 139 | 1165 | |
| | F | 86 | 72 | 107 | 97 | 82 | 132 | 144 | 1075 |
| 55 - 64 | M | 69 | 80 | 87 | 109 | 102 | 115 | 138 | 2112 |
| | F | 68 | 96 | 100 | 96 | 111 | 99 | 128 | 1752 |
| 65 - 74 | M | 94 | 88 | 103 | 92 | 100 | 117 | 124 | 4383 |
| | F | 87 | 99 | 95 | 105 | 67 | 106 | 123 | 4187 |
| 75 + | M | 72 | 91 | 103 | 106 | 93 | 100 | 142 | 11170 |
| | F | 93 | 98 | 101 | 100 | 96 | 101 | 105 | 14804 |

*rates per 1,000 population

TABLE 7.6   BEDS USED* BY HEALTH BOARD OF TREATMENT AND AREA OF RESIDENCE: 1981 HEALTH BOARD OF RESIDENCE

| Health Board providing treatment | All areas | Argyll & Clyde | Ayrshire & Arran | Borders | Dumfries & Galloway | Fife | Forth Valley | Grampian | Greater Glasgow | Highland | Lanarkshire | Lothian | Tayside | Islands |
|---|---|---|---|---|---|---|---|---|---|---|---|---|---|---|
| Scotland | 24,521 | 2,212 | 1,546 | 652 | 669 | 1,412 | 1,073 | 2,284 | 5,104 | 939 | 2,404 | 3,569 | 2,042 | 430 |
| Argyll & Clyde | 1,897 | 1,776 | 61 | 0 | 0 | 0 | 3 | 0 | 33 | 3 | 1 | 1 | 1 | 0 |
| Ayrshire & Arran | 1,370 | 7 | 1,347 | 0 | 8 | 0 | 0 | 0 | 2 | 0 | 1 | 1 | 0 | - |
| Borders | 541 | 0 | 0 | 535 | 0 | 0 | 9 | 0 | 0 | 0 | 0 | 2 | 0 | - |
| Dumfries & Galloway | 640 | 0 | 6 | 0 | 618 | 0 | 0 | 0 | 1 | 0 | 1 | 0 | 2 | 0 |
| Fife | 1,191 | 0 | 0 | 0 | 0 | 1,182 | 0 | 0 | 1 | 0 | 0 | 4 | 3 | - |
| Forth Valley | 947 | 0 | 0 | 0 | - | 5 | 918 | 0 | 1 | 1 | 3 | 8 | 5 | 0 |
| Grampian | 2,288 | 1 | 0 | 1 | 0 | 4 | 0 | 2,207 | 1 | 18 | 1 | 1 | 5 | 39 |
| Greater Glasgow | 5,910 | 408 | 119 | 0 | 21 | 1 | 86 | 1 | 4,875 | 10 | 311 | 5 | 0 | 16 |
| Highland | 938 | 2 | 0 | 0 | 1 | 1 | 1 | 15 | 1 | 893 | 1 | 1 | 0 | 15 |
| Lanarkshire | 2,283 | 12 | 9 | 6 | 0 | 0 | 1 | 0 | 181 | 0 | 2,066 | 3 | 17 | 0 |
| Lothian | 3,984 | 4 | 3 | 109 | 20 | 133 | 62 | 5 | 5 | 11 | 18 | 3,540 | 1 | 4 |
| Tayside | 2,178 | 2 | 1 | 0 | 0 | 87 | 3 | 53 | 5 | 2 | 1 | 3 | 2,008 | 5 |
| Islands | 354 | 0 | 0 | 0 | - | 0 | 0 | 1 | 0 | 0 | 0 | 0 | 0 | 351 |

*Figures for beds used represent the average beds used daily
#"Islands" consists of Orkney, Shetland and Western Isles Health Boards

TABLE 7.7   AVAILABLE BEDS PER 1,000 POULATION FOR RESIDENT AND CATCHMENT
POPULATIONS BY HEALTH BOARD AND HEALTH DISTRICT 1981

| | All Beds | | Acute Beds | |
|---|---|---|---|---|
| | Resident | Catchment | Resident | Catchment |
| Argyll & Clyde | 5.35 | 6.57 | 3.08 | 4.21 |
| Argyll & Bute | 6.85 | 8.79 | 3.60 | 5.83 |
| Dunbarton | 5.19 | 6.72 | 2.79 | 4.17 |
| Inverclyde | 5.85 | 6.02 | 3.82 | 3.91 |
| Renfrew | 4.70 | 6.15 | 2.68 | 3.99 |
| Ayr & Arran | 4.62 | 5.26 | 2.92 | 3.57 |
| North Ayrshire | 3.38 | 5.06 | 1.88 | 3.43 |
| South Ayrshire | 6.34 | 5.42 | 4.37 | 3.65 |
| Borders | 5.75 | 7.63 | 3.47 | 5.13 |
| Dumfries & Galloway | 5.35 | 5.91 | 3.14 | 3.70 |
| Fife | 4.25 | 5.13 | 2.64 | 3.58 |
| East Fife | 4.91 | 5.91 | 3.02 | 4.12 |
| West Fife | 3.12 | 3.79 | 2.00 | 2.68 |
| Forth Valley | 4.84 | 5.74 | 2.82 | 3.52 |
| Falkirk | 4.06 | 5.22 | 2.60 | 3.50 |
| Stirling | 5.22 | 6.24 | 2.57 | 3.33 |
| Grampian | 5.90 | 6.17 | 3.96 | 4.17 |
| South Grampian | 8.16 | 6.40 | 6.06 | 4.16 |
| North Grampian | 2.98 | 5.63 | 1.22 | 4.70 |
| West Grampian | 4.05 | 5.61 | 2.30 | 3.84 |
| Greater Glasgow | 8.06 | 6.75 | 5.82 | 4.46 |
| Eastern | 9.46 | 6.87 | 7.12 | 4.38 |
| Northern | 7.32 | 5.65 | 4.83 | 4.85 |
| South East | 6.56 | 7.34 | 5.08 | 5.01 |
| South West | 7.99 | 6.44 | 5.02 | 4.26 |
| West | 8.83 | 6.51 | 6.63 | 4.09 |
| Highland | 6.43 | 6.68 | 4.42 | 4.55 |
| Northern | 5.24 | 7.64 | 2.18 | 3.94 |
| Southern | 6.74 | 6.52 | 5.02 | 4.64 |
| Lanark | 5.11 | 5.73 | 3.34 | 4.og |
| Monklands | 4.46 | 5.45 | 2.88 | 3.79 |
| Motherwell | 6.50 | 5.75 | 3.43 | 4.41 |
| Hamilton | 4.21 | 5.99 | 3.67 | 4.02 |
| Lothian | 6.90 | 6.41 | 5.09 | 4.49 |
| North Lothian | 5.97 | 6.58 | 4.03 | 4.38 |
| South Lothian | 8.87 | 6.62 | 6.98 | 4.70 |
| West Lothian | 4.34 | 5.23 | 3.01 | 3.87 |
| Tayside | 7.47 | 7.32 | 5.23 | 4.93 |
| Dundee | 8.17 | 7.02 | 5.81 | 4.47 |
| Perth & Kinross | 6.62 | 7.03 | 4.80 | 5.18 |
| Angus | 7.17 | 8.55 | 4.63 | 6.08 |

| Orkney | 6.30 | 8.81 | 3.12 | 4.72 |
| Shetland | 5.75 | 7.94 | 2.72 | 4.29 |
| Western Isles | 5.90 | 7.38 | 2.39 | 3.81 |
| SCOTLAND | 6.34 | 6.34 | 4.28 | 4.28 |

Catchment populations are based on allocating postcode sector populations as stated except for Fife; since postecoded data were not available the allocation of poulations was at health district level.

TABLE 7.8    DISTANCE TO HOSPITAL SERVICES
% OF POPULATION*

| miles | DGH facilities % | Basic acute facilities % |
|---|---|---|
| 0 < 1 | 13.7 | 17.8 |
| 1 < 2 | 17.9 | 20.8 |
| 2 < 5 | 30.7 | 31.3 |
| 5 < 10 | 16.6 | 15.8 |
| 10 < 15 | 7.0 | 6.5 |
| 15 < 20 | 2.5 | 2.3 |
| 20 < 50 | 8.7 | 5.3 |
| 50 < 100 | 1.9 | 0.2 |
| 100 or more | 1.2 | - |

*excludes Fife, Annandale, Eskdale which are not included in the hospital analysis

TABLE 7.9    DEPRIVATION, MORTALITY AND HOSPITAL VARIABLES:
CORRELATION MATRIX
(N = 928 SECTORS)

| | DEP | SMR | | | | BEDUSE | | | | |
|---|---|---|---|---|---|---|---|---|---|---|
| | | All | 0-64 | 0-74 | 65+ | All | Acute: All | 0-64 | 65+ | Long stay |
| SMRS | | | | | | | | | | |
| all | 0.73 | | | | | | | | | |
| 0-64 | 0.76 | 0.81 | | | | | | | | |
| 0-74 | 0.78 | 0.88 | 0.90 | | | | | | | |
| 65+ | 0.53 | 0.90 | 0.48 | 0.67 | | | | | | |
| BEDUSE | | | | | | | | | | |
| all | 0.25 | 0.25 | 0.22 | 0.24 | 0.20 | | | | | |
| acute | 0.41 | 0.33 | 0.35 | 0.34 | 0.22 | 0.45 | | | | |
| acute64 | 0.60 | 0.48 | 0.56 | 0.54 | 0.31 | 0.40 | 0.75 | | | |
| acute65 | 0.10 | 0.09 | 0.07 | 0.07 | 0.09 | 0.34 | 0.84 | 0.30 | | |
| longstay | 0.10 | 0.16 | 0.12 | 0.14 | 0.15 | 0.87 | 0.07 | 0.12 | -0.01 | |

TABLE 7.9   DEPRIVATION, MORTALITY AND HOSPITAL VARIABLES:
CORRELATION MATRIX
(N = 928 SECTORS)   CONTD.

| | DEP | SMR | | | | BEDUSE | | | | |
| | | All | 0-64 | 0-74 | 65+ | All | Acute: All | 0-64 | 65+ | Long stay |
|---|---|---|---|---|---|---|---|---|---|---|
| **BEDSUP** | | | | | | | | | | |
| all | -0.06 | 0.13 | -0.12 | -0.15 | -0.11 | 0.12 | 0.28 | 0.19 | 0.26 | -0.01 |
| acute | -0.07 | -0.16 | -0.13 | -0.6 | -0.14 | 0.14 | 0.32 | 0.23 | 0.29 | -0.00 |
| longstay | 0.01 | -0.02 | -0.03 | -1.05 | -0.02 | 0.12 | 0.09 | 0.07 | 0.07 | 0.10 |
| **DISTANCE** | | | | | | | | | | |
| acute | -0.17 | -0.13 | -0.15 | -0.18 | -0.09 | 0.07 | 0.01 | -0.12 | 0.11 | 0.00 |
| DGH | -0.14 | -0.11 | -0.11 | -0.15 | -0.09 | 0.06 | 0.06 | -0.06 | 0.13 | 0.00 |
| **PERM SICK** | 0.84 | 0.68 | 072 | 0.73 | 0.49 | 0.23 | 0.34 | 0.55 | 0.05 | 0.13 |

TABLE 7.10   BEDS AVAILABLE* AND BEDS USED BY HEALTH BOARDS
RATIOS: ALL = 100

| Health Board | Beds* Available | Beds+ Used |
|---|---|---|
| Argyll & Clyde | 104 | 105 |
| Ayr & Arran | 83 | 86 |
| Borders | 120 | 107 |
| Dumfries & Galloway | 93 | 91 |
| Fife | 81 | 87 |
| Forth Valley | 91 | 82 |
| Grampian | 97 | 99 |
| Greater Glasgow | 106 | 106 |
| Highland | 105 | 100 |
| Lanark | 90 | 104 |
| Lothian | 101 | 98 |
| Tayside | 115 | 98 |
| Rate = 100 = | 6.34 | 4.74 |

*beds in the health board per 1,000 catchment population
+beds occupied per 1,000 resident population, in any health board

TABLE 7.11   REGRESSION OF BED-DAYS ON SMR, DIS, SUP AND DEP

| | SMR all ages | | | | SMR 0-74 | | | | SMR 0-64 | | | |
| | S r | MR | $R^2$% | b | S r | MR | $R^2$% | b | S r | MR | $R^2$% | b |
|---|---|---|---|---|---|---|---|---|---|---|---|---|
| **All beds** | | | | | | | | | | | | |
| SMR | 0.294 | o.294 | 8.7 | 0.63 | 0.282 | 0.282 | 7.9 | 0.45 | 0.266 | 0.266 | 7.1 | 0.33 |
| DIS | 0.005 | 0.297 | 0.2 | 0.65 | 0.005 | 0.288 | 0.3 | 0.47 | 0.005 | 0.270 | 0.2 | 0.34 |
| SUP | 0.122 | 0.338 | 2.6 | 0.69 | 0.112 | 0.332 | 2.8 | 0.51 | 0.122 | 0.310 | 2.4 | 0.36 |
| DEP | 0.283 | 0.351 | 0.9 | 0.47 | 0.283 | 0.343 | 0.7 | 0.33 | 0.283 | 0.333 | 1.5 | 0.19 |
| | | 12.3 | | | | 11.8 | | | | 11.1 | | |

Acute beds

| | r | R | R²% | b | r | R | R²% | b | r | R | R²% | b |
|---|---|---|---|---|---|---|---|---|---|---|---|---|
| SMR | 0.331 | 0.331 | 11.0 | 0.53 | 0.343 | 0.343 | 11.8 | 041 | 0.357 | 0.357 | 12.7 | 0.33 |
| DIS | 0.061 | 0.346 | 0.9 | 0.55 | 0.061 | 0.361 | 1.3 | 0.43 | 0.061 | 0.370 | 1.0 | 0.34 |
| SUP | 0.324 | 0.5l4 | 14.4 | 0.65 | 0.324 | 0.526 | 14.6 | 0.51 | 0.324 | 0.526 | 13.9 | 0.39 |
| DEP | 0.407 | 0.560 | 5.0 | 0.56 | 0.407 | 0.560 | 3.7 | 0.21 | 0.404 | 0.563 | 4.0 | 0.17 |
| | | | 31.4 | | | | 31.4 | | | | 31.6 | |

Acute beds 0-64

| | r | R | R²% | b | r | R | R²% | b | r | R | R²% | b |
|---|---|---|---|---|---|---|---|---|---|---|---|---|
| SMR | 0.490 | 0.490 | 24.0 | 0.81 | 0.543 | 0.543 | 29.5 | 0.67 | 0.564 | 0.564 | 31.9 | 0.54 |
| DIS | 0.063 | 0.490 | 0.0 | 0.81 | 0.0631 | 0.544 | 0.0 | 0.67 | -0.063 | 0.564 | 0.0 | 0.54 |
| SUP | 0.226 | 0.578 | 9.4 | 0.89 | 0.226 | 0.628 | 9.9 | 0.74 | 0.226l | 0.641 | 9.2 | 0.57 |
| DEP | 0.604 | 0.671 | 11.5 | 0.28 | 0.604 | 0.680 | 6.8 | 0.32 | 0.604 | 0.690 | 6.5 | 0.29 |
| | | | 44.9 | | | | 46.2 | | | | 47.6 | |

S r = correlation coefficients with bed-days

M R = multiple correlation coefficient

$R^2$ % = percentage change in r-squared at each step

b = b-coefficient of the SMR with bed-days at each step, SMR±100

TABLE 7.12  PREDICTORS OF BEDUSE ACUTE 0-64

| | | % variance explained | SMR b-coeff. | DEP b-coeff. |
|---|---|---|---|---|
| 1 | SMR 0-64 alone | 31.7 | 0.54 | |
| 2 | SMR 0-64 (DIS/SUP) | 40.9 | 0.57 | - |
| 3 | DEP alone | 36.5 | - | 0.045 |
| 4 | DEP (DIS/SUP) | 43.6 | - | 0.046 |
| 5 | SMR 0-64 (DIS/SUP) + DEP (simple model) | 47.5 | 0.29 | 0.029 |
| 6 | SMR 0-64 (DIS/SUP) + DEP (2-stage model) | 44.1 | 0.57 | 0.011 |
| 7 | DEP (DIS/SUP) + SMR 0-64 (2-stage model) | 45.8 | 0.11 | 0.046 |

TABLE 7.13   ASSOCIATION OF DEP WITH BED-DAYS FOR HEALTH BOARD GROUPS CORRELATIONS\*, B-COEFFCIENTS AND CONFIDENCE INTERVALS

| Beds | SMR#<br>(simple r) | Correlation<br>(slope) | b coefficient<br>limits | 95% confidence | | |
|------|------|------|------|------|------|------|
| | Scotland | 0.28 | 0.027 | 0.021 | - | 0.033 |
| all | West | 0.39 | 0.034 | 0.026 | - | 0.042 |
| | East | 0.13 | 0.015 | 0.003 | - | 0.027 |
| | Rural | 0.01 | 0.001 | 0.034 | - | 0.036 |
| | Scotland | 0.41 | 0.029 | 0.025 | - | 0.034 |
| acute | West | 0.56 | 0.035 | 0.030 | - | 0.039 |
| all ages | East | 0.40 | 0.036 | -0.027 | - | 0.045 |
| | Rural | 0.00 | -0.001 | -0.028 | - | 0.027 |
| | Scotland | 0.60 | 0.045 | 0.041 | - | 0.049 |
| acute | West | 0.70 | 0.047 | 0.043 | - | 0.050 |
| 0-64 | East | 0.55 | 0.049 | 0.041 | - | 0.057 |
| | Rural | 0.17 | 0.028 | 0.003 | - | 0.053 |

TABLE 7.14   ASSOCIATION OF SMR WITH BED-DAYS FOR HEALTH BOARD GROUPS CORRELATIONS\*, B-COEFFICIENTS AND CONFIDENCE INTERVALS

| Beds | SMR# | Correlation<br>(multiple r) | b-coefficient<br>(slope) | 95% confidence<br>limits | | |
|------|------|------|------|------|------|------|
| all | all | | | | | |
| | Scotland | 0.34 | 0.70 | 0.57 | - | 0.83 |
| | West | 0.43 | 0.86 | 0.67 | - | 1.05 |
| | East | 0.23 | 0.52 | 0.25 | - | 0.80 |
| | Rural | 0.15 | 0.15 | -0.26 | - | 0.57 |
| acute | all | | | | | |
| all | Scotland | 0.51 | 0.65 | 0.56 | - | 0.74 |
| ages | West | 0.65 | 0.80 | 0.68 | - | 0.91 |
| | East | 0.44 | 0.70 | 0.50 | - | 0.91 |
| | Rural | 0.40 | 0.48 | 0.18 | - | 0.79 |
| acute | 0-64 | | | | | |
| 0-64 | Scotland | 0.64 | 0.57 | 0.52 | - | 0.61 |
| | West | 0.72. | 0.62 | 0.56 | - | 0.68 |
| | East | 0.60 | 0.62 | 0.52 | - | 0.72 |
| | Rural | 0.31 | 0.32 | 0.16 | - | 0.47 |

\*No. of sectors = Scotland 918, West 405, East 343, Rural 170
#DIS/SUP taken into account

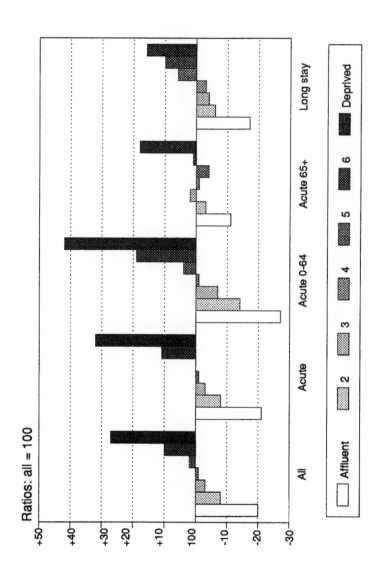

FIGURE 7.1 BED DAYS 1981 BY DEPCAT

Acute bed-days (0 - 64) vs. SMR (0 - 64)

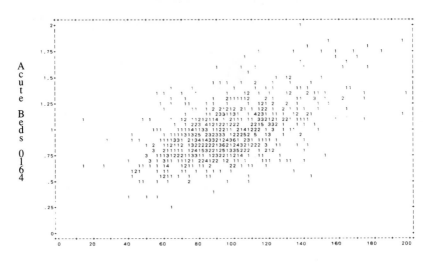

746 cases plotted                SMR 0 - 64

FIGURE 7.2

All bed-days (all ages) vs. SMR (all ages)

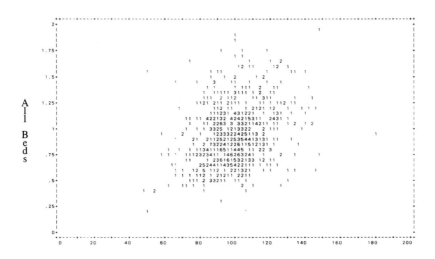

727 cases plotted                SMR all ages

FIGURE 7.2

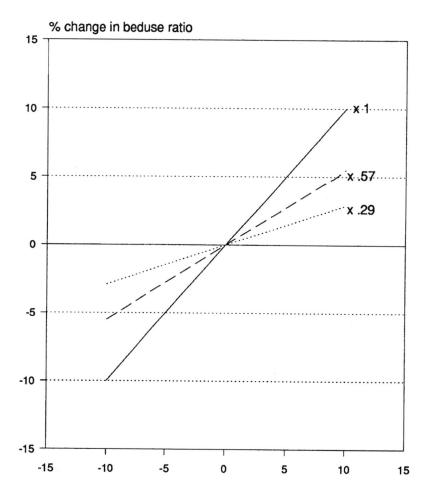

FIGURE 7.3    RELATIONSHIP BETWEEN BEDUSE AND SMR
(BEDS ACUTE 0 - 64, SMR 0 - 64)

CHAPTER 8

# Resource Allocation in the Health Service

The relationship between beduse, mortality and deprivation leads on to consideration of these in respect of the formula used for resource allocation in the health service.

Resource allocation refers to the process of distributing the sum voted by Parliament to run the health service between the fifteen health boards in Scotland. The formula for distribution was set out in the Report of the Working Party on Revenue Resource Allocation (SHARE) in 1977[1] and, with some modifications, the procedures described in that document continue to provide the basis for distribution. Similar though slightly different proposals are detailed in the RAWP report for England and Wales.[2] Recent proposals for reorganisation of the health service imply some change in many elements of this formula but indicate that weighting 'to reflect the health and age distribution of the population' will remain.[3]

The main principle underlying both the SHARE and RAWP formulae rests in providing funding to health boards on an equitable basis in relation to the needs of the population. One intention, and effect, of the introduction of the formula was to move away from previous methods of allocation which related essentially to established levels of funding; these were determined in large part by the level of resources available in an area which was to some extent a matter of historical accident. Since there was no apparent equation between this level of resources and any identifiable need a new approach to resource allocation was required which would relate as objectively as possible to the needs in different areas.

The measurement of need for health care of course presents considerable problems since no valid and absolutely comparative measures can be identified. Both the SHARE and RAWP working parties concluded that one of the main determinants of need for health care was the age and sex composition of a population. This is obvious to all and is documented in the data in tables 7.1 and 7.2 showing use of (general) hospital services by age group; use of these services increases with age and the elderly use a high proportion of the resources. Much preventive care however is directed mainly at younger ages (children and mothers) and the formula in respect of community services (child health, ante-natal, community dental services, etc.) is weighted towards the other end of the age range.

Over and above adjustments due to age and sex structure differentials in morbidity between populations in health board areas were also considered to exist and the working parties recognised that a component in respect of these differentials should be incorporated in the formula. Fully objective and comparable measures of total (or general) morbidity are not however available and, in lieu of an acceptable measure, the standardised mortality ratio was adopted as the most reliable,accessible and objective proxy for differences in health state between the populations of health boards and regional authorities. In the Scottish formula the SMR used is that for the age group 0-64 and this weighting is applied in various parts of the formula in calculating the allocation for specific services (see fig.8.1.); it functions to augment the allocations to boards with SMRs greater than 100 and to diminish those to boards with SMRs below that level. In England and Wales the SMR adopted in the formula was for all ages and condition-specific (ICD chapters), weighted by the beds used for that group of conditions. Current proposals have recently changed that basis to the all-causes SMR 0-74.[4]

The SHARE working group also considered the possibility of introducing a weighting specifically related to the extra burden which can be expected to fall on  the health service in areas of multiple deprivation but concluded that none of the measures could be directly related to a quantified level of bed utilisation.

This analysis now provides some evidence of this relationship, and also of the weighting which might be appropriate in respect of the SMR.

The SMR 0-64 was selected in Scotland rather than the all ages SMR on the basis that mortality in old age and need for health care may well be inversely related, i.e. if more people die than fewer remain in the population requiring care for conditions of old age and vice versa. This argument is contrary to that for the younger age group where mortality and ill health are considered to be linked in the same direction. The argument may have some validity since we may assume that on balance there is a proportionately greater incidence of acute disease in younger age groups and that treatment may restore a high proportion of persons receiving care to previous levels of functional capacity; in the elderly on the other hand long-term disabling conditions will be more prevalent, treatment will be less effective in achieving restorative outcome and residual pathology will more often remain and require continuing care.

Some evidence on needs for hospital care in the elderly comes from the hospital discharge data, which show that among the elderly discharge rates for men are higher than for women at each age group but beduse rates are higher for women, and this differential increases with age. At age 85 and over discharge rates for women are 22% lower than for men and beduse rates 36% higher (table 8.1).

These data suggest greater morbidity (as evidenced by discharges) in men, who also have higher SMRs - i.e. a positive association between mortality and morbidity. Greater 'need' for hospital care (beds used) is evident however in women, in particular for those aged 75 and over; in view of their lower mortality this indicates a negative association between mortality and need for care. Women aged 75 and over account for over 50% of the beds used by both males and females aged 65 and over so that the needs for care in this group are not insignificant to the debate.

Most of the excess stay in hospital is likely to be attributable to social factors, women being less likely to have a spouse available who could play a role in preventing admission or providing care after discharge; some of the longer stay could also possibly reflect the enhanced capacity for survival which is observed in women and thus imply a true morbidity factor.

The influence of social factors may be seen in table 8.2 which shows clearly the lesser demand on hospital beds by the married than by the single and widowed.

These differentials are particularly marked for the long-stay beds with the single and widowed making two to four times as much use as the married. Divorced women provide an exception to the general pattern for the unmarried, but are relatively few in number in these two age groups. Of course fewer women in these two age groups are married: 32% compared with 68% of men (table 8.2).

In the Scottish formula the effect of the SMR weighting is to increase or decrease the allocation (for the age group 0-64) for specific elements of the formula (as seen in fig. 8.1) by 1% for every unit of SMR above or below 100.

The use of the SMR in the formulae has attracted a considerable amount of debate, not to say criticism, on two counts. Firstly, its value as a proxy for morbidity (or need for health care) has been brought into question , and secondly, the gearing (or elasticity) of one percent for each unit of SMR has also never been fully justified. The use of the all-causes SMR in Scotland however has made it impervious to the additional criticism which has been directed at the use of cause-specific SMRs in the English RAWP formula. In addition the proposition has been advanced that deprivation creates needs for health care which are not fully reflected in the SMR and that it would be appropriate to incorporate a component for deprivation in the formula.[5]

This analysis has allowed some of these issues to be explored in the case of the general (non-psychiatric/non-obstetric) hospital beds.

Firstly the value of the SMR 0-64 as a proxy for differential needs for health care in this age group is supported by the finding that SMR64 (SUP and DIS taken into account) explains 40.9% of the variance in BEDUSE (table 7.12). It is hardly to be expected that mortality will explain a major part of the variance in bed-days since clearly other factors such as referral practice, admitting practice and the availability of alternative forms of care will all have an influence over and above both true morbidity and the social factors which are inherent in the variations in mortality.

Considerable support is also provided for the Scottish decision to select the SMR 0-64 for use in the SHARE formula (applied to the allocation to that age group), since DEP and SMR64 are most highly correlated with BEDUSE acute 64 (most of the beduse by this group) but only at low levels with all beds, acute beduse 65 and over and long-stay beds.

The increment in bed-days (0-64) per unit of SMR (0-64) is shown to be below the level of one percent currently used in the formula, and analysis for three area groups within Scotland shows this relationship to be constant (table 7.15). This was not the case for all beds or all acute beds for both of which the gradient was steeper in the West than in the other two areas.

The value of using SMR64 in relation to bed use by this age group in SHARE is thus further endorsed.

These conclusions lead on to consideration of the implications of the evidence for resource allocations to specific health boards.

## The Implications for Resource Allocation to Health Boards

The information which emerges from the regression analyses showing the relationship between bed days. mortality and deprivation (chapter 7) provides the basis for calculating allocations to health boards.

The various coefficients for SMR and DEP in relation to BEDUSE in table 7.12 show that the increment in bed-days in relation to mortality in considerably less than the value of unity which has hitherto provided the basis in the formula, and implementation of these findings would thus imply some fairly major gains and losses in the funding to health boards. The value of 0.54 attaching to SMR-64 alone would obviously result in losses for health boards with high mortality and gains for those with low since the former would gain less and the latter lose less by the use of an incremental value of 0.54% than of 1%. Introduction of a crude change in this value on its own does not appear equitable since it ignores a great deal of information emerging from the analysis which shows that deprivation contributes to bed-days over and above SMR. Equally a change which substituted DEP for SMR would be equally inefficient, DEP alone explaining only 36.5% of the variance in bed-days (and SMR 31.7%) compared with 44% and 47% when the two variables are considered jointly.

The formulae which use SMR and DEP jointly to explain bed-days therefore provide the basis for calculating the estimated requirements for health boards.

The coefficients which emerge from the regression analyses are used to calculate the effects for health boards for the allocation of resources in relation to general hospital beds which in the 1989-90 SHARE calculation[6] accounted for 54.2% of the allocations which are determined by the formula.

The method of weighting populations for mortality and deprivation is shown in figure 8.2 and the simple and two-stage formulae are given in table 7.12. The calculations follow the SHARE procedure although ignoring the adjustment which is normally made in respect of costs for older patients (see figure 8.2). The age/sex beduse rates which are used to effect the adjustment on these factors in the first stage of the formula are seen in table 7.2. The SMRs (0-64) used are those for 1980-82 (see table 8.3) which provide the basis for the SHARE 1984-85 distribution; these differ slightly from those reported earlier (chapter 3) in including deaths of persons resident outwith Scotland. SMRs have also seen some change since that date, although for 1985-87 all boards with SMRs below 100 in 1980-82 were still in that range;[7] two boards with higher levels in 1980-82 show a considerable decrease in 1985-87, albeit still remaining at 100 or more. It must be remembered that actual death rates continue to decline, the SMR showing the variation around the mean. It should be noted that adjustments in respect of cross-border flow - patients treated in a board other than the one they live in - are introduced at a later stage in the calculation and are not considered here.

The results in table 8.3 and figure 8.3 show the effects of using a weighting of unity for SMR (i.e. change from the age/sex basis) as well as the use of both the simple and two-stage models which give precedence to SMR (equations 5 and 6 in table 7.12), the effects in these cases being compared with allocations based on a weighting of one per cent for SMR. The changes shown are for the total populations with the SMR weighting being applied only at 0-64. The effect of the mortality weighting is thus modified by the addition of estimates for the age group 65 and over, with the result for instance that, with an SMR weighting of one percent, the 16% excess in mortality (0-64) for Glasgow attracts an increment of around six percent over the total age group, and Grampian with an SMR of 83 suffers a reduction of around six percent. In considering the changes implied it must be borne in mind that SHARE is a distributive formula and the total resources remain constant; the formula does not calculate absolute requirements but relative SHARES.

On either formula all boards with SMRs above 100 would suffer reductions compared with present funding; for the simple model these result in reductions of, for instance, -1.61% in Argyll & Clyde and -1.34% in Greater Glasgow, with Highland experiencing a reduction of over two percent (-2.69%) due to having both a high SMR and a low DEP score. Boards with low SMRs gain for the most part with Tayside and Grampian being the biggest gainers with increments respectively of +2.83% and +2.50%. Dumfries & Galloway and the Islands both show losses despite SMRs below 100, due to their low scores on deprivation. The two-stage model shows generally less drastic change from the present position with the reduction being greatest for Glasgow at -1.36 (similar to the simple model), while Argyll & Clyde would lose -1.10% and Highland -1.21%. Grampian would be the biggest gainer on this model (+2.0%) followed by Tayside (+1.84%).

The effect of using a revised value for the SMR only can also be seen in the table, and the additional effect of DEP in each instance. Amending the formula only to reduce the weighting for SMR from one to a lower weighting (0.29% or 0.57%) would generally effect bigger change than with DEP also included since boards with high SMR values also tend to have high DEP scores and the inclusion of deprivation into the formula tends to compensate these for losses suffered through a reduction in the gearing or elasticity of SMR, and vice versa. The exceptions are Ayr & Arran and Highland; the latter loses on both counts having both high mortality (see chapter 4) and low deprivation while Ayr & Arran with a very low positive DEP score suffers a negative effect which results from the distributional constraint that requires total resources to remain constant.

Some of these adjustment may seem small but need to be viewed in the context of expenditure on the health service. In 1987/88 expenditure on all services totalled £2,233 million. [8] Current expenditure on hospital services amounted to £1,365 million with approximately 60% going to general hospitals i.e. £819 million.

The largest board, Greater Glasgow, would spend around £218 million (estimate) on general hospital services so that a downward shift of -1.34% (table 8.3) in the allocation represents a potential reduction of £2.9 million (at 1987/88 prices) in the resource available.

Table 8.3 shows also the change effected by SMR x 1 from the age/sex basis which provides the first stage in the formula. These effects can also be seen in figure 8.3.

These results are also expressed in table 8.4 as weighted populations and in table 8.5 as bed ratios. The weighted population base (table 8.4) is that actually used in SHARE calculations and of course incorporates the element of population size; it shows the proportionate share of resources going to each board. The bed ratios in table 8.5 remove the element of population size and show comparative bed requirements for each health board. It should be remembered that these reflect 1981 levels of provision and refer to occupied beds, i.e. no allowance is made for the time the bed remains empty between patients. For interest the results of the basic age/sex weighting adjustments are also shown, in the first column: Lanarkshire with its younger population attracts a considerable downward adjustment, from 4.74 to 3.94, and the values of 5.77 for the Borders and 5.27 for Tayside reflect the more elderly profile in these boards. Adjustment for SMR x 1 modifies the range in the values although Lanarkshire and Borders still remain at the extremes. Population factors are seen to outweigh all others, since Borders with low SMR and low DEP displays the highest ratios on all adjustments and Lanark, with high SMR and positive DEP, the lowest.

In the models considered so far mortality has been given precedence over DEP in explaining bed-days, and SMR clearly makes the biggest contribution to the adjustment to the estimated requirements for health boards. A formula which gives precedence to deprivation is also a feasible alternative: the simple formula, number 5 in table 7.12, provides one model and the other is given by the two-stage formula, number 7, which explains slightly more of the variation in bed-days (45.8%) than does the two-stage formula, number 6; in which SMR is allowed to account for most of the explanation, in this case explaining 40.9% and DEP adding only 3.2% (44.1% in total). DEP entered first explains 43.6% of the variance, with SMR adding only 2.2%. Using the simple formula the results, with DEP entered first, are exactly the same as when SMR is entered first (table 8.6), most of the total adjustment occurring at the first stage of adjusting for DEP.

Using the two-stage model with DEP making the major contribution presents a somewhat different picture with health board allocations in general showing more extreme deviation from the current basis than either of the other two formulae (figure 8.4). The biggest loss is seen for Highland (-3.97%) since its favourable deprivation score means that it loses heavily (compared with an incremental value of one percent for SMR) and the low weighting of 0.11% for SMR does little to compensate for this. Tayside attracts the largest gains since the negative effect from DEP is small compared with the gain from reduction of the SMR weighting. For all except three boards the effects on the allocations of using any of these three models is always in the same direction, boards gaining or losing consistently. The exceptions are the three boards for which the effects are somewhat marginal: Fife, Forth Valley and the Islands. The former two attract losses on the final model considered since they lose from the SMR adjustment more than they gain from DEP; the results for the Islands is more complex but only on the two-stage model with SMR in first do they gain more from the SMR lower weighting of 0.57% (i.e. lose less than SMR x 1%), than they lose in respect of their relatively low deprivation score.

These results show that the simple model provides the best result since not only does it explain the greatest proportion of the variance but the end results for health board are the same whether deprivation or mortality is given precedence in the formula. The two-stage model with SMR in first and given the greatest weighting shows lesser deviation from the present basis for allocation, for most but not all boards. It is the case that all boards with positive deprivation scores lose on all of these models so that expectations that an adjustment for deprivation would direct more resources to them are not realised, the reason being that, with SMRs in excess of 100, all of these boards suffer greater losses from a reduction in the weighting for each unit of SMR to less than 1% than they gain in respect of their more severe deprivation.

## Bed-Days as a Measure of Need

The validity of these models and therefore the question of whether they provide a more equitable basis than does the present formula for the allocations to health boards rests on whether beduse provides an adequate measure of need for these particular services and can therefore be defended as a basis on which to determine the weighting for the SMR. The use of bed-days in this way requires some justification since bed-days was rejected by the working parties which originally developed the formulae, for the very good reason that as between health authorities the level of bed-days (or beduse) will directly reflect the level of bed provision; and at this level it is likely that this is the case (see table 7.10). Since then bed use has featured in a number of analyses (in England and Wales) concerned with developing alternatives to the SMR, and this use has been heavily criticised on the basis that demand and supply are inextricably intertwined and that high rates of hospital use by deprived populations are a product both of high levels of need and a high level of supply since 'deprived populations in the UK tend to be concentrated in inner city areas that have a relatively plentiful supply of hospital beds'.[9] Within Scotland however this relatively plentiful supply of beds in the cities is available to populations which are widespread geographically, and the influence of supply is more reliably observed since the ratio of beds to population will be relatively invariable across a wide range of sectors at all levels of deprivation and mortality, and each level of deprivation and mortality will be associated with varying levels of supply. The analysis of the relationships between these factors at sector level has shown the factor of bed availability (supply) to be relatively less important than both deprivation and mortality in explaining variations in beduse (table 7.9). The measure of bed supply employed is also believed to be more reliable than has been achieved in other studies since the comprehensive database available for Scotland allows the calculation of the catchment populations with some certainty.

Apart form considerations of supply, beduse is accused of having imperfections as a measure of need for health care which stem from the lack of a perfect equivalence between need and use and critics comment the current utilisation provides no indication of the appropriateness of different rates of hospital use among socio-economic groups.[9] Not only morbidity but patient tolerance, general practitioners' behaviour, the availability and acceptability of alternative modes of care and variations in hospital doctors' practice style will influence hospital use.[10] Both the fact of admission and the length of time spent in hospital are factors susceptible to varying fashions and constraints, and the need for hospital care is not a constant which can readily be identified. While there are obvious conditions involving the use of sophisticated techniques and equipment, and specialised facilities and environments where the need for hospital care is beyond doubt, for many conditions considerable elasticity exists in the demand for hospital care which may be influenced by the availability or standard of other forms of care, in the community, or in private, voluntary or local authority institutional services.

Critics who argue that existing use reflects not only morbidity in a population but many extraneous factors relating to the circumstances of patients or doctors surely overlook the fact that 'met' demand not 'theoretical' demand reflects the realities of the situation and that, for the most part, these theoretical demands cannot be quantified. Indeed, since 'for more than 80% of medical conditions and large numbers of surgical conditions the need for hospital care is not clearly defined and there is little professional consensus as to the appropriate form of management'[11] the measurement of 'appropriate' demand or theoretical need is unlikely to be attainable in the near future although met and appropriate demand may possibly come closer together as time progresses. Although it may not provide a perfect measure of need for hospital care, nevertheless the correlation of beduse 0-64 not only with mortality and deprivation but also with permanent sickness (r=0.55), provides some confidence that variations in morbidity within the population account for some of the variations in morbidity within the population account for some of the variations observed in beduse.

It is notable that critics of health service use as an indicator of need universally ignore the first stage of the formula, which weights local populations by age/sex beduse rates at national level. Comments about 'appropriate' use would also apply to these adjustments which have been shown (table 8.5) to make an important contribution to the end results. Even at this stage then both RAWP and SHARE reflect 'existing practices'. Beduse therefore is already accepted as a valid measure of variation in need for hospital care by age and sex in the the resource allocation formula and despite its imperfections, arguably recommends itself more as a measure of need for hospital care than discharges in theory total stay for an episode of care should not be subject to the same vagaries in practice (organisational, clinical or recording) which affect discharges, although still of course susceptible to some degree since clinicians will have varying discharge policies and some may treat on a day case or outpatients basis (where appropriate), thus avoiding any length of stay.

Since it is not possible to create a model (particularly at small area level) which would quantify all of these possible influences we are inevitably left with an imperfect measure of need in terms of demand whether utilising patient demand (discharges) or resources used (bed-days). Hospital use however reflects the realities of the (met) demand for hospital care which is clearly determined by many factors other than true morbidity.

## *Mortality, Deprivation, Morbidity*

Both mortality and deprivation have been shown to be determinants of hospital use, with both explaining very similar proportions of the variation in beduse by the age group 0-64. The respective merits of these alternative measures as candidates for use in the formula must take into account other considerations. Commenting on a study in North East Thames, in which the outcome was to supplant mortality with socio-economic groups, the point was made that since both SMRs and SEGs were found to be highly correlated, 'the choice of which indicator to use ought to have hinged on factors such as which was nearer to being a direct measure of population health status, more comprehensive, more independent of supply and so on'. [12] In this context deprivation could be viewed more as a determinant, and mortality more as an outcome which is affected by deprivation, with mortality conceptually being more closely akin to health state. Deprivation would certainly be viewed as more independent of supply. Mays' comment that 'the mortality data used in RAWP had the advantage of being independent of the existing unequal supply of health service resource' [12] comes close to suggesting that health service provision does not affect mortality. The relationship between these two inputs and outputs has never been adequately determined although Blaxter concludes that there have been some measurable beneficial effects [13] and Charlton that the fall which has occurred in mortality from causes amenable to medical intervention can probably be attributed to health care. [14] It appears a more reasonable hypothesis that health services effect some reduction (i.e. postponement) of mortality in the population. The use of SMR as a proxy for morbidity in the resource allocation formula and the redistribution of resources to give more to authorities with high mortality and less to those with low was not accompanied by any explicit statement about an expected influence on this outcome measure. Although some reduction in the variation between health boards of mortality over the decade in which SHARE came into operation has been reported[15] it appears improbable that most of those changes could be attributed to the reallocations which had occurred.

Another consideration might be the stability of a measure since 'sudden and unpredictable shifts' in allocations are forecast in 1991, following a decision to include a measure of deprivation in the RAWP formula.[16] Although characteristics of small areas may change it appears improbable however that major variation would occur in the relative position of health boards in Scotland; it is the case also that SMRs, even averaged over three years, exhibit fluctuations from year to year.[7] Since, at present, deprivation measures are available only from census material, they might be expected to bring additional stability into the formula.

The SMR itself has been subject to much criticism 'mainly hostile'[9] with a great deal of effort directed at attempting to measure the association of mortality and morbidity, and with a recent reviewer concluding that it is 'now commonly agreed that RAWP's choice of mortality as a surrogate for morbidity was inadequate - although it is much less clear what should be put in its place'[17] but with other protagonists in this arena arguing that 'there is no convincing empirical case for displacing SMRs and that SMRs remain valid since a better proxy for morbidity has not yet been developed'.[16]

We would agree with this conclusion since the results from this analysis indicate that the SMR does provide a reasonable proxy for needs for general hospital care for the age group 0-64, and that it reflects also at least one aspect of morbidity (permanent sickness in the population of working age), with this measure also correlating strongly with beduse by the younger age group. Mortality thus appears to incorporate much of the variation in morbidity which stems from deprivation, although deprivation makes an independent additional contribution to demand for hospital care, presumably reflecting a variation in those elements of the illness experience which do not lead to death. Steeper gradients seen in both the temporary and permanent sickness measures compared with mortality suggest that this may be the case.

Measures of mortality have much to recommend them for use in the resource allocation formulae and the original reasons for their selection still hold good: at the all causes level they are comprehensive and reasonably reliable, the event carries an unequivocal meaning and the measures are available on a yearly basis as a by-product of the registration process.

The need to 'address directly questions of the distribution of morbidity rather than relying on evermore indirect proxies for health resource need'[9] is still on the agenda and the search for a reliable and objective measure of differences in morbidity has given rise to an extensive literature on this topic, much of it at the conceptual level due to the absence of good data.[18] This search is likely to continue.

None of the various measures examined in this analysis suggests that it could unarguably fill this role. The cancer registration data emerge as the most reliable since the fact of disease has been established, registrations should be reasonably complete and duplication of registration should not occur, but the measure suffers the limitation that registrations cover only a part of the total spectrum of disease and their relationship to this total spectrum is unknown; the recording of many other specific health events suffers from these same problems.

The infant measure of low weight also provides an objective and reliable measure but not one that would be acceptable as an indicator of morbidity in the population generally. Other hospital-based measures suffer from various problems

— the influence of supply, multiple admissions, other treatment alternatives — which negate their usefulness as an indicator of morbidity at health board level.

Temporary and permanent sickness measures from the census relate mainly to the population of working age and are susceptible to economic change, deriving as they do from a question aimed primarily at identifying the working status of the respondent. Levels of unemployment, it has been suggested, may influence the response to this census question, older persons of working age in particular being more ready to identify themselves as sick rather than unemployed when the prospects of re-employment are poor [19] and Piachaud has shown that an increase in the prevalence of long-term sickness and early retirement has largely been a result of the declining labour market. [20]

Extending consideration beyond those used in this enquiry, measures which are both comprehensive and general come in the main from population sample surveys with the General Household Survey (GHS) providing an established and reputable example of a continuing enquiry which covers the entire population of Great Britain. [21] The health measures are based on self-reporting and therefore not wholly objective but individual's assessments of their own health have been shown to correlate well with the incidence of a wide range of symptoms and the results from physical tests in the recent one-off Health and Lifestyle survey. [22] The excess mortality of those declaring themselves as sick in the census, shown in table 6.5, also provides evidence for the validity of self-reported measures. Some doubts must remain nevertheless about how far people's perceptions influence their readiness to declare themselves as sick: despite the higher mortality in Scotland compared with England and Wales (table 3.9) self-reported measures from the GHS are not higher in Scotland for either acute or chronic sickness [28] a finding which must at least raise a query whether the Scots are less likely to consider themselves as sick compared with their counterparts in the south.

All sample surveys, including the GHS, suffer from the problem of inadequate sample size for the purposes of identifying differences between populations; the Scottish sample of around 2500 in a year does not even permit reliable estimates to emerge for some sub-groups of the entire population and regional breakdowns within Scotland are out of the question.

The limitations of present measures should result in a welcome for the proposal to include a question similar to the GHS question on long-standing illness in the 1991 census [23] for people of all ages and not tied to a question on economic activity as present sickness measures are, since apparently this should provide a robust basis for examining regional differences. As with most sample surveys however (including the GHS) the census measure is likely to fall into the error of failing to include a section of the population which should make a potentially large contribution: those who are sick and in hospital or other institutional care on census day.

Persons who had been resident more than six months in 'non-private households' were counted in the 1981 census as resident there and postcode of their home residence was not collected for them. Those resident less than six months would normally appear in the database in the area where they live only if a household was present to complete a census form and enter them as absent member of the household. The proportion of persons who are classed as residents varies considerably, from 13% in hotels and boarding houses to 84% in psychiatric hospitals and 91% in old people's homes (see Appendix A5), and unless there is any change in the procedures for assigning area of residence for this group in the population (which presents obvious problems for long-term residents) then considerable numbers of people who might reasonably be expected to fall into the category of long-standing illness will not be included in the counts. Long-stay hospital patients are demonstrably making demands on the most expensive sector of the health service and any attempt to identify needs for health care (in terms of long-standing illness) without including them would be bound to lack credibility. Variations in the local level of supply of long-term facilities could of course impinge on the numbers living in the community with long-standing illness and a measure based solely on those living in private households could not be considered to be free of the supply problem which has loomed large in criticisms of beduse as an indicator of need for services. Even if achieved, the leap from this (partial) measure of morbidity to determining the health care needs of the entire population is a large one and should provide endless opportunities for further debate and research.

Enough has been said to illustrate the complexities and problems which emerge in relation to this apparently simple proposition to measure the nation's health on a comprehensive basis. An objective reliable and certain measure of morbidity or need for health care does not appear to be just on the horizon, and the indisputable qualities of the SMR look even more attractive in the light of these considerations.

## Other Elements in the Formula

Results from the analysis which have been considered in this chapter would apply in respect of the part of the formula that relates to general (non-psychiatric/non-maternity) beds which in the 1989-90 calculation accounted for 54.2% of the allocations relating to weighted populations and the total composite weighted population (see figure 8.1) would therefore be moderated by the remaining components of the formula; i.e.

> maternity inpatients
> mental illness inpatients
> mental handicap inpatients
> day and outpatient services
> community services

Of these components day and outpatient services are currently weighted, for the age-group 0-64, by SMR x 1%, as is the allocation in respect of community services; neither of these two components has been examined in this study. In respect of maternity and mental illness inpatient services strong evidence has emerged of lesser need, or demand, in affluent areas and greater need or demand in deprived, although we are not able to quantify the exact relationship in respect of mental illness beds. For maternity services beduse is shown to be 20% higher in deprived than in affluent areas (table 6.2b), all of this excess relating to the ante-natal period and presumably reflecting enhanced needs for care. At present no differential weighting for morbidity is incorporated in either the maternity or the mental illness components of the resource allocation formula.

Use of the Jarman underprivileged area (UPA) scores has featured in a method proposed by the Royal College of Psychiatrists [24] for determining acute bed requirements for the age group 0-64 for mental illness beds. This calculates expected admission rates in relation to the UPA score for an area; in comparison with the norm these then provide the basis to adjust the target level of beds for the region to reflect local 'need'. While this method preserves the principle of estimation of requirements it relies on the assumption that bed requirements are proportional to admissions; this may be reasonable for the category of bed under consideration, but is unlikely to be so for the 64% of beds occupied (in Scotland) by patients aged 65 and over so that this method has limitations , which are recognised, in respect of estimating requirements for all beds.

All of these data, for three different types of hospital, indicate greater need for health services in deprived than affluent populations and provide ample evidence for differential weighting of the allocation of resources if health services are to be provided on an equitable basis in relation to need.

Hospital services of course respond to the needs of those who are already ill and appropriate strategies to reduce the differentials in morbidity in the population do not lie in the main within that sector of the health service but in those more directly concerned with changing the incidence of disease by means of disease prevention and health promotion - tasks falling mainly within the sectors of primary care and community services.

TABLE 8.1    INPATIENT DISCHARGE AND BEDUSE RATES,1986 BY AGE AND SEX

|  | Rates per million population | |
|---|---|---|
|  | Males | Females |
| 65-74 |  |  |
| Discharges | 2866 | 2071 |
| Beds used | 117 | 118 |
| 75-84 |  |  |
| Discharges | 4315 | 3218 |
| Beds used | 270 | 334 |
| 85+ |  |  |
| Discharges | 6195 | 4818 |
| Beds used | 555 | 754 |

TABLE 8.2    BEDUSE RATES BY MARITAL STATE 1981

Ratios- married = 100

| 1. Acute beds | Males | | Females | |
|---|---|---|---|---|
| | 65-74 | 75+ | 65-74 | 75+ |
| married | 100 | 100 | 100 | 100 |
| single | 119 | 134 | 126 | 123 |
| widowed | 163 | 166 | 123 | 119 |
| divorced | 117 | 129 | 82 | 84 |
| 100*= | 2555 | 3987 | 2118 | 4305 |
| 2. Long-stay beds | | | | |
| married | 100 | 100 | 100 | 100 |
| single | 382 | 236 | 369 | 267 |
| widowed | 435 | 302 | 330 | 221 |
| divorced | 153 | 270 | 95 | 161 |
| 100*= | 845 | 3194 | 733 | 4628 |

*rate per 1,000

TABLE 8.3    (SEE NEXT PAGE)

TABLE 8.4    WEIGHTED POPULATIONS (SHARE %)
(including age/sex weighting)*

| | SMR x 1 | SMR x0.29 DEP x0.029 | SMR x0.57 DEP x0.011 |
|---|---|---|---|
| Argyll & Clyde | 8.69 | 8.58 | 8.60 |
| Ayr & Arran | 7.42 | 7.32 | 7.36 |
| Borders | 2.23 | 2.28 | 2.27 |
| Dumfries & Galloway | 3.01 | 2.98 | 3.00 |
| Fife | 6.36 | 6.37 | 6.38 |
| Forth Valley | 4.91 | 4.91 | 4.92 |
| Grampian | 8.83 | 9.05 | 9.00 |
| Greater Glasgow | 21.29 | 21.01 | 21.00 |
| Highland | 3.75 | 3.65 | 3.70 |
| Lanarkshire | 9.57 | 9.53 | 9.52 |
| Lothian | 14.29 | 14.48 | 14.43 |
| Tayside | 8.06 | 8.29 | 8.21 |
| Islands | 1.59 | 1.59 | 1.60 |

*does not include adjustment for geriatric cost factor or any grossing to ISD(S)l levels

Note: the percent change shown in table 8.4 is more precise than the same measure calculated using the values in this table since rounding to 2 decimal places results in some loss of precision in the data.

TABLE 8.3  SHARE ALLOCATIONS TO HEALTH BOARDS: SMR GIVEN PRIORITY

| | SMR[b] 0—64 | %change from age/sex | | percent change from SMR x 1 basis[a] simple model | | | 2-stage model | | |
| --- | --- | --- | --- | --- | --- | --- | --- | --- | --- |
| | | DEP | SMR x 1 | SMR x 0.29 | DEP x 0.029 | Combined | SMR x 0.57 | DEP x 0.011 | Combined |
| Argyll & Clyde | 108.0 | +0.49 | +3.04 | -2.09 | +0.48 | -1.61 | -1.27 | +0.17 | -1.10 |
| Ayr & Arran | 105.3 | +0.05 | +1.96 | -1.36 | -0.00 | -1.36 | -0.82 | -0.02 | -0.84 |
| Borders | 83.7 | -1.80 | -4.85 | +3.62 | -1.59 | +2.03 | +2.19 | -0.59 | +1.60 |
| Dumfries & Galloway | 99.1 | -1.22 | -0.34 | +0.24 | -1.27 | -1.03 | +0.14 | -0.50 | -0.35 |
| Fife | 94.5 | -1.18 | -2.01 | +1.46 | -1.30 | +0.16 | +0.88 | -0.50 | +0.38 |
| Forth Valley | 95.7 | -0.91 | -1.71 | +1.24 | -1.10 | +0.14 | +0.75 | -0.43 | +0.32 |
| Grampian | 82.9 | -1.95 | -6.04 | +4.56 | -2.07 | +2.50 | +2.76 | -0.76 | +2.00 |
| Greater Glasgow | 116.1 | +2.50 | +5.75 | -3.86 | +2.52 | -1.34 | -2.34 | +0.98 | -1.36 |
| Highland | 103.0 | -1.82 | +1.06 | -0.74 | -1.95 | -2.69 | -0.45 | -0.76 | -1.21 |
| Lanarkshire | 104.8 | +0.87 | +2.09 | -1.45 | +1.04 | -0.41 | -0.88 | +0.38 | -0.50 |
| Lothian | 91.0 | -0.94 | -3.21 | +2.35 | -1.02 | +1.33 | +1.42 | -0.39 | +1.03 |
| Tayside | 86.1 | -0.55 | -4.58 | +3.41 | -0.58 | +2.83 | +2.06 | -0.22 | +1.84 |
| Islands | 95.4 | -1.26 | -1.44 | +1.03 | -1.17 | -0.14 | +0.66 | -0.45 | +0.17 |

a - it should be noted that the values in this table depend not only on SMR and DEP but also on the ratio of beds used by 0-64 and 65 and over, and the constraint that the resource requirement over all boards remains constant

b - 0-64 1980-82

TABLE 8.5    BED RATIOS PER 1,000 POPULATION FOR HEALTH BOARDS
AGE/SEX BASIS, PLUS:

|  | Age/sex basis | SMR x 1 | SMR x 0.29 DEP x 0.029 | SMR x 0.57 DEP x 0.011 |
|---|---|---|---|---|
| Argyll & Clyde | 4.53 | 4.67 | 4.59 | 4.62 |
| Ayr & Arran | 4.64 | 4.73 | 4.66 | 4.69 |
| Borders | 5.77 | 5.49 | 5.60 | 5.58 |
| Dumfries & Galloway | 5.09 | 5.07 | 5.02 | 5.05 |
| Fife | 4.77 | 4.67 | 4.68 | 4.69 |
| Forth Valley | 4.45 | 4.37 | 4.38 | 4.39 |
| Grampian | 4.85 | 4.55 | 4.67 | 4.64 |
| Greater Glasgow | 4.87 | 5.15 | 5.08 | 5.08 |
| Highland | 4.74 | 4.79 | 4.66 | 4.73 |
| Lanark | 3.94 | 4.02 | 4.01 | 4.00 |
| Lothian | 4.87 | 4.72 | 4.78 | 4.77 |
| Tayside | 5.27 | 5.03 | 5.17 | 5.12 |
| Islands | 5.37 | 5.29 | 5.28 | 5.30 |
| Scotland | 4.74 | 4.74 | 4.74 | 4.74 |

TABLE 8.6    ADJUSTMENTS TO SHARE ALLOCATIONS FOR HEALTH BOARDS:
DEP GIVEN PRIORITY

|  | % change from SMR x 1 | | | | | |
|---|---|---|---|---|---|---|
|  | Simple model | | | 2-stage model | | |
|  | DEP x 0.029 | SMR* x 0.29 | Combined | DEP x 0.046 | SMR* x 0.11 | Combined |
| Argyll & Clyde | -2.43 | +0.82 | -1.61 | -2.13 | +0.31 | -1.82 |
| Ayr & Arran | -1.88 | +0.52 | -1.36 | -1.85 | +0.18 | -1.67 |
| Borders | +3.46 | -1.43 | +2.03 | +2.50 | -0.53 | +1.97 |
| Dumfries & Galloway | -0.90 | -0.13 | -1.03 | -1.62 | -0.06 | -1.68 |
| Fife | +0.78 | -0.62 | +0.16 | +0.03 | -0.23 | -0.20 |
| Forth Valley | +0.68 | -0.54 | +0.14 | +0.05 | -0.21 | -0.16 |
| Grampian | +4.30 | -1.80 | +2.50 | +3.05 | -0.67 | +2.38 |
| Greater Glasgow | -2.99 | +1.65 | -1.34 | -1.55 | +0.64 | -0.91 |
| Highland | -2.94 | +0.25 | -2.69 | -4.05 | +0.08 | -3.97 |
| Lanarkshire | -0.97 | +0.56 | -0.41 | -0.33 | +0.20 | -0.13 |
| Lothian | +2.31 | -0.98 | +1.33 | +1.72 | -0.38 | +1.34 |
| Tayside | +4.24 | -1.41 | +2.83 | +3.91 | -0.54 | +3.37 |
| Islands | +0.31 | -0.45 | -0.14 | -0.37 | -0.17 | -0.54 |

*shows the marginal change (+ or -) from DEP

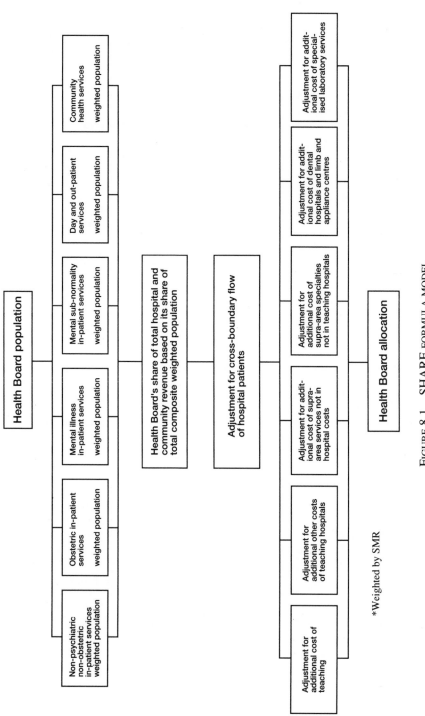

FIGURE 8.1   SHARE FORMULA MODEL

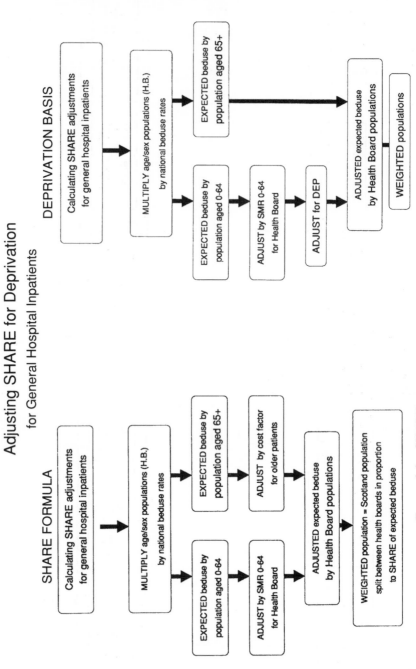

FIGURE 8.2    SHARE FORMULA ADJUSTED FOR DEPRIVATION: METHOD

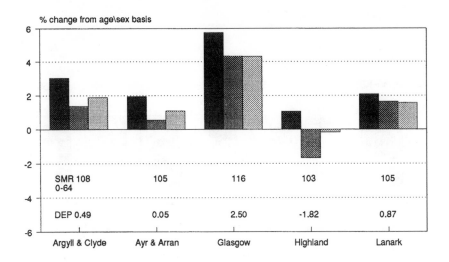

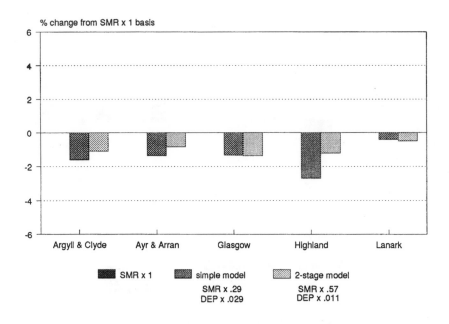

FIGURE 8.3A    ADJUSTMENTS TO SHARE: GENERAL HOSPITALS
HEALTH BOARDS WITH SMRs>100

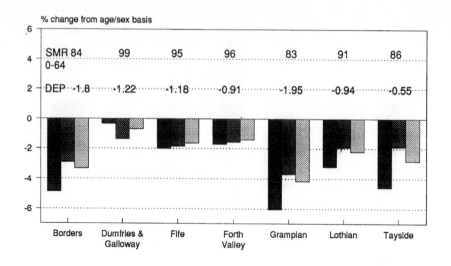

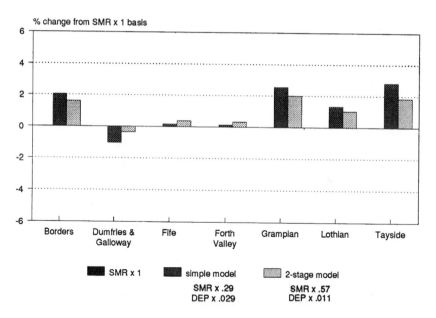

FIGURE 8.3B    ADJUSTMENTS TO SHARE: GENERAL HOSPITALS
HEALTH BOARDS WITH SMRS<100

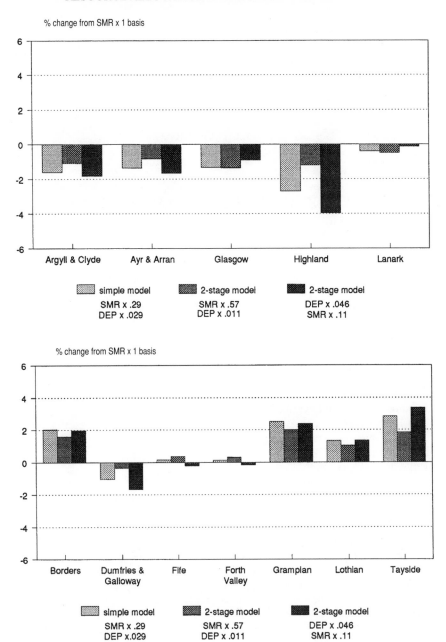

FIGURE 8.4    ADJUSTMENTS TO SHARE: GENERAL HOSPITALS
TOP HEALTH BOARDS WITH SMRS>100
BOTTOM HEALTH BOARDS WITH SMRS<100

CHAPTER 9

# Conclusions and Explanations

The links between health and deprivation which have been amply demonstrated in this report are drawn together in table 9.1 which documents the differentials which exist in various aspects of the pattern of health. The more favourable health enjoyed by people living in affluent areas and the adverse health experience of those living in deprived areas starts with the risks associated with birth — weight at birth and perinatal and infant deaths —, followed by morbidity in the population of working age — as seen in the census measures of temporarily and permanently sick —, and in the population generally — as observed in cancer registrations —, and culminates at life's termination with the gradients in mortality being steepest in younger adults but nevertheless continuing into older ages.

In his analysis of deprivation and health in the Northern Region Townsend combined three measures - mortality in the age group 0-64, permanent sickness, and low birthweight - into a health index, assigning equal weights to each of these.[1] The temptation to do the same has been resisted since doubts remain about appropriate weights and sufficient evidence of differentials is provided by the individual measures, which would probably not be further illuminated by deriving a combined health measure.

It is possible nevertheless to consider the way in which levels of health tend to cluster on an area basis by examining the correlation matrix for a number of health measures (table 9.2). Mortality, in particular for the younger age group (0-64), is shown to be most highly associated with permanent and temporary sickness and to a lesser degree with acute beduse in the same age group although not with all beduse. Links with the other hospital measures, mental illness admissions, low birthweight and cancer are somewhat weaker. Temporary and permanent sickness are also strongly inter-correlated, areas with high levels of permanent sickness also tending to have high levels of temporary sickness, and vice versa. Cancer registrations at 0-64 are fairly strongly associated with those at all ages but these two indicators are no more than moderately associated with any of the other health measures. No doubt for the approximately one-third of cancer sites which show strong positive links with deprivation the correlations would be stronger.

As would be expected these data indicate a tendency for various aspects of ill-health to cluster: in areas with high mortality there will be more people with temporary and permanent sickness, more low birthweight births, and more mental illness admissions; all cancer registrations will obviously show a somewhat different distribution and, except for the age group 0-64, general hospital beduse is not strongly linked to other health measures. Despite these exceptions, as also for a few specific causes of death, the overall pattern that emerges is of overwhelming differentials in health experience in relation to the characteristics of the area in which people live, with the strength of that relationship varying for different measures and at different ages. Mortality overall is only 50% greater in the most deprived than in the most affluent areas but at age 0-64 the difference is two-fold and at 25-44 three-fold with these differentials emerging equally for women as for men; thus it is in the younger adult population of both sexes that socio-economic factors make the biggest impact on mortality. The only other data to be broken down into specific age groups, for general beduse, do not show any consistent trend with age although the most extreme ratio, of 193, is found for all sites do not show differential which are more extreme at age 0-64 than at 65 and over, and they are only slightly wider for lung cancer at 0-64 that at all ages. The differentials in low birthweight are two-fold and those for infant deaths show a 50% excess. Measures of temporary and permanent sickness, which relate in the main to population of working age, are unfortunately not available by an age breakdown but the former (which relates only to the working age group) displays the most extreme variation between deprived and affluent areas with a gradient which is slightly stronger for men than women; both also exhibit a wider range than is seen for all causes mortality at 0-64.

Apart from the general picture which emerges analysis by cause of death and cancer site throws more light on the particular diseases which influence the overall picture, with deaths from chronic respiratory diseases showing the strongest gradient, steeper at 0-64, followed by lung cancer, with cancer of the cervix, pneumonia and liver disease and cirrhosis also exhibiting strong differentials between affluent and deprived areas. Among cancer registrations lung cancer emerges with the most pronounced gradients, followed by cancer of the cervix, with cancers of the oesophagus and stomach also showing major variation. With the exception of pneumonia all of these causes are strongly influenced by patterns of behaviour.

Differentials found in morbidity measures in the population must point to the conclusion that these underlie those seen in mortality, with the gradients for cancer registrations and cancer deaths providing particularly convincing evidence.

The distribution of deaths by DEPCAT (table 9.3) shows a slightly higher proportion (40%) occurring in more affluent categories (1, 2 and 3) than in areas that are more deprived than the average, which account for 34.2% of deaths at all ages, about four percent more than would be expected. At 0-64, the picture is reversed with the more deprived categories having 40.6% of observed deaths, seven percent above the level expected.

Excess deaths are based on the number of deaths observed compared with those expected if death rates in an area were the same as in Scotland as a whole: just over 7,000 excess deaths occurred in more deprived areas in the three years, of which 48% were in the age group 0-64 due to the much steeper gradients found at younger ages. In affluent areas of course the deaths occurring were fewer than those expected by about the same number. The most affluent DEPCAT had SMR values 17% below the Scottish average at all ages, and 36% below at age 0-64, but since the proportion of deaths in this category was very low the levels of mortality in categories 1, 2 and 3 combined provide a target which may be more capable of realisation. Mortality in the most deprived category is 37% above the level in DEPCATS 1, 2 and 3 combined at all ages and 71% greater at 0-64 and the excess deaths in DEPCATS 5 to 7 are very substantial. Nearly 5,000 excess deaths a year occur at all ages and just above 3,000 at 0-64, increasing to over 7,000 and just below 4,000 if DEPCAT 4 is also included, these 'premature' deaths accounting for 59% of the total excess. Although all excess deaths amount to only 10% of the total, those for the age group 0-64 represent 20% of deaths in that age group, a heavy toll in terms of premature mortality.

Explanation of these age-related effects points to a conclusion that vulnerable individuals and those without reserves to resist various adverse influences on health succumb to these in early adult years; with their progressive removal the population becomes relatively more robust (the survival of the fittest) and the effects of these adverse influences gradually diminish. This leads on to consideration of what these influences may be.

## Explanatory Models

Much of the work which has examined differentials in health has been confined to determination of those differences and explanation of them continues to lag behind these expositions. Causative theories attempt to probe beyond the facts to examine some of the processes involved in the determination of the health differentials and the risk factors associated with them.

Theoretical structures which provide a basis for considering the relationships between health and social measures were set out in the Black Report[2] and have provided the framework for most examinations of the relationships observed. They may be divided into roughly four categories:

>  artefactual explanations
>  theories of natural or social selection
>  social explanation: cultural/behavioural
>  social explanation: structural/material

In reviewing these various explanations the Black Report concluded that 'there is much that is convincingly explained in alternative terms: cultural, social selection and so on. Moreover, it may well be that different kinds of factors or forms of explanation apply more strongly or more appropriately to different stages of the life cycle'. The authors nevertheless express their belief that 'it is in some forms of the materialist approach that the best answer lies'.[2]

These various explanatory bases have been ably reviewed by Macintyre[3] and by Blanes specifically in relation to the Black report[4] and are considered here briefly in relation to the socio-economic measures employed and the data which emerge from this study.

*Artefactual* explanation tries to explain away the differentials observed by suggesting that the relationship is mediated by another factor which is the true cause of the variation seen, and in so far as deprivation per se is not a primary cause of health differences this will undoubtedly be true. It does not lead to a denial that these differentials exist nevertheless but as a further spur to the search for those factors and for the mechanisms and processes involved. The other artefactual effect seeks to suggest that the differences observed are a product of the inadequacy of the recording process, being influenced in particular by lack of agreement between the attribution of events and populations to the same social category, with the inflation of the SMRs for social class 5 in the latest supplement on Occupational Mortality [5] providing an example of this effect. Such lack of agreement could obviously exist in data at an area level with an event being registered in a sector other than that in which the individual was enumerated in the census. For bias to exist and to influence the gradients observed unduly however it would be necessary for the events — deaths and cancer registrations — to be systematically registered in an area more deprived than that in which an individual was enumerated at the census, and this seems improbable. Census data show that nine percent of the population had moved to their current address in the previous year; some moves will be within not between postcode sectors and others no doubt to a sector with a similar level of deprivation so that moves which could create such bias will be much fewer. Both deprivation and mortality are found to vary negatively with the level of people moving into a sector (r=0.28, -0.15); that is movers are more common in less deprived areas, and mortality is lower in areas with more movers. If movers (in general) are more healthy then they could be having some influence in enhancing the gradients but the small proportion moving and the low levels of association suggest that this effect cannot be large. Mobility in the population also leads on to consideration of *selection* process arguments which suggest that persons with poor health risks are likely to drift down the social scale, into less skilled jobs or out of employment for instance, while those with better health are more likely to be upwardly mobile. The possibility that selection processes affect the mortality differentials seen in social class data have been exhaustively examined, with the conclusion that any possible effect is very small. [6] In this area-based analysis the comparable process would be one of individuals with poor health moving into deprived and those with good health moving into affluent areas. The information relating to movers (above) points in the direction of greater movement into sectors which are more affluent and with lower mortality so that one can infer some upward mobility of more healthy families and individuals, although the level of association is quite low and this pattern will therefore not represent the norm. Such upward mobility of healthy people will presumably result in those with poorer health risks tending to be left in more deprived areas, so that the evidence provides some support for a selection process affecting the health differentials, although it is not particularly strong. Social drift explanations, i.e. downward mobility, have been invoked in the exploration of variations in mental illness in a number of studies, and the presence of lodging houses and short term shelters for the homeless in inner city areas may point to dynamics of this kind determining some elements of area demography.

Both of these two types of explanation search for reasons to explain away the differentials which are observed and thus to weaken the need to search for reasons why these inequalities exist in society. The remaining two models accept their existence and seek to identify what lies behind them with the cultural/behavioural model placing the emphasis on health-related behaviour and personal responsibility for health. Evidence that life-style factors influence health has grown over recent decades, with smoking, alcohol, diet and physical exercise providing the best-known examples. One of these factors, smoking, was found to be strongly associated with area characteristics, smoking levels being much higher in deprived than affluent districts (see chapter 5). Data on other risk factors for the same districts [7] also show strong links between deprivation and other behaviours relevant to health, in particular in respect of the population not eating fruit and greens, with a slightly lower correlation for alcohol consumption in men, although this link is not apparent for women (table 9.4). Vigorous exercise at work and at home is also found to be positively associated with deprivation for women, i.e. in this case women in deprived areas appear more likely to engage in this beneficial health practice, although a link is not observed for men (reliable comparative information is not easy to obtain).

Other information refers to biological measures which constitute particular risk factors in relation to cardiovascular disease, and which are considered in many instances to be largely determined by diet. Of these the Body Mass Index (i.e. weight in relation to height) is positively and highly correlated with deprivation for women, although for men; triglyceride levels demonstrate a moderately strong association, with measures of blood pressure tending to be modestly associated with deprivation. All cholesterol measures show negative association with DEP, although only for HDL (high density lipoproteins) in women is it significant; finally, for measure of fibrinogen the associations are low and not significant. Most of these correlations are in the direction expected, with health practices and biological measures being more favourable in affluent districts and more adverse in deprived. The exception, cholesterol level, displays an inverse relationship with deprivation although the result is not significant. Similar findings appear in the British Regional Heart Study with men in non-manual classes having slightly higher mean levels of serum total cholesterol than those in manual classes,[8] and in the Whitehall Study of civil servants, with upper grades having higher levels than the lowest, other, grades.[9] These observations are somewhat contrary to expectation since the higher consumption of polyunsaturated margarine in upper compared with lower social classes might be expected to result in lower cholesterol levels in upper social classes (and more affluent areas) and vice versa. Fat-specific consumption however accounts for only a small proportion of total fat intake which is high in all social classes, with all classes having serum total cholesterol levels substantially in excess of communities with low risk of ischaemic heart disease.[8]

Dietary intake for a sample of men within Scotland has recently been reported in relation both to social class and to smoking, the main differences lying in the intake of fibre and polyunsaturated fatty acids, especially linoleic acid.[10] Fibre intake varied significantly by both social class and smoking habits being highest in the non-manual/non-smoking group and lowest in the manual/smoking group, with the effect by class being explained by differences in smoking. The intake of polyunsaturated fats was also highest in the non-manual/non-smoking group. Information on the food sources relating to these nutrient intakes showed the most striking differences to be in the intake of cereal and cereal products, which were eaten more by non-smokers, and of fruit and polyunsaturated margarine which were consumed by non-manual/non-smokers than by the manual/smoking group. Alcohol consumption was also higher (although not significantly so) in manual groups and in smokers. In a further comment on the diet in Scotland in relation to coronary risks it has been stated that 'coronary-prone people and coronary patients for some reason do not eat much food that contains linoleic acid, with the low intake of polyunsaturated fats (and linoleic acid) in cigarette smokers being striking and significant'. It is suggested that 'smoking increases fibrinogen and platelet adhesiveness, lowers high density lipoproteins and favours endothelial injury and more atheromatous lesions'.[11] In other words smoking appears to be associated with dietary practices which render smokers more susceptible to coronary disease; in addition of course to the more direct influence on the respiratory system and a number of other diseases.

While the adverse effects of smoking are now fully accepted debate about the ideal diet still continues, with the specific role of polyunsaturated fat and its attendant risks still remaining in doubt. Another recent report on a sample of the Scottish population for example found the higher levels of mortality from coronary heart disease in both men and women with higher cholesterol levels were accompanied by lower levels of cancer cases and cancer deaths with an inverse relationship emerging between cholesterol levels and deaths from cancers.[12] Other explanations than that a low cholesterol concentration predisposes directly to cancer may be considered but the complexity of the biochemical processes involved produces only hypotheses rather than explanations of possible processes, and uncertainty still attaches to the determination of risks for this particular constituent of the blood.

Overall, evidence from these various studies indicates that smoking behaviour, alcohol consumption (in men), nutritional intake, and obesity (in women) probably lie behind some of the health differentials observed. Smoking-related diseases account for 18% of deaths in the population and there can be little doubt that much of the difference seen in mortality from this group of causes may be attributed to differences in smoking habit, on the assumption (not too unreasonable) that these differentials remain reasonably constant over time, since current mortality will be a product of past experience in this respect.

Differences in smoking habit between men and women in this century, together with alcohol assumption, have also been singled out as the most probable determining factors in the higher mortality evident in men, with men turning to both of these 'drugs' as a means of relieving stress while housewives have dealt with stress in other ways, more recently by resort to medically-prescribed drugs. With the entry of women into employment, giving them more income and control over it, the marked rise which has occurred in their cigarette consumption points to the probable consequence that women may 'pay the price by forfeiting their distinctive advantage in longevity'.[13] The differential between men and women is already diminishing, with a steady decline in excess deaths for men from 16% in 1961-65 to only three percent in 1986 and 1987.

Set against the increase in smoking following the last war more recent years have witnessed a steady decline in cigarette smoking in both sexes which has been steeper for men in whom the proportion smoking cigarettes in Scotland fell from 54% in 1972 to 38% in 1986, but only from 43% to 36% in women,[14] consumption in 1986 being above the levels of 35% and 31% in Great Britain overall. This reduction in smoking has not been experienced equally by all social groups; data available for Great Britain, but not separately for Scotland, show the falls to be steepest in the non-manual groups with reductions of 40% in men and 35% in women by 1986 compared with 1972, while in the three manual groups the reduction has been by 31% in men and only 20% in women; current (1986) levels of smoking range from 18% in professional groups in men to 43% in unskilled manual, and from 19% to 33%-36% in the three manual classes in women.[15] This pattern of change, which will be reflected across the deprivation categories, may well portend a widening of the differentials in mortality by deprivation or other social category.

Smoking has been firmly indicted as the most important specific factor contributing to deaths from coronary heart disease and lung cancer but it has also been shown that conventional risk factors are found not to explain all of the differences observed in mortality and further explanation must be sought among other influences on health.

The fourth of the explanatory models, relating to materialistic factors, puts the emphasis on the social structure with its explanatory role extending not only to differences in health but also to those in health behaviour, proponents arguing that behaviour is not autonomous but rather tied to social structure through factors such as access to education, new knowledge and facilities and through shared ways of seeing the world. [4] Behaviour is seen as determined, in large part, by the social background and social conditioning of the individual, so that behavioural and structural explanations should not be viewed as necessarily mutually exclusive since behaviour will depend very much on the culture and pressures existing in communities and the control individuals are able to exert over their personal circumstances - not everyone 'has the resources and autonomy to effect the necessary changes in behaviour and lead healthier lives'. [4] Individuals and families in deprived circumstances may have neither the physical (including financial) or psychical resources to allow them to adopt or participate in health promoting practices. Moreover lack of resources and inability to control or determine various aspects of living which provide enhancement of self-image and life satisfaction, may result in individuals in such circumstances too readily resorting to behaviours which provide easily-available gratification and relief from stress at the expense of health.

The four components which constitute the deprivation index may be viewed as aspects of the social structure with car ownership in some measure reflecting an individual's or household's command over material resources and all this implies in terms of the ability to make choices in life, and with unemployment, overcrowding and low social class (unskilled manual occupations) possibly having more direct implications for health consequences. Of these four factors unemployment appears as the most likely candidate for direct effects on health, although evidence of these effects has been slow to emerge due to the difficulties in isolating morbidity resulting from or consequent on becoming unemployed from that which may already have been present and possibly a causal factor in becoming unemployed. Evidence from a number of studies which examine mortality and illness is now building up although the findings are not all consistent and evidence for a causal role for unemployment remains somewhat equivocal.

Some of the strongest evidence on mortality emerges from the Longitudinal Study for men who reported themselves as unemployed in the 1971 and 1981 censuses: men unemployed in 1971 had higher mortality than those employed in the period up to 1981, after taking into account various social factors, in particular from suicide, lung cancer and ischaemic heart disease. Mortality was increased also in the wives of these men and this finding among others was considered to support the suggestion that raised mortality was a consequence of unemployment rather than of pre-existing illness. [16] By 1981 unemployment levels had risen considerably and it was argued that this category in the census was less likely (than in 1971) to include persons with existing health problems since the number of older men declaring themselves as 'retired' or 'permanently sick' had increased, most probably reflecting a realistic appraisal of the prospects of obtaining further employment in the circumstances of high unemployment which prevailed at the time. For men unemployed in 1981 mortality ratios increased over the three years of follow-up (1981-83) for men aged 45-64, with low SMRs in the first two years leading to the conclusion that this was a group of initially healthy men, and the SMR of 145 in the third year (1983) providing a measure of the increase in mortality which may be viewed as a consequence of unemployment. In this three-year period of follow-up no significant excess mortality was found in the wives of men unemployed in 1981.

Time series analysis has provided another methods for examining changes in both employment and health measures; a study specific to Scotland which examined time trends in male unemployment and mortality in the post-war period found little evidence to support the hypothesis that unemployment exerts an impact on mortality from all causes, and found moreover that over the longer term the associations were negative. [17] A similar study in England and Wales related changes in unemployment form 1977 to 1981 to changes in mortality rates from 1975 to 1983 in Family Practitioner areas and equally reported only slight effects in younger age groups for death from suicide, ischaemic heart disease and cerebrovascular disease and all causes, which were not statistically significant. [18]

Evidence of increased levels of illness comes from an analysis of General Household Survey data for the years 1981 and 1982 combined [19] which found levels of limiting long-standing illness to be 43% higher in men in the unemployed (in the age group 20-59) and 16% higher in women, but with housewives also reporting levels 23% above the population generally. In part these differences were accounted for by the fact that more unemployed persons are found in lower social groups, which have higher levels of limiting long-standing illness, but although these links were apparent in both the employed and unemployed the gradients in the health measure were much more pronounced for those not in employment (although these include persons declaring themselves retired or sick as well as the unemployed), and were stronger for men than for women. Although there was no possibility of assessing the initial health state of those reporting themselves as unemployed the evidence from this analysis provides fairly strong support for increased morbidity in this group.

Also in the area of morbidity, information on parasuicide (non-fatal deliberate self-harm), from a series of analyses of data for Edinburgh, [20] has reported very strong links between hospital admissions for parasuicide and unemployment in men, both in the year by year variations in both variables from 1968 to 1982 and across the 31 wards in Edingburgh in 1970-72 and 1980-82, with levels of poverty in 1970-72 explaining much of the variation for that period and leading to the conclusion that 'unemployment causes parasuicide via its impact on standards of living'. Parasuicide rates based on event for employed and unemployed individuals provide more convincing evidence than the statistically-based analyses of aggregate data: over the period 1968-82 the incidence of parasuicide declined in the unemployed probably reflecting a change in the composition of this group as the unemployed increased in number, but the relative risk for the unemployed nevertheless remained dramatically high, only in one year being below a level of ten times that of the employed and being apparent in all social classes and higher for men with longer terms of unemployment. [20]

For suicide itself the strongest evidence for individuals comes from the Longitudinal Study which reported a two to three-fold increase in suicide in the unemployed in England and Wales. [16] Within Scotland however an apparently strong correlation over the period 1976 to 1986 between unemployment and suicide (for men aged 25-64) disappeared when these time trends were analysed by health board areas or aggregates of local government districts. [21] The contrast between these findings and those from the individually-based LS could reflect not only the differing methods but also regional differences in the impact of unemployment in terms of local attitudes to or the chances of re-employment, or adaptation to these circumstances, a feature which has been reported from another enquiry which assessed the mental health of unemployed men registered in one area of England and Wales, and found that scores for ill-health were significantly lower in areas of particularly high unemployment, a result supporting the authors' hypothesis that communities with high rates of unemployment develop resilience that is beneficial to the unemployed. [22] Mental health in this cohort also improved after long periods of continuous unemployment, due it is suggested to changes in aspiration, autonomy and competence, which are likely to underpin the changes seen in well-being. Others have also suggested that the widening experience of unemployment may result in a reduction in the stigma associated with this condition, and possibly also in the strengthening of networks of support available to the unemployed and their families. [16]

Data from our own analysis show a strong association between male unemployment and mortality all causes (table 4.1) and for a number of specific causes (table 5.7), the link being strongest for chronic respiratory diseases (0-74), and with deaths from suicide and undetermined causes producing a moderately strong correlation, of 0.45, calculated over the 56 local government districts. These data nevertheless are not considered to support any hypothesis that higher mortality is a consequence of unemployment; unemployment rather appears to form part of a complex of adverse social conditions and poor life chances, being highly associated (at sector level) with the proportion of population lacking car ownership (r=0.85), in overcrowding housing (0.81), in large households (0.65), being council tenants (0.65), in one-parent households (0.79), young people unemployed (0.96) men and women out of work because of temporary sickness (0.78, 0.61), or because of permanent sickness and disability (0.75), and with being in low social class occupations (0.71) (Appendix table B1.1). Sectors with high unemployment also exhibit lesser morbidity with fewer of the population having been born outside of Scotland (born in rest of United Kingdom, -0.53) or having moved into the sector within the last year (-0.26), and have a smaller proportion of population with vocational or educational qualifications above those obtained at school (-0.60). Any or all of these circumstances might equally be implicated in the association of mortality with unemployment — mortality rates are for instance more than three times greater than average in people declaring themselves temporarily or permanently sick (table 6.5) — and, as with the composite measure of deprivation, unemployment is likely to serve as a marker for a whole range of adverse social conditions and rather than having an independent influence probably acts to exacerbate other stresses already present.

Housing characteristics may also impinge on health, (with the unemployed being more likely to live in overcrowded housing) and overcrowding has been reported in one study as having a significant effect on mental rather than physical health in women, with the presence of pre-school children significantly increasing that distress. [23] A recent review concludes however that the effects on health of various housing characteristics are hard to prove since results from most studies do not reach levels of statistical significance or take confounding factors into account and, although they are usually consistent in suggesting adverse outcomes for poorer quality of various aspects of housing, evidence that overcrowding remains a major risk to health after poverty and social class are taken into account is still lacking. [24]

Features of housing other than overcrowding may also be relevant, and Lowry examines temperature and humidity, indoor air quality, noise, space and light, electro-magnetic radiation, homelessness, accidents and sanitation in her review.[24] She cites a finding that the incidence of domestic fires is significantly associated with unemployment and low socio-economic status, and inversely with owner occupation, so that not only illness but accidents also claim to be linked, via these circumstances, to housing characteristics. Alternatively, as with unemployment, other stresses and strains may be influential in their determination. Dampness in housing has attracted particular attention and 'a considerable body of evidence now exists that supports the contention that dampness and mould may adversely affect health', with damp housing conditions, and the presence of fungal mould, resulting in more symptoms of illness in both adults and children; after controlling for other confounding factors a recent study found that the mean number of symptoms reported rose with increasing dampness.[25]

It seems likely that families in more deprived circumstances will be found in poorer quality housing and will also be less well endowed in terms of aids to coping with domestic tasks. Although very few families now lack basic facilities (bath, lavatory, shower) ownership of other amenities varies considerably; homes with central heating for instance range from 53% in unskilled to 90% in professional groups[15] and, while ownership of consumer durables is widespread in the population — with 98% overall owning a television, 94% a refrigerator, 78% a washing machine and 75% a telephone — a trend with income nevertheless exists, with ownership being at a lower level in poorer households: about 10% of households with incomes below £60 a week owned a tumbler drier in 1984 for instance compared with 50% in the two income groups of £300 a week or more, and 60% or less owned a washing machine compared with more than 90% in upper income groups.

Low social class is one of the four deprivation components, and for workers in semi-skilled or unskilled manual occupations the risks associated with direct occupational hazards such as exposure to noxious substances and the possibility of work-related accidents are without doubt higher than for those in upper social class occupations and will contribute to some of the excess morbidity for men in manual occupations. But although there are big differences between social groups in deaths due to accidents at work, these account for only around one percent of total deaths,[4] while the effects of occupation on morbidity are more difficult to measure. Workers in manual occupations could, on the other hand, be protected from risks associated with a sedentary life-style and from the stress engendered by competitive demands and pressures to achieve which may be a feature of some upper social class occupations . Direct occupational effects will also apply only to the workers in a family and other associated features of social class are needed to explain the influence on families.[26]

Indeed any direct causal influence of each of the four components of deprivation is likely to be limited and to explain only a minor part of the variations seen. It is necessary therefore to look among other influences on health which may exhibit socially-related differences within populations for further explanations.

## *Influences on Health*

Various influences may be considered in the chain from good health to death, which include factors in the environment (mainly external to the individual), those mainly determined by or intrinsic to the individual, and influences from the health services (figure 9.1). Each of these three main axes encompasses many specific aspects; environmental influences for instance include both physical and socio-economic conditions. Some physical aspects — pollution for example — may act directly to create ill-health, while the influence of others, e.g. climate, probably lies in exacerbating ill-health once it is present. The socio-economic environment may be conceived as both general and specific the former being characterised by those features which are shared by all persons living in a neighbourhood — the availability of and access to services, leisure and recreational facilities and access to open countryside — as well as features which characterise an area on a dimension from tranquil to stressful: noise, traffic and crime among others. Stress (and threat) in the environment is certainly likely to vary on an area basis and reinforce social adversity at individual level but, since people's lives are not contained within the area in which they live, many may experience the stress attaching to other areas in pursuing the occupational and social aspect of their lives. Other aspects of the socio-economic environment are more specific to the household or the individual; the quality of housing, employment status, occupation, financial resources; many of these specific socio-economic aspects have been shown to be at higher levels of disadvantage in deprived than affluent areas.

The experience of life events may be classified as external since in the main the individual or family does not have direct control over them in the shorter term, and they are largely determined by position within society. Their role is not fully determined but adverse and threatening life events have been shown to impact on emotional health and to be more commonly experienced in working class women who were also less well supplied with the resources and support which appeared to protect middle class women from these events. [27]

Evidence on the influence of social networks and social contacts on health is so far suggestive rather than convincing [28] but it would seem reasonable to suppose that the kind and level of support from others can modify its effects and influence the capacity to cope. Little evidence exists of the way in which such support varies with social position. The 'health enhancing consequences of prestige, deference and power in social relations' also fits within this social spectrum as does the 'lack of personal control over circumstances' identified by the Black Report as constituting one important possible factor influencing health, with both of these being very much determined by position in the social structure.

Individual or intrinsic influences include genetic factors, still implicated in some disease in the population although the determination of genetic risks and ante-natal screening are reducing the burden from this source. Deaths from congenital anomalies have been shown not to be linked to deprivation but these account of course for only a small part of the spectrum of congenitally determined disadvantage in the population.

Although only a small number of births may be affected a poorer start in life for infants in deprived than in affluent areas is indicated by the gradients in low birthweight, which may reflect genetic factors or mother's (smoking) behaviour, and may stand as a signal for a spectrum of further disadvantage in the new-born.

Height has also been identified as an independent risk factor in mortality from coronary heart disease, and other causes[9], with height reflecting of course not only genetic factors but also social/nutritional experience in infancy.

Suggestions that early experience in life, perhaps related to levels of nutrition in infancy and housing conditions, including overcrowding, may make an important contribution to mortality in adult life have recently been reported.[29] This study was based on the health experience of the populations living in specific areas at two different time periods and the adults in which mortality is examined will not consist entirely of survivors of the infancy experience in these locations. Reporting on the experience of individuals, the British Regional Heart Study found the geographic zone in which people reside to be a more important determinant of the risk of a major coronary event than the place of birth.[31] Although suggestive this report does not altogether dispose of the proposition that early experience affects adult morbidity and mortality since the zones that provided the basis for analysis are large (Scotland being one) and therefore heterogeneous. The possibility of selective migration (in relation to inborn risk) affecting these results was examined, and disposed of, in respect of the international migrants, who were few in number, but not for the internal migrants who constituted over 50% of the sample. Infant experience may clearly range very widely within any one zone and more detailed examination of the risks in relation to more specific characteristics of the environment experienced in infancy or early life is needed in order to refute this hypothesis. Adverse illness experience in childhood has also been reported as associated with serious illness in adults, with serious illness in childhood being more common in families with fathers in lower social class occupations.[31] It appears therefore more reasonable to conclude at the present time that both past and current circumstances may have a role in determining an individual's health potential and the experience of disease.

Data are lacking but it may be supposed that the population currently living in deprived circumstances are more likely to have experienced adverse conditions in infancy than those living in affluent areas, although the upward social mobility which has been a feature of post-war society would presumably result in residents in more affluent areas being more diverse in their origins.

Evidence on the importance of life-style and behavioural factors in determining health has emerged over the last quarter of a century — cigarette smoking, alcohol consumption, diet and nutrition, the abuse of addictive substances, exercise — the (adverse) effects on health have been fully explored, and the list is still being enlarged, sexual practices now being added in view of their very important role in respect of AIDS. Some at least of these life-style factors have been shown to be strongly linked to deprivation.

The availability and quality of health care are factors in the main external to the individual; use of services relating to health promotion and disease prevention however are more likely to be determined by the individual, influenced to some extent by local availability. Practices in this respect will play a role in the healthy (or apparently healthy) since neglecting to use preventive services or those for early detection of disease, or to respond to health promotion messages, may have a direct influence on susceptibility to or even the incidence of disease, as also the possibility of effective treatment. Individuals carry responsibility not only for their own health state but also for that of any children in their care: child-rearing practices, the monitoring of growth and development and making use (or not) of services to prevent disease or promote health will have consequences for them.

Evidence from other studies tends to point in the direction of people in lower social groups making less use of preventive and health promoting services and less effective use of general practitioner services. [32]

Once illness is present the health service will have a major role in the treatment of disease and in the eventual outcome although individuals still exert influence by the way in which medical care is moderated, through use of health (or alternative) services, and by the extent of compliance with medical treatment or advice.

In this study increased utilisation of hospital services was found in more deprived categories, with gradients in beduse in the age group 0-64 being somewhat less steep than the range found in both mortality in the same age group and in measures of temporary and permanent sickness (table 9.1). These data nevertheless cannot be regarded as statistically sound enough to reach a conclusion on whether the differentials in service use match those for morbidity or need for health care particularly as alternatives to inpatient care have not been examined.

This list adds up to an impressive array of factors all of which may influence health in differing degrees; while documentation of all of them in relation to social circumstances is not possible it is clear that they are not equally distributed in society. Families in disadvantaged social circumstances are likely to be located at the more unfavourable end of the spectrum of many of these influences on health; and to lack moreover the resources which enable individuals and families to avoid stressful circumstances in the first place or to cope with them or shield themselves from their consequences when they arise.

## General or specific explanation

These various influences may be considered as specific or general. While specific factors such as infection, pollution, smoking, may lead directly to the development of particular diseases, more general effects in terms of lower resistance to a variety of specific influences are a more likely consequence from factors such as stress and social contacts. Cassel, one of the most influential protagonists of this view, has postulated that the social environment may contribute to differences in general susceptibility to or capacity to resist influences in the environment and suggested that increased susceptibility to disease should occur when, for a variety of reasons, individuals do not receive any evidence that their actions are leading to desirable and anticipated consequences. [33] Antonovsky has put forward the proposition that a capacity to resist disease stems from a sense of coherence which is characterised by 'comprehensibility, manageability and meaningfulness' in the stimuli of everyday life, and suggested that those in lower socio-economic groups have less money, knowledge, intelligence and social contacts to help them cope successfully in adversity. [34] The 'lack of personal control over circumstances' singled out by the Black Report as an important intermediary influence in the equation between low social position and ill-health fits within these frameworks of psychosocial influences on the individual.

A general factor common to many diseases has been advanced as a possible explanation for the similarity in the relative risks of death from a wide range of specific causes as between lower and higher grades of civil servants, conventional and measurable risk factors accounting for only 40% of the differences found in coronary heart disease deaths in this cohort, for which the specific risk factors are well established. [35] The Scottish heart health study equally concluded that the considerable variations in risk factors and lifestyle across Scottish districts do not appear to account for more than a part of the differences in coronary heart disease mortality.[7] A wide range of individual income and behavioural risk factors also failed to explain the 30% increase in mortality in poverty areas found in the Alameda County study.[36]

Psychosocial influences are likely to prove much more difficult to identify and quantify than the more conventional risk factors and so far most research has centred on the workplace, Marmot reporting marked differences among employment grades of civil servants in various measures of control and satisfaction at work as well as in social networks and activities outside work.[35] Strong gradients in measures of life satisfaction and a stress symptoms score across the occupational classes, the gradients being more marked for men than for women, have also been reported in a study from Finland.[37]

## *Will differentials diminish?*

The means to reduce health and socio-economic differential in the population are located within various areas of social, economic and fiscal policy. The Black Report contained a large number of general and specific recommendations, the abolition of child poverty being identified as the most critical.[2] Many of these policy recommendations remain relevant and it would be invidious to repeat them here.

Health services clearly have a key role to play but changing the patterns of morbidity in the population presents a more formidable challenge than responding to the needs for care generated, and one which will require a greater commitment to strategies for disease prevention and health promotion. Community services, which provide the main vehicle for these functions, absorbed only eight percent of the budget in 1987/88 and not all of this expenditure is relevant since caring services such as district nursing are included in this total. Some commitment to a change in this direction may be detected in recent government statements. The SHARPEN report on priorities in the health service issued by the Scottish Home and Health Department is one example; it puts considerable emphasis on tackling the problem of deprivation, with a general recommendation that services for people living in deprived circumstances should have the highest priority in each service programme, and more specific recommendations which include both increasing the accessibility of primary care services and the deployment of higher ratios of community nursing staff in these areas.[38]

Increased delivery of preventive and other community services to deprived areas with high SMRs has also been identified by Womersley as one means of effecting improvement in health[39]. Current proposals to restructure the contract for general practitioners to emphasise that health promotion and disease prevention fall within the definition of general medical services must represent a step forward in this context, particularly as the general proposal is backed up by extra payments for reaching specific targets in respect of childhood immunisation and cervical cytology examinations in women, and by sessional fees for clinics which put emphasis on health promotion for those without as well as with health problems.[40] The intention behind the health department's proposal to pay enhanced capitation payments to general practitioners for patients living in deprived areas is not spelt out however and no expectation is expressed that these fairly substantial payments should result in any reduction in the inequalities rather than merely compensate for the additional workload generated by these conditions.

Improving the provision of health promoting services will not be enough on its own since disadvantaged groups currently fail to make full use of relevant services, and increased effort is required to encourage them to do so. Lesser uptake by then of preventive and screening services for early detection of disease, cancer of the breast or cervix [41] for instance, may well mean that the expected reductions in mortality overall could nevertheless be accompanied by a widening in the mortality gradients.

Remedial strategies aimed at reducing the level of specific health risks in the population have so far equally shown little capacity to lessen the differentials in these factors and thus in the illness experience associated with them, since upper social groups more readily adopt healthier life-style than those in manual classes, the widening gap in smoking behaviour (p 221) providing one example. Unless health education programmes can find ways to increase their influence on those at the bottom of the social scale their impact appears likely to presage a widening rather than a narrowing of the differentials presently observed in illness and death in the population.

Health services have a substantial role to play but reduction of the inequalities in health does not lie wholly, perhaps not even mainly, within their sphere of influence. Other areas of social policy in both local and central government have more fundamental contributions to make in redressing the inequalities in the social and economic circumstances of which the differential health experience is an inevitable consequence. These structural features in society influencing health potential exhibit little sign of lessening divisions within society, despite social and economic policies aimed at improving the circumstances of the population generally. Restructuring of the economy has had some impact on overall levels of unemployment but despite job creation chronic unemployment has not been eradicated and remains more prevalent in the unskilled; levels of homelessness are increasing, particularly among young people in the wake of the withdrawal of social security benefits; single-parent families are growing in number with consequences in terms of low levels of income and lack of support for mother and children. Trends in income levels indicate a widening of the earnings distribution, for those who are in employment, families in the highest decile of earnings having achieved much greater increases in the last two decades than those at the lower end of the distribution. [42] Since disposable income provides the basis for much of the ability to 'exert control over personal circumstances' and probably to 'achieve desirable and anticipated consequences' these temporal trends equally with those observed in health-related behaviour do not augur well for any reduction in the inequalities in social circumstances or in the health consequences in the population.

TABLE 9.1  RANGE AND RATIOS: MOST DEPRIVED, MOST AFFLUENT
FOR SELECTED HEALTH INDICATORS

|  | Range | Ratio |
|---|---|---|
| Low birthweight | 67-142 | 2.1 |
| Perinatal deaths | 73-110 | 1.5 |
| Infant deaths | 82-122 | 1.5 |
| Temp. sick | 36-216 | 6.0 |
| Perm. sick | 52-153 | 2.9 |
| Cancer registrations | | |
| - all ages | 95-125 | 1.3 |
| - 0-64 | 92-119 | 1.3 |
| - lung | 67-192 | 2.9 |
| Deaths | | |
| - all ages | 81-125 | 1.2 |
| - 0-64 | 64-141 | 2.2 |
| - 65+ | 89-118 | 1.3 |
| ca. cervix | 44-163 | 3.7 |
| chronic respiratory | 63-203 | 3.2 |
| ca. lung | 67-176 | 2.6 |

TABLE 9.2  CORRELATION MATRIX: DEPRIVATION AND HEALTH VARIABLES

| | DEP | SMR all | SMR 0-64 | SMR 65+ | TEMP SICK | PERM SICK | LOW WT. | CAN CER all | CAN CER 0-64 | MEN TAL all | MEN TAL 0-64 | BEDS USE all |
|---|---|---|---|---|---|---|---|---|---|---|---|---|
| DEP | | | | | | | | | | | | |
| SMR all | 0.72 | | | | | | | | | | | |
| SMR 64 | 0.75 | 0.80 | | | | | | | | | | |
| SMR 65 | 0.53 | 0.88 | 0.48 | | | | | | | | | |
| TEMPSICK | 0.72 | 0.58 | 0.61 | 0.45 | | | | | | | | |
| PERMSICK | 0.83 | 0.67 | 0.72 | 0.48 | 0.76 | | | | | | | |
| LOW WEIGHT | 0.58 | 0.44 | 0.44 | 0.34 | 0.41 | 0.48 | | | | | | |
| CANCER all | 0.37 | 0.35 | 0.32 | 0.26 | 0.18 | 0.31 | 0.23 | | | | | |
| CANCER 64 | 0.28 | 0.26 | 0.36 | 0.09 | 0.18 | 0.27 | 0.14 | 0.72 | | | | |
| MENTAL all | 0.50 | 0.40 | 0.43 | 0.28 | 0.34 | 0.40 | 0.31 | 0.49 | 0.35 | | | |
| MENTAL 64 | 0.53 | 0.44 | 0.48 | 0.29 | 0.39 | 0.45 | 0.32 | 0.46 | 0.35 | 0.96 | | |
| BEDUSE all | 0.25 | 0.25 | 0.22 | 0.20 | 0.22 | 0.23 | 0.14 | 0.14 | 0.15 | 0.21 | 0.23 | |
| BEDUSE 64 | 0.60 | 0.48 | 0.56 | 0.31 | 0.45 | 0.55 | 0.38 | 0.41 | 0.38 | 0.53 | 0.56 | 0.40 |

TABLE 9.3 DISTRIBUTION OF DEATHS BY DEPCAT AND EXCESS DEATHS

| | DEPCAT | | | |
|---|---|---|---|---|
| Percent distribution | | | | |
| All ages | 1/2/3 | 4 | 5/6/7 | 100%= |
| observed | 40.3 | 25.4 | 34.2 | 190274 |
| expected | 44.2 | 25.3 | 30.4 | |
| 0-64 | | | | |
| observed | 33.7 | 25.4 | 40.6 | 48735 |
| expected | 40.9 | 25.7 | 33.5 | |
| Excess deaths | | | | |
| Scotland = 100 | | | | annual average |
| all ages | 0 | 0 | 7137 | 2379 |
| 0-64 | 0 | 0 | 3402 | 1134 |
| DEPCATS 1,2,3 = 100 | | | | |
| all ages | 0 | 4841 | 15291 | 6711 |
| 0-64 | 0 | 2348 | 9546 | 3965 |

TABLE 9.4 RISK FACTORS AND DEPRIVATION IN 22 DISTRICTS IN
SCOTLAND FOR MEN AND WOMEN AGED 40-59

| | Correlation* with DEP | | Mean# value | |
|---|---|---|---|---|
| | M | F | M | F |
| % smoking | 0.90 | 0.90 | 41.6 | 39.6 |
| alcohol units | 0.70 | -0.37 | 12.6 | 2.5 |
| % not eating: | | | | |
| - fruit | 0.85 | 0.75 | 12.5 | 7.6 |
| - greens | 0.81 | 0.87 | 22.0 | 11.5 |
| vigorous exercise: | | | | |
| - at work | 0.33 | 0.80 | 18.2 | 15.1 |
| - at home | 0.04 | 0.84 | 13.7 | 11.4 |
| body mass index | -0.42 | 0.75 | 25.9 | 25.7 |
| blood pressure: | | | | |
| - systolic | 0.55 | 0.41 | 134 | 132 |
| - diastolic | 0.29 | 0.55 | 84 | 82 |
| cholesterol: | | | | |
| - total | -0.23 | -0.20 | 6.3 | 6.6 |
| - HDL | -0.18 | -0.49 | 1.4 | 1.7 |
| triglycerides | 0.65 | 0.59 | 2.3 | 1.7 |
| fibrinogen | -0.15 | -0.01 | 2.3 | 2.4 |

(coefficients below 0.41 are not sig. at 5% level)
*population weighted
#% or units
Source: reference

## EXTERNAL / ENVIRONMENTAL FACTORS

*Physical environment*

- climate       - heat/ventilation
- water         - infection
- soil          - pollution
- air           - toxicity
- food          - trace elements
- waste         - radiation
- disasters

*Socio-economic environment*

(a) - general

- local services
- transport / traffic
- recreation / open space / leisure
- noise / crime / security
  urbanisation

(b) - specific ⟩

- housing
- employment / unemployment
- occupation /working situation
- disposable income / resources
- life events
- social networks

## INTERNAL / INDIVIDUAL FACTORS

*Genetic / biological / ethnicity*

- genetically determined disease
  or biological status
- susceptibility or resistance
  to trauma and disease

*Early experience*

- nutrition/housing
  pollution/illness

*Life-styles / health-related behaviour*

- smoking
- alcohol
- diet
- addiction
- physical exercise
- sexual practices

## HEALTH CARE

*Service Supply*

- availability
- accessibility
- quality/effectiveness
- medically determined disease

*Use of health services and
health care practices*

- health promotion

- illness prevention
- early detection
- seeking help
- alternative medicine
- compliance with treatment

FIGURE 9.1 INFLUENCES ON HEALTH

# CHAPTER 10

# Considering Deprivation and
# Area-Based Methods

In this chapter some of the strengths and weaknesses of deprivation measures and the area-based approach are considered; pitfalls are also examined and suggestions made for ways of dealing with these and for further developments which could overcome some of the limitations. First however the performance of the particular measure, DEP, used throughout this analysis in explaining variations in the health measures is compared with other indexes of deprivation.

## *Which Deprivation?*

Critics of deprivation measures have attacked their composition referring to the limited menu of variables available on the census, and the arbitrary basis for selection of variables. Our own measure, DEP, as with others, cannot avoid this charge since the decision on the inclusion of variables finally rests in a value judgement about their relevance to the measurement of material disadvantage. Our selection is limited to four indicators but it should be noted that many social variables other than those included are also highly correlated with DEP, council tenure 0.75, one-parent households 0.80, higher qualifications -0.75, and permanent sickness 0.77 for example, and the measure therefore encapsulates a number of other aspects which might be considered as indicators of social advantage/disadvantage even though these are not explicitly included in the measure.

Since external validators of deprivation scores are not available one test of utility at least lies in the power of any measure to explain variations in the health measures. DEP itself has been shown to provide a strong basis for explaining these differences but the performance of a number of other indexes which have been considered in detail in chapter 1 is now examined. Two further measures proposed for health services use, by Thunhurst[1] and Scott-Samuel[2] are not included here since the specification of these is too imprecise to allow them to be calculated. Of the five examined only three were designed specifically for use in the context of health, but since the DOE measure was considered by DHSS in its review of

RAWP[3] it appears appropriate to include both this and its Scottish equivalent (SDDEP). These indexes include a variety of indicators which are listed in Figure 10.1. Even where these appear to be the same, subtle differences in definition often exist, and the methods used for combining the components into one score also vary. These variations on the theme have been considered in more detail elsewhere.[4] The indexes examined are:

DEP         as used throughout this analysis
TOWN        used by Townsend in exploring health
JAR         designed by Jarman as a measure of need for primary care services[6]
DOEB ⎱      designed by the two government departments
SDDEP ⎰     in relation to urban policy and planning[7,8]

The five measures were each calculated for all postcode sectors to replicate the originals as closely as possible, although in all cases 'persons' rather than 'households' provide the basis for calculation. The correlations between them are seen in table 10.1

As might be expected there is a high degree of inter-correlation between these measures although JARMAN shows weaker association than others. The strongest coefficient is between DEP and TOWN (0.960), not surprisingly since three of the four components are common to both measures. The two government measures exhibit a relatively weak level of association (0.862) between themselves although showing strong association with DEP.

These deprivation measures as well as the single indicator of 'no car' are also correlated with selected health measures: mortality, bed-days and permanent and temporary sickness, with the results seen in table 10.2

These coefficients indicate very little difference in the results for mortality as between DEP, TOWN and DOEB, with JAR showing the lowest levels of association and SDDEP and NOCAR giving similar results, although with NOCAR performing better at 0-64 and SDDEP at 65 and over.

For bed-days DEP serves better than TOWN as an explanatory variable but DOEB shows a stronger association at 0-64, with NOCAR surpassing it. JAR however, although just worse than DEP at 0-64, acts better to explain the variation for 65 and over and longstay, as does DOEB, and these associations also enhance the results for all beds.

Finally, for permanent and temporary sickness, DEP emerges as the best explanatory measure with JAR having the lowest coefficient, and other indexes falling in between.

DEP therefore as used throughout this report performs as well as or better than most indexes examined in respect of the pure health measures (mortality and permanent and temporary sickness) followed closely by TOWN.

The lesser association of the Townsend measure than of DEP with bed-days suggest that low social class (in DEP) provides a better explanatory variable than does tenure (in TOWN) in relation to need for care in Scotland.

Bed-days in the elderly are better explained by JAR and DOEB and in the younger age-group by DOEB and NOCAR. Both JAR and DOEB include 'lone pensioners' in their index and the inclusion of that variable has been shown to enhance these associations as far as JAR is concerned.[4] Elderly persons *per se* should not affect the variation in bed-days since the ratios have been standardised to take account of differences in population age and sex structure. Marital state does influence beduse however (table 8.2) and it seems realistic to conclude that the lone pensioners variable is capturing some of the extra demand from the unmarried elderly. Being old and alone may indeed be an indicator of disadvantage but not necessarily, we suggest, of material disadvantage: high proportions of lone pensioners may be found living in wealthy retirement areas and indeed lone pensioners are only weakly and negatively associated with DEP, with a correlation of -0.05.

SDDEP, which comprises 12 variables, consistently exhibits lower coefficients than the English equivalent, DOEB. It has some indicators in common with DEP but 'no car' is not among them while both demographic and housing variables are included, as also the indicator of permanent sickness; SODEP nevertheless does not result in a stronger association with the health indicator of permanent sickness than is produced by DOEB, although temporary sickness does emerge more strongly.

All the differentials observed in the health measures clearly will not be accounted for by material deprivation; sickness experience will underlie variations in mortality as well as in hospital use, and although the link between DEP and temporary and permanent sickness is strong (see table 6.6) it does not nevertheless explain all of the variation, and these two sickness measures also cannot lay claim to reflecting all aspects of the sickness experience. Social factors other than those captured in the DEP measures equally have a contribution to make, as do variations in practice. If the aim were to identify circumstances which most fully explain the variations in the health variables then it might be desirable to include a whole host of factors which would serve to enhance the correlation coefficients. Between DEP and SMR0-64 for instance the coefficient could be raised to a higher level by the inclusion of one-person households, men/women in work, permanently sick, students, one-parent households, agricultural occupations, and having higher qualifications (see Appendix A8). With the aim of examining differences due to material disadvantage however both DEP and TOWN adhere more closely than others to this concept and both are seen to function well in explaining variations in mortality and morbidity although the single variable NOCAR also gives consistently high correlations across all measures, with DEP performing marginally better. Conceptually however a composite measure is to be preferred since it is likely to capture aspects of disadvantage which are not fully reflected in not having a car.

The use to which measures are to be put may have some impact on their composition. Jarman scores for example may well serve to explain needs for primary care, but the decision by DHSS to adopt this basis for measuring social deprivation in relation to the RAWP formula, in preference to TOWNSEND or DOEB, must be questioned since it is less strongly correlated with the health measures than both of these two indexes and the stronger coefficient for BEDUSE by the elderly appears to be due to demographic factors (lone pensioners) which would probably be better dealt with at the first stage of the formula (which adjusts for age/sex differences) than incorporated in a measure of social deprivation. [4]

Unless other indicators than those currently available appear on the scene general consensus about the composition of such a measure is unlikely to emerge since judgement on the part of individual researchers plays a large part in this process, notwithstanding that:

> Diff'ring judgements (may) serve to declare that truth lies somewhere,
> if we knew but where (Cowper).

# Strengths and Weaknesses of Area-Based Methods

## Deprivation vs social class

The most overwhelming benefit of the area approach is obviously the opportunity offered to examine (in relation to area characteristics) a wide range of records which are based on individual events and contain a postcode reference. This overcomes one of the major limitations of the traditional social class basis, individual social class information not being available for most health records. Where social class analysis is undertaken, mainly in respect of mortality, it suffers in that the attribution to social class is never complete, both in the census population base and in the death records. The census failure to record an occupation and classify to social class, varies by sex, age and marital state, with 51% of women aged 16 and over (in Scotland) not being classified by their own occupation compared with 12.6% of men, and the proportion ranging (in men) from 4.3% to over 19% at 20-24 and 75 and over, and 43.5% at 16-19.[9] Death certificates also show deficits in terms of occupation, 5% of certificates for men aged 20-64 not recording an occupation, and those for married women classified by husband's occupation in the same age group having a shortfall of 23%. Scottish data do not indicate the proportion of women with an own occupation recorded on the death certificate but for England and Wales at age 20-59 only 32% of death certificates could be classified on this basis.[9]

Data reported in relation to social class suffer also from the so-called numerator/denominator bias, i.e. lack of agreement in the attribution of occupation, and social class, as between death certificates and the census record. These deficiencies are considered in detail in the latest decennial supplement on occupational mortality[9] with the authors concluding that the less specific occupational information recorded on the death certificate than on the census record has resulted in considerable bias, in particular for labourers and unskilled workers, leading to overestimation of the SMRs for social class 5 which 'will be balanced by artificially lowered mortality in other classes'. A more recent analysis has suggested that this bias may be less extreme than was formerly thought[10] but strong reservations nevertheless remain as to the reliability of social class in mortality analyses and thus about the strength of the differentials which emerge. Although the high rates reported for social class 5 have been in question an alternative view argues that the true impact of socio-economic inequalities on health will be understated by social class analysis, due to the inflexible nature of the social class classification and the failure of occupational class to produce a neat ordering of the population in terms of fundamental socio-economic circumstances.[11] This contention is supported by data from the Whitehall Study which found civil servants in the lowest grade to have a mortality rate three times greater than those in the administrative grade[12], a range considerably wider than that observed between the extremes of the social classes.

The problems of numerator/denominator bias are overcome by the methods of the Longitudinal Study which links the death record, and other events, to the individual census record and produces more reliable mortality gradients by social class as well as a range of other social variables, including for older age groups[13], and for cancer registrations[14] as well as deaths.

Problems of non-allocation to an occupation nevertheless are not avoided and, since higher mortality is observed in the group not classified, this impinges on the gradients observed between the social classes.[10]

Analysis by area overcomes the problems of lack of comprehensiveness since the use of the postcode means that most events can now be allocated to an area of residence. In this study all mortality records were allocated to a postcode sector and the shortfall in other types of records was very small (see Appendix A1); greater efforts to capture information and validate address codes should enable this shortfall to be reduced even further.

As with the Occupational Mortality analysis problems of numerator/denominator bias may exist with mobility in the population resulting in individuals moving from the sector in which they were enumerated in the census, and this may influence the accuracy of the rates calculated for individual sectors. Since some movements will be between sectors with similar deprivation characteristics any error will be mitigated when considering the gradients observed by deprivation for the health measures.

Much of the recent criticism of social class-based mortality analysis has been concerned with the problems of analysis over time, with changes in the composition and size of social classes (with a declining proportion in SC5) raising questions about the validity of comparing mortality for specific social classes over successive decennial supplements. [15] This analysis has not included a historical perspective but compared with social class another advantage of the DEP score is its superior statistical properties since it provides a continuous variable, albeit based on artificial units which should be considered as having the properties of a ranking measure than those of a numerical score. It nevertheless enables correlation and regression analyses to be carried out and also offers greater flexibility for the determination of class intervals, which could overcome the problems associated with interpretation of trends over time in social class based analysis. A deprivation measure of the kind we employ could be used in future years to examine health characteristics on the basis of the same allocation inrto categories (i.e. on a distributional basis) or for areas grouped on the basis of the same scores. Trends across time however imply some continuity in the measures and we have to acknowledge that identification of relative advantage/disadvantage will need to keep in step with contemporary circumstances and definitions; lack of housing amenities has been excluded from the measure used in 1981 as no longer useful for example, and in which decade of this century would car ownership have become relevant?

Finally, populations have been shown to be much more diverse in respect to deprivation than in terms of social class and this greater discrimination enhances its value as an explanatory factor in relation to differentials in health.

Social class is not of course the only measure of social disadvantage but occupation must be considered as the only socio-economic information that it is feasible to collect on death and health service records and social class is likely to remain the only basis for routine analysis which uses information for individuals. The methodological approach of the Longitudinal Study provides a research alternative, but one which is both technically complex and expensive, and its restriction to a small sample of the population carries the attendant disadvantage of low numbers for some types of events and specific cause of death.

## Problems of availability of data and potential solutions

As with other similar measures DEP relies on the census as the source of indicators and this constraint results in one of the main apparent deficits in area-based analysis, present also for most social class analysis of routine data, that the necessary tools — populations and social characteristics — are comprehensively available for small areas only at ten-yearly intervals. Since smaller areas are more likely to be affected by demographic and social change than larger ones this thereby limits their utility for the analysis of events between census years. Solutions to the provision of population data seem likely to emerge: at least one commercial agency is supplying population updates for wards and enumeration districts which are consistent with the annual population estimates[16] although only the 1991 census population data will show whether the methods used are robust; local authorities are also making efforts to obtain population data for their area — the introduction of the community charge will presumably have some input into this process though whether this influence will be wholly beneficial (in terms of accuracy of population counts) remains to be seen; finally health authorities also hold registers of the population living in their area and registered with general practitioner, in the form of the Family Practitioner Committee lists (England and Wales) or the Community Health Index (in Scotland). Inadequate levels of accuracy in the lists have recently been reported in a number of studies in relation to screening programmes in England and Wales, with an eighth to a third of women on the register no longer living at the address on the record[17] but with a study within Scotland (Tayside) reporting only 10% of the population not at the address on the index, which is subject to more continuous upgrading, from hospital as well as primary care sources.[18] The need for accurate age/sex registers has been highlighted[19] in relation to meeting targets for preventative activities, generating income and managing resources in the wake of proposals for primary care in the recent white paper setting out the government's strategy for the future of the NHS[20] and these requirements point in the direction of improved population data becoming available within the framework of the health service.

The provision of small area characteristics appears as more of a problem but various sources of relevant information exist that could be exploited, including some of the components of the deprivation measure. Unemployment statistics for instance are made available by the Department of Employment at ward level[21] the data including both the numbers and duration of unemployment; although workforce denominators are presently available from this source only for travel to work areas based on aggregates of wards, other population denominators e.g. for the population of working age could provide a reasonable alternative.

Car ownership data also exist in the form of car licences issued, and since postcodes are entered on the application form and licensing is at least on an annual basis, it should prove possible to count licences current at small area level to provide a ratio of cars to population, which might serve as well as the census measure of the percentage of population without a car. Even more direct information on disadvantage lies currently inaccessible in government computers: levels of income held by the Inland Revenue and benefits provided by the Department of Social Security. Since one government department, Employment, has shown the way could others not follow suit? Release of these data could put an end to the continuing debate about the construction of a deprivation measure and the selection of indicators, although determination of the most appropriate and relevant measures would obviously need consideration.[11] We should not despair therefore of charting differentials in the socio-economic circumstances of populations from sources other than the census, which have the benefit of being available on a continuing basis. The Department of Social Security in addition holds valuable data on health characteristics — sickness and invalidity benefit, attendance and mobility allowances — which could equally be of use in assessing differentials in the health of the populations.

## Boundary problems

This analysis has been undertaken at the postcode sector level but addresses may also be allocated to many other area levels, of which the ward is the obvious alternative and possibly preferable in view of being less diverse in population size and conforming more closely to local communities. Allocation to any area other than the sector however requires recourse to the Postcode Directory, maintained by the Registrars General [22], using the unit postcode [23], and some failure to link addresses must be expected; not all of the death records for 1980 to 1982 for instance could be allocated to an Enumeration District. Problems may lie in the unit postcode or in the directory and sorting out these failures for individual records in time consuming. Use of the sector levels avoids such problems (although we implicitly assume absence of error at this level) and sectors have been shown to aggregate up into relevant communities by Greater Glasgow health boards. [24] Sectors present other problems however, relating to boundaries, since they have not been designed to conform to administrative areas and some span local authorities. For purposes of this analysis this problem was dealt with by allocating unit postcodes to 'part' postcode sectors, this being necessary in order to maintain the ability to attribute an event correctly to local government districts and health boards (by aggregation over sectors) but this attribution to a part postcode sector encounters the same problem of use of the postcode directory. Health boards and local government districts wishing to carry out analysis of data for their area could construct specific look-up tables to enable unit postcodes to be correctly allocated for the few sectors which would be involved. Sectors which are split across local government district boundaries within health boards could be amalgamated to provide populations (and sector characteristics) for whole sectors, thus reducing the problems of small part sectors with low numbers of events. Within England and Wales use of the Postcode directory is necessary to allocate unit postcodes to wards since postcode sector data are not available in the 1981 census output; wards do not of course suffer from the problem of crossing administrative boundaries.

Every encouragement should be given to the Post Office to take steps to overcome this problem by aligning postcode boundaries with the administrative area base.

## Rural areas

The composition of the deprivation measure appears less appropriate for rural than urban areas, with high levels of mortality in some rural local government districts appearing to be inconsistent with deprivation scores in the more affluent part of the distribution. Higher levels of car ownership occur in rural areas and may account for bias towards the more affluent end of the spectrum, although NOCAR has been shown (table 10.2) to provide a useful explanatory variable in relation to health measures. Poorer quality of housing is likely to be a more common feature in rural than urban areas but inclusion of the census variable of 'lacking housing amenities' did not act to improve the correlation of mortality with deprivation in rural health boards to any great extent. Further work is required to identify ways of measuring deprivation in rural areas.

## Bias resulting from institutions

Analysis at local level must also take note of the bias in mortality which may arise from large institutional populations within a small area (see Appendix A4). The effects are not always adverse (greater mortality) since some institutions, prisons and borstals for instance, have younger populations. Standardising for age/sex differences does not invariably produce a reliable measure when the population structure does not conform to the general pattern. Accuracy in death rates may also be affected by the procedures for determining the residence of the deceased in Scotland, which are not in accordance with the rules in the census for determining persons who are resident and form part of the institutional population. In the census persons in institutions are counted as resident after six months of stay while deaths are allocated back to the previous area of residence when the deceased has been resident less than ten years in respect of most institutions, but less than one year in the case of old people's homes. The best solution might be for both institutional deaths and institutional populations to be excluded from analysis for some purposes. At present it is not easy to identify when a death has been allocated to an institution (the disclosure of a Special Enumeration District on the Postcode Directory is the main clue), and the Registrar General could assist by including an item in the computerised death details.

At a larger area level the effect of institutions on death rates is less pronounced since most residents of institutions in an area now come from within the area itself and such deaths form a smaller proportion of total deaths. [25] It has been shown nevertheless that the flow of patients into a terminal care home considerably enhanced the mortality for a small rural district in England and that this problem would not be entirely eliminated by grouping up to the larger district level. [26]

## The ecological fallacy

Area-based methods have been criticised for falling into the error of the ecological fallacy [27] with the implication that the population in an area is homogeneous and shares equally in its characteristics. This is of course not the case and obviously households in some categories of deprivation will be more similar in their characteristics to those in other categories and deprived households will be found in non-deprived areas and vice versa. Nevertheless evidence in this report shows an increasing proportion of deprived households as the severity of area deprivation increases (table 2.8), and enumeration districts within sectors tending to be similar in characteristics to the sector in which they are located (Appendix A3). Mortality for social classes has also been shown to vary by the area characteristics, death rates for each social class increasing from the most affluent to most deprived areas (table 4.8). All of these results support the claim for the area basis to have some validity in discriminating between populations which in some degree are exposed to and share in the environment in which they live. Analysis at a smaller area level than postcode sector would of course produce populations with greater homogeneity in their characteristics but the alternative level of enumeration district (pop. c.300) suffers from two problems: data which are coded only for 10% of records in the census (e.g. social class) become very unreliable, and events at ED level are few and any rates are unreliable with large standard errors attached. Aggregation over EDs with similar characteristics could provide one strategy to overcome this particular problem.

Criticism of this kind apparently overlooks the fact that social classes also do not consist of homogeneous categories, since the numerous occupations which go to make up a social class experience diverse working conditions and very varying mortality experience. [28] Like social class, deprivation categories do not contain individuals or households which are unambiguously alike, and although this may impose limitations it does not render either measure useless for epidemiological investigation.

## Conclusion

A strong case can thus be made both for area-based methods and for deprivation as a relevant concept for the analysis of health events. Concern about inequalities in health will endure and strategies for their reduction should be included in health service policies at national and local level. Monitoring of these policies would be eased by the inclusion of one or more deprivation measures in the small area output from the 1991 census, since health and other authorities will not necessarily be in a position to calculate scores for their own area on a national base. Such measures would also provide a useful tool for much health-related research. A measure composed in the same manner as DEP would provide an obvious basis to allow comparison in the next decade with the gradients and relationships which have been observed in this report, and would also supply a standard for calibration of newly-constructed measures that can profit from the emergence of further relevant information.

## Innovation or Reincarnation?

This analysis has shown that area-based methods provide a powerful tool for the examination of variations in health in relation to socio-economic characteristics. The area approach has of course been utilised in a number of epidemiological studies examining the link between health and physical features of the environment, [29] air pollution [30] and the hardness of water [31,32] for instance, but use of the area base to examine variations by social factors has been a more recent innovation. [33] Despite its apparent recent emergence on the scene the use of the small area basis for the observation and interpretation of health events is not nevertheless a novel approach; reports of Medical Officers of Health for instance routinely examined mortality rates for the wards within their area and as long as a century ago Russell (one time Medical Officer of Health for Glasgow) was commenting 'it is undeniable that the inhabitants of towns differ in the physical conditions of health which they enjoy; it is but fair to take those differences into account in comparing their vital statistics' [34] which he did by examining death rates in relation to area density, rooms per house, persons per room, and population living in one apartment, and 5+ apartment houses. A necessary correction for institutions also attracted his attention, in particular for districts within towns; at this level the calculation of 'mean size of house and occupancy being in many instances vitiated as pure expressions of the accommodation of private householders, particularly since all institutions having under 200 inmates are classed as "houses"! Fortunately most of the inaccuracies in registration of deaths against which he struggled to measure the health experience of various communities no longer present problems, although that of dealing with the institutional populations and deaths remains, as do inaccuracies in respect of causes of deaths. [35]

The objectives Russell set himself still remain at the forefront of epidemiological analysis but out capacity to address them would have been beyond his comprehension. While the high quality, uniformity and comprehensiveness of the database might have been within his vision, the arrival on the scene of the computer would no doubt have exceeded his wildest dreams. This essential tool is joined by others: the postcode system to provide an area reference, together with the central postcode directory to provide the attribution to an area, the small area database in the census output to provide both population denominators and area characteristics, the increasing involvement of medical geographers, and the development of computerised mapping systems; all of these join in making the analysis of health data more accessible to investigation and rendering these objectives capable of attainment.

TABLE 10.1     CORRELATION BETWEEN SELECTED DEPRIVATION INDEXES*

| DEP | | | | | |
|---|---|---|---|---|---|
| TOWN | 0.960 | | | | |
| JAR | 0.826 | 0.801 | | | |
| DOEB | 0.910 | 0.896 | 0.870 | | |
| SDDEP | 0.955 | 0.908 | 0.804 | 0.862 | |
| | DEP | TOWN | JAR | DOEB | SDDEP |

*over 928 sectors

TABLE 10.2   CORRELATION OF FIVE DEPRIVATION INDEXES WITH
SELECTED HEALTH MEASURES

|            | DEP  | TOWN | JAR  | DOEB | SDDEP | NOCAR |
|------------|------|------|------|------|-------|-------|
| SMR all    | 0.73 | 0.72 | 0.65 | 0.73 | 0.71  | 0.69  |
| 0-64       | 0.75 | 0.73 | 0.67 | 6.76 | 0.72  | 0.74  |
| 65+        | 0.53 | 0.53 | 0.47 | 0.52 | 0.51  | 0.49  |
| BEDUSE all | 0.25 | 0.21 | 0.28 | 0.29 | 0.24  | 0.24  |
| acute 0-64 | 0.60 | 0.56 | 0.59 | 0.62 | 0.59  | 0.64  |
| acute 65+  | 0.10 | 0.07 | 0.16 | 0.14 | 0.08  | 0.12  |
| longstay   | 0.10 | 0.09 | 0.13 | 0.13 | 0.10  | 0.10  |
| PERMSICK   | 0.83 | 0.80 | 0.67 | 0.80 | 0.79  | 0.80  |
| TEMPSICK   | 0.75 | 0.73 | 0.60 | 0.70 | 0.75  | 0.68  |

|                      | SCOTDEP | JAR | TOWN | DOE | SDD |
|----------------------|---------|-----|------|-----|-----|
| Unemployment         | X       | X   | X    | X   | X   |
| - youth unemployment |         |     |      |     | X   |
| No car               | X       |     | X    |     |     |
| Low social class     | X       |     |      |     |     |
| - unskilled          |         | X   |      |     | X   |
| Overcrowding         | X       | X   | X    | X   |     |
| - below occ norm     |         |     |      |     | X   |
| Not owner occupied   |         |     | X    |     |     |
| Lacking amenities    |         |     |      | X   | X   |
| Single parent        |         | X   |      | X   | X   |
| Under 5              |         | X   |      |     |     |
| Elderly households   |         |     |      |     | X   |
| Lone pensioners      |         | X   |      | X   |     |
| 1-year migrants      |         | X   |      |     |     |
| Ethnic minorities    |         | X   |      | X   |     |
| Vacant dwellings     |         |     |      |     | X   |
| Level & access (old) |         |     |      |     | X   |
| Level & access (<5)  |         |     |      |     | X   |
| Permanent sickness   |         |     |      |     | X   |
| Large households     |         |     |      |     | X   |

Figure 10.1 RANGE OF VARIABLES INCLUDED IN FIVE MEASURES OF DEPRIVATION

# REFERENCES

CHAPTER 1 PP 1 TO 13

1   Registrar general, Seventy-fourth annual report of the Registrar General, HMSO London 1913

2   Office of Population Censuses and Surveys, General Household Survey (series GHS) annual reports, HMSO London

3   Blaxter M, Evidence on inequality in health from a national survey, *Lancet* 1982, 2: 30-3

4   Townsend P, Davidson N, Whitehead M, *Inequalities in health: the Black report and The Health Divide,* Penguin, London 1988

5   Wilkinson R G, Socio-economic differences in mortality: interpreting the data on their size and trends, in Wilkinson R G (ed) *Class and health*, Tavistock, London 1986: 1-20

6   Carr-Hill R, The inequalities in health debate: a critical review of the issues, *J Social Policy* 1987, *16*, 4: 509-42

7   Office of Population Censuses and Surveys and Registrar General, Scotland. Occupational mortality, decennial supplement 1979-80, 1982-83, DS No.4, HMSO London 1986

8   Fox A J, Goldblatt P O, Jones D R, Socio-demographic mortality differentials: Longitudinal Study 1971-75, LS No.1,.HMSO London 1982

9   Fox A J, Goldblatt P O, Jones D R, Social class mortality differentials: artefact, selection or life circumstances, *J Epidemiol Commun Health* 1985, *39*: 1-8

10  Office of Population Censuses and Surveys and General Register Office Scotland, Census 1981, Central postcode directory, User Guide 2

11  Office of Population Censuses and Surveys and General Register Office, Scotland, Census 1981 Small area statistics prospectus, User Guides 50 and 52, 2 and 4

12  Information & Statistics Division, *A guide to the work of ISD*, ISD publications Edinburgh 1989

13  Carr-Hill R, Revising the RAWP formula: indexing deprivation and modelling demand, Discussion paper 41, Centre for Health Economics, York University 1988

14  Townsend P, Deprivation, *J Social Policy* 1987, 16, 2: 125-46

15  Holterman S, Areas of deprivation in Great Britain: an analysis of 1971 Census data, Social Trends 1975, *6*. HMSO London

16  Department of Health & Social Security, NHS Management Board, Review of the resource allocation working party (RAWP) formula: Final report, DHSS London, 1988

17  Department of the Environment, Urban deprivation, Information Note No.2, DOE London, 1983

18  Duguid G & Grant R, Areas of special need in Scotland, Central Research Unit, Scottish Development Department Edinburgh 1983

19  Duguid G, Multiply deprived households in Scotland, Scottish Development Department; General Register Office, Scotland, 1981 Census Multiply deprived household tables, User Guide 21, GRO Edinburgh 1983

20  Jarman B, Identification of underprivileged areas, *Br Med J* 1983, *286*: 1705-9

    Jarman B, Underprivileged areas: validation and distribution of scores, *Br Med J* 1984, *289*: 1587-92

21  Hirsch S R (Chairman), *Psychiatric beds and resources: factors influencing bed use and service planning*, Gaskell, London 1988

22  Scott-Samuel A, Need for primary health care: an objective indicator, *Br Med J* 1984, *288*: 457-8

23  Fox A J, Social network interaction: new jargon in inequalities, *Br Med J* 1988, *297*: 373-4

24  Townsend P, Phillimore P, Beattie A, *Health and deprivation: inequality and the North*, Croom Helm, London 1988

25  Thunhurst C, The analysis of small area statistics and planning for health, *The Statistician* 1985, *34*: 93-106

26  Carstairs V, Multiple deprivation and health state, *Commun Med* 1981, 3: 4-13

27  Office of Population Censuses and Surveys and General Register Office, Scotland, Census 1981, Key statistics for urban areas, Scotland HMSO 1986

28  Wilkinson R G, Socio-economic differences in mortality, in Wilkinson R G (ed), *Class & Health*, Tavistock publications, London 1986, 1-20

29  Morris R, Carstairs V, Which deprivation? A comparison of selected deprivation measures in relation to health (in press)

30  Greater Glasgow Health Board, 10-year Report, 1973-1984, 1985

31  Lothian Regional Council Health Committee, Mortality differentials in the 0-64 year old population of Lothian, 1974-85

32  Scottish Home & Health Department, report of the working party on revenue resource allocation (SHARE), HMSO Edinburgh 1977

CHAPTER 2  PP 14 TO 42

1  Duguid G, Multiply deprived households in Scotland, Scottish Development Department; General Register Office, Scotland, 1981 Census Multiply deprived household tables, User Guide 21, GRO Edinburgh 1983

2  Knox P L, Disadvantaged households and areas of deprivation: microdata from the 1981 Census of Scotland, Environment & Planning A, 1985, *17:* 413-25

3   Denham C, Urban Britain, Population Trends 36, Summer 1984 HMSO London 1984

4   Registrar General Scotland, Census 1981, Housing and household report, HMSO Edinburgh 1984

5   Holterman S, Areas of deprivation in Great Britain: an analysis of 1971 Census data, Social Trends 1975, *6*, 33-47, HMSO London 1975

CHAPTER 3  PP 43 TO 66

1   Registrar General for Scotland, Annual Report, HMSO Edinburgh

2   Hume D & Womersley J, Analysis of death rates in the population aged 60 years and over of Greater Glasgow by postcode sector of residence. *J Epidemiol Commun Health* 1985, *39*: 357-363

3   Office of Population and Censuses and Surveys, Mortality Statistics, series DH1, 1980, 1981, 1982, HMSO London

4   Office of Population Censuses and Surveys and Registrar General, Scotland, Occupation Mortality, decennial supplement 1979-1980, 1982-83, HMSO London 1986

5   Britton M, Mortality & Geography, Population Trends 56, Summer 1989: 16-23, HMSO London 1989

6   Townsend P, Phillimore P, Beattie A, *Health and deprivation: Inequality and the North*, Croom Helm, London 1988

CHAPTER 4  PP 67 TO 99

1   Townsend P, Phillimore P, Beattie A, *Health and deprivation: Inequality and the North*, Croom Helm, London 1987

2   Office of Population Censuses and Surveys and Registrar General, Scotland, Occupation Mortality, decennial supplement 1979-1980, 1982-83, DS No.4, HMSO London 1986

3   Goldblatt P, Mortality by social class, 1971-85, OPCS, Population Trends 56: 6-11, Summer 1989

4   Fox A J, Goldblatt P O, Jones D R, Social class mortality differentials: artefact, selection or life circumstances, *J Epidemiol Commun Health* 1985, *39:* 1-8

5   Jones I G, Cameron D, Social class analysis: an embarrassment to epidemiology, *Commun Med* 1984, *6*: 37-46

6   Carstairs V, Morris R, Deprivation: explaining differences in mortality between Scotland and England and Wales, *Br Med J* 1989, 299: 886-9

CHAPTER 5 PP 100 TO 143

1   Acheson R M, Williams DRR, Does consumption of fruit and vegetables protect against stroke? *Lancet* 1983, *1*: 1191-3

2    Rutstein D D, Berenberg W, *et al*, Measuring the quality of medical care, *N England J Med* 1976, 294: 582-8

3    Carstairs V, Differentials in mortality, *Health Bulletin* 1988, *46*, 4: 226-36

4    Holland W W, European Community atlas of avoidable deaths, CEC Health services research series No.3, Oxford 1988

5    Doll R, Tobacco related disease, WHO First European conference on tobacco policy, Madrid 1988

6    Doll R, Peto R, Mortality in relation to smoking: 20 years' observations on male British doctors, *Br Med J*, 1976, 2: 1525-36

7    US Department of Health and Human Services, Reducing the consequences of smoking, Maryland USA 1989

8    Office of Population Censuses and Surveys, General Household survey, Annual reports, HMSO London

9    Tunstall-Pedoe H, Smith W C S, Crombie K, Tavendale R, Coronary risk factors and lifestyle variations across Scotland: results from the Scottish heart health study, *Scot Med J* 1989, *34*: 556-60

10   Smith W C S, Crombie K, Tunstall-Pedoe H D, Tavendale R, Riemersma R A, Cardiovascular risk factor profile and mortality in two Scottish cities, *Acta Med Scand* 1988, Suppl 728: 113-18

11   Crombie I K, Kenicer M G, Smith W C S, Tunstall-Pedoe H D, Unemployment, socioenvironmental factors and coronary heart disease in Scotland, *Br Heart J* 1989, *61*: 172-7

12   Marmot M G, Shipley M J, Rose G, Inequalities in death - specific explanations of a general pattern, *Lancet* 1984, *1*: 1003-6

13   Office of Population Censuses and Surveys and Registrar General, Scotland, Occupational mortality, decennial supplement 1979-80, 1982-83, DS No.4, HMSO London 1986

14   Registrar General, Scotland. A relative mortality analysis of Scottish local government districts 1974-84. Vital Statistics Return weeks 45-48, 1986

CHAPTER 6 PP 144 TO 175

1    Office of Population Censuses and Surveys, General Household Survey (series GHS) annual reports, HMSO London

2    Royal College of General Practitioners, Office of Population Censuses and Surveys, Department of health and Social Security, Morbidity Statistics from General Practice, 3rd national study, series MB No.1, HMSO London 1986

3    Brooke O G, Anderson H R, *et al*, Effects on birth weight of smoking, alcohol, caffeine, socioeconomic factors and psychosocial stress, *Br Med J* 1989, 298: 795-801

4    Registrar General Scotland, Annual report 1985, HMSO Edinburgh 1986

5    Registrar General Scotland, Illegitimate births in Scotland 1970-85, Vital Statistics Report weeks 25-8 1986

6    Knox E G et al, Social and health care determinants of area variations on mortality, Commun Med 1980, 2: 282-90

7    Registrar General, Scotland, Annual reports 1980, 81, 82, HMSO Edinburgh

8    Fox A J, Goldblatt P O, Socio-demographic mortality differentials: Longitudinal Study 1971-75, LS No.1, HMSO London 1982

9    Townsend P, Phillimore P, Beattie A, *Health and deprivation, inequality and the North*, Croom Helm, London 1988

10   Kemp I, Boyle P, Smans P, Muir C (eds.), *Atlas of cancer in Scotland 1975-80*, IARC Scientific Publications No.72, Oxford and WHO, Lyon 1985

11   Waterhouse J A *et al* (eds.) *Cancer incidence in five continents*, vol V, IARC Scientific Publications No.88, WHO Lyon 1987

12   Hirayama T (ed.), Cancer risks by site, International Union Against Cancer, Geneva 1980

13   Armstrong B, Doll R, Environmental factors and cancer incidence and mortality in different countries with special reference to dietary practices, *Intl J Cancer*, 1975, *15*: 617-31

14   Leon D, Longitudinal Study 1971-75, Social distribution of cancer, OPCS series LS No.3, HMSO London 1988

19   Doll R, Tobacco related disease, WHO First European conference on tobacco policy, Madrid 1988

20   Dooley C P, Cohen H, The clinical significance of campylobacter pylori, *Annals of Internal Med* 1988, *108*: 70

17   Goldberg D P, Huxley P C, *Mental illness in the community*, Tavistock Publications, London 1980

18   Goldberg D P, Morrison S L, Schizophrenia and social class, *Br J Psychiat* 1963, *109*: 785-802

19   Hirsch S R (chairman), Psychiatric beds and resources: factors influencing beduse and service planning. *Report of a working party of the Royal College of Psychiatrists*, Gaskell, London 1988

CHAPTER 7  PP 176 TO 195

1    Information and Statistics Division, *Scottish health statistics 1989, ISD publications*, Edinburgh 1989

2    Department of Health and Social Security, Final report of the NHS Management Board, *Review of the resource allocation* (RAWP) *formula*, Final report, DHSS London 1988

3    Carstairs V, Morris R, Deprivation, mortality and resource allocation, *Commun Med* 1989, 4: 364-72

CHAPTER 8  PP 196 TO 215

1    Scottish Home and Health Department. Report of the working party on revenue resource allocation (SHARE), HMSO Edinburgh 1977

2    Department of Health and Social Security, Sharing Resources for Health in England. Report of the resource allocation working party, HMSO London 1976

3    Secretaries of State for Health. Wales, Northern Ireland Working for patients, Parliamentary paper CM555, HMSO London 1989

4    Department of Health and Social Security. Final report by the NHS Management Board of the review of the resource allocation formula, DHSS 1988

5    Forwell G. Scottish Health Authorities Revenue Equalisation: a community medicine view of the SHARE report, *Scot Med J* 1978, *23*: 207-12

6    Information and Statistics Division, SHARE tables, 1989/90, ISD Publications Edinburgh 1989

7    Information and Statistics Division, Trend tables from SHARE 1979/80 - 1986/87, ISD publications, Edinburgh 1988

8    Information and Statistics Division, Scottish Health Statistics 1988, ISD Publications Edinburgh 1988

9    Morgan M, Mays N, Holland W, Can hospital use be a measure of need for health care? *J Epidemiol Commun Health* 1987, *41*: 269-74

10   Bloor M, Venters G, An epidemiological and sociological study of variations in the incidence of operation on the tonsils and adenoids, University of Aberdeen, Institute of medical sociology, Occasional paper No.2, 1978

11   Wennberg J, Which rate is right? *New Eng J Med*, 1986, 314: 310-11

12   Mays N, Measuring morbidity for resource allocation, *Br med J*, 1987, *295*, 703-6

13   Blaxter M, Health services as a defence against the consequences of poverty in industrialised societies, *Soc Sci Med* 1983, 17: 1139-48

14   Charlton J R H, Velez R, Some international comparisons of mortality amenable to medical intervention, *Br Med J* 1986, *292*: 295-301

15   Carstairs V, Ten years after reorganisation: changes in mortality measures 1974-1983 in Scotland and health boards, *Health Bulletin*, 1986, *44*. 4: 203-17

16   Carr-Hill R, Revising the RAWP formula: indexing deprivation and modelling demand, York University Centre for Health Economics, Discussion paper 41, 1988

17   Mays N, Bevan G, Resource allocation in the health service: a review of the methods of RAWP, London, Bedford Square Press 1987 (Occasional Papers on Social Administration, 81)

18   Carr-Hill R,. The inequalities in health debate: a critical review of the issues, *J Social Policy*, 1987, *16*. 4: 509-42

19   Moser K A, Goldblatt P O, Fox A J, Jones D R, Unemployment and Mortality: comparison of the 1971 and 1981 longitudinal study samples, *Br Med J*, 1987, *294*: 86-90

20   Piachaud D, Disability, retirement and unemployment of older men. *J Social Policy*, 1986, *15*: 145-62

21   Office of Population Censuses and Surveys, General Household Survey, Series GHS (annual reports)

22   Cox B, et al. The health and lifestyle survey, Health Promotion Research trust, London 1987

23    White paper on the 1991 Census, London, HMSO (Cm430) 1988

24    Hirsch S R (Chairman), Psychiatric beds and resources: factors influencing beduse
      and service planning. Report of a working party of the Royal College of Psychiatrists,
      Gaskell London 1988


CHAPTER 9  PP 216 TO 233


1     Townsend P, Phillimore P, Beattie A, *Health and deprivation: inequality and the
      North*, Croom Helm, London 1988

2     Townsend P, Davidson N, Whitehead M, I*nequalities in health: The Black report and
      The health divide*, Penguin London 1988

3     Macintyre S, The patterning of health by social position in contemporary Britain:
      directions for sociological research, Soc Sci Med, 1986, 23. 4: 393-415

4     Blane D, An assessment of the Black Report's 'explanations' of health inequalities,
      *Sociology of Health & Illness*, 1985, 7, 3: 423-45

5     Office of population Censuses and Surveys and Registrar General, Scotland,
      Occupational mortality, decennial supplement 1979-80, 1982-83, DS No.4, HMSO
      London 1986

6     Fox A J, Goldblatt P O, Jones D R, Social class mortality differentials: artefact,
      selection or life circumstances, *J Epidemiol Commun Health,* 1985, *39*: 1-8

7     Tunstall-Pedoe H, Smith W C S, Crombie K, Tavendale R, Coronary risk factors and
      lifestyle variations across Scotland: results from the Scottish heart health study, *Scot
      Med J*, 1989, *34*: 550-5, 556-60

8     Pocock S J, Cook D G, Shaper A G, Social class difference in ischaemic heart disease
      in British men, *Lancet*, 1987, *2*: 197-201

9     Marmot M G, Shipley M J, Rose G, Inequalities in death - specific explanations of a
      general pattern? *Lancet*, 1984, 1: 1003-6

10    Fulton M, Thomson M, Elton R A, *et al*, Cigarette smoking, social class and nutrient
      intake: relevance to coronary heart disease, *European J Chem Nutr*, 1988,
      *42*: 797-803

11    Oliver M F, Cigarette smoking, polyunsaturated fats, linoleic acid and coronary heart
      disease. *Lancet*, 1989, 1: 124-43

12    Isles C G, Hole D J, Gillis C R, *et al*, Plasma cholesterol, coronary heart disease and
      cancer in the Renfrew & Paisley survey, *Br Med J*, 1989, *298*: 920-4

13    Hart N, Sex, gender and survival: inequalities in life chances between European men
      and women, in Fox J (ed.) *Health inequalities in European countries*, Gower,
      London 1989

14    Information and Statistics Division Scottish Health Statistics 1988, ISD Publications,
      Edinburgh 1988

15    Office of Population Censuses and Surveys, General household Survey 1986, HMSO
      London 1988

16    Moser K A, Goldblatt P O, Fox A J, Jones D R, Unemployment and mortality:
      comparison of the 1971 and 1981 longitudinal study samples, *Br Med J,* 1987, *29*,
      4: 86-90

17  Forbes J F, McGregor A, Male unemployment and cause-specific mortality in post-war Scotland, *Int J Health Serv*, 1987, *17*, 2: 233-40

18  Charlton J R, Bauer R, Thakhore A et al, Unemployment and mortality: a small area analysis, *J Epidemiol Commun Health*, 1987, *41*: 10-13

19  Arber S, Social class, non-employment and chronic illness: continuing the inequalities in health debate, *Br Med J*, 1987, *294*: 1069-73

20  Platt S, Kreitman N, Trends in parasuicide and unemployment among men in Edinburgh, 1968-82, *Br Med J*, 1984, *289*: 1029-32

21  Crombie I K, Trends in suicide and unemployment in Scotland, 1976-86, *Br Med J*, 1989, *298*: 782-4

22  Jackson P R, Warr P, Mental health of unemployed men in different parts of England and Wales, *Br Med J*, 1987, *295*: 525-7

23  Gabe J, Williams P, Is space bad for your health? The relationship between crowding in the home and emotional distress in women, *Sociology of Health & Illness*, 1986, *8*, 4: 351-70

24  Lowry S, Housing and Health, *Br Med J* 1989, *299:* 1261-2, 1326-8, 1388-90, 1439-42, 1990, *300*: 32-4, 104-6

25  Platt S D, Martin C J, Hunt S M, Lewis C W, Damp housing, mould growth and symptomatic health state, *Br Med J*, 1989, *298*: 1673-8

26  Fox A J, Adelstein A M, Occupational mortality: Work or way of life? *J Epidemiol Commun Health*, 1978, *32*: 73-7

27  Brown G W, Harris T, *Social origins of depression*, Tavistock, London 1978

28  Fox J, Social network interaction: new jargon in health inequalities, *Br Med J,* 1988, *297*: 373-4

29  Barker D J P, Osmond C, Inequalities in health in Britain: specific explanations in three Lancashire towns, *Br Med J*, 1987, *294*: 749-52

30  Elford J, Phillips A, Thomson A G, Shaper, A G, Migration and geographic variations in ischaemic heart disease in Great Britain, *Lancet*, 1989, *1*: 343-46

31  Wadsworth M E J, Serious illness in childhood and its association with later-life achievement, in Wilkinson R G (ed.) *Class & health*, Tavistock London 1986

32  Cartwright a, O'Brien M, Social class variations in health care, in Stacey M (ed.), *The Sociology of the N.H.S.*, Keele Univ, 1976

33  Cassel J C, The contribution of the social environment to host resistance, *Am J Epidemiol*, 1976, *104*: 107-23

34  Antonovsky A, Social inequalities in health: a complementary perspective, in Fox J (ed.) *Health inequalities in European countries*, Gower, Aldershot 1989: 386-97

35  Marmot M G, Kogevinas M, Elston M A, Social/economic status and disease, *Ann Rev Public Health*, 1987, *8*: 111-35

36  Kaplan G A, *Twenty years of health in Alameda County, Society for Prospective Medicine*, 1985, San Francisco, Calif.

37  Hasan J, Way of life, stress and differences in morbidity between occupational classes in Fox J (ed.) *Health inequalities in European countries*, Gower Aldershot 1989: 372-85

38    Scottish Home & Health Department, Scottish Health Authorities Review of Priorities for the Eighties and Nineties (SHARPEN), HMSO Edinburgh 1988

39    Womersley J, McCauley D, Tailoring health services to the needs of individual communities, *J Epidemiol Commun Health* 1987, *41*, 3, 190-5

40    Roberts M M, Alexander F E, *et al*, Edinburgh trial of screening for breast cancer: mortality at seven years, *Lancet*, 1990, *1*, 241-6

41    Health Departments of Great Britain: General practice in the National health Service, the 1990 contract, August 1989

42    Central Statistical Office, Social Trends 1989, HMSO London 1989


CHAPTER 10  PP 234 TO 244


1    Thunhurst C, The analysis of small area statistics and planning for health, *The Statistician* 1985, *34*: 93-106

2    Scott-Samuel A, Need for primary health care: an objective indicator, *Br Med J* 1984, *288*: 457-8

3    Department of Health & Social Security, NHS Management Board, Review of the resource allocation working party (RAWP) formula: Final report, DHSS London 1988

4    Morris R, Carstairs V, Which deprivation? a comparison of selected deprivation measures in relatrion to health (in press)

5    Townsend P, Phillimore P, Beattie A, *Health and deprivation: inequality and the North*, Croom Helm, London 1988

6    Jarman B, Identification of underprivileged areas, *Br Med J* 1983, *286*: 1075-9

7    Department of the Environment, Urban deprivation, Information Note No.2, DOE London 1983

8    Duguid G, Grant R, Areas of special need in Scotland, Central research Unit, Scottish Development Department, Edinburgh 1983

9    Office of Population Censuses and Surveys and Registrar General, Scotland, Occupational mortality, decennial supplement 1979-80, 1982-83, DS No.4, HMSO London 1986

10    Goldblatt P, Mortality by social class 1971-85, OPCS, Population trends 56, Summer 1989: 6-12, HMSO London 1989

11    Wilkinson R G, Socio-economic differences in mortality: interpreting the data on their size and trends, in Wilkinson R G (ed) *Class and health*, Tavistock, London 1986

12    Marmot M G, Shipley M J, Rose G A, Inequalities in death - specific explanations of a general pattern, *Lancet* 1984, *1*: 1003-6

13    Fox A J, Goldblatt P O, Jones D R, Social class mortality differentials: artefact, selection or life circumstances, *J Epidemiol Commun Health* 1985, *39*: 1-8

14    Leon D A, Longitudinal Study 1971-75: Social distribution of cancer, OPCS Series LS No.3, HMSO London 1988

15    Stern J, Social mobility and the interpretation of social class mortality differentials, *J Social Policy* 1983 *12*: 27-49

16    Office of Population Censuses and Surveys, Census Newsletter No.9, May 1989

17    Bowling A, Jacobson B, Screening: the inadequacy of population registers, *Br Med J*, 1989, *298*: 545-6

18    Robertson A J, Reid G S, *et al*, Evaluation of a call programme for cervical cytology screening in women aged 50-60, *Br Med J*, 1989, *299*: 163-6

19    Armstrong E M, The politics of inadequate registers, *Br Med J* 1989, 299: 73

20    Secretaries of State for Health, Wales, Northern Ireland & Scotland, Working for Patients, CM555, HMSO London 1989

21    Department of Environment, Unemployment statistics for small areas, *Employment Gazette* 1984: *92*, 9: 393-9

22    Office of Population Censuses and Surveys and General register Office Scotland, census 1981, Central postcode directory, User Guide 2

23    Carstairs V, Lowe M, Small area analysis: creating an area base for environmental monitoring and epidemiological analysis, *Community Medicine*, 1986, *8*, 1: 15-28

24    Greater Glasgow health Board, Maternity & child health statistics 1982

25    Bulusu L, Area mortality comparisons and institutional deaths, OPCS Population Trends 42, Winter 1985: 36-41, HMSO London 1985

26    Gardner M J, Winter P D, Mapping small area cancer mortality: a residential coding story, *J Epidemiol Commun Health*, 1984, *38*: 81-4

27    Carr-Hill R A, Mays N B, Need for health care, social deprivation and the NHS management board review of the RAWP formula: a critique of the research, York & St. Thomas' 1988

28    Jones I G, Cameron D, Social class analysis-an embarrassment to epidemiology, *Community Medicine* 1984, *6*: 37-46

29    Gardner M J, using the environment to explain and predict mortality, *J R Statist Soc A*, 1973, *136*, 3: 421-40

30    Chinn S, Florey C du V, Baldwin I G, Gorgol M, The relation of mortality in England & Wales 1969-73 to measurements of air pollution, *J Epidemiol Commun Health* 1981, *35*: 174-9

31    Pocock S J, Shaper A G, Cook D G et al, British Regional Heart Study: geographic variations in cardiovascular mortality and the role of water quality, *Br Med J* 1980, *280*: 1243-9

32    Smith W C S, Crombie I K, Heart disease and water hardness in Scotland - is there a relationship? *J Epidemiol Commun Health* 1987, *41*: 227-8

33    Carstairs V, Small area analysis and health service research, Community Medicine 1981, 3: 131-9

34    Chalmers A K (ed.) *Public health administration in Glasgow: a memorial volume of the writings of J B Russell*, Maclehose & Sons, Glasgow 1905

35    Bloor M, Samphier M, Prior L, Artefact explanations of inequalities in health: an assessment of the evidence, *Sociology of Health and Illness* 1987, *9*, 3: 231-64

# Appendices

# A - Methods

## 1   Composition of the Database

Details of the database, below, show the number of records used in the study, compared with published statistics, and the percent of eligible records which were valid. Eligible records exclude the areas stated: residents from outside Scotland for deaths, Fife for all hospital records, since Fife was not supplying specific postcodes for its own residents in 1981, and Annandale & Eskdale local government district for general hospitals due to some patients crossing the border into Carlisle for treatment. Patients from other areas treated in England were very few. Exclusions due to problems with postcodes include out of Scotland residents (if any). The highest percentage of excluded records was for mental illness (4.7%) and the lowest for cancer (1.9%). For SMR 1, general hospitals, the % of records not allocated ranged from 7% in Orkney, to less than 1% in Greater Glasgow. Maternity records fail to capture births taking place at home or in private hospitals, and a few probably fail to get recorded. Analysis is in respect of deliveries, in relation to characteristics of the mother, and of these the 180,925 events represent 97.4% of eligible records (omitting the area exclusions shown). Analysis relating to infants is for 179,296 singleton births, an unknown proportion of eligible births. Singleton births registered in the period numbered 204,427, with the SMR 2 system capturing 97.7% of these. Exclusions due to inadequate postcodes (delivery events) ranged from 1.0% in Glasgow to 3.9% in Forth Valley health boards. In Orkney and Shetlands the proportion was 17% and 14% but, there being only six postcode sectors in these two boards the values will have little influence on the analysis. For cancer registrations later additions increased the number of cases over those published, to 95,020 and the % of valid records is based on this number.

MORTALITY AND MORBIDITY RECORDS

| Records Yr(s) | Published | Used in Study | Valid (%) | Details of excluded records | | |
|---|---|---|---|---|---|---|
| | | | | Area | | Postcode not known/ recorded |
| Deaths  1980-82 | 192,149 | 190,502 | 100.0 | O/S | 1,647 | |
| Deaths  1980-85 | 381,915 | 378,456 | 100.0 | O/S | 3,274 | 185 |
| SMR1     1981 All Discharges | 671,688 | 611,269 | 97.8 | O/S Fife Annan | 5,953 37,578 3,176 | 13,712 |

| SMR2 1980-82 | | | | | | |
|---|---|---|---|---|---|---|
| Deliveries | 199,804 | 180,925 | 97.4 | O/S | 412 | 4,857 |
| Singleton births | 198,044 | 179,296 | N/K | Fife | 13,610 | |

| SMR4 1980-82 | | | | | | |
|---|---|---|---|---|---|---|
| M.I. Admissions | 75,930 | 67,807 | 95.3 | Fife | 4,750 | 3,373 |

| SMR6 1979-82 | 93,312 | 93,175 | 98.1 | None | 1,845 | |
|---|---|---|---|---|---|---|
| Cancer Regs | (95,020) | | | | | |

* O/S out of Scotland

The number of events, the all-Scotland rates and the standard deviations of the standardised ratios around 100 are shown in the next table.

## MORTALITY AND MORBIDITY DATA STATISTICS

|  |  | Number | Rate | S.D. $ |
|---|---|---|---|---|
| Deaths | all | 190,502 | 12.6 | 15.1 |
|  | 0-64 | 48,779 | 3.8 | 26.1 |
|  | 65+ | 141,723 | 66.4 | 14.4 |
| Discharges | all | 614,445 | 131 | 19.6 |
|  | acute | 594,779 | 126 | 20.1 |
|  | acute 0-64 | 443,600 | 110 | 21.3 |
|  | acute 65+ | 151,179 | 228 | 23.5 |
|  | long stay | 19,666 | 4 | 51.2 |
| Beduse (days) | all | 8,161,215 | 1,733 | 36.8 |
|  | acute | 4,969,545 | 1,055 | 24.9 |
|  | acute 0-64 | 2,566,943 | 635 | 25.5 |
|  | acute 65+ | 2,402,602 | 3,626 | 35.4 |
|  | long stay | 3,191,670 | 678 | 72.8 |
| Mental Illness Admissions |  | 67,807 | 4.8 | 46.2 |
|  | 0-64 | 49,310 | 4.1 | 53.0 |
|  | 65+ | 18,497 | 9.3 | 54.0 |
|  | first | 26,277 | 1.9 | 40.6 |
|  | first 0-64 | 17,344 | 1.4 | 48.9 |
|  | first 65+ | 8,933 | 4.5 | 50.7 |
| Cancer Registrations | all | 93,175 | 4.6 | 16.7 |
|  | malignant | 89,505 | 4.5 | 16.3 |
|  | malignant 0-64 | 35,042 | 2.0 | 20.6 |
|  | malignant 65+ | 55,103 | 19.0 | 20.0 |
| Infant Mortality | perinatal | 4,524 | 11.3 | 1.8 * |
| 1980-85 | infant deaths | 4,261 | 10.7 | 1.5 * |
|  | neonatal | 2,625 | 6.6 | 1.3 * |
|  | post-neonatal | 1,636 | 4.2 | 0.8 * |
| Low Birth Weight singletons | 10,830 | 60.4 | 36.7 | |

$ standard deviation around 100
* standard deviation of the crude rate

The rates are all annual and are per 1,000 population except for perinatal which is per 1,000 all births; infant deaths, neo-natal and post-neonatal which are per 1,000 live births; and low birth weight which is per 1,000 singleton births. The standard deviations are evaluated over postcode sectors.

## 2   Variable Specifications

Listed below are the SAS cell numbers of components of deprivation and other variables used in this study.

Deprivation indicator :

| | |
|---|---|
| MUNP Male unemployment | 402/388 |
| NOCAR No car | 1177/937 |
| SC45 Social class IV & V | (5421+5424)/(5439-30-33-36) |
| OVERC >1 pers per room | (947+948)/937 |

Other socioeconomic measures :

| | |
|---|---|
| PAR1H One-parent h/holds | 2430/929 |
| QUALS Higher qualifications | (4805+4808+4811)/387 |
| OWNOC Owner occupier | 975/937 |
| BEWUK Born UK, not Scotland | (323+329+332)/(323+326+329+332) |
| MIGRT 1-year migration | 642/320 |

Health measures :

| | |
|---|---|
| TSICK Temporarily sick | 408/387 |
| PSICK Permanently sick | 1664/1629 |

## 3   Postcode Sectors

There are about 900 GPO postcode sectors in Scotland. However, in the census data sectors are split when they cross local authority district boundaries, resulting in 1,155 sectors (excluding the 56 shipping sectors). Sectors vary considerably in size, as can be seen in the frequency distribution of postcode sectors (PCS) by population size below, and 145 sectors in the census SAS have data suppressed for reasons of confidentiality since they contain less than 25 population or 8 households.

DISTRIBUTION OF POSTCODE SECTORS BY POPULATION SIZE

| Population in PCS | Number of PCS | Percent of PCS | Total of Pop | Percent of Pop |
|---|---|---|---|---|
| 0 | 16 | 1.4 | 0 | 0.0 |
| 1 - | 118 | 10.2 | 1,237 | 0.0 |
| 26 - | 76 | 6.6 | 4,204 | 0.1 |
| 100 - | 115 | 10.0 | 29,460 | 0.6 |
| 500 - | 51 | 4.4 | 38,627 | 0.8 |
| 1,000 - | 79 | 6.8 | 116,881 | 2.3 |
| 2,000 - | 58 | 5.0 | 149,109 | 3.0 |
| 3,000 - | 76 | 6.6 | 264,416 | 5.3 |
| 4,000 - | 84 | 7.3 | 381,613 | 7.6 |

| | | | | |
|---|---|---|---|---|
| 5,000 - | 96 | 8.3 | 530,138 | 10.5 |
| 6,000 - | 88 | 7.6 | 572,911 | 11.4 |
| 7,000 - | 71 | 6.2 | 530,736 | 10.5 |
| 8,000 - | 66 | 5.7 | 557,466 | 11.1 |
| 9,000 - | 52 | 4.5 | 494,519 | 9.8 |
| 11,000 - | 31 | 2.7 | 324,853 | 6.5 |
| 12,000 - | 27 | 2.3 | 311,206 | 6.2 |
| 13,000 - | 17 | 1.5 | 212,115 | 4.2 |
| 14,000 - | 6 | 0.5 | 80,227 | 1.6 |
| 15,000 - | 10 | 0.9 | 144,431 | 2.9 |
| 16,000 - | 11 | 1.0 | 169,577 | 3.4 |
| 17,000 - | 5 | 0.4 | 82,794 | 1.6 |
| 18,000 - | 1 | 0.1 | 17,558 | 0.4 |
| 19,000 + | 1 | 0.1 | 19,887 | 0.4 |
| TOTAL | 1,155 | 100 | 5,033,965 | 100 |

The postcode sector is used in this analysis since the population size provides a reasonable basis to observe adequate numbers of many types of events. Although the average size of population over all PCS is around 4,400, for sectors with population size greater than 500 this value rises to 6,000 (see table below) and it can be seen that only 20% of the population live in sectors of less than 5,000 population.

POSTCODE SECTOR POPULATION SIZE STATISTICS (1981 SAS TABLE 45, C4442)

| Description | No. PCS | Mean | Std Dev | Total |
|---|---|---|---|---|
| All | 1,211 | 4,200 | 4,100 | 5,035,315 |
| Excl. Shipping PCS | 1,155 | 4,400 | 4,000 | 5,033,965 |
| Whole Sectors | 898 | 5,600 | 3,800 | 5,033,965 |
| With Valid DEP score | 1,010 | 5,000 | 4,000 | 5,032,295 |
| With pop > 500 | 830 | 6,000 | 3,600 | 4,999,064 |
| Excl. Institutional PCS | 810 | 6,100 | 3,600 | 4,917,130 |

Over the three years of the mortality data a population of 6,000 would experience around 200 deaths for all ages, and around 50 for 0-64. Sectors with smaller populations will experience fewer events, and the rates will of course be less reliable, and for this reason the correlation analysis is weighted by sector population (see Section A.4). From the viewpoint of population size, ward data would have been preferable since there would have been a lesser variation in size but the 1981 Census Small Area Statistics output for wards was not available in Scotland when the analysis started.

It was possible to calculate the deprivation score for only 1,010 sectors, because of data suppression in the small sectors; most of the analysis is carried out on this basis and gradients in health measures over deprivation categories are calculated over these sectors. In many parts of the report data are reported for only the 830 sectors with a population size greater than 500, or alternatively, an 810 subset of sectors which exclude a further twenty sectors which have large Institutional populations (see Section A.5). The 180 small PCS (18% of total) which are excluded contain only 33,231 population (0.7% of the total).

Population and other data are aggregated to higher levels - local authority district, health board, and Scotland — over all 1,155 sectors to ensure that data for these areas are complete (DEPCAT over 1,010). Observed and expected values for the events data (eg. deaths) are calculated at sector level and aggregated to higher levels including Scotland to provide the basis for calculation of standardised values.

One of the benefits of small area analysis lies in the ability to observe populations with similar characteristics but the larger the population size of an area the less homogeneous it is likely to be. This consideration might point towards the use of Enumeration Districts (EDs) but the average size of EDs ($\mu = 300$, $N = 17418$) is too small to provide reliable rates for analysis.

The matter of homogeneity at sector level is explored in two ways, firstly, Enumeration Districts (EDs) as well as sectors were classified into a deprivation category (although it should be noted that the 10% measure of social class will be less reliable at this level). Not all EDs fall into the same deprivation category as the sector in which they are located but there is nevertheless general agreement between the two measures with between 60% and 93% of the population in EDs living either at the same level of deprivation as the sector, or within one level on either side (see table below). Greater diversity is apparent in the middle DEPCATS.

DEPRIVATION CATEGORY OF ENUMERATION DISTRICTS POPULATIONS BY DEPCAT OF POSTCODE SECTOR. PERCENT EDs WITHIN PCS.

| ED DEPCAT | Sector DEPCAT | | | | | | |
|---|---|---|---|---|---|---|---|
| | Affluent 1 | 2 | 3 | 4 | 5 | 6 | Deprived 7 |
| 1 Affluent | 81 | 41 | 21 | 10 | 5 | 2 | - |
| 2 | 11 | 26 | 20 | 11 | 6 | 3 | - |
| 3 | 4 | 17 | 22 | 17 | 11 | 4 | 1 |
| 4 | 2 | 10 | 17 | 23 | 17 | 8 | 1 |
| 5 | 1 | 4 | 11 | 19 | 21 | 17 | 5 |
| 6 | - | 2 | 7 | 15 | 27 | 32 | 20 |
| 7 Deprived | - | - | 2 | 5 | 14 | 33 | 72 |

In addition, the analysis relating to multiply and severely deprived households (chapter 2) provides evidence that deprivation in households is strongly aligned with area deprivation (at local government district level), the proportion of multiply deprived households ranging from 6% in the most affluent district to 29% in the most deprived. Wards or sectors both have the merit of being more homogeneous than local government districts.

## 4   Weighting

The postcode sectors vary considerably in size, from 0 to 19,900 (m = 5000, Std Dev = 4000, N = 1010) so the statistical analysis must use some method of weighting to ensure that small sectors (often with extreme values) do not carry undue influence in the results. Various methods have been proposed in the analysis of SMRs. One simple method is to weight by population size (a measure which is readily available). More sophisticated intermediate methods have been proposed by Pocock et al [1] and Breslow [2]; a Poisson weighted method is suggested.

These methods have been tested using data for 829 postcode sectors and six census variables [3] and the results are shown below together with the output from this study. The smaller dataset excludes sectors with population less than 500, and a further sector with no recorded deaths (DD9.7P).

CORRELATION OF SMR WITH CENSUS VARIABLES

| Weight = | Study results (N = 1010) | | Subset of sectors [3] (N = 829) | | |
|---|---|---|---|---|---|
| | Unweighted | Pop | Unweighted | Poisson | Pop |
| Male Unemployment | 0.38 | 0.70 | 0.65 | 0.70 | 0.72 |
| No Car | 0.40 | 0.69 | 0.66 | 0.70 | 0.71 |
| Overcrowding | 0.32 | 0.64 | 0.57 | 0.63 | 0.67 |
| Single-parent | 0.19 | 0.48 | 0.45 | 0.48 | 0.50 |
| Social Class I | -0.01 | -0.45 | -0.41 | -0.46 | -0.48 |
| Social Class V | 0.15 | 0.59 | 0.52 | 0.59 | 0.61 |

The two population weighted analyses (which use different numbers of sectors) produce very similar results which are just slightly higher for the first three variables on the 829 subset of sectors, while the results using Poisson weighted coefficients are almost identical to the population weighted results for 1010 sectors. They suggest that there is not much to be lost by including the smaller sectors (so long as population weighting is used). The data show that the correlation coefficients are improved by weighting, particularly when the low population sectors are included in the analysis. Weighting by population size on all sectors with unsuppressed data (N = 1010) is the method adopted.

## 5   The Effect of Institutions

The census populations includes persons enumerated in institutions of various kinds. A person is counted as resident in an institution if they have been there more than six months. The type of institutions and numbers of persons present and the percentage classified as usually resident are shown below.

| | Persons present | * Usually resident (%) |
|---|---|---|
| Hotels and boarding houses | 28,935 | 13 |
| Childrens homes | 3,667 | 73 |
| Old people's homes | 16,056 | 91 |
| Psychiatric hospitals | 22,476 | 84 |
| Other hospitals | 35,698 | 30 |
| Schools and colleges | 9,651 | 14 |
| Prisons and other penal institutions | 4,508 | 46 |
| Hostels and lodging houses | 6,357 | 65 |
| Other establishments | 19,918 | 39 |

* not staff; resident more than six months

This table shows a wide range of different kinds of establishment and the presence of some of these could be expected to have an influence on the death rate for a sector containing an institution because of the age structure resulting in either a greater or lesser probability of deaths occurring. The death rate for an area depends however not only on the presence of the institution but also on the way deaths are treated in the registration process; the rule (in Scotland) is to allocate back to their previous area of residence the deaths of all persons resident less than ten years except for old people's homes when a stay of one year applies. This differs from the census basis which counts as resident all persons with a period of stay of six months or more. It is not known how far the procedure for allocating a death to an area achieves its aim but the the possibility of a death being allocated to a sector should obviously be lower in those containing institutions which do not have long-stay residents and higher in those that do. Death rates in the former would be likely to be artificially low because of the lack of agreement between the numerator and the denominator populations. The length of stay of the residents is not known but among the establishments listed, psychiatric hospitals — which include both those for mental illness and mental handicap — are probably most likely to accommodate residents with a length of stay of more than ten years, such length of stay in 'other' hospitals being the exception rather than the rule. Despite a high average age on entry a majority of residents in old people's homes will probably achieve one year of stay. Most prisons and borstals will have shorter stay populations as will most of the other types of institution although previous residence may be difficult to identify in some cases.

The possibility of the death rate for a sector being influenced by the presence of an institution depends therefore on two factors :

Whether the age distribution within the sector is affected in such a way that fewer or more deaths would be expected in relation to total population.

Whether a death occurring in an institution is allocated to the area.

The 51 postcode sectors with an institutional population (total) which constituted more than 10% of the total were therefore examined to see if there was any undue bias present in their death rates. Twenty-two of these sectors had populations of less than 500 (usually very much less) and these would therefore carry very little weight in the analysis (see section - A.4). Information on the twenty-nine sectors with more than 500 population shows the very considerable variety of establishments and populations within these sectors, the % in institutions ranging from 10% to over 75%, and the population aged less than 65 from 54% up to 99%. This statistic also disguises variations within this group, one sector (G1.5), despite having an above average proportion of elderly also having an excess of males in the younger age groups and particularly at 45–64; this is the case also for sectors G4.0, G40.2 and G69.8 (data not shown). Several sectors have high proportions of population under 65, with DD9.7P having 99% in this age group and 87% under 45. At the other end of the scale the proportion of the elderly ranges from 2% in DD9.7P to 46% in G69.8P, in comparison with 14% for Scotland as a whole.

The type of institution in a sector shows that the picture is often confused by the presence of more than one type of institution, with different population profiles. The diversity of these institutional sectors thus presents some problems for the analysis of mortality and many of the SMRs for these particular postcode sectors display very extreme values, including one sector with no deaths. SMRs range from 57 to 173 (all ages); from 34 to 257 (0-64) and from 49 to 173 (65 and over) and a very high proportion of the SMRs fall outwith the range of less than 80 or more than 120, i.e. 56% of the total values, compared with 23% for sectors with populations of 500 or more. Only four sectors of the 29 had all three values within the range 80–120.

It is of course possible that some of the extreme values are true measures but even though some of these are shown to be statistically significant there must be some doubt about their authenticity; the disparate distributions of age groups and deaths within most of these sectors means that these SMRs are unreliable for comparison with those populations which conform to the norm. These sectors are included in the analysis in order to maintain the completeness of the database, but twenty of these sectors with significantly high or low SMRs (5% level of significance) have been excluded from the output tables. These are shown in the table (below):

POSTCODE SECTORS EXCLUDED FROM ANALYSIS - POPULATIONS AND SMRs.

| Sector | Total pop | % Total Inst | Pop% 65+ | Residential Pop 1 | 2 | 3 | 4 | SMR All | 0-64 | 65+ |
|--------|-----------|--------------|----------|-------------------|---|---|---|---------|------|-----|
| AB1.5P | 598 | 11 | 13 | - | - | - | 100 | 81 | 34 | 99 |
| DD1.1 | 565 | 16 | 14 | 19 | - | - | 80 | 145 | 101 | 167 |
| DD9.7P | 715 | 16 | 2 | - | - | - | 100 | - | - | - |
| EH1.1 | 815 | 21 | 19 | - | - | - | 100 | 173 | 205 | 163 |
| EH10.5 | 8,462 | 15 | 29 | 39 | 47 | 8 | 5 | 96 | 67 | 100 |
| EH24.9 | 1,432 | 16 | 12 | - | 100 | - | - | 160 | 136 | 173 |
| EH8.8 | 2,867 | 12 | 27 | 43 | - | 56 | - | 157 | 130 | 162 |
| FK5.4P | 11,236 | 17 | 16 | - | 99 | - | - | 87 | 104 | 82 |
| G1.5 | 934 | 28 | 34 | - | - | - | 100 | 146 | 257 | 120 |
| G12.0 | 8,127 | 15 | 22 | 37 | 43 | 3 | 15 | 116 | 85 | 122 |
| G4.0 | 6,012 | 19 | 31 | - | - | 1 | 98 | 121 | 144 | 115 |
| G40.2 | 1,659 | 32 | 27 | - | - | - | 100 | 158 | 250 | 132 |
| G53.7P | 11,981 | 10 | 16 | 29 | 66 | 4 | - | 112 | 142 | 104 |
| G65.7 | 5,087 | 26 | 13 | - | 100 | - | - | 113 | 152 | 97 |
| G69.8P | 803 | 75 | 46 | - | 100 | - | - | 67 | 143 | 59 |
| KA6.6P | 2,785 | 21 | 20 | - | 97 | - | 2 | 74 | 76 | 73 |
| KY15.5 | 6,842 | 10 | 20 | - | 100 | - | - | 72 | 79 | 70 |
| ML7.4P | 7,055 | 17 | 19 | - | 96 | - | 3 | 95 | 135 | 86 |
| PA11.3 | 713 | 73 | 16 | - | - | 49 | 50 | 57 | 110 | 49 |
| TD6.9P | 3,246 | 11 | 26 | 2 | 97 | - | - | 73 | 111 | 65 |

where '% Residential Population' number key is:

1. Old people's homes
2. Psychiatric hospitals
3. Other hospitals
4. Other institutions

## 6    Standardised Ratios

Standardardised ratios for various measures are calculated within the database at postcode sector and other area levels using both the events data and the 1981 census populations. This ensures that observed (O) and expected (E) events in total are always in agreement. The rates which provide the basis for standardisation will differ slightly from published data because of the use of census populations, and also because of the exclusion of the 'out of Scotland' residents who are not allocated to a sector but the differences between the rates computed on these two bases are small. The exclusion of non-residents amounts to less than 1% of total deaths but varies between 0.3% in Glasgow health board and 3.0% in Highland health board and this factor helps to explain differences to published data at this area level.

The standardised ratio (SR) = Observed/Expected and is expressed in relation to 100. A ratio higher than 100 implies observed events are higher than expected, and vice versa. The expected number of events for any area is calculated by the summation of the values which result from muliplying the populations (by age and sex) in the area by the respective national rates. The rates used for standardisation will be found in the body of the report (eg. death rates in table 3.10). The expected events thus take into account the structure of the area population. The expected number is given by:

$$E = \sum N_i R_i$$

and $SR = 100*O/E$

Where:    $N_i$ = Number of persons in age/sex group i

$R_i$ = Event rate of age/sex group i in the reference population

The standardised ratios used in this study, as is usual, employs indirect age-standardisation; a standard set of rates derived from the reference population (Scotland) is applied to an area population to obtain the expected number of events (deaths, cancer registrations, number of bed days, etc). This indirect method is preferred since the rates are based on larger numbers and are therefore more reliable than the direct standardised ratios, which use area rates (often based on small numbers) applied to a standard population.

**Significance Testing of Standardised Ratios** Significance testing is achieved by first calculating the $100(1 - \alpha)\%$ confidence interval for the population value of O/E. The O can be regarded as a Poisson variable:

$$\chi^2 = (|O - E| - \tfrac{1}{2})^2/E$$

This is the simple continuity corrected chi-square statistic with mean and variance both equal to E. The $\frac{1}{2}$ correction in the numerator improves the correspondence between the percentiles of the discrete Poisson distribution and the continuous normal one. The confidence intervals are derived from tables when the number of observed cases is 5 or less for 95% and 99% intervals. When the number of observed cases exceeds 5, we have used Byar's approximation which is quite precise [4]. The confidence limits are obtained by first finding the lower (L) and upper (U) limits $\mu_L$ and $\mu_U$ for the mean $\mu = E(O)$ of the Poisson distributed observation O, and then computing $SR_L = \mu L/E$ and $SR_U = \mu U/E$. Then for $100(1 - \alpha)\%$ confidence interval we have:

$$\mu L = O(1 - 1/9O - Z_{\alpha/2}/3\sqrt{O})^3$$

and:

$$\mu U = (O + 1)(1 - 1/9(O + 1) - Z_{\alpha/2}/3\sqrt{(O + 1)})^3$$

Where $Z_{\alpha/2}$ denotes the $100(1 - \alpha/2)$ percentile of the unit normal distribution (1.96 for the 5% level of significance). Once $\mu_L$ and $\mu_U$ are computed, $SR_L$ and $SR_U$ are calculated. Then the SR is tested to see if it lies outwith this range to determine whether or not it is significantly low or high.

## 7  Significance of Correlation Coefficients

Since the standardised rates and deprivation indicators are  continuous variables, Pearsons product moment correlation coefficient, $r$, is  used throughout. The value or $r$ can lie between -1 and +1. If it is either -1 or +1 then the two variables have total dependence. If $r$ is zero there is no relationship between them, they are stochastically independent.

In testing the statistical significance of an $r$ it is usual to assume the null hypothesis that its population value is zero, HO: r=0. When the sample size, N, is large then the standard error of $r$ is approximately $(1-r^2)/\sqrt{N}$ [5]. Correlation coefficients are calculated for a varying number of areal units depending on the type of analysis; from 56 (local government districts) to 1010 (postcode sectors). The significant limits of $|r|$ at the 95% level of significance are approximately equal to $\sqrt{(3.84/(1.84+N))}$ where N is the number of areal units in the analysis [6]. The following table gives the level $|r|$ needs to exceed to be significant at the 95%, 99% and 99.9% level for the area levels used in the study:

| Analysis level | No. Areal units | Significance level (%) | | |
|---|---|---|---|---|
| | | 95 | 99 | 99.9 |
| LGD's | 56 | 0.26 | 0.34 | 0.43 |
| HBG - Rural | 185 | 0.14 | 0.19 | 0.24 |
| HBG - East | 405 | 0.10 | 0.13 | 0.16 |
| HBG - West | 420 | 0.10 | 0.13 | 0.16 |
| PCS | 1010 | 0.06 | 0.08 | 0.10 |

Indication of significance is not given in the text.

## 8  Derivation of the Measure of Deprivation

The determination of the variables to be included in the deprivation measure was mainly based on a previous analysis of 1971 data for Glasgow and Edinburgh which used the variables of overcrowding, male unemployment, lacking amenities, 1–3 rooms, no car, SEG 11 [7]. These were based on a list of indicators used by the Scottish Development Department  in identifying areas for  priority treatment;

selection from among these however was on the basis of correlation with the health indicators. On this occasion the intention was to select those indicators which best appear to represent material disadvantage (see chapter 1). The list nevertheless includes three of the same variables: overcrowding, male unemployment and no car. Since social class is available in the 1981 Census output this is used (social class IV and V) in preference to SEG. Although lack of amenities still appeared relevant this indicator had fallen by 1981 to a level where it no longer carried much weight. Households with 1-3 rooms does not carry conviction as an indicator of deprivation; three rooms might be considered quite generous space for one inhabitant, and measures of space per person are in our view to be preferred. So the four indicators chosen to be combined into the deprivation score are no car, male unemployment, overcrowding and social class IV & V. The deprivation score is a simple (unweighted) combination of these four variables. But to ensure that the variables are on the same scale (with zero mean and unit deviation), they are standardised (or Z-scored) before combination. Standardisation is accomplished by subtracting the mean from the observed value then dividing by its respective standard deviation. The population means and standard deviations (calculated over 1010 sectors) are shown below:

MEANS AND STANDARD DEVIATIONS OF DEPRIVATION SCORE VARIABLES (%)

|  | Mean | Stan Dev |
|---|---|---|
| No Car | 41.2 | 18.5 |
| Male Unem. | 12.5 | 7.3 |
| Overcrowding | 25.3 | 11.4 |
| SC IV & V | 24.1 | 10.4 |

An example of the calculation of the score for one sector is given in chapter 1. These four variables are all based on individuals rather than households, the Census SAS cell specifications appear at A.2. They are highly inter-correlated with a range of other census measures as may be seen in the full correlation matrix at (Appendix B Table 1.1). Correlations between the four variables and the composite indicator are shown below:

CORRELATIONS BETWEEN DEPRIVATION INDICATORS AND SCORE (N = 1010)

| | | | | |
|---|---|---|---|---|
| 1. No Car | * | | | |
| 2. Male Unemployment | 0.85 | * | | |
| 3. Overcrowding | 0.78 | 0.81 | * | |
| 4. Social Class IV & V | 0.69 | 0.71 | 0.72 | * |
| Deprivation | 0.92 | 0.93 | 0.91 | 0.86 |
| | 1 | 2 | 3 | 4 |

For some analyses the deprivation score for a postcode sector is recoded into a categorical variable, DEPCAT, which ranges from 1 (most affluent) to 7 (most deprived). The table (below) shows the distribution of the deprivation score and DEPCAT by number of sectors and population.

FREQUENCY DISTRIBUTION OF DEPRIVATION SCORE AND DEPCAT

| | Deprivation Score | | | | | DEPCAT | | | | |
|---|---|---|---|---|---|---|---|---|---|---|
| Range | Sectors | | Population | | DEP | Sectors | | Population | |
| | No. | % | No. | % | CAT | No. | % | No. | % |
| -9 to -8 | 5 | 1 | 231 | 0 | | | | | |
| -8 to -7 | 14 | 1 | 26,012 | 1 | 1 | 105 | 10 | 305,868 | 6 |
| -7 to -6 | 32 | 3 | 97,633 | 2 | | | | | |
| -6 to -5 | 54 | 5 | 181,992 | 4 | | | | | |
| -5 to -4 | 80 | 8 | 267,718 | 5 | 2 | 180 | 18 | 691,280 | 14 |
| -4 to -3 | 100 | 10 | 423,562 | 8 | | | | | |
| -3 to -2 | 126 | 12 | 543,593 | 11 | 3 | 253 | 25 | 1,095,583 | 22 |
| -2 to -1 | 127 | 13 | 551,990 | 1 | | | | | |
| -1 to 0 | 116 | 11 | 649,422 | 13 | 4 | 219 | 22 | 1,282,976 | 25 |
| 0 to 1 | 103 | 10 | 633,554 | 13 | | | | | |
| 1 to 2 | 66 | 7 | 383,420 | 8 | 5 | 117 | 12 | 743,689 | 15 |
| 2 to 3 | 51 | 5 | 360,269 | 7 | | | | | |
| 3 to 4 | 43 | 4 | 285,353 | 6 | | | | | |
| 4 to 5 | 22 | 2 | 101,079 | 2 | 6 | 91 | 9 | 571,901 | 11 |
| 5 to 6 | 26 | 3 | 185,469 | 4 | | | | | |
| 6 to 7 | 10 | 1 | 81,022 | 2 | | | | | |
| 7 to 8 | 11 | 1 | 97,459 | 2 | | | | | |
| 8 to 9 | 6 | 1 | 41,210 | 0 | | | | | |
| 9 to 10 | 7 | 1 | 55,325 | 1 | 7 | 45 | 4 | 340,998 | 7 |
| 10 to 11 | 6 | 1 | 55,126 | 1 | | | | | |
| 11 to 12 | 3 | 0 | 2,632 | 0 | | | | | |
| 12 to 13 | 2 | 0 | 8,224 | 0 | | | | | |
| TOTAL | 1,010 | 100 | 5,032,295 | 100 | | 1,010 | 100 | 5,032,295 | 100 |

***Explaining Mortality*** The contribution of additional variables over and above the deprivation score in explaining mortality has been examined using multiple regression. A subset of variables (35 in number) were chosen as possible candidates for entry into a regression with mortality the the independent variable. The variables comprising the deprivation score were excluded, and the analysis was carried out using the smaller 810 sector dataset (see A.3) to ensure a more robust analysis. Variables were selected for entry (or removal) using stepwise selection and terminating when no further variables met the standard (default) entry and removal criteria [8]. Some of the variables have a negative association with mortality such as 'M in work' ($r = -0.74$), 'Students' ($r = -0.56$) and 'Agriculture Employees' ($r = -0.26$). The analysis was carried out on SMR all ages, 0-64 and 65+. The multiple correlation coefficient and percentage change in explained variance ($R^2$) at each step for each SMR is shown below:

MULTIPLE REGRESSION RESULTS

| SMR All | Mult R | Cha | SMR 0-64 | Mult R | Cha | SMR 65+ | Mult R | Cha |
|---|---|---|---|---|---|---|---|---|
| Deprivation | 0.748 | 55.9 | Deprivation | 0.777 | 60.3 | Deprivation | 0.562 | 31.6 |
| M in work | 0.755 | 1.1 | 1-Person HH | 0.791 | 2.3 | Pens ON<0 | 0.570 | 0.9 |
| 1-Parent HH | 0.762 | 1.0 | F in work | 0.798 | 1.1 | Manuf Emp | 0.580 | 1.1 |
| Pens ON<0 | 0.765 | 0.6 | Perm Sick | 0.803 | 0.7 | Change Addr | 0.584 | 0.5 |
| Students | 0.769 | 0.5 | Students | 0.805 | 0.4 | 16-24 Unemp | 0.589 | 0.5 |
| Agricul Emp | 0.771 | 0.3 | M in work | 0.810 | 0.8 | Perm Sick | 0.593 | 0.4 |
| F Econ Inac | 0.776 | 0.7 | 1-Parent P | 0.813 | 0.5 | Temp Sick | 0.596 | 0.4 |
| M Retired | 0.778 | 0.4 | Agricul Emp | 0.815 | 0.3 | E & W Emp | 0.599 | 0.4 |
| 1-Person HH | 0.782 | 0.5 | Pers ON>0 | 0.817 | 0.4 | | | |
| Qualified | 0.785 | 0.5 | Pens ON<0 | 0.820 | 0.4 | Additional $R^2$ | : 4.34 | |
| Students | 0.785 | -0.1 | Qualified | 0.822 | 0.4 | Adjusted $R^2$ | : 3.79 | |
| Lone Pens | 0.787 | 0.4 | Pers ON<0 | 0.823 | 0.2 | | | |
| LA Tenure | 0.789 | 0.3 | 1-Parent P | 0.823 | -0.1 | | | |
| | | | 1-3 Rooms | 0.824 | 0.2 | | | |

Additional $R^2$    : 6.32
Adjusted $R^2$    : 5.86

Additional $R^2$    : 7.56
Adjusted $R^2$    : 7.12

The $R^2$ statistics (or *coefficients of determination*) do not increase by a great deal after the deprivation score has been entered. The *adjusted* $R^2$, which (by taking into account the number of independent variables in the equation) is a more realistic measure of the goodness of fit of the model in the population, show that the contribution of variables over and above the deprivation score is highest for mortality in the age group 0–64 at 7%, 6% for all ages and 4% in the age group 65+. This shows that a very high proportion (about 95%) of the variance in mortality which *can* be explained by census variables, is explained by the deprivation score. It can also be seen that many of the variables which have been selected for entry into the models are variations of measures already included in the deprivation score — measures of overcrowding and employment.

## 9    Derivation of the Distance Measure

The distance measure had the aim of measuring distance to the main general hospital services, and two types of facilities were defined in the derivation of this measure:

**1. Acute District General Hospital (DGH) beds.** The criteria used were beds in:

at least general surgery and one other (adult) surgical specialty, plus general medicine and one other (adult) medical specialty; or

Four or more specialties (not necessarily the mix as specified above) with 200 or more beds. In practice hospitals with these combinations also contain a range of other specialties. By definition these hospitals provide the services at 2.

**2. Other combinations of acute beds.** To include at least general surgery and general medicine. These hospitals are mostly based away from large centres of population and provide a restricted range of services.

Both definitions exclude maternity, general practitioner, single specialty hospitals providing very specialised care and children's hospitals. Maternity beds are excluded since this specialty is not included in the examination of general hospital measures. The other types of hospitals listed above provide only a minor part of patient care and cannot be conceived as providing a route to the bulk of hospital services. The same consideration applies to long-stay beds which are also excluded but although these are rarely located in DGH hospitals access to these is mainly under the control of geriatric assessment services which tend to be located within the acute hospital services.

One or two hospitals were located so close to one another that they were considered to constitute a single unit for purposes of calculating distance. Fifty-four hospitals or combined hospitals fell within the criteria, and of these thirty-two were defined as an acute DGH facility.

Grid reference co-ordinates for the hospitals were obtained from the Postcode directory, and the cartesian co-ordinates of postcode sector population centroid were obtained from 1981 Census SAS, thus enabling crow-fly distances to be calculated for all sectors in Scotland, except Fife health board, Annandale & Eskdale local authority district, a further 15 sectors with zero population, and Shipping Sectors, leaving a total of 1063 sectors. Population weighted distances (in miles) are shown below:

|                       | Mean | Stan Dev | Minimum | Maximum |
|-----------------------|------|----------|---------|---------|
| DGH hospital distance | 9.9  | 21.6     | 0.11    | 222.5   |
| Other hospitals       | 5.3  | 7.3      | 0.05    | 62.2    |

Distributions for the two measures are given below:

| | DGH hospitals | | Other hospitals | |
|---|---|---|---|---|
| Distance (Miles) | Number of Sectors | Population (thousands) | Number of Sectors | Population (thousands) |
|---|---|---|---|---|
| 0 -   1   | 104 | 629 | 135 | 817 |
| 1 -   2   | 120 | 823 | 138 | 956 |
| 2 -   3   | 96  | 700 | 105 | 701 |
| 3 -   4   | 75  | 427 | 81  | 410 |
| 4 -   5   | 67  | 285 | 83  | 327 |
| 5 -   10  | 196 | 762 | 208 | 729 |
| 10 -  15  | 94  | 322 | 96  | 299 |
| 15 -  20  | 41  | 113 | 60  | 107 |
| 20 -  30  | 76  | 161 | 92  | 155 |
| 30 -  40  | 56  | 154 | 31  | 67  |
| 40 -  50  | 33  | 83  | 11  | 24  |
| 50 -  60  | 25  | 27  | 7   | 8   |
| 60 -  70  | 26  | 9   | 1   | 1   |
| 70 -  80  | 11  | 12  | 0   | 0   |
| 80 -  90  | 9   | 20  | 0   | 0   |
| 90 - 100  | 5   | 17  | 0   | 0   |
| 100 - 200 | 2   | 34  | 0   | 0   |
| 200 +     | 2   | 22  | 0   | 0   |

Fife Health Board, Annandale & Eskdale District are excluded since these areas are excluded from hospital based analyses (see A.3).

For hospitals of type 1 (acute DGH) 14% of the population were within 1 mile of the facility and for type 2 (any acute facilities), 18%. For type 2 only 1% of the population was more than 40 miles distant while for type 1 5% of the population was at this distance with 1% being more than 100 miles from this particular type of service.

## 10  Derivation of the Supply Function

The calculation of the bed supply measure was calculated on beds available at health district level as described below:

### a. Calculation of bed supply per 1,000 catchment population.

1. Catchment populations were first calculated for the thirty-seven health districts which existed in 1981 by allocating the population of postcode sectors (PCS) to districts in proportion to (a) the discharges and (b) the bed-days from a PCS which occured in each health district. This procedure augments the population of districts which receive patients and diminishes the population of those which export patients. Criticisms have been made of this proportional method [10] but these are relevant mainly at larger area levels within which access to resources may vary; the populations of PCS are small enough to assume equality of access to any beds available for all parts of the sector.
2. The numbers of beds available (for all, acute and long-stay specialties) for health districts were extracted for 1981.
3. From (1) and (2) the bed ratios per 1,000 catchment population were calculated for each health district. Bed ratios per 1,000 resident and catchment population are given in table 7.7 for health boards and health districts.

### b. Calculating bed supply at sector level

1. To calculate the bed supply rate for a PCS, the proportion of (a) discharges and (b) bed-days from each sector which occurred in each of the health districts was first computed. These proportions were then multiplied by the appropriate available bed rates for the health district (from a.3 above) and summed to give an average rate for the sector.

   Hypothetical Example

   Sector
   xx2.1   3 discharges  (30%)   30 bed-days  (28%)   to District A
           5 discharges  (50%)   60 bed-days  (57%)   to District B
           2 discharges  (20%)   16 bed-days  (15%)   to District C
   Total  10                    106

   Suppose:

   |            | Bed Supply Ratio (a) * | Bed Supply Ratio (b) * |
   |------------|------------------------|------------------------|
   | District A | 7.8                    | 7.6                    |
   | District B | 6.3                    | 6.5                    |
   | District C | 6.1                    | 7.0                    |

   Then BEDSUP for Sector xx2.1 =

   (a) = (0.30 x 7.8) + (0.50 x 6.3) + (0.20 x 6.1) = 6.71
   (b) = (0.28 x 7.6) + (0.57 x 6.5) + (0.15 x 7.0) = 6.88

   * Supply based on: (a) flow of discharges; (b) flow of bed-days.

It should be noted that this method does not use the volume of discharges or bed supply as part of the formula.

These rates were calculated for all 898 GPO postcode sectors and the rates for the complete sector were applied to any adjacent part-postcode sectors. Ratios were calculated for acute and long-stay specialties in addition to all specialties and separately on the basis of discharges and bed-days.

The bed supply for all beds had an average value (m) of 6.4 per 1,000 catchment population for all the postcode sectors. It ranged from 4.0 (in one sector) to over 9.0. The mean for acute beds was 4.3 per 1000 catchment population and ranged from 3.5 to 5.1. The table (below) shows the % of population in sectors with bed supply ratios less than and more than one standard deviation from the mean, and also the health board value of the bed supply ratio.

BED SUPPLY RATIOS FOR HEALTH BOARDS

| | All beds | | | Acute beds | | |
|---|---|---|---|---|---|---|
| | Bed * Ratio /1000 | Percent PCS: <1 SD % | > 1 SD % | Bed * Ratio /1000 | Percent PCS: <1 SD % | > 1 SD % |
| Argyll & Clyde | 6.6 | - | 14 | 4.0 | - | 14 |
| Ayrshire & Arran | 5.3 | 97 | - | 3.6 | 94 | - |
| Borders | 7.6 | - | 89 | 5.1 | - | 89 |
| Dumfries & Galloway | 5.9 | - | - | 3.7 | 95 | - |
| Fife | 5.1 | n/a | 3.7 | n/a | | |
| Forth Valley | 5.7 | 51 | - | 3.5 | 96 | - |
| Grampian | 6.2 | 5 | 2 | 4.2 | - | 2 |
| Greater Glasgow | 6.7 | - | 14 | 4.5 | - | 22 |
| Highland | 6.7 | - | 20 | 4.5 | - | 1 |
| Lanarkshire | 5.7 | 23 | - | 4.1 | - | - |
| Lothian | 6.4 | 18 | - | 4.5 | - | - |
| Tayside | 7.3 | - | 31 | 4.9 | - | 50 |
| SCOTLAND | 6.4 | | | 4.3 | | |

* Catchment basis.

As would be expected, boards with low bed ratios tend to have a high proportion in sectors with bed supply ratios at the lower end of the distribution and those with high ratios — Borders, Glasgow, Highland and Tayside (all beds only) — to have PCS and population at the upper end.

## 11 Definitions

### Perinatal, Neonatal and Infant Deaths:

Perinatal: Stillbirths and first week deaths per 1,000 total births.
Neonatal: Deaths in the first four weeks of life per 1,000 live births.
Post-neonatal: Deaths in the first year of life excluding the first four weeks per 1,000 live births.
Infant: Deaths in first year per 1,000 live births.

**Social Class** is determined according to a persons occupation and occupations are grouped into social classes as shown below:

**1.** Professional etc occupations

**2.** Intermediate occupations.

**3N.** Skilled non-manual occupations.

**3M.** Skilled manual occupations.

**4.** Partly skilled occupations.

**5.** Unskilled occupations.

The allocation of specific occupations to social classes is detailed in reference 9.

## References

1.  Pocock SJ, Cook D.G. & Beresford S.A., 'Regression of area mortality rates on explanatory variables: what weighting is appropiate?', *Applied Statistics*, 30, pp 286-95, 1981

2.  Breslow NE, 'Extra-poisson variation in log-linear models', *Applied Statistics*, 33, pp 38-44, 1984

3.  Amfoh KK, *Statistical investigation of spatial models of mortality variation in Scotland and its relation to social deprivation*, MPhil Thesis, University of Edinburgh, 1988

4.  Breslow NE & Day NE, *Statistical methods in cancer research: Volume II — the design and analysis of cohort studies*, OUP, 1987.

5.  Armitage P, *Statistical methods in medical research*, Blackwell Scientific Publications, 1971.

6.  Diem K (ed), *Scientific tables (6th edition)*, Geigy Pharmaceutical Company Limited, 1962.

7.  Carstairs V, 'Multiple deprivation and health state', *Community Medicine*, 3, pp 4-13, 1981

8.  Norusis MJ, *SPSSx Advanced statistics guide*, McGraw-Hill, 1985.

9.  OPCS, *Classification of Occupations*, HMSO, 1980.

10. Pinder DC, 'Catchment populations: the properties and accuracy of various methods for their estimation', *Community Medicine*, 4, pp 188-195, 1982

# *B - Tables*

TABLE B1.1  DEPRIVATION VARIABLES - CORRELATION MATRIX

| Variable | 1 | 2 | 3 | 4 | 5 | 6 | 7 | 8 | 9 | 10 | 11 | 12 | 13 | 14 | 15 | 16 |
|---|---|---|---|---|---|---|---|---|---|---|---|---|---|---|---|---|
| 1. Deprivation | * | | | | | | | | | | | | | | | |
| 2. No Car | .92 | * | | | | | | | | | | | | | | |
| 3. 2+ Cars | -.81 | -.88 | * | | | | | | | | | | | | | |
| 4. Overcrowding | .91 | .78 | -.71 | * | | | | | | | | | | | | |
| 5. Occupancy Norm <O | .90 | .86 | -.69 | .90 | * | | | | | | | | | | | |
| 6. Persons per room | .83 | .70 | -.69 | .93 | .80 | * | | | | | | | | | | |
| 7. 1-3 Rooms | .68 | .80 | -.70 | .57 | .72 | .52 | * | | | | | | | | | |
| 8. 1-Person Households | .06 | .32 | -.21 | -.20 | .08 | -.36 | .48 | * | | | | | | | | |
| 9. 6+Person Households | .64 | .45 | -.36 | .76 | .62 | .69 | .02 | -.42 | * | | | | | | | |
| 10. 4+Children Households | .60 | .40 | -.33 | .70 | .57 | .66 | .02 | -.42 | .93 | * | | | | | | |
| 11. Council Tenure | .75 | .63 | -.68 | .76 | .55 | .80 | .44 | -.26 | .52 | .46 | * | | | | | |
| 12. Owner Occupied | -.78 | -.66 | .69 | -.76 | -.58 | -.75 | -.49 | .15 | -.49 | -.45 | -.94 | * | | | | |
| 13. Vacant Dwellings | .19 | .18 | -.05 | .05 | .23 | -.06 | .20 | .34 | .03 | .10 | -.20 | .01 | * | | | |
| 14. Lack Amenities-Persons | .12 | .24 | -.15 | -.03 | .23 | -.13 | .32 | .57 | -.14 | -.12 | -.32 | .17 | .57 | * | | |
| 15. Lack Amenities-H.holds | .06 | .19 | -.10 | -.08 | .18 | -.19 | .27 | .58 | -.16 | -.13 | -.37 | .22 | .57 | .99 | * | |
| 16. 1-Parent Families-Persons | .71 | .64 | -.58 | .67 | .61 | .68 | .48 | -.12 | .42 | .48 | .62 | -.61 | .14 | -.09 | -.13 | * |
| 17. 1-Parent Families-H.holds | .80 | .69 | -.60 | .80 | .72 | .79 | .41 | -.24 | .66 | .67 | .68 | -.66 | .12 | -.13 | -.17 | .92 |
| 18. Children (Under 5) | .07 | -.12 | .02 | .21 | .05 | .34 | -.18 | -.60 | .28 | .43 | .13 | -.11 | .04 | -.20 | -.21 | .36 |
| 19. Level & Access (Under 5) | .72 | .76 | -.62 | .69 | .77 | .66 | .65 | .11 | .41 | .43 | .41 | -.43 | .21 | .17 | .13 | .75 |
| 20. Lone Pensioners | -.03 | .23 | -.14 | -.28 | -.03 | -.42 | .42 | .95 | -.49 | -.49 | -.25 | .18 | .23 | .45 | .46 | -.21 |
| 21. Overcrowding - Pensioners | .73 | .72 | -.65 | .73 | .76 | .79 | .66 | .02 | .45 | .42 | .59 | -.60 | .12 | .13 | .07 | .55 |
| 22. Retired - Households | -.14 | .07 | .02 | -.36 | -.15 | -.53 | .25 | .84 | -.48 | -.51 | -.29 | .23 | .16 | .33 | .34 | -.33 |
| 23. Level & Access (75+) | .18 | .46 | -.35 | -.02 | .27 | -.10 | .52 | .77 | -.23 | -.25 | -.19 | .13 | .23 | .53 | .52 | -.02 |
| 24. Qualified Workforce | -.75 | -.63 | .71 | -.73 | -.56 | -.71 | -.50 | .12 | -.44 | -.41 | -.78 | .82 | -.08 | .04 | .08 | -.52 |
| 25. Unemployed M+F | .87 | .74 | -.61 | .77 | .76 | .69 | .46 | -.03 | .66 | .67 | .60 | -.62 | .24 | .11 | .06 | .65 |
| 26. Unemployed & Temp Sick | .92 | .82 | -.68 | .82 | .82 | .75 | .54 | .01 | .67 | .65 | .65 | -.66 | .19 | .10 | .05 | .67 |
| 27. Youth Unemployment | .89 | .75 | -.63 | .85 | .80 | .79 | .43 | -.14 | .77 | .73 | .68 | -.68 | .13 | -.05 | -.09 | .69 |
| 28. Unemployed with 2+ kids | .92 | .83 | -.68 | .85 | .84 | .78 | .55 | -.02 | .69 | .67 | .67 | -.67 | .17 | .06 | .01 | .69 |
| 29. Male unemployment | .93 | .85 | -.70 | .81 | .83 | .74 | .57 | .05 | .65 | .62 | .65 | -.65 | .20 | .11 | .06 | .70 |
| 30. in work | -.74 | -.76 | .55 | -.54 | -.66 | -.37 | -.57 | -.42 | -.39 | -.34 | -.40 | .43 | -.23 | -.24 | -.20 | -.41 |
| 31. self-employed | .54 | .63 | -.71 | .55 | .51 | .70 | .52 | -.09 | .25 | .21 | .63 | -.55 | .15 | .13 | .08 | .46 |
| 32. temp sick | .78 | .71 | -.56 | .72 | .77 | .64 | .37 | .06 | .58 | .56 | .52 | -.53 | .18 | .13 | .00 | .61 |
| 33. Female unemployment | .76 | .62 | -.55 | .70 | .65 | .64 | .42 | -.10 | .61 | .63 | .56 | -.59 | .04 | .04 | .01 | .61 |
| 34. temp sick | .62 | .55 | -.47 | .61 | .62 | .56 | .59 | .00 | .47 | .47 | .48 | -.47 | .15 | .05 | .03 | .36 |
| 35. Permanently Sick M+F | .77 | .75 | -.61 | .63 | .68 | .50 | -.59 | .27 | .43 | .38 | .56 | -.57 | -.09 | .15 | .11 | .41 |
| 36. Social Class I & II | -.85 | -.76 | .83 | -.80 | -.67 | -.77 | -.09 | .04 | -.48 | -.44 | -.81 | .84 | -.19 | -.02 | .03 | -.60 |
| 37. IIIN | -.45 | -.23 | .16 | -.41 | -.29 | -.32 | .38 | .18 | -.39 | -.39 | -.41 | .48 | -.11 | -.11 | .08 | -.30 |
| 38. IIIM | .56 | .50 | -.64 | .61 | .41 | .63 | .53 | -.18 | .48 | .31 | .73 | -.71 | .26 | .10 | -.14 | .39 |
| 39. IV & V | .86 | .69 | -.63 | .72 | .66 | .62 | .57 | .05 | .48 | .46 | .67 | -.62 | .23 | .16 | .06 | .57 |
| 40. SEG 11 | .82 | .73 | -.61 | .72 | .73 | .65 | .57 | .08 | .48 | .46 | .59 | -.55 | .10 | .04 | .11 | .57 |
| 41. SEG 10 & 11 | .87 | .74 | -.73 | .78 | .69 | .74 | .55 | -.03 | .50 | .47 | .77 | -.77 | .28 | .10 | .00 | .60 |
| 42. Low SEG (EA & Retired) | .87 | .72 | -.65 | .75 | .69 | .64 | -.04 | .06 | .51 | .49 | .70 | -.78 | .16 | .10 | .06 | .62 |
| 43. Not in private households | -.14 | -.10 | .12 | -.20 | -.12 | -.24 | .41 | .16 | -.16 | -.15 | -.22 | .13 | -.21 | -.13 | .13 | -.15 |
| 44. Born in Scotland | .56 | .49 | -.52 | .58 | .46 | .60 | -.50 | -.13 | .36 | .30 | .63 | -.51 | .17 | -.02 | -.17 | .34 |
| 45. - rest of UK | -.59 | -.58 | .58 | -.60 | -.55 | -.60 | -.01 | -.02 | -.36 | -.29 | -.56 | .46 | .18 | -.11 | .02 | -.34 |
| 46. - elsewhere | -.20 | -.05 | .12 | -.24 | -.06 | -.28 | -.10 | .34 | -.18 | -.16 | -.45 | .34 | .35 | .34 | .37 | -.16 |
| 47. 1-year Migration | -.28 | -.17 | .14 | -.36 | -.23 | -.34 | | .23 | -.29 | -.19 | -.42 | .28 | | .30 | .33 | -.07 |

TABLE B1.1  DEPRIVATION VARIABLES - CORRELATION MATRIX CONTD.

| Variable | 17 | 18 | 19 | 20 | 21 | 22 | 23 | 24 | 25 | 26 | 27 | 28 | 29 | 30 | 31 | 32 |
|---|---|---|---|---|---|---|---|---|---|---|---|---|---|---|---|---|
| 1. Deprivation | .80 | .07 | .72 | -.03 | .73 | -.14 | .18 | -.75 | .87 | .92 | .89 | .92 | .93 | -.74 | .54 | .78 |
| 2. No Car | .69 | -.12 | .76 | .23 | .72 | .07 | .46 | -.63 | .74 | .82 | .75 | .83 | .85 | -.76 | .63 | .71 |
| 3. 2+ Cars | -.60 | .02 | -.62 | -.14 | -.65 | .02 | -.35 | .71 | -.61 | -.68 | -.63 | -.68 | -.70 | .55 | -.71 | -.56 |
| 4. Overcrowding | .80 | .21 | .69 | -.28 | .73 | -.36 | -.02 | -.73 | .77 | .82 | .85 | .85 | .81 | -.54 | .55 | .72 |
| 5. Occupancy Norm <O | .72 | .05 | .77 | -.03 | .76 | -.15 | .27 | -.56 | .76 | .82 | .80 | .84 | .83 | -.66 | .51 | .77 |
| 6. Persons per room | .79 | .34 | .66 | -.42 | .79 | -.53 | -.10 | -.71 | .69 | .75 | .79 | .78 | .74 | -.37 | .70 | .64 |
| 7. 1-3 Rooms | .41 | -.18 | .65 | .42 | .66 | .25 | .52 | -.50 | .46 | .54 | .43 | .55 | .57 | -.57 | .52 | .52 |
| 8. 1-Person Households | -.24 | -.60 | .11 | .95 | .02 | .84 | .77 | .12 | -.03 | .01 | .14 | -.02 | .05 | -.42 | -.09 | .06 |
| 9. 6+Person Households | .66 | .28 | .41 | -.49 | .45 | -.48 | -.23 | -.44 | .66 | .65 | .77 | .69 | .65 | -.39 | .25 | .58 |
| 10. 4+Children Households | .67 | .43 | .43 | -.49 | .42 | -.51 | -.25 | -.41 | .67 | .65 | .73 | .67 | .62 | -.34 | .21 | .56 |
| 11. Council Tenure | .68 | .13 | .41 | -.25 | .59 | -.29 | -.19 | -.78 | .60 | .66 | .68 | .67 | .65 | -.40 | .63 | .52 |
| 12. Owner Occupied | -.66 | -.11 | -.43 | .18 | -.60 | .23 | .13 | .82 | -.62 | -.66 | -.68 | -.67 | -.65 | .43 | -.55 | -.53 |
| 13. Vacant Dwellings | .12 | .04 | .21 | .23 | .12 | .16 | .23 | -.08 | .24 | .19 | .05 | .17 | .20 | -.23 | -.23 | .15 |
| 14. Lack Amenities-Persons | -.13 | -.20 | .17 | .45 | .13 | .33 | .53 | .04 | .11 | .10 | -.09 | .06 | .06 | -.24 | -.14 | .13 |
| 15. Lack Amenities-H.holds | -.17 | -.21 | .13 | .46 | .07 | .34 | .52 | .08 | .06 | .05 | -.09 | .01 | .06 | -.20 | -.20 | .08 |
| 16. 1-Parent Families-Persons | .92 | .36 | .75 | -.21 | .55 | -.33 | -.02 | -.52 | .65 | .67 | .69 | .69 | .70 | -.41 | .47 | .46 |
| 17. 1-Parent Families-H.holds | * | .34 | .21 | -.33 | .60 | -.42 | -.08 | -.57 | .75 | .76 | .82 | .79 | .79 | -.47 | .49 | .57 |
| 18. Children (Under 5) | .34 | * | .21 | -.67 | .15 | -.73 | .47 | -.11 | .21 | .15 | .19 | .15 | .10 | .30 | .09 | .04 |
| 19. Level & Access (Under 5) | .75 | .21 | * | .00 | .64 | -.16 | .32 | -.42 | .60 | .66 | .63 | .68 | .69 | -.50 | .48 | .57 |
| 20. Lone Pensioners | -.33 | -.67 | .00 | * | -.05 | .93 | .73 | .12 | -.12 | -.08 | -.23 | -.11 | -.04 | -.38 | -.11 | -.08 |
| 21. Overcrowding - Pensioners | .60 | .15 | .64 | -.05 | * | -.22 | .19 | .08 | .59 | .65 | .62 | .65 | .66 | -.43 | .58 | .57 |
| 22. Retired - Households | -.42 | -.73 | -.16 | .93 | -.22 | * | .58 | .14 | -.18 | -.18 | -.30 | -.20 | -.15 | -.34 | -.28 | -.08 |
| 23. Level B Access (75+) | -.08 | .47 | .32 | .73 | .19 | .58 | * | .08 | .06 | .13 | .00 | .11 | .18 | -.40 | .18 | .16 |
| 24. Qualified Workforce | -.57 | -.11 | -.42 | .12 | .08 | .14 | .08 | * | -.58 | -.60 | -.61 | -.62 | -.60 | .38 | -.43 | -.47 |
| 25. Unemployed M+F | .75 | .21 | .60 | -.12 | .59 | -.18 | .06 | -.58 | * | .98 | .91 | .93 | .96 | -.74 | .36 | .76 |
| 26. Unemployed a Temp Sick | .76 | .15 | .66 | -.08 | .65 | -.18 | .13 | -.60 | .98 | * | .93 | .96 | .98 | -.79 | .46 | .84 |
| 27. Youth Unemployment | .82 | .19 | .63 | -.23 | .62 | -.30 | .00 | -.61 | .91 | .93 | * | .94 | .92 | -.67 | .48 | .75 |
| 28. Unemployed with 2+ kids | .79 | .15 | .68 | -.11 | .65 | -.20 | .11 | -.62 | .93 | .96 | .94 | * | .96 | -.75 | .49 | .80 |
| 29. Male unemployment | .79 | .10 | .69 | -.04 | .66 | -.15 | .18 | -.60 | .96 | .98 | .92 | .96 | * | -.80 | .48 | .78 |
| 30. in work | -.47 | .30 | -.50 | -.38 | -.43 | -.34 | -.40 | .38 | -.74 | -.79 | -.67 | -.75 | -.80 | * | -.26 | -.74 |
| 31. self-employed | .49 | .09 | .48 | -.11 | .58 | -.28 | .18 | -.43 | .36 | .46 | .48 | .49 | .48 | -.26 | * | .41 |
| 32. temp sick | .57 | .04 | .54 | .00 | .57 | -.08 | .16 | -.47 | .76 | .84 | .75 | .80 | .78 | -.74 | .41 | * |
| 33. Female unemployment | .68 | .31 | .52 | -.20 | .51 | -.27 | -.03 | -.54 | .91 | .89 | .86 | .85 | .83 | -.60 | .33 | .65 |
| 34. temp sick | .42 | .10 | .40 | -.05 | .48 | -.12 | .08 | -.39 | .61 | .71 | .61 | .66 | .61 | -.57 | .38 | .80 |
| 35. Permanently Sick M+F | .47 | -.19 | .43 | .24 | .49 | .21 | .23 | -.57 | .71 | .76 | .69 | .76 | .75 | -.82 | .33 | .75 |
| 36. Social Class   I & II | -.65 | -.11 | -.52 | .08 | -.63 | .15 | -.03 | .91 | -.66 | -.70 | -.68 | -.71 | -.70 | .48 | -.57 | -.57 |
| 37.                IIN | -.35 | -.20 | -.13 | .19 | -.20 | .15 | .28 | .41 | -.48 | -.45 | -.45 | -.43 | -.41 | .30 | .03 | -.36 |
| 38.                IIIM | .43 | .12 | .31 | -.17 | .47 | -.20 | -.10 | -.77 | .43 | .47 | .47 | .47 | .46 | -.25 | .50 | .35 |
| 39.                IV & V | .62 | .06 | .47 | -.01 | .54 | -.05 | .02 | -.75 | .70 | .71 | .68 | .71 | .71 | -.57 | .31 | .60 |
| 40. SEG 11 | .63 | .07 | .55 | .00 | .59 | -.08 | .13 | -.61 | .69 | .73 | .71 | .71 | .72 | -.57 | .41 | .62 |
| 41. SEG 10 B 11 | .65 | .10 | .51 | -.09 | .62 | -.18 | .03 | -.76 | .69 | .78 | .71 | .73 | .73 | -.53 | .53 | .61 |
| 42. Low SEG (EA B Retired) | .68 | .07 | .50 | -.01 | .58 | -.06 | .01 | -.77 | .77 | .78 | .74 | .76 | .78 | -.64 | .33 | .65 |
| 43. Not in private households | -.16 | -.08 | -.10 | .16 | -.14 | .14 | .09 | .21 | -.10 | -.10 | -.20 | -.17 | -.12 | -.16 | -.12 | .03 |
| 44. Born in Scotland | .40 | -.04 | .31 | -.08 | .47 | -.10 | -.02 | -.60 | .43 | .49 | .49 | .51 | .49 | -.39 | .44 | .45 |
| 45.      - rest of UK | -.39 | .10 | -.42 | -.01 | -.53 | .05 | -.15 | .53 | -.44 | -.52 | -.24 | -.53 | -.53 | .46 | -.47 | -.49 |
| 46.      - elsewhere | -.20 | -.08 | .06 | .23 | -.10 | .15 | .35 | .41 | -.18 | -.18 | -.24 | -.19 | -.16 | .05 | -.15 | -.14 |
| 47. 1-year Migration | -.16 | .20 | -.06 | .13 | -.15 | .01 | .19 | .35 | -.20 | -.23 | -.27 | -.26 | -.23 | .23 | -.14 | -.26 |

TABLE B1.1  DEPRIVATION VARIABLES - CORRELATION MATRIX CONTD.

| Variable | 33 | 34 | 35 | 36 | 37 | 38 | 39 | 40 | 41 | 42 | 43 | 44 | 45 | 46 | 47 |
|---|---|---|---|---|---|---|---|---|---|---|---|---|---|---|---|
| 1. Deprivation | .76 | .62 | .77 | -.85 | -.45 | .56 | .86 | .82 | .87 | .87 | -.14 | .56 | -.59 | -.20 | -.28 |
| 2. No Car | .62 | .55 | .75 | -.76 | -.23 | .50 | .69 | .73 | .74 | .72 | -.10 | .49 | -.58 | -.05 | -.17 |
| 3. 2+ Cars | -.55 | -.47 | -.61 | .83 | .16 | -.64 | -.63 | -.61 | -.73 | -.65 | .12 | -.52 | .58 | .12 | .14 |
| 4. Overcrowding | .70 | .61 | .63 | -.80 | -.41 | .61 | .72 | .72 | .78 | .75 | -.20 | .58 | -.60 | -.24 | -.36 |
| 5. Occupancy Norm <0 | .65 | .62 | .68 | -.67 | -.29 | .41 | .66 | .73 | .69 | .69 | -.12 | .46 | -.55 | -.06 | -.23 |
| 6. Persons per room | .64 | .56 | .50 | -.77 | -.32 | .63 | .62 | .65 | .74 | .64 | -.24 | .60 | -.50 | -.28 | -.34 |
| 7. 1-3 Rooms | .37 | .42 | .59 | -.59 | -.09 | .38 | .53 | .57 | .57 | .55 | -.04 | .41 | -.50 | -.01 | -.10 |
| 8. 1-Person Households | -.10 | .00 | .27 | .04 | .18 | -.18 | .05 | .08 | -.03 | .06 | .16 | -.13 | -.02 | .34 | .23 |
| 9. 6+Person Households | .61 | .47 | .43 | -.48 | -.39 | .36 | .48 | .48 | .50 | .51 | -.16 | .36 | -.36 | -.18 | -.29 |
| 10. 4 + Children Households | .63 | .47 | .38 | -.44 | -.39 | .31 | .46 | .46 | .47 | .49 | -.15 | .30 | -.29 | -.16 | -.19 |
| 11. Council Tenure | .56 | .48 | .56 | -.81 | -.41 | .73 | .67 | .59 | .77 | .70 | -.22 | .63 | -.56 | -.45 | -.42 |
| 12. Owner Occupied | -.59 | -.47 | -.57 | .84 | .48 | -.71 | -.74 | -.62 | -.77 | -.78 | .13 | -.51 | .46 | .34 | .28 |
| 13. Vacant Dwellings | .18 | .04 | .15 | -.09 | -.19 | -.11 | .26 | .23 | .10 | .28 | .16 | -.21 | .17 | .18 | .35 |
| 14. Lack Amenities-Persons | .04 | .05 | .15 | -.02 | .07 | -.14 | .10 | .16 | .04 | .10 | .13 | -.13 | -.02 | .34 | .30 |
| 15. Lack Amenities-H.holds | .00 | .01 | .11 | .03 | .08 | -.10 | .06 | .11 | .00 | .06 | .13 | -.17 | -.34 | .37 | .33 |
| 16. 1-Parent Families-Persons | .61 | .36 | .41 | -.60 | -.30 | .39 | .57 | .57 | .60 | .62 | -.15 | .34 | -.39 | -.16 | -.07 |
| 17. 1-Parent Families-H.holds | .68 | .42 | .47 | -.65 | -.35 | .43 | .62 | .63 | .65 | .68 | -.16 | .40 | -.42 | -.20 | -.16 |
| 18. Children (Under 5) | .31 | .10 | -.19 | -.11 | -.20 | .12 | .06 | .07 | .10 | .07 | -.08 | -.04 | -.04 | -.08 | -.20 |
| 19. Level & Access (Under 5) | .52 | .40 | .43 | -.52 | -.13 | .31 | .47 | .55 | .51 | .50 | -.10 | .31 | -.01 | .06 | -.06 |
| 20. Lone Pensioners | -.20 | -.05 | .24 | .08 | .19 | -.17 | -.01 | .00 | -.09 | -.01 | .16 | -.08 | -.53 | .23 | .13 |
| 21. Overcrowding - Pensioners | .51 | .48 | .49 | -.63 | -.20 | .47 | .54 | .59 | .62 | .58 | -.14 | .47 | .05 | -.10 | -.15 |
| 22. Retired - Households | -.27 | -.12 | .21 | .15 | .15 | -.20 | -.05 | -.08 | -.18 | -.06 | .14 | -.10 | -.15 | -.15 | -.01 |
| 23. Level & Access (75+) | -.03 | .08 | .23 | -.03 | .28 | -.10 | .02 | .13 | .03 | .01 | .09 | -.02 | .53 | .35 | .19 |
| 24. Qualified Workforce | -.54 | -.39 | -.57 | .91 | .41 | -.77 | -.75 | -.61 | -.76 | -.77 | .21 | -.60 | -.44 | .41 | .35 |
| 25. Unemployed M+F | .91 | .61 | .71 | -.66 | -.48 | .43 | .70 | .69 | .69 | .77 | -.10 | .43 | -.52 | -.18 | -.20 |
| 26. Unemployed & Temp Sick | .89 | .71 | .76 | -.70 | -.45 | .47 | .71 | .71 | .73 | .78 | -.10 | .49 | -.49 | -.18 | -.23 |
| 27. Youth Unemployment | .86 | .61 | .69 | -.68 | -.45 | .47 | .68 | .67 | .71 | .74 | -.20 | .49 | -.53 | -.24 | -.23 |
| 28. Unemployed with 2+ kids | .85 | .66 | .76 | -.71 | -.43 | .47 | .71 | .71 | .73 | .76 | -.17 | .51 | -.53 | -.19 | -.26 |
| 29. Male unemployment | .83 | .61 | .75 | -.70 | -.41 | .46 | .71 | .72 | .73 | .78 | -.12 | .49 | -.53 | -.16 | -.23 |
| 30. in work | -.60 | -.57 | -.82 | .48 | .30 | -.25 | -.57 | -.57 | -.53 | -.64 | -.16 | -.39 | .46 | .05 | .23 |
| 31. self-employed | .33 | .38 | .33 | -.57 | .03 | .50 | .31 | .41 | .53 | .33 | -.12 | .44 | -.47 | -.15 | -.14 |
| 32. temp sick | .65 | .80 | .75 | -.57 | -.36 | .35 | .60 | .62 | .61 | .65 | .03 | .45 | -.49 | -.14 | -.26 |
| 33. Female unemployment | * | .60 | .61 | -.62 | -.48 | .43 | .61 | .58 | .62 | .68 | -.15 | .34 | -.33 | -.18 | -.12 |
| 34. temp sick | .60 | * | .63 | -.48 | -.28 | .33 | .48 | .49 | .52 | .52 | .04 | .42 | -.45 | -.16 | -.23 |
| 35. Permanently Sick M+F | .61 | .63 | * | -.64 | -.39 | .43 | .66 | .65 | .63 | .71 | -.12 | .51 | -.53 | -.22 | -.34 |
| 36. Social Class  I & II | -.62 | -.48 | -.64 | * | .37 | -.81 | -.80 | -.69 | -.83 | -.82 | .18 | -.58 | .57 | .31 | .28 |
| 37.  IIIN | -.48 | -.28 | -.39 | .37 | * | -.38 | -.56 | -.41 | -.47 | -.58 | .05 | -.17 | .08 | .26 | .15 |
| 38.  IIIM | .43 | .33 | .43 | -.81 | -.38 | * | .45 | .40 | .56 | .54 | -.23 | .60 | -.56 | -.38 | -.37 |
| 39.  IV & V | .61 | .48 | .66 | -.80 | -.56 | .45 | * | .79 | .89 | .90 | -.10 | .46 | -.43 | -.28 | -.24 |
| 40. SEG 11 | .58 | .49 | .65 | -.69 | -.41 | .40 | .79 | * | .82 | .76 | -.10 | .43 | -.44 | -.19 | -.21 |
| 41. SEG 10 & 11 | .62 | .52 | .63 | -.83 | -.47 | .56 | .89 | .82 | * | .84 | -.15 | .58 | -.56 | -.32 | -.29 |
| 42. Low SEG (EA & Retired) | .68 | .52 | .71 | -.82 | -.58 | .54 | .90 | .76 | .84 | * | -.05 | .46 | -.44 | -.27 | -.24 |
| 43. Not in private households | -.15 | .04 | -.12 | .18 | .05 | -.23 | -.10 | -.10 | -.15 | -.05 | * | -.26 | .21 | .22 | .32 |
| 44. Born in Scotland | .34 | .42 | .51 | -.58 | -.17 | .60 | .46 | .43 | .58 | .46 | -.26 | * | -.92 | -.64 | -.63 |
| 45.  - rest of UK | -.33 | -.45 | -.53 | .57 | .08 | -.56 | -.43 | -.44 | -.56 | -.44 | .21 | -.92 | * | .28 | .53 |
| 46.  - elsewhere | -.18 | -.16 | -.22 | .31 | .26 | -.38 | -.28 | -.19 | -.32 | -.27 | .22 | -.64 | .28 | * | .51 |
| 47. 1-year Migration | -.12 | -.23 | -.34 | .28 | .15 | -.37 | -.24 | -.21 | -.29 | -.24 | .32 | -.63 | .53 | .51 | * |

TABLE B2.1 DEPRIVATION COMPONENTS STATISTICS - NO CAR

| AREA | Popul.n | No Car (%) | | | | Sectors |
|---|---|---|---|---|---|---|
| | | Mean | Stan Dev | Minimum | Maximum | |
| Group 1 - WEST | 2315779 | 47.9 | 19.4 | 3.8 | 89.1 | 338 |
| Group 2 - EAST | 2117570 | 37.0 | 15.8 | 3.4 | 79.1 | 337 |
| Group 3 - RURAL | 483781 | 28.6 | 8.6 | 9.2 | 55.1 | 135 |
| SCOTLAND | 4917130 | 41.3 | 18.3 | 3.4 | 89.1 | 810 |

| AREA | Popul.n | No Car (%) | | | | Sectors |
|---|---|---|---|---|---|---|
| | | Mean | Stan Dev | Minimum | Maximum | |
| Group 1 - WEST | | | | | | |
|   Argyll & Clyde | 437953 | 43.5 | 15.9 | 6.6 | 83.2 | 77 |
|   Ayr & Arran | 371043 | 38.8 | 11.2 | 7.0 | 60.0 | 71 |
|   Greater Glasgow | 948125 | 56.7 | 23.4 | 3.8 | 89.1 | 128 |
|   Lanarkshire | 558653 | 42.5 | 10.8 | 17.8 | 60.7 | 62 |
| Group 2 - EAST | | | | | | |
|   Fife | 317302 | 36.2 | 10.4 | 11.4 | 54.9 | 49 |
|   Forth Valley | 254887 | 35.5 | 12.1 | 10.2 | 62.1 | 44 |
|   Grampian | 458931 | 29.9 | 14.7 | 3.4 | 64.2 | 62 |
|   Lothian | 706334 | 41.6 | 16.7 | 4.0 | 79.1 | 113 |
|   Tayside | 380116 | 38.9 | 17.6 | 8.0 | 73.7 | 69 |
| Group 3 - RURAL | | | | | | |
|   Borders | 92543 | 29.7 | 8.9 | 9.2 | 44.5 | 27 |
|   Dumfries & Galloway | 141028 | 28.7 | 9.9 | 11.2 | 49.8 | 35 |
|   Highland | 179119 | 28.8 | 7.5 | 13.8 | 55.1 | 59 |
|   The Islands | 71091 | 26.4 | 7.4 | 14.1 | 39.7 | 14 |
| SCOTLAND | 4917130 | 41.3 | 18.3 | 3.4 | 89.1 | 810 |

Notes:
    Sectors >500, excluding 20 with large institutional populations

TABLE B2.1   Deprivation Component Statistics - No Car Contd.

| AREA | Popul.n | No Car (%) | | | | Sectors |
|---|---|---|---|---|---|---|
| | | Mean | Stan Dev | Minimum | Maximum | |
| Argyll & Clyde | | | | | | |
| Argyll & Bute | 57760 | 34.3 | 9.1 | 13.0 | 54.6 | 20 |
| Dumbarton | 76166 | 40.0 | 11.7 | 15.6 | 63.5 | 13 |
| Inverclyde | 98833 | 51.2 | 16.9 | 13.9 | 75.0 | 13 |
| Renfrew | 205199 | 43.6 | 16.6 | 6.6 | 83.2 | 31 |
| Ayr & Arran | | | | | | |
| Cumnoch & Doon V | 44657 | 43.6 | 7.0 | 16.5 | 49.2 | 8 |
| Cunninghame | 135412 | 42.6 | 9.2 | 19.3 | 60.0 | 28 |
| Kilmarnock & Loudoun | 81633 | 37.3 | 9.1 | 18.5 | 56.5 | 16 |
| Kyle & Carrick | 109341 | 33.3 | 13.3 | 7.0 | 55.6 | 19 |
| Borders | | | | | | |
| Berwickshire | 17148 | 24.5 | 6.0 | 14.5 | 32.2 | 6 |
| Ett. & Lauderdale | 27204 | 31.3 | 7.4 | 16.6 | 42.1 | 8 |
| Roxburgh | 34518 | 31.7 | 9.3 | 12.6 | 44.5 | 7 |
| Tweeddale | 13673 | 28.3 | 10.4 | 9.2 | 40.5 | 6 |
| Dumfries & Galloway | | | | | | |
| Ann. & Eskdale | 34744 | 28.7 | 6.5 | 15.2 | 38.0 | 9 |
| Nithsdale | 54437 | 31.2 | 11.7 | 16.0 | 49.8 | 11 |
| Stewartry | 22310 | 21.3 | 5.1 | 11.2 | 27.3 | 6 |
| Wigtown | 29537 | 29.5 | 9.7 | 20.4 | 48.0 | 9 |
| Fife | | | | | | |
| Dunfermline | 121692 | 37.1 | 11.5 | 11.4 | 54.9 | 16 |
| Kirkcaldy | 142706 | 39.2 | 8.5 | 26.0 | 52.9 | 20 |
| N. E. Fife | 52904 | 26.4 | 5.5 | 16.1 | 40.2 | 13 |
| Forth Valley | | | | | | |
| Clackmannan | 47168 | 34.7 | 9.6 | 11.3 | 53.7 | 8 |
| Falkirk | 132004 | 38.5 | 9.3 | 21.2 | 54.2 | 20 |
| Stirling | 75715 | 31.1 | 15.9 | 10.2 | 62.1 | 16 |
| Grampian | | | | | | |
| Aberdeen City | 199552 | 38.7 | 15.3 | 7.0 | 64.2 | 20 |
| Banff & Buchan | 79331 | 27.8 | 9.3 | 10.6 | 36.9 | 11 |
| Gordon | 61324 | 13.5 | 7.3 | 3.4 | 33.6 | 11 |
| Kincar. & Deeside | 39277 | 16.6 | 4.9 | 9.5 | 28.5 | 7 |
| Moray | 79447 | 29.0 | 5.9 | 10.2 | 38.6 | 13 |
| Greater Glasgow | | | | | | |
| Bears. & Milngavie | 39335 | 14.2 | 7.8 | 7.0 | 29.4 | 7 |
| Clydebank | 51995 | 54.2 | 9.7 | 33.0 | 63.7 | 7 |
| Eastwood | 53389 | 13.9 | 7.6 | 3.8 | 51.0 | 9 |
| Glasgow City | 722303 | 65.6 | 16.7 | 12.0 | 89.1 | 90 |
| Strathkelvin | 81103 | 27.9 | 12.5 | 10.6 | 60.7 | 15 |
| Highland | | | | | | |
| Badenoch & Strathspey | 8366 | 24.7 | 3.7 | 18.2 | 30.2 | 5 |
| Caithness | 26076 | 30.4 | 5.0 | 16.0 | 35.2 | 6 |
| Inverness | 53821 | 31.2 | 9.8 | 16.1 | 55.1 | 9 |
| Lochaber | 16813 | 33.4 | 4.9 | 17.5 | 41.6 | 7 |
| Nairn | 9488 | 28.3 | 3.9 | 24.3 | 32.1 | 2 |
| Ross & Cromarty | 44624 | 25.5 | 5.8 | 13.8 | 35.6 | 19 |
| Skye & Lochalsh | 7603 | 25.5 | 2.8 | 22.0 | 29.6 | 4 |
| Sutherland | 12328 | 25.5 | 4.8 | 20.8 | 35.7 | 7 |
| Lanarkshire | | | | | | |
| Cumbernauld | 61112 | 40.0 | 7.9 | 27.3 | 49.0 | 7 |
| E. Kilbride | 81865 | 31.6 | 7.5 | 19.8 | 42.3 | 9 |
| Hamilton | 107784 | 42.1 | 10.0 | 27.8 | 60.4 | 12 |
| Clydesdale | 56138 | 29.4 | 6.9 | 17.8 | 40.9 | 7 |
| Monklands | 109597 | 50.2 | 6.7 | 38.8 | 60.7 | 12 |
| Motherwell | 142157 | 49.3 | 6.0 | 38.1 | 59.0 | 15 |
| Lothian | | | | | | |
| E. Lothian | 78327 | 34.5 | 10.9 | 15.1 | 49.6 | 16 |
| Edinburgh City | 410951 | 45.5 | 19.1 | 4.8 | 79.1 | 61 |
| Midlothian | 80006 | 34.0 | 11.4 | 7.0 | 48.8 | 15 |
| W. Lothian | 137050 | 38.1 | 8.6 | 4.0 | 52.5 | 21 |
| Tayside | | | | | | |
| Angus | 90927 | 32.8 | 10.6 | 8.0 | 58.4 | 18 |
| Dundee City | 176668 | 48.5 | 17.9 | 10.9 | 73.7 | 22 |
| Perth & Kinross | 112521 | 28.9 | 13.6 | 8.5 | 62.1 | 29 |
| The Islands | | | | | | |
| Orkney | 18419 | 21.1 | 6.2 | 14.1 | 27.1 | 3 |
| Shetland | 22768 | 22.5 | 6.2 | 17.3 | 30.6 | 3 |
| Western Isles | 29904 | 32.7 | 3.2 | 27.6 | 39.7 | 8 |
| SCOTLAND | 4917130 | 41.3 | 18.3 | 3.4 | 89.1 | 810 |

Notes:

    Sectors >500, excluding 20 with large institutional populations

Table B2.2   Deprivation Component Statistics - Male Unemployment

| AREA | Popul.n | Male Unemployment (%) | | | | Sectors |
|------|---------|------|----------|---------|---------|---------|
|      |         | Mean | Stan Dev | Minimum | Maximum |         |
| Group 1 - WEST | 2315779 | 15.9 | 7.7 | 2.0 | 39.3 | 338 |
| Group 2 - EAST | 2117570 | 9.7 | 5.4 | 1.7 | 31.6 | 337 |
| Group 3 - RURAL | 483781 | 8.7 | 3.8 | 0.5 | 24.0 | 135 |
| SCOTLAND | 4917130 | 12.5 | 7.2 | 0.5 | 39.3 | 810 |

| AREA | Popul.n | Male Unemployment (%) | | | | Sectors |
|------|---------|------|----------|---------|---------|---------|
|      |         | Mean | Stan Dev | Minimum | Maximum |         |
| Group 1 - WEST |  |  |  |  |  |  |
|   Argyll & Clyde | 437958 | 13.3 | 6.6 | 2.0 | 39.3 | 77 |
|   Ayr & Arran | 371043 | 15.3 | 5.7 | 4.8 | 31.4 | 71 |
|   Greater Glasgow | 948125 | 18.0 | 9.6 | 3.2 | 38.6 | 128 |
|   Lanarkshire | 558653 | 14.6 | 4.1 | 6.7 | 25.9 | 62 |
| Group 2 - EAST |  |  |  |  |  |  |
|   Fife | 317302 | 10.0 | 3.6 | 3.2 | 18.6 | 49 |
|   Forth Valley | 254887 | 11.5 | 4.2 | 3.4 | 22.1 | 44 |
|   Grampian | 458931 | 6.3 | 2.9 | 1.7 | 12.3 | 62 |
|   Lothian | 706334 | 10.0 | 5.7 | 2.0 | 31.6 | 113 |
|   Tayside | 380116 | 11.8 | 6.9 | 2.1 | 30.9 | 69 |
| Group 3 - RURAL |  |  |  |  |  |  |
|   Borders | 92543 | 7.5 | 1.9 | 2.8 | 11.1 | 27 |
|   Dumfries & Galloway | 141028 | 9.7 | 3.8 | 4.3 | 17.6 | 35 |
|   Highland | 179119 | 8.3 | 3.0 | 3.7 | 22.2 | 59 |
|   The Islands | 71091 | 9.3 | 5.9 | 0.5 | 24.0 | 14 |
| SCOTLAND | 4917130 | 12.5 | 7.2 | 0.5 | 39.3 | 810 |

Notes:
  Sectors >500, excluding 20 with large institutional populations

TABLE B2.2  DEPRIVATION COMPONENT STATISTICS - MALE UNEMPLOYMENT  CONTD.

| AREA | Popul.n | Male Unemployment (%) | | | | Sectors |
|---|---|---|---|---|---|---|
| | | Mean | Stan Dev | Minimum | Maximum | |
| Argyll & Clyde | | | | | | |
| Argyll & Bute | 57760 | 10.1 | 2.9 | 4.3 | 17.7 | 20 |
| Dumbarton | 76166 | 14.1 | 6.0 | 2.0 | 26.5 | 13 |
| Inverclyde | 98833 | 15.9 | 7.3 | 4.9 | 30.5 | 13 |
| Renfrew | 205199 | 12.6 | 6.7 | 3.4 | 39.3 | 31 |
| Ayr & Arran | | | | | | |
| Cumnoch & Doon V | 44657 | 17.1 | 4.3 | 6.3 | 23.9 | 8 |
| Cunninghame | 135412 | 17.5 | 5.0 | 5.5 | 31.4 | 28 |
| Kilmarnoch & Loudoun | 61633 | 15.0 | 6.2 | 5.1 | 29.1 | 16 |
| Kyle & Carrich | 109341 | 12.1 | 5.1 | 4.8 | 22.0 | 19 |
| Borders | | | | | | |
| Berwickshire | 17148 | 6.9 | 2.0 | 4.0 | 9.6 | 6 |
| Ett.& Lauderdale | 27204 | 7.3 | 1.5 | 4.2 | 9.7 | 8 |
| Roxburgh | 34518 | 8.3 | 2.0 | 5.4 | 11.1 | 7 |
| Tweeddale | 13673 | 7.1 | 1.8 | 2.8 | 9.2 | 6 |
| Dumfries & Galloway | | | | | | |
| Ann.& Eskdale | 34744 | 9.4 | 2.9 | 4.4 | 14.5 | 9 |
| Nithsdale | 54437 | 9.8 | 4.6 | 4.3 | 17.0 | 11 |
| Stewartry | 22310 | 7.9 | 2.2 | 4.7 | 11.7 | 6 |
| Wigtown | 29537 | 11.5 | 3.2 | 7.3 | 17.6 | 9 |
| Fife | | | | | | |
| Dunfermline | 121692 | 8.3 | 3.1 | 3.4 | 17.7 | 16 |
| Kirkcaldy | 142706 | 12.5 | 2.7 | 9.0 | 18.6 | 20 |
| N.E. Fife | 52904 | 7.3 | 2.0 | 3.2 | 11.5 | 13 |
| Forth Valley | | | | | | |
| Clackmannan | 47168 | 10.7 | 3.7 | 5.3 | 20.4 | 8 |
| Falkirk | 132004 | 12.9 | 3.1 | 6.4 | 20.8 | 20 |
| Stirling | 75715 | 9.8 | 5.2 | 3.4 | 22.1 | 16 |
| Grampian | | | | | | |
| Aberdeen City | 199552 | 6.6 | 3.2 | 1.7 | 12.3 | 20 |
| Banff & Buchan | 79331 | 7.5 | 1.8 | 3.8 | 10.0 | 11 |
| Gordon | 61324 | 3.2 | 1.2 | 2.1 | 6.4 | 11 |
| Kincar. & Deeside | 39277 | 4.1 | 1.0 | 2.7 | 5.6 | 7 |
| Moray | 79447 | 7.9 | 1.9 | 4.0 | 11.8 | 13 |
| Greater Glasgow | | | | | | |
| Bears.a MiIngavie | 39335 | 4.7 | 1.6 | 3.5 | 8.1 | 7 |
| Clydebank | 51995 | 17.9 | 3.0 | 11.6 | 21.4 | 7 |
| Eastwood | 53389 | 4.6 | 1.3 | 3.2 | 10.6 | 9 |
| Glasgow City | 722303 | 20.8 | 8.9 | 3.9 | 38.6 | 90 |
| Strathkelvin | 81103 | 8.7 | 3.5 | 3.9 | 15.7 | 15 |
| Highland | | | | | | |
| Badenoch & Strathspey | 8366 | 7.8 | 1.8 | 6.3 | 12.7 | 5 |
| Caithness | 26076 | 8.5 | 2.8 | 5.6 | 20.1 | 6 |
| Inverness | 53821 | 8.2 | 2.4 | 5.0 | 11.7 | 9 |
| Lochaber | 16813 | 11.3 | 1.8 | 7.2 | 13.5 | 7 |
| Nairn | 9488 | 9.0 | 1.1 | 7.9 | 10.1 | 2 |
| Ross & Cromarty | 44624 | 6.3 | 1.9 | 3.7 | 13.5 | 19 |
| Skye & Lochalsh | 7603 | 14.0 | 4.3 | 8.5 | 22.2 | 4 |
| Sutherland | 12328 | 8.4 | 3.3 | 3.7 | 15.6 | 7 |
| Lanarkshire | | | | | | |
| Cumbernauld | 61112 | 12.7 | 1.8 | 10.5 | 14.9 | 7 |
| E.Kilbride | 81865 | 10.9 | 2.4 | 6.8 | 15.8 | 9 |
| Hamilton | 107784 | 15.2 | 4.7 | 8.4 | 25.9 | 12 |
| Clydesdale | 56138 | 9.7 | 2.2 | 6.7 | 13.9 | 7 |
| Monklands | 109597 | 18.1 | 3.0 | 13.0 | 22.3 | 12 |
| Motherwell | 142157 | 16.2 | 2.5 | 10.9 | 20.6 | 15 |
| Lothian | | | | | | |
| E.Lothian | 78327 | 8.2 | 2.9 | 3.3 | 13.3 | 16 |
| Edinburgh City | 410951 | 9.8 | 6.4 | 2.4 | 31.6 | 61 |
| Midlothian | 80006 | 7.1 | 2.3 | 2.0 | 10.1 | 15 |
| W.Lothian | 137050 | 13.4 | 4.0 | 2.5 | 21.6 | 21 |
| Tayside | | | | | | |
| Angus | 90927 | 8.7 | 2.7 | 2.8 | 15.6 | 18 |
| Dundee City | 176668 | 15.7 | 7.7 | 4.0 | 30.9 | 22 |
| Perth & Kinross | 112521 | 8.4 | 4.1 | 2.1 | 18.2 | 29 |
| The Islands | | | | | | |
| Orkney | 18419 | 7.0 | 1.5 | 5.5 | 9.6 | 3 |
| Shetland | 22768 | 4.0 | 0.6 | 0.5 | 4.2 | 3 |
| Western Isles | 29904 | 14.7 | 5.2 | 5.4 | 24.0 | 8 |
| SCOTLAND | 4917130 | 12.5 | 7.2 | 0.5 | 39.3 | 810 |

Notes:

     Sectors >500, excluding 20 with large institutional populations

TABLE B2.3 DEPRIVATION COMPONENT STATISTICS - OVERCROWDING

| AREA | Popul.n | Overcrowding (%) | | | | Sectors |
|------|---------|------|----------|---------|---------|---------|
|      |         | Mean | Stan Dev | Minimum | Maximum |         |
| Group 1 - WEST | 2315779 | 30.1 | 12.5 | 2.4 | 59.8 | 338 |
| Group 2 - EAST | 2117570 | 21.7 | 8.6 | 1.7 | 46.9 | 337 |
| Group 3 - RURAL | 483781 | 19.4 | 5.5 | 9.4 | 44.3 | 135 |
| SCOTLAND | 4917130 | 25.4 | 11.3 | 1.7 | 59.8 | 810 |

| AREA | Popul.n | Overcrowding (%) | | | | Sectors |
|------|---------|------|----------|---------|---------|---------|
|      |         | Mean | Stan Dev | Minimum | Maximum |         |
| Group 1 - WEST |  |  |  |  |  |  |
|   Argyll & Clyde | 437958 | 28.8 | 11.7 | 5.9 | 55.0 | 77 |
|   Ayr & Arran | 371043 | 23.1 | 7.5 | 5.6 | 35.7 | 71 |
|   Greater Glasgow | 948125 | 33.0 | 15.0 | 2.4 | 59.8 | 128 |
|   Lanarkshire | 558653 | 30.8 | 8.4 | 15.0 | 51.2 | 62 |
| Group 2 - EAST |  |  |  |  |  |  |
|   Fife | 317302 | 21.7 | 6.0 | 6.7 | 35.6 | 49 |
|   Forth Valley | 254887 | 21.8 | 6.8 | 5.9 | 35.3 | 44 |
|   Grampian | 458931 | 20.8 | 7.8 | 5.4 | 44.8 | 62 |
|   Lothian | 706334 | 21.8 | 10.1 | 1.7 | 46.9 | 113 |
|   Tayside | 380116 | 22.4 | 9.3 | 6.0 | 41.2 | 69 |
| Group 3 - RURAL |  |  |  |  |  |  |
|   Borders | 92543 | 16.3 | 3.9 | 9.6 | 24.6 | 27 |
|   Dumfries & Galloway | 141028 | 19.4 | 5.4 | 12.2 | 30.9 | 35 |
|   Highland | 179119 | 20.6 | 5.1 | 9.4 | 35.1 | 59 |
|   The Islands | 71091 | 20.4 | 6.6 | 13.5 | 44.3 | 14 |
| SCOTLAND | 4917130 | 25.4 | 11.3 | 1.7 | 59.8 | 810 |

Notes:
    Sectors >500, excluding 20 with large institutional populations

# DEPRIVATION AND HEALTH IN SCOTLAND

TABLE B2.3  DEPRIVATION COMPONENT STATISTICS - OVERCROWDING  CONTD.

| AREA | Popul.n | Overcrowding (%) | | | | Sectors |
|------|---------|------|---------|---------|---------|---------|
|      |         | Mean | Stan Dev | Minimum | Maximum |         |
| **Argyll & Clyde** | | | | | | |
| Argyll & Bute | 57760 | 19.6 | 4.5 | 10.1 | 32.0 | 20 |
| Dumbarton | 76166 | 26.5 | 10.3 | 5.9 | 38.6 | 13 |
| Inverclyde | 98833 | 33.6 | 12.8 | 10.4 | 52.5 | 13 |
| Renfrew | 205199 | 30.0 | 11.3 | 6.0 | 55.0 | 31 |
| **Ayr & Arran** | | | | | | |
| Cumnock & Doon V | 44657 | 27.6 | 4.0 | 11.5 | 31.9 | 8 |
| Cunninghame | 135412 | 24.2 | 8.0 | 7.0 | 35.7 | 28 |
| Kilmarnoch & Loudoun | 81633 | 23.4 | 5.0 | 8.3 | 28.6 | 16 |
| Kyle & Carrick | 109341 | 19.7 | 8.1 | 5.6 | 31.3 | 19 |
| **Borders** | | | | | | |
| Berwickshire | 17148 | 16.5 | 3.3 | 12.0 | 20.9 | 6 |
| Ett.& Lauderdale | 27204 | 16.2 | 3.9 | 9.6 | 21.3 | 8 |
| Roxburgh | 34518 | 16.4 | 4.6 | 10.0 | 24.6 | 7 |
| Tweeddale | 13673 | 16.0 | 1.9 | 10.9 | 18.5 | 6 |
| **Dumfries & Galloway** | | | | | | |
| Ann & Eskdale | 34744 | 18.0 | 2.6 | 13.1 | 21.0 | 9 |
| Nithsdale | 54437 | 20.1 | 6.8 | 12.2 | 29.9 | 11 |
| Stewartry | 22310 | 17.2 | 3.3 | 13.0 | 23.3 | 6 |
| Wigtown | 29537 | 21.3 | 5.2 | 15.0 | 30.9 | 9 |
| **Fife** | | | | | | |
| Dunfermline | 121692 | 22.9 | 6.5 | 7.0 | 35.6 | 16 |
| Kirkcaldy | 142706 | 22.6 | 4.7 | 13.7 | 32.3 | 20 |
| N.E. Fife | 52904 | 16.5 | 5.1 | 6.7 | 24.1 | 13 |
| **Forth Valley** | | | | | | |
| Clackmannan | 47168 | 23.3 | 6.0 | 7.5 | 33.5 | 8 |
| Falkirk | 132004 | 22.3 | 5.6 | 8.3 | 35.3 | 20 |
| Stirling | 75715 | 20.0 | 8.5 | 5.9 | 31.8 | 16 |
| **Grampian** | | | | | | |
| Aberdeen City | 199552 | 22.9 | 10.3 | 5.4 | 44.8 | 20 |
| Banff & Buchan | 79331 | 22.5 | 3.3 | 15.4 | 27.8 | 11 |
| Gordon | 61324 | 17.6 | 3.8 | 11.6 | 22.5 | 11 |
| Kincar. & Deeside | 39277 | 15.3 | 1.2 | 13.6 | 17.7 | 7 |
| Moray | 79447 | 19.1 | 4.6 | 7.9 | 25.7 | 13 |
| **Greater Glasgow** | | | | | | |
| Bears. & Milngavie | 39335 | 10.8 | 5.7 | 4.8 | 21.4 | 7 |
| Clydebank | 51995 | 33.7 | 6.6 | 20.6 | 42.9 | 7 |
| Eastwood | 53389 | 9.5 | 6.1 | 2.4 | 22.2 | 9 |
| Glasgow City | 722303 | 37.1 | 13.5 | 5.3 | 59.8 | 90 |
| Strathkelvin | 81103 | 22.8 | 8.6 | 10.1 | 44.3 | 15 |
| **Highland** | | | | | | |
| Badenoch & Strathspey | 8366 | 15.2 | 5.9 | 9.5 | 25.1 | 5 |
| Caithness | 26076 | 22.8 | 4.6 | 16.0 | 26.8 | 6 |
| Inverness | 53821 | 20.2 | 3.6 | 13.2 | 25.2 | 9 |
| Lochaber | 16813 | 26.7 | 4.8 | 16.4 | 35.1 | 7 |
| Nairn | 9488 | 17.3 | 3.0 | 14.2 | 20.1 | 2 |
| Ross & Cromarty | 44624 | 20.4 | 5.2 | 9.4 | 29.7 | 19 |
| Skye & Lochalsh | 7603 | 21.4 | 2.0 | 16.9 | 22.6 | 4 |
| Sutherland | 12328 | 16.2 | 3.5 | 11.6 | 23.5 | 7 |
| **Lanarkshire** | | | | | | |
| Cumbernauld | 61112 | 21.9 | 6.7 | 15.0 | 35.0 | 7 |
| E. Kilbride | 81865 | 26.7 | 5.8 | 16.4 | 36.4 | 9 |
| Hamilton | 107784 | 28.8 | 6.2 | 20.4 | 42.5 | 12 |
| Clydesdale | 56138 | 23.7 | 3.8 | 17.2 | 28.5 | 7 |
| Monklands | 109597 | 38.4 | 6.6 | 25.9 | 51.2 | 12 |
| Motherwell | 142157 | 35.6 | 5.9 | 25.6 | 49.3 | 15 |
| **Lothian** | | | | | | |
| E.Lothian | 78327 | 21.4 | 6.3 | 9.2 | 30.9 | 16 |
| Edinburgh City | 410951 | 20.4 | 11.8 | 1.7 | 46.9 | 61 |
| Midlothian | 80006 | 23.8 | 7.3 | 6.3 | 36.1 | 15 |
| W. Lothian | 137050 | 25.3 | 6.1 | 9.9 | 38.3 | 21 |
| **Tayside** | | | | | | |
| Angus | 90927 | 21.2 | 5.0 | 10.2 | 29.8 | 1B |
| Dundee City | 176668 | 25.3 | 11.3 | 6.0 | 41.2 | 22 |
| Perth & Kinross | 112521 | 19.0 | 7.0 | 6.5 | 30.0 | 29 |
| **The Islands** | | | | | | |
| Orkney | 18419 | 15.1 | 1.9 | 13.5 | 17.5 | 3 |
| Shetland | 22768 | 17.8 | 2.1 | 15.5 | 20.5 | 3 |
| Western Isles | 29904 | 25.6 | 7.1 | 18.5 | 44.3 | 8 |
| **SCOTLAND** | 4917130 | 25.4 | 11.3 | 1.7 | 59.8 | 810 |

Notes:

Sectors >500, excluding 20 with large institutional populations

TABLE B2.4   DEPRIVATION COMPONENT STATISTICS - LOW SOCIAL CLASS

| AREA | Popul.n | Social Class IV & V (%) | | | | Sectors |
|---|---|---|---|---|---|---|
| | | Mean | Stan Dev | Minimum | Maximum | |
| Group 1 - WEST | 2315779 | 25.1 | 11.1 | 0.0 | 62.9 | 338 |
| Group 2 - EAST | 2117570 | 22.5 | 9.3 | 0.5 | 52.9 | 337 |
| Group 3 - RURAL | 483781 | 25.8 | 6.9 | 0.0 | 47.4 | 135 |
| SCOTLAND | 4917130 | 24.0 | 10.1 | 0.0 | 62.9 | 310 |

| AREA | Popul.n | Social Class IV & V (%) | | | | Sectors |
|---|---|---|---|---|---|---|
| | | Mean | Stan Dev | Minimum | Maximum | |
| Group 1 - WEST | | | | | | |
| Argyll & Clyde | 437958 | 23.9 | 10.6 | 0.0 | 62.9 | 77 |
| Ayr & Arran | 371043 | 24.2 | 7.9 | 5.7 | 45.5 | 71 |
| Greater Glasgow | 948125 | 26.4 | 13.9 | 1.8 | 55.1 | 128 |
| Lanarkshire | 558653 | 24.3 | 7.3 | 11.3 | 44.1 | 62 |
| Group 2 - EAST | | | | | | |
| Fife | 317302 | 22.1 | 6.8 | 4.7 | 39.6 | 49 |
| Forth Valley | 254887 | 23.4 | 7.3 | 1.8 | 44.9 | 44 |
| Grampian | 458931 | 23.4 | 9.4 | 1.9 | 46.8 | 62 |
| Lothian | 706334 | 21.3 | 10.5 | 0.5 | 52.9 | 113 |
| Tayside | 380116 | 23.4 | 9.3 | 2.4 | 47.5 | 69 |
| Group 3 - RURAL | | | | | | |
| Borders | 92543 | 28.0 | 5.8 | 1O.2 | 45.2 | 27 |
| Dumfries & Galloway | 141028 | 27.9 | 7.1 | 14.6 | 47.4 | 35 |
| Highland | 179119 | 22.1 | 6.7 | 0.0 | 44.4 | 59 |
| The Islands | 71091 | 28.2 | 3.9 | 19.3 | 39.7 | 14 |
| SCOTLAND | 4917130 | 24.0 | 10.1 | 0.0 | 62.9 | 810 |

Notes:
Sectors >500. excluding 20 with large institutional populations

TABLE B2.4   DEPRIVATION COMPONENT STATISTICS - LOW SOCIAL CLASS CONTD.

| AREA | Popul.n | Social Class IV & V (%) | | | | Sectors |
|---|---|---|---|---|---|---|
| | | Mean | Stan Dev | Minimum | Maximum | |
| Argyll & Clyde | | | | | | |
| Argyll & Bute | 57760 | 22.3 | 7.4 | 0.0 | 42.0 | 20 |
| Dumbarton | 76166 | 19.0 | 7.8 | 0.0 | 32.8 | 13 |
| Inverclyde | 98833 | 26.8 | 10.5 | 8.5 | 46.7 | 13 |
| Renfrew | 205199 | 24.8 | 11.6 | 0.0 | 62.9 | 31 |
| Ayr & Arran | | | | | | |
| Cumnock & Doon V | 44657 | 27.1 | 5.7 | 6.3 | 34.2 | 8 |
| Cunninghame | 135412 | 26.2 | 8.0 | 8.4 | 45.5 | 28 |
| Kilmarnoch & Loudoun | 81633 | 24.6. | 6.7 | 5.8 | 34.2 | 16 |
| Kyle & Carrick | 109341 | 20.2 | 7.8 | 5.7 | 34.2 | 19 |
| Borders | | | | | | |
| Berwickshire | 17146 | 31.6 | 2.4 | 24.5 | 36.7 | 6 |
| Ett.& Lauderdale | 27204 | 26.5 | 7.2 | 10.2 | 34.0 | 8 |
| Roxburgh | 34518 | 27.5 | 4.3 | 20.3 | 33.2 | 7 |
| Tweeddale | 13673 | 27.9 | 6.9 | 21.9 | 45.2 | 6 |
| Dumfries & Galloway | | | | | | |
| Ann. & Eshdale | 34744 | 25.8 | 6.0 | 17.4 | 34.3 | 9 |
| Nithsdale | 54437 | 28.1 | 7.5 | 14.6 | 38.3 | 11 |
| Stewartry | 22310 | 29.8 | 3.6 | 17.3 | 33.5 | 6 |
| Wigtown | 29537 | 28.8 | 8.6 | 19.0 | 47.4 | 9 |
| Fife | | | | | | |
| Dunfermline | 121692 | 20.2 | 7.2 | 4.7 | 32.4 | 16 |
| Kirkcaldy | 142706 | 23.6 | 5.7 | 12.7 | 34.2 | 20 |
| N.E. Fife | 52904 | 22.5 | 7.6 | 9.0 | 39.6 | 13 |
| Forth Valley | | | | | | |
| Clackmannan | 47168 | 21.3 | 4.9 | 5.1 | 25.1 | 8 |
| Falkirk | 132004 | 26.0 | 5.9 | 16.3 | 44.9 | 20 |
| Stirling | 75715 | 20.2 | 8.9 | 1.8 | 33.2 | 16 |
| Grampian | | | | | | |
| Aberdeen City | 199552 | 21.5 | 8.9 | 1.9 | 36.9 | 20 |
| Banff & Buchan | 79331 | 33.3 | 8.1 | 16.9 | 43.4 | 11 |
| Gordon | 61324 | 17.8 | 4.4 | 10.2 | 25.0 | 11 |
| Kincar. & Deeside | 39277 | 20.5 | 8.1 | 13.9 | 36.0 | 7 |
| Moray | 79447 | 24.1 | 7.7 | 9.4 | 46.8 | 13 |
| Greater Glasgow | | | | | | |
| Bears.& Milngavie | 39335 | 6.4 | 3.4 | 2.4 | 13.4 | 7 |
| Clydebank | 51995 | 24.8 | 6.3 | 13.6 | 31.4 | 7 |
| Eastwood | 53389 | 6.3 | 4.8 | 1.8 | 30.6 | 9 |
| Glasgow City | 722303 | 30.5 | 12.4 | 2.1 | 55.1 | 90 |
| Strathkelvin | 81103 | 13.9 | 8.1 | 2.7 | 35.0 | 15 |
| Highland | | | | | | |
| Badenoch & Strathspey | 8366 | 23.0 | 3.3 | 17.0 | 26.8 | 5 |
| Caithness | 26076 | 24.3 | 6.3 | 14.9 | 35.6 | 6 |
| Inverness | 53821 | 19.0 | 4.5 | 12.2 | 27.2 | 9 |
| Lochaber | 16813 | 24.1 | 6.5 | 13.3 | 32.1 | 7 |
| Nairn | 9488 | 18.5 | 6.5 | 11.7 | 24.7 | 2 |
| Ross & Cromarty | 44624 | 22.4 | 7.4 | 0.0 | 44.4 | 19 |
| Skye & Lochalsh | 7603 | 28.7 | 8.1 | 10.5 | 44.4 | 4 |
| Sutherland | 12323 | 25.0 | 6.3 | 18.5 | 35.4 | 7 |
| Lanarkshire | | | | | | |
| Cumbernauld | 61112 | 20.7 | 3.3 | 15.2 | 28.2 | 7 |
| E.Kilbride | 81865 | 16.4 | 4.3 | 11.3 | 30.7 | 9 |
| Hamilton | 107784 | 22.0 | 7.3 | 11.7 | 36.0 | 12 |
| Clydesdale | 56138 | 21.9 | 4.7 | 15.9 | 27.4 | 7 |
| Monklands | 109597 | 29.8 | 4.8 | 22.2 | 42.9 | 12 |
| Motherwell | 142157 | 28.9 | 5.9 | 19.6 | 44.1 | 15 |
| Lothian | | | | | | |
| E Lothian | 78327 | 21.4 | 6.9 | 0.8 | 29.1 | 16 |
| Edinburgh City | 410951 | 19.3 | 11.2 | 0.5 | 40.5 | 61 |
| Midlothian | 80006 | 20.8 | 7.8 | 3.0 | 31.0 | 15 |
| W.Lothian | 137050 | 27.3 | 8.8 | 3.7 | 52.9 | 21 |
| Tayside | | | | | | |
| Angus | 90927 | 22.9 | 6.1 | 4.0 | 37.1 | 18 |
| Dundee City | 176668 | 24.8 | 11.2 | 2.4 | 42.9 | 22 |
| Perth & Kinross | 112521 | 21.6 | 7.6 | 3.0 | 47.5 | 29 |
| The Islands | | | | | | |
| Orkney | 18419 | 28.6 | 2.5 | 26.7 | 33.4 | 3 |
| Shetland | 22768 | 28.0 | 1.6 | 21.6 | 29.7 | 3 |
| Western Isles | 29904 | 28.2 | 5.4 | 19.3 | 39.7 | 8 |
| SCOTLAND | 4917130 | 24.0 | 10.1 | 0.0 | 62.9 | 810 |

Notes:

    Sectors >500, excluding 20 with large institutional populations

TABLE B2.5 DEPRIVATION SCORE STATISTICS

| AREA | Popul.n | Deprivation Score | | | | Sectors |
|---|---|---|---|---|---|---|
| | | Mean | Stan Dev | Minimum | Maximum | |
| Group 1 - WEST | 2315779 | 1.34 | 4.02 | -7.31 | 12.27 | 338 |
| Group 2 - EAST | 2117570 | -1.08 | 2.82 | -7.17 | 7.62 | 337 |
| Group 3 - RURAL | 483781 | -1.55 | 1.62 | -4.51 | 4.09 | 135 |
| SCOTLAND | 4917130 | 0.02 | 3.59 | -7.31 | 12.27 | 810 |

| AREA | Popul.n | Deprivation Score | | | | Sectors |
|---|---|---|---|---|---|---|
| | | Mean | Stan Dev | Minimum | Maximum | |
| Group 1 - WEST | | | | | | |
| Argyll & Clyde | 437958 | 0.52 | 3.50 | -6.61 | 12.27 | 77 |
| Ayr & Arran | 371043 | 0.07 | 2.56 | -6.40 | 6.13 | 71 |
| Greater Glasgow | 948125 | 2.50 | 5.05 | -7.31 | 10.88 | 128 |
| Lanarkshire | 558653 | 0.86 | 2.35 | -3.68 | 5.92 | 62 |
| Group 2 - EAST | | | | | | |
| Fife | 317302 | -1.11 | 1.87 | -5.79 | 3.16 | 49 |
| Forth Valley | 254887 | -0.81 | 2.30 | -6.61 | 3.60 | 44 |
| Grampian | 45B931 | -1.92 | 2.28 | -7.17 | 3.46 | 62 |
| Lothian | 706334 | -0.90 | 3.24 | -7.16 | 7.62 | 113 |
| Tayside | 380116 | -0.53 | 3.31 | -6.14 | 6.19 | 69 |
| Group 3 - RURAL | | | | | | |
| Borders | 92543 | -1.71 | 1.20 | -4.49 | 0.49 | 27 |
| Dumfries & Galloway | 141028 | -1.21 | 1.92 | -4.32 | 3.00 | 35 |
| Highland | 179119 | -1.85 | 1.40 | -4.51 | 1.39 | 59 |
| The Islands | 71091 | -1.27 | 1.77 | -4.04 | 4.09 | 14 |
| SCOTLAND | 4917130 | 0.02 | 3.59 | -7.31 | 12.27 | 810 |

Notes:
   Sectors >500. excluding 20 with large institutional populations

# DEPRIVATION AND HEALTH IN SCOTLAND

TABLE B2.5   DEPRIVATION SCORE STATISTICS CONTD.

| AREA | Popul.n | Deprivation Score | | | | Sectors |
|------|---------|------|---------|---------|---------|---------|
| | | Mean | Stan Dev | Minimum | Maximum | |
| **Argyll & Clyde** | | | | | | |
| Argyll & Bute | 57760 | -1.37 | 1.09 | -3.74 | 0.46 | 20 |
| Dumbarton | 76166 | -0.22 | 2.96 | -6.55 | 4.77 | 13 |
| Inverclyde | 98833 | 1.99 | 3.79 | -5.08 | 7.43 | 13 |
| Renfrew | 205199 | 0.62 | 3.67 | -6.61 | 12.27 | 31 |
| **Ayr & Arran** | | | | | | |
| Cumnoch & Doon V | 44657 | 1.25 | 1.70 | -5.11 | 3.47 | 8 |
| Cunninghame | 135412 | 0.86 | 2.41 | -4.87 | 6.13 | 28 |
| Kilmarnoch & Loudoun | 81633 | 0.01 | 2.14 | -5.49 | 3.60 | 16 |
| Kyle & Carrick | 109341 | -1.33 | 2.66 | -6.40 | 2.78 | 19 |
| **Borders** | | | | | | |
| Berwickshire | 17148 | -1.73 | 1.01 | -3.67 | -0.38 | 6 |
| Ett. & Lauderdale | 27204 | -1.82 | 1.35 | -4.49 | -0.44 | 8 |
| Roxburgh | 34518 | -1.54 | 1.26 | -3.45 | 0.49 | 7 |
| Tweeddale | 13673 | -1.89 | 0.85 | -3.49 | 0.28 | 6 |
| **Dumfries & Galloway** | | | | | | |
| Annan & Eskdale | 34744 | -1.59 | 1.10 | -3.65 | 0.06 | 9 |
| Nithsdale | 54437 | -0.98 | 2.38 | -4.12 | 2.32 | 11 |
| Stewartry | 22310 | -1.88 | 1.05 | -4.32 | -0.13 | 6 |
| Wigtown | 29537 | -0.67 | 2.00 | -2.98 | 3.00 | 9 |
| **Fife** | | | | | | |
| Dunfermline | 121692 | -1.38 | 2.15 | -5.79 | 3.16 | 16 |
| Kirkcaldy | 142706 | -0.39 | 1.36 | -2.57 | 2.50 | 20 |
| N.E.Fife | 52904 | -2.43 | 1.40 | -5.2B | -0.24 | 13 |
| **Forth Valley** | | | | | | |
| Clackmannan | 47168 | -1.04 | 1.83 | -5.74 | 2.57 | 8 |
| Falkirk | 132004 | -0.17 | 1.70 | -3.90 | 3.34 | 20 |
| Stirling | 75715 | -1.77 | 3.00 | -6.61 | 3.60 | 16 |
| **Grampian** | | | | | | |
| Aberdeen City | 199552 | -1.41 | 2.63 | -7.17 | 3.46 | 20 |
| Banff & Buchan | 79331 | -0.77 | 1.60 | -4.04 | 0.84 | 11 |
| Gordon | 61324 | -4.05 | 1.04 | -5.93 | -1.49 | 11 |
| Kincar. & Deeside | 39277 | -3.70 | 1.17 | -4.73 | -1.15 | 7 |
| Moray | 79447 | -1.83 | 1.26 | -4.60 | 0.36 | 13 |
| **Greater Glasgow** | | | | | | |
| Bears. & Milngavie | 39335 | -5.51 | 1.39 | -6.96 | -2.61 | 7 |
| Clydebank | 51995 | 2.25 | 1.90 | -1.37 | 3.97 | 7 |
| Eastwood | 53389 | -5.65 | 1.51 | -7.31 | 0.63 | 9 |
| Glasgow City | 722303 | 4.11 | 4.30 | -6.43 | 10.88 | 90 |
| Strathkelvin | 81103 | -2.45 | 2.59 | -5.72 | 3.48 | 15 |
| **Highland** | | | | | | |
| Badenoch & Strathspey | 8366 | -2.52 | 1.02 | -3.48 | -0.90 | 5 |
| Caithness | 26076 | -1.32 | 1.29 | -3.16 | 0.33 | 6 |
| Inverness | 53821 | -2.08 | 1.40 | -4.20 | -0.13 | 9 |
| Lochaber | 16813 | -0.46 | 1.31 | -3.33 | 1.00 | 7 |
| Nairn | 9488 | -2.42 | 1.25 | -3.72 | -1.22 | 2 |
| Ross & Cromarty | 44624 | -2.30 | 1.15 | -4.51 | -0.52 | 19 |
| Skye & Lochalsh | 7603 | -0.54 | 0.98 | -1.75 | 1.39 | 4 |
| Sutherland | 12328 | -2.11 | 0.88 | -3.62 | -0.95 | 7 |
| **Lanarkshire** | | | | | | |
| Cumbernauld | 61112 | -0.66 | 1.41 | -2.49 | 1.60 | 7 |
| E.Kilbride | 81865 | -1.36 | 1.39 | -3.68 | 0.65 | 9 |
| Hamilton | 107784 | 0.52 | 2.30 | -2.64 | 5.52 | 12 |
| Clydesdale | 56138 | -1.36 | 1.19 | -2.89 | 0.72 | 7 |
| Monklands | 109597 | 2.95 | 1.54 | -0.18 | 5.40 | 12 |
| Motherwell | 142157 | 2.32 | 1.43 | -0.51 | 5.92 | 15 |
| **Lothian** | | | | | | |
| E Lothian | 78327 | -1.55 | 1.99 | -5.91 | 1.46 | 16 |
| Edinburgh City | 410951 | -1.04 | 3.75 | -7.16 | 7.62 | 61 |
| Midlothian | 80006 | -1.58 | 2.21 | -6.82 | 0.99 | 15 |
| W.Lothian | 137050 | 0.26 | 2.20 | -6.39 | 5.09 | 21 |
| **Tayside** | | | | | | |
| Angus | 90927 | -1.45 | 1.67 | -5.89 | 2.37 | 18 |
| Dundee City | 176668 | 0.89 | 3.86 | -5.94 | 6.19 | 22 |
| Perth & Kinross | 112521 | -2.03 | 2.26 | -6.14 | 1.75 | 29 |
| **The Islands** | | | | | | |
| Orkney | 18419 | -2.30 | 0.81 | -3.21 | -1.30 | 3 |
| Shetland | 22768 | -2.46 | 0.68 | -4.04 | -1.60 | 3 |
| Western Isles | 29904 | 0.27 | 1.60 | -1.55 | 4.09 | 8 |
| **SCOTLAND** | 4917130 | 0.02 | 3.59 | -7.31 | 12.27 | 810 |

Notes:

Sectors >500, excluding 20 with large institutional populations

TABLE B2.6 Deprivation Scores. Health Board: Argyll & Clyde

| L. A. District | Sector | Pop | Dep | DEPCAT | NOCAR* | MUNP* | OVERC* | SC45* |
|---|---|---|---|---|---|---|---|---|
| Argyll & Bute | FK20.8P | 4 | n/a | - | 0 | 0 | 0 | 0 |
| Argyll & Bute | G83.7P | 214 | -0.79 | 4 | 42 | 3 | 28 | 27 |
| Argyll & Bute | PA20.0 | 4057 | 0.27 | 4 | 55 | 16 | 14 | 24 |
| Argyll & Bute | PA20.9 | 3254 | -1.43 | 3 | 46 | 12 | 14 | 18 |
| Argyll & Bute | PA21.2 | 874 | -1.91 | 3 | 23 | 10 | 14 | 28 |
| Argyll & Bute | PA22.3 | 343 | -1.96 | 3 | 16 | 6 | 24 | 29 |
| Argyll & Bute | PA23.7 | 5382 | -1.87 | 3 | 39 | 12 | 15 | 16 |
| Argyll & Bute | PA23.8 | 7713 | -2.81 | 3 | 36 | 8 | 16 | 12 |
| Argyll & Bute | PA24.8 | 425 | -2.04 | 3 | 23 | 8 | 9 | 34 |
| Argyll & Bute | PA25.8 | 74 | -6.67 | 1 | 10 | 6 | 6 | 0 |
| Argyll & Bute | PA26.8 | 109 | -5.30 | 1 | 13 | 5 | 20 | 0 |
| Argyll & Bute | PA27.8 | 736 | -2.67 | 3 | 13 | 4 | 17 | 31 |
| Argyll & Bute | PA28.6 | 8879 | -0.63 | 4 | 37 | 11 | 23 | 25 |
| Argyll & Bute | PA29.6 | 2524 | 0.30 | 4 | 28 | 9 | 23 | 42 |
| Argyll & Bute | PA30.8 | 1407 | -1.75 | 3 | 24 | 7 | 21 | 28 |
| Argyll & Bute | PA31.8 | 4290 | -2.73 | 3 | 20 | 6 | 20 | 22 |
| Argyll & Bute | PA32.8 | 1155 | -0.59 | 4 | 23 | 16 | 19 | 29 |
| Argyll & Bute | PA33.1 | 731 | -1.42 | 3 | 21 | 6 | 22 | 33 |
| Argyll & Bute | PA34.4 | 5537 | -0.71 | 4 | 34 | 11 | 22 | 26 |
| Argyll & Bute | PA34.5P | 3501 | -1.63 | 3 | 35 | 6 | 22 | 22 |
| Argyll & Bute | PA35.1 | 1090 | -3.41 | 2 | 24 | 8 | 25 | 6 |
| Argyll & Bute | PA36.4 | 70 | -6.33 | 1 | 18 | 0 | 13 | 0 |
| Argyll & Bute | PA37.1 | 2523 | -0.75 | 4 | 24 | 11 | 25 | 28 |
| Argyll & Bute | PA38.4P | 423 | -0.89 | 4 | 13 | 9 | 25 | 35 |
| Argyll & Bute | PA41.7 | 153 | -3.27 | 2 | 23 | 2 | 25 | 15 |
| Argyll & Bute | PA42.7 | 1307 | 0.46 | 4 | 38 | 13 | 32 | 24 |
| Argyll & Bute | PA43.7 | 1026 | -0.32 | 4 | 35 | 11 | 31 | 21 |
| Argyll & Bute | PA44.7 | 305 | -1.20 | 3 | 18 | 8 | 12 | 43 |
| Argyll & Bute | PA15.7 | 179 | 1.56 | 5 | 38 | 9 | 18 | 53 |
| Argyll & Bute | PA46.7 | 292 | 0.39 | 4 | 21 | 6 | 24 | 50 |
| Argyll & Bute | PA47.7 | 162 | 5.22 | 6 | 35 | 9 | 19 | 92 |
| Argyll & Bute | PA48.7 | 313 | -1.86 | 3 | 32 | 7 | 10 | 32 |
| Argyll & Bute | PA49.7 | 208 | -0.35 | 4 | 18 | 10 | 9 | 52 |
| Argyll & Bute | PA60.7 | 228 | -0.13 | 4 | 26 | 11 | 19 | 39 |
| Argyll & Bute | PA61.7 | 136 | 3.17 | 6 | 35 | 12 | 17 | 71 |
| Argyll & Bute | PA62.6 | 28 | -7.73 | 1 | 14 | 0 | 0 | 0 |
| Argyll & Bute | PA63.6 | 1 | n/a | - | 0 | 0 | 0 | 0 |
| Argyll & Bute | PA64.6 | 67 | -3.44 | 2 | 15 | 12 | 30 | 0 |
| Argyll & Bute | PA65.6 | 162 | -5.11 | 1 | 25 | 12 | 5 | 0 |
| Argyll & Bute | PA66.6 | 135 | -2.18 | 3 | 37 | 18 | 20 | 0 |
| Argyll & Bute | PA67.6 | 218 | 0.82 | 4 | 28 | 14 | 20 | 43 |
| Argyll & Bute | PA68.6 | 13 | n/a | - | 0 | 0 | 0 | 0 |
| Argyll & Bute | PA69.6 | 13 | n/a | - | 29 | 0 | 0 | 0 |
| Argyll & Bute | PA70.6 | 70 | -5.83 | 1 | 10 | 10 | 8 | 0 |
| Argyll & Bute | PA71.6 | 42 | n/a | - | 0 | 0 | 21 | 0 |
| Argyll & Bute | PA72.6 | 403 | -3.37 | 2 | 17 | 9 | 13 | 19 |
| Argyll & Bute | PA73.6 | 65 | 3.01 | 6 | 13 | 5 | 21 | 86 |
| Argyll & Bute | PA74.6 | 11 | -2.22 | 3 | 27 | 0 | 55 | 0 |
| Argyll & Bute | PA75.6 | 1014 | -1.79 | 3 | 26 | 10 | 19 | 23 |
| Argyll & Bute | PA76.6 | 122 | -4.99 | 2 | 31 | 0 | 21 | 0 |
| Argyll & Bute | PA77.6 | 760 | -3.74 | 2 | 26 | 18 | 10 | 0 |
| Argyll & Bute | PA78.6 | 131 | -1.81 | 3 | 21 | 9 | 12 | 33 |
| Dumbarton | G60.5P | 450 | 1.56 | 5 | 36 | 15 | 25 | 40 |
| Dumbarton | G63.0P | 205 | -3.63 | 2 | 12 | 6 | 24 | 14 |
| Dumbarton | G82.1 | 2979 | -1.71 | 3 | 44 | 9 | 15 | 19 |
| Dumbarton | G82.2 | 6175 | -0.89 | 4 | 40 | 12 | 25 | 17 |
| Dumbarton | G82.3 | 8112 | 1.60 | 5 | 44 | 17 | 38 | 21 |
| Dumbarton | G82.4 | 5397 | 4.77 | 6 | 63 | 27 | 35 | 33 |
| Dumbarton | G82.5 | 6085 | 1.36 | 5 | 43 | 17 | 36 | 20 |
| Dumbarton | G83.0 | 7568 | 0.81 | 4 | 49 | 15 | 28 | 22 |
| Dumbarton | G83.7P | 717 | -3.14 | 2 | 24 | 10 | 30 | 0 |
| Dumbarton | G83.8P | 8207 | 0.54 | 4 | 39 | 17 | 26 | 24 |
| Dumbarton | G83.9P | 9261 | 2.51 | 5 | 47 | 19 | 39 | 26 |
| Dumbarton | G84.0 | 4787 | -4.10 | 2 | 22 | 7 | 16 | 8 |
| Dumbarton | G84.7 | 6443 | -1.00 | 4 | 38 | 12 | 22 | 19 |
| Dumbarton | G84.8 | 5358 | -4.79 | 2 | 25 | 6 | 10 | 7 |
| Dumbarton | G84.9 | 5077 | -6.55 | 1 | 16 | 2 | 6 | 3 |
| Inverclyde | PA10.2P | 7 | n/a | - | 0 | 0 | 0 | 0 |
| Inverclyde | PA11.3P | 713 | -3.62 | 2 | 6 | 24 | 15 | 0 |
| Inverclyde | PA13.4P | 4007 | -5.08 | 1 | 14 | 7 | 10 | 9 |
| Inverclyde | PA14.5 | 10239 | 0.87 | 4 | 49 | 13 | 31 | 23 |
| Inverclyde | PA14.6P | 12466 | 4.40 | 6 | 61 | 21 | 43 | 31 |
| Inverclyde | PA15.1 | 2289 | 3.50 | 6 | 75 | 26 | 19 | 28 |

*percent of population

| L. A. District | Sector | Pop | Dep | DEPCAT | NOCAR* | MUNP* | OVERC* | SC45* |
|---|---|---|---|---|---|---|---|---|
| Inverclyde | PA15.2 | 7873 | 7.43 | 7 | 74 | 26 | 44 | 47 |
| Inverclyde | PA15.3 | 5535 | 7.13 | 7 | 75 | 31 | 52 | 29 |
| Inverclyde | PA15.4 | 9740 | 2.25 | 5 | 63 | 13 | 32 | 29 |
| Inverclyde | PA16.0 | 12110 | 5.06 | 6 | 56 | 20 | 48 | 36 |
| Inverclyde | PA16.7 | 10436 | 3.24 | 6 | 52 | 17 | 39 | 34 |
| Inverclyde | PA16.8 | 6660 | -4.40 | 2 | 25 | 5 | 10 | 12 |
| Inverclyde | PA16.9 | 4922 | -0.74 | 4 | 44 | 10 | 27 | 16 |
| Inverclyde | PA18.6 | 1460 | -4.98 | 2 | 14 | 5 | 13 | 9 |
| Inverclyde | PA19.1 | 11096 | -2.64 | 3 | 31 | 8 | 20 | 14 |
| Renfrew | G52.3P | 29 | n/a | - | 21 | 0 | 38 | 0 |
| Renfrew | G52.4P | 10 | n/a | - | 0 | 0 | 0 | 0 |
| Renfrew | G53.7P | 60 | -1.49 | 3 | 41 | 12 | 36 | 0 |
| Renfrew | G77.6P | 4 | n/a | - | 0 | 0 | 0 | 0 |
| Renfrew | G78.1P | 8484 | 0.76 | 4 | 45 | 14 | 31 | 23 |
| Renfrew | G78.2P | 9965 | 1.10 | 5 | 44 | 12 | 38 | 23 |
| Renfrew | G78.3 | 5049 | -1.51 | 3 | 35 | 9 | 27 | 15 |
| Renfrew | G78.4P | 716 | -6.53 | 1 | 7 | 3 | 6 | 6 |
| Renfrew | PA1.1 | 5443 | 3.76 | 6 | 70 | 16 | 37 | 32 |
| Renfrew | PA1.2 | 6493 | 2.14 | 5 | 64 | 13 | 29 | 30 |
| Renfrew | PA1.3P | 8247 | -5.08 | 1 | 23 | 5 | 9 | 8 |
| Renfrew | PA10.2P | 4289 | -3.74 | 2 | 22 | 8 | 18 | 10 |
| Renfrew | PA11.3P | 5150 | -3.46 | 2 | 22 | 8 | 16 | 14 |
| Renfrew | PA12.4 | 2777 | -2.33 | 3 | 26 | 10 | 18 | 18 |
| Renfrew | PA13.4P | 21 | n/a | - | 0 | 0 | 0 | 0 |
| Renfrew | PA14.6P | 816 | -6.61 | 1 | 9 | 5 | 8 | 0 |
| Renfrew | PA2.0 | 10115 | 2.50 | 5 | 50 | 16 | 41 | 26 |
| Renfrew | PA2.6 | 9902 | 0.89 | 4 | 53 | 12 | 25 | 28 |
| Renfrew | PA2.7 | 7307 | -0.38 | 4 | 36 | 9 | 29 | 24 |
| Renfrew | PA2.8 | 9925 | 2.78 | 5 | 49 | 13 | 39 | 35 |
| Renfrew | PA2.9 | 6897 | -2.10 | 3 | 28 | 8 | 23 | 19 |
| Renfrew | PA3.1 | 8171 | 12.27 | 7 | 83 | 39 | 55 | 63 |
| Renfrew | PA3.2 | 4607 | 5.57 | 6 | 68 | 18 | 37 | 49 |
| Renfrew | PA3.3 | 12407 | 2.40 | 5 | 45 | 15 | 43 | 28 |
| Renfrew | PA3.4 | 7393 | 3.04 | 6 | 59 | 13 | 35 | 36 |
| Renfrew | PA4.0 | 10746 | -2.27 | 3 | 33 | 7 | 24 | 14 |
| Renfrew | PA4.8P | 8101 | 2.08 | 5 | 58 | 14 | 33 | 27 |
| Renfrew | PA4.9 | 4643 | 0.09 | 4 | 45 | 11 | 28 | 22 |
| Renfrew | PA5.0 | 10160 | 2.94 | 5 | 48 | 18 | 43 | 28 |
| Renfrew | PA5.8 | 8246 | 2.23 | 5 | 57 | 17 | 29 | 28 |
| Renfrew | PA5.9 | 8063 | -0.19 | 4 | 39 | 11 | 31 | 20 |
| Renfrew | PA6.7 | 3593 | -5.24 | 1 | 8 | 5 | 14 | 9 |
| Renfrew | PA7.5 | 6002 | -5.20 | 1 | 13 | 4 | 11 | 10 |
| Renfrew | PA8.6 | 5892 | -3.22 | 2 | 29 | 7 | 14 | 15 |
| Renfrew | PA8.7 | 4329 | -3.39 | 2 | 29 | 7 | 10 | 18 |
| Renfrew | PA9.1 | 1271 | -2.09 | 3 | 24 | 12 | 21 | 17 |

Deprivation Scores. Health Board: Ayrshire & Arran

| L. A. District | Sector | Pop | Dep | DEPCAT | NOCAR* | MUNP* | OVERC* | SC45* |
|---|---|---|---|---|---|---|---|---|
| Cumnock & Doon Valley | DG4.6P | 0 | n/a | - | 0 | 0 | 0 | 0 |
| Cumnock & Doon Valley | DG7.3P | 2 | n/a | - | 0 | 0 | 0 | 0 |
| Cumnock & Doon Valley | KA1.5P | 16 | n/a | - | 0 | 0 | 0 | 0 |
| Cumnock & Doon Valley | KA18.1 | 7287 | 0.01 | 4 | 37 | 13 | 24 | 26 |
| Cumnock & Doon Valley | KA18.2 | 5873 | 1.47 | 5 | 46 | 16 | 30 | 27 |
| Cumnock & Doon Valley | KA18.3 | 6827 | 1.22 | 5 | 49 | 17 | 27 | 25 |
| Cumnock & Doon Valley | KA18.4P | 5218 | 1.05 | 5 | 47 | 15 | 26 | 28 |
| Cumnock & Doon Valley | KA4.8P | 63 | -5.79 | 1 | 0 | 4 | 24 | 0 |
| Cumnock & Doon Valley | KA5.5P | 1480 | -5.11 | 1 | 16 | 6 | 12 | 6 |
| Cumnock & Doon Valley | KA5.6 | 5845 | 0.71 | 4 | 41 | 15 | 28 | 25 |
| Cumnock & Doon Valley | KA6.6P | 1527 | -0.15 | 4 | 32 | 17 | 32 | 15 |
| Cumnock & Doon Valley | KA6.7P | 10600 | 3.47 | 6 | 48 | 24 | 32 | 34 |
| Cunninghame | G78.4P | 68 | n/a | - | 0 | 0 | 0 | 0 |
| Cunninghame | KA11.1 | 10272 | -0.71 | 4 | 38 | 18 | 11 | 24 |
| Cunninghame | KA11.2.P | 229 | -4.65 | 2 | 14 | 7 | 9 | 14 |
| Cunninghame | KA11.3 | 1524 | 6.13 | 7 | 60 | 31 | 31 | 45 |
| Cunninghame | KA11.4 | 4076 | 0.58 | 4 | 36 | 14 | 25 | 31 |
| Cunninghame | KA11.5P | 345 | -0.24 | 4 | 19 | 17 | 24 | 29 |
| Cunninghame | KA12.0 | 9683 | 2.04 | 5 | 46 | 20 | 25 | 32 |
| Cunninghame | KA12.8 | 3997 | 1.81 | 5 | 50 | 22 | 25 | 24 |
| Cunninghame | KA12.9 | 8592 | 2.83 | 5 | 50 | 21 | 33 | 30 |
| Cunninghame | KA13.6 | 10087 | 0.45 | 4 | 40 | 15 | 26 | 26 |
| Cunninghame | KA13.7P | 6648 | 2.20 | 5 | 45 | 19 | 27 | 34 |
| Cunninghame | KA14.3 | 769 | 2.22 | 5 | 47 | 25 | 27 | 25 |
| Cunninghame | KA15.1 | 3234 | -1.36 | 3 | 36 | 10 | 23 | 18 |

| L. A. District | Sector | Pop | Dep | DEPCAT | NOCAR* | MUNP* | OVERC* | SC45* |
|---|---|---|---|---|---|---|---|---|
| Cunninghame | KA15.2 | 3397 | -1.02 | 3 | 31 | 11 | 22 | 24 |
| Cunninghame | KA2.0P | 31 | n/a | - | 13 | 0 | 26 | 0 |
| Cunninghame | KA20.3 | 5952 | 2.76 | 5 | 52 | 23 | 30 | 27 |
| Cunninghame | KA20.4 | 5461 | 3.78 | 6 | 53 | 24 | 33 | 34 |
| Cunninghame | KA21.5 | 6754 | 1.76 | 5 | 52 | 20 | 23 | 28 |
| Cunninghame | KA21.6 | 6141 | 3.48 | 6 | 51 | 22 | 35 | 32 |
| Cunninghame | KA22.7 | 7676 | 3.41 | 6 | 51 | 22 | 34 | 32 |
| Cunninghame | KA22.8 | 3807 | -0.74 | 4 | 42 | 17 | 20 | 15 |
| Cunninghame | KA23.9 | 4535 | -3.04 | 2 | 25 | 10 | 14 | 16 |
| Cunninghame | KA24.4 | 3846 | 1.13 | 5 | 47 | 18 | 28 | 22 |
| Cunninghame | KA24.5 | 2629 | -1.39 | 3 | 27 | 13 | 22 | 20 |
| Cunninghame | KA25.6 | 4903 | 4.69 | 6 | 52 | 21 | 36 | 45 |
| Cunninghame | KA25.7 | 3380 | -0.39 | 4 | 37 | 17 | 22 | 20 |
| Cunninghame | KA27.8 | 3845 | -2.24 | 3 | 25 | 14 | 12 | 20 |
| Cunninghame | KA28.0 | 1306 | -2.75 | 3 | 42 | 11 | 10 | 11 |
| Cunninghame | KA29.0 | 1365 | -3.77 | 2 | 19 | 9 | 10 | 16 |
| Cunninghame | KA3.2P | 188 | -3.01 | 2 | 4 | 5 | 16 | 33 |
| Cunninghame | KA3.3P | 22 | n/a | - | 0 | 0 | 0 | 0 |
| Cunninghame | KA3.4P | 17 | n/a | - | 0 | 0 | 0 | 0 |
| Cunninghame | KA30.8 | 3861 | -4.87 | 2 | 26 | 5 | 7 | 8 |
| Cunninghame | KA30.9 | 5913 | -1.96 | 3 | 38 | 11 | 18 | 15 |
| Cunninghame | PA17.5 | 1759 | -3.51 | 2 | 20 | 8 | 20 | 10 |
| Kilmarnock & Loudoun | G77.6P | 4 | n/a | - | 0 | 0 | 0 | 0 |
| Kilmarnock & Loudoun | G78.4P | 15 | n/a | - | 0 | 0 | 0 | 0 |
| Kilmarnock & Loudoun | KA1.1 | 2551 | -5.49 | 1 | 18 | 5 | 8 | 6 |
| Kilmarnock & Loudoun | KA1.2 | 4760 | -2.54 | 3 | 36 | 9 | 11 | 18 |
| Kilmarnock & Loudoun | KA1.3 | 7939 | 0.45 | 4 | 40 | 13 | 25 | 29 |
| Kilmarnock & Loudoun | KA1.4 | 8759 | 3.05 | 6 | 49 | 24 | 27 | 34 |
| Kilmarnock & Loudoun | KA1.5P | 4583 | 1.63 | 5 | 44 | 17 | 29 | 31 |
| Kilmarnock & Loudoun | KA11.2P | 11 | n/a | - | 0 | 0 | 0 | 0 |
| Kilmarnock & Loudoun | KA13.7P | 39 | -8.48 | 1 | 0 | 0 | 0 | 0 |
| Kilmarnock & Loudoun | KA16.9 | 3526 | -1.82 | 3 | 34 | 9 | 20 | 19 |
| Kilmarnock & Loudoun | KA17.0P | 3782 | -2.19 | 3 | 32 | 7 | 21 | 17 |
| Kilmarnock & Loudoun | KA2.0P | 3449 | 0.06 | 4 | 33 | 13 | 23 | 31 |
| Kilmarnock & Loudoun | KA2.9P | 41 | 2.68 | 5 | 7 | 8 | 0 | 0 |
| Kilmarnock & Loudoun | KA3.1 | 6023 | 3.60 | 6 | 56 | 29 | 25 | 30 |
| Kilmarnock & Loudoun | KA3.2P | 9099 | 1.21 | 5 | 40 | 19 | 28 | 26 |
| Kilmarnock & Loudoun | KA3.3P | 3198 | -0.56 | 4 | 28 | 13 | 28 | 22 |
| Kilmarnock & Loudoun | KA3.4P | 1335 | -1.54 | 3 | 22 | 8 | 20 | 30 |
| Kilmarnock & Loudoun | KA3.5 | 3708 | -3.06 | 2 | 23 | 10 | 18 | 12 |
| Kilmarnock & Loudoun | KA3.6 | 2716 | -1.52 | 3 | 28 | 12 | 22 | 20 |
| Kilmarnock & Loudoun | KA3.7 | 10430 | -0.62 | 4 | 32 | 11 | 25 | 25 |
| Kilmarnock & Loudoun | KA4.8P | 5775 | -0.61 | 4 | 36 | 14 | 22 | 20 |
| Kyle & Carrick | DG8.0P | 13 | n/a | - | 0 | 0 | 0 | 0 |
| Kyle & Carrick | DG8.6P | 8 | n/a | - | 0 | 0 | 0 | 0 |
| Kyle & Carrick | KA1.5P | 1930 | -2.67 | 3 | 17 | 9 | 22 | 19 |
| Kyle & Carrick | KA10.6 | 9540 | -3.62 | 2 | 28 | 8 | 12 | 13 |
| Kyle & Carrick | KA10.7 | 4643 | -3.66 | 2 | 21 | 10 | 13 | 12 |
| Kyle & Carrick | KA11.5P | 10 | n/a | - | 0 | 0 | 0 | 0 |
| Kyle & Carrick | KA19.7P | 4517 | -0.31 | 4 | 37 | 11 | 23 | 27 |
| Kyle & Carrick | KA19.8 | 2994 | -0.70 | 4 | 28 | 9 | 26 | 29 |
| Kyle & Carrick | KA2.9P | 2944 | -0.98 | 4 | 26 | 13 | 21 | 26 |
| Kyle & Carrick | KA26.0P | 6739 | 1.29 | 5 | 38 | 15 | 27 | 34 |
| Kyle & Carrick | KA26.9 | 5569 | -1.20 | 3 | 33 | 12 | 20 | 22 |
| Kyle & Carrick | KA5.5P | 2494 | 0.80 | 4 | 36 | 19 | 27 | 24 |
| Kyle & Carrick | KA6.5 | 4062 | 1.16 | 5 | 39 | 14 | 29 | 32 |
| Kyle & Carrick | KA6.6P | 2785 | -2.02 | 3 | 20 | 8 | 16 | 30 |
| Kyle & Carrick | KA6.7P | 114 | 5.30 | 6 | 6 | 14 | 22 | 0 |
| Kyle & Carrick | KA7.4 | 1807 | -1.97 | 3 | 47 | 12 | 10 | 16 |
| Kyle & Carrick | KA7.2 | 5636 | -4.44 | 2 | 20 | 7 | 10 | 12 |
| Kyle & Carrick | KA7.3 | 12200 | -0.90 | 4 | 32 | 13 | 24 | 20 |
| Kyle & Carrick | KA7.1 | 8440 | -6.40 | 1 | 7 | 5 | 6 | 6 |
| Kyle & Carrick | KA8.0 | 8525 | 2.63 | 5 | 54 | 22 | 31 | 25 |
| Kyle & Carrick | KA8.8 | 4048 | 0.07 | 4 | 54 | 16 | 20 | 18 |
| Kyle & Carrick | KA8.9 | 8651 | 2.78 | 5 | 56 | 20 | 30 | 29 |
| Kyle & Carrick | KA9.1 | 7361 | -2.79 | 3 | 32 | 9 | 13 | 17 |
| Kyle & Carrick | KA9.2 | 7241 | -3.36 | 2 | 26 | 7 | 13 | 17 |

Deprivation Scores. Health Board: Borders

| L. A. District | Sector | Pop | Dep | DEPCAT | NOCAR* | MUNP* | OVERC* | SC45* |
|---|---|---|---|---|---|---|---|---|
| Berwickshire | TD10.6 | 1028 | -2.23 | 3 | 17 | 6 | 18 | 30 |
| Berwickshire | TD11.3P | 6147 | -2.36 | 3 | 22 | 5 | 14 | 31 |
| Berwickshire | TD12.4 | 2436 | -2.41 | 3 | 22 | 6 | 14 | 29 |
| Berwickshire | TD13.5P | 474 | -3.56 | 2 | 18 | 1 | 10 | 30 |
| Berwickshire | TD14.5 | 5884 | -0.38 | 4 | 32 | 10 | 21 | 33 |
| Berwickshire | TD15.1 | 982 | -2.35 | 3 | 14 | 6 | 12 | 37 |

| L. A. District | Sector | Pop | Dep | DEPCAT | NOCAR* | MUNP* | OVERC* | SC45* |
|---|---|---|---|---|---|---|---|---|
| Berwickshire | TD2.6P | 12 | n/a | - | 0 | 0 | 0 | 0 |
| Berwickshire | TD3.6P | 671 | -3.67 | 2 | 15 | 4 | 13 | 25 |
| Berwickshire | TD4.6P | 32 | -5.46 | 1 | 0 | 0 | 34 | 0 |
| Berwickshire | TD5.7P | 230 | -4.04 | 2 | 10 | 12 | 10 | 15 |
| Ettrick & Lauderdale | EH37.5P | 5 | n/a | - | 0 | 0 | 0 | 0 |
| Ettrick & Lauderdale | EH38.5P | 288 | 3.81 | 6 | 16 | 4 | 15 | 0 |
| Ettrick & Lauderdale | EH43.6P | 10 | n/a | - | 0 | 0 | 0 | 0 |
| Ettrick & Lauderdale | EH44.6P | 0 | n/a | - | 0 | 0 | 0 | 0 |
| Ettrick & Lauderdale | TD1.1 | 4821 | -0.92 | 4 | 42 | 8 | 17 | 29 |
| Ettrick & Lauderdale | TD1.2 | 5904 | -0.44 | 4 | 37 | 9 | 21 | 31 |
| Ettrick & Lauderdale | TD1.3P | 3500 | -4.16 | 2 | 27 | 7 | 10 | 10 |
| Ettrick & Lauderdale | TD2.6P | 1415 | -4.49 | 2 | 17 | 4 | 10 | 17 |
| Ettrick & Lauderdale | TD3.6P | 75 | -5.64 | 1 | 7 | 4 | 23 | 0 |
| Ettrick & Lauderdale | TD4.6P | 1937 | -1.87 | 3 | 25 | 5 | 15 | 34 |
| Ettrick & Lauderdale | TD5.7P | 33 | -1.43 | 3 | 21 | 33 | 15 | 0 |
| Ettrick & Lauderdale | TD5.8P | 74 | -6.46 | 1 | 8 | 8 | 5 | 0 |
| Ettrick & Lauderdale | TD6.0 | 2750 | -2.57 | 3 | 22 | 7 | 13 | 27 |
| Ettrick & Lauderdale | TD6.9P | 3246 | -4.40 | 2 | 16 | 4 | 9 | 19 |
| Ettrick & Lauderdale | TD7.4 | 4296 | -2.10 | 3 | 30 | 6 | 16 | 26 |
| Ettrick & Lauderdale | TD7.5P | 2581 | -0.66 | 4 | 27 | 10 | 21 | 33 |
| Ettrick & Lauderdale | TD9.7P | 22 | n/a | - | 0 | 0 | 0 | 0 |
| Roxburgh | DG14.0P | 5 | n/a | - | 0 | 0 | 0 | 0 |
| Roxburgh | TD3.6P | 8 | n/a | - | 0 | 0 | 0 | 0 |
| Roxburgh | TD5.7P | 5616 | -2.23 | 3 | 23 | 7 | 16 | 27 |
| Roxburgh | TD5.8P | 3282 | -3.45 | 2 | 13 | 5 | 12 | 27 |
| Roxburgh | TD6.9P | 55 | -4.60 | 2 | 9 | 0 | 7 | 29 |
| Roxburgh | TD8.6 | 5641 | -1.92 | 3 | 27 | 7 | 14 | 30 |
| Roxburgh | TD9.0P | 4933 | -0.28 | 4 | 45 | 11 | 15 | 30 |
| Roxburgh | TD9.7P | 4389 | -1.65 | 3 | 32 | 9 | 20 | 22 |
| Roxburgh | TD9.8 | 5967 | 0.49 | 4 | 40 | 11 | 25 | 33 |
| Roxburgh | TD9.9 | 4690 | -2.75 | 3 | 36 | 7 | 10 | 20 |
| Tweeddale | EH26.8P | 3 | n/a | - | 0 | 0 | 0 | 0 |
| Tweeddale | EH26.9P | 91 | 2.17 | 5 | 12 | 0 | 4 | 0 |
| Tweeddale | EH43.6P | 773 | 0.28 | 4 | 41 | 7 | 14 | 45 |
| Tweeddale | EH44.6P | 2700 | -1.08 | 3 | 33 | 6 | 16 | 35 |
| Tweeddale | EH45.8 | 4446 | -1.82 | 3 | 37 | 8 | 16 | 22 |
| Tweeddale | EH45.9 | 3045 | -2.14 | 3 | 23 | 9 | 19 | 23 |
| Tweeddale | EH46.7P | 1899 | -2.98 | 3 | 9 | 5 | 14 | 32 |
| Tweeddale | ML12.6P | 810 | -3.49 | 2 | 14 | 3 | 11 | 30 |
| Tweeddale | TD1.3P | 12 | n/a | - | 0 | 0 | 0 | 0 |

Deprivation Scores. Health Board: Dumfries & Galloway

| L. A. District | Sector | Pop | Dep | DEPCAT | NOCAR* | MUNP* | OVERC* | SC45* |
|---|---|---|---|---|---|---|---|---|
| Annandale & Eskdale | CA6.5 | 3124 | -0.51 | 4 | 35 | 15 | 17 | 27 |
| Annandale & Eskdale | DG1.3P | 5 | n/a | - | 0 | 0 | 0 | 0 |
| Annandale & Eskdale | DG1.4P | 244 | -2.03 | 3 | 18 | 5 | 14 | 37 |
| Annandale & Eskdale | DG10.9P | 3125 | -2.50 | 3 | 26 | 12 | 15 | 17 |
| Annandale & Eskdale | DG11.1P | 4006 | -3.03 | 2 | 21 | 6 | 16 | 21 |
| Annandale & Eskdale | DG11.2 | 4610 | -2.58 | 3 | 26 | 6 | 20 | 20 |
| Annandale & Eskdale | DG11.3 | 3071 | -1.01 | 3 | 20 | 11 | 21 | 32 |
| Annandale & Eskdale | DG12.5P | 5763 | 0.06 | 4 | 38 | 11 | 20 | 34 |
| Annandale & Eskdale | DG12.6 | 6450 | -1.32 | 3 | 32 | 11 | 20 | 23 |
| Annandale & Eskdale | DG13.0 | 3293 | -1.74 | 3 | 30 | 6 | 13 | 33 |
| Annandale & Eskdale | DG14.0P | 1302 | -3.65 | 2 | 15 | 4 | 14 | 23 |
| Annandale & Eskdale | TD7.5P | 5 | n.a | - | 0 | 0 | 0 | 0 |
| Annandale & Eskdale | TD9.0P | 0 | n/a | - | 0 | 0 | 0 | 0 |
| Nithsdale | DG1.1 | 5762 | -1.52 | 3 | 26 | 9 | 21 | 26 |
| Nithsdale | DG1.2 | 2356 | -1.13 | 3 | 50 | 12 | 13 | 20 |
| Nithsdale | DG1.3P | 4764 | -4.12 | 2 | 20 | 5 | 13 | 15 |
| Nithsdale | DG1.4P | 9326 | -3.93 | 2 | 16 | 5 | 12 | 20 |
| Nithsdale | DG11.1P | 309 | -4.65 | 2 | 8 | 11 | 10 | 11 |
| Nithsdale | DG12.5P | 42 | -7.41 | 1 | 5 | 0 | 9 | 0 |
| Nithsdale | DG2.0P | 8294 | 2.26 | 5 | 43 | 16 | 30 | 37 |
| Nithsdale | DG2.7 | 4617 | -1.94 | 3 | 32 | 8 | 15 | 25 |
| Nithsdale | DG2.8P | 1982 | -1.98 | 3 | 19 | 4 | 19 | 34 |
| Nithsdale | DG2.9P | 7602 | 0.70 | 4 | 40 | 12 | 27 | 31 |
| Nithsdale | DG3.4P | 2068 | -2.18 | 3 | 20 | 6 | 15 | 32 |
| Nithsdale | DG3.5 | 2357 | -1.99 | 3 | 22 | 4 | 17 | 33 |
| Nithsdale | DG4.6P | 5309 | 2.32 | 5 | 46 | 17 | 26 | 38 |
| Nithsdale | KA18.4P | 1 | n/a | - | 0 | 0 | 0 | 0 |
| Nithsdale | ML12.6P | 127 | -4.92 | 2 | 24 | 13 | 6 | 0 |
| Stewartry | DG2.0P | 6 | n./a | - | 0 | 0 | 0 | 0 |
| Stewartry | DG2.8P | 1195 | -4.32 | 2 | 11 | 5 | 13 | 17 |

| | | | | | | | | |
|---|---|---|---|---|---|---|---|---|
| Stewartry | DG2.9P | 21 | n/a | - | 0 | 0 | 0 | 0 |
| Stewartry | DG3.4P | 30 | n/a | - | 3 | 14 | 34 | 0 |
| Stewartry | DG5.4 | 4801 | -0.13 | 4 | 27 | 12 | 23 | 34 |
| Stewartry | DG6.4 | 5190 | -2.08 | 3 | 23 | 7 | 16 | 29 |
| Stewartry | DG7.1 | 5133 | -2.08 | 3 | 24 | 7 | 16 | 28 |
| Stewartry | DG7.2P | 2083 | -2.73 | 3 | 18 | 5 | 14 | 30 |
| Stewartry | DG7.3P | 3908 | -2.30 | 3 | 14 | 7 | 15 | 32 |
| Stewartry | KA6.7P | 3 | n/a | - | 0 | 0 | 0 | 0 |
| Wigtown | DG7.2P | 28 | n/a | - | 24 | 0 | 0 | 0 |
| Wigtown | DG7.3P | 10 | n/a | - | 0 | 0 | 0 | 0 |
| Wigtown | DG8.0P | 1964 | -2.98 | 3 | 20 | 7 | 15 | 22 |
| Wigtown | DG8.6P | 3946 | -1.78 | 3 | 28 | 11 | 21 | 19 |
| Wigtown | DG8.7 | 1330 | 0.80 | 4 | 26 | 10 | 22 | 47 |
| Wigtown | DG8.8 | 2447 | -0.60 | 4 | 33 | 11 | 19 | 30 |
| Wigtown | DG8.9 | 3003 | -1.66 | 3 | 23 | 9 | 15 | 32 |
| Wigtown | DG9.0 | 4083 | -2.06 | 3 | 23 | 9 | 20 | 23 |
| Wigtown | DG9.7 | 5836 | 3.00 | 6 | 48 | 18 | 31 | 39 |
| Wigtown | DG9.8 | 4461 | -2.15 | 3 | 24 | 11 | 18 | 20 |
| Wigtown | DG9.9 | 2467 | -0.44 | 4 · | 21 | 12 | 20 | 36 |
| Wigtown | KA26.0P | 4 | n/a | - | 0 | 0 | 0 | 0 |

Deprivation Scores. Health Board: Fife

| L. A. District | Sector | Pop | Dep | DEPCAT | NOCAR* | MUNP* | OVERC* | SC45* |
|---|---|---|---|---|---|---|---|---|
| Dunfermline | FK10.3P | 43 | -2.68 | 3 | 2 | 25 | 26 | 0 |
| Dunfermline | FK10.4P | 3392 | -1.27 | 3 | 25 | 8 | 25 | 27 |
| Dunfermline | FK14.7P | 10 | n/a | - | 0 | 0 | 0 | 0 |
| Dunfermline | KY11.1 | 6723 | -0.86 | 4 | 43 | 9 | 22 | 22 |
| Dunfermline | KY11.2 | 12871 | -2.15 | 3 | 44 | 5 | 19 | 16 |
| Dunfermline | KY11.3 | 3401 | -2.46 | 3 | 33 | 7 | 19 | 17 |
| Dunfermline | KY11.4 | 16432 | -0.10 | 4 | 40 | 10 | 28 | 25 |
| Dunferm]ine | KY11.5 | 10845 | -5.79 | 1 | 11 | 3 | 12 | 6 |
| Dunfermline | KY12.0 | 8127 | -2.01 | 3 | 39 | 8 | 20 | 16 |
| Dunfermline | KY12.7 | 3815 | -5.26 | 1 | 20 | 5 | 7 | 9 |
| Dunfermline | KY12.8 | 9732 | -2.06 | 3 | 28 | 9 | 21 | 20 |
| Dunfermline | KY12.9 | 10437 | -1.89 | 3 | 33 | 7 | 24 | 17 |
| Dunfermline | KY13.7P | 5 | n/a | - | 0 | 0 | 0 | 0 |
| Dunfermline | KY2.5P | 25 | n/a | - | 0 | 13 | 20 | 0 |
| Dunfermline | KY3.0P | 1630 | -5.19 | 1 | 20 | 6 | 10 | 5 |
| Dunfermline | KY4.0P | 5684 | 0.48 | 4 | 46 | 11 | 28 | 27 |
| Dunfermline | KY4.8 | 5677 | -0.64 | 4 | 46 | 9 | 25 | 20 |
| Dunfermline | KY4.9 | 8485 | 0.37 | 4 | 46 | 9 | 27 | 28 |
| Dunfermline | KY5.0P | 4 | n/a | - | 0 | 0 | 0 | 0 |
| Dunfermline | KY5.8P | 7116 | 3.16 | 6 | 55 | 18 | 36 | 32 |
| Dunfermline | KY5.9 | 7325 | 0.44 | 4 | 49 | 9 | 28 | 27 |
| Kirkcaldy | KY1.1 | 5294 | -1.21 | 3 | 47 | 14 | 14 | 16 |
| Kirkcaldy | KY1.2 | 6531 | 0.77 | 4 | 51 | 16 | 23 | 24 |
| Kirkcaldy | KY1.3 | 5570 | 1.68 | 5 | 50 | 16 | 23 | 34 |
| Kirkcaldy | KY1.4 | 4585 | -0.77 | 4 | 43 | 10 | 24 | 21 |
| Kirkcaldy | KY2.5P | 10274 | -1.40 | 3 | 39 | 12 | 16 | 20 |
| Kirkcaldy | KY2.6 | 19887 | -1.29 | 3 | 32 | 9 | 27 | 19 |
| Kirkcaldy | KY3.0P | 2935 | 0.77 | 4 | 46 | 16 | 29 | 21 |
| Kirkcaldy | KY3.9 | 5806 | -2.57 | 3 | 32 | 9 | 14 | 18 |
| Kirkcaldy | KY5.0P | 7704 | 0.71 | 4 | 48 | 12 | 26 | 28 |
| Kirkcaldy | KY5.8P | 7 | n/a | - | 0 | 0 | 0 | 0 |
| Kirkcaldy | KY6.1 | 5631 | -0.62 | 4 | 31 | 11 | 21 | 30 |
| Kirkcal~y | KY6.2 | 9737 | -1.94 | 3 | 27 | 11 | 23 | 16 |
| Kirkcaldy | KY6.3P | 3770 | -2.14 | 3 | 31 | 12 | 21 | 13 |
| Kirkcaldy | KY7.4 | 9130 | -0.01 | 4 | 36 | 14 | 24 | 26 |
| Kirkcaldy | KY7.5 | 4634 | -0.43 | 4 | 36 | 11 | 25 | 25 |
| Kirkcaldy | KY7.6P | 7486 | -2.00 | 3 | 26 | 10 | 14 | 25 |
| Kirkcaldy | KY8.1 | 5566 | 1.06 | 5 | 51 | 15 | 25 | 27 |
| Kirkcaldy | KY8.2 | 6638 | 2.50 | 5 | 50 | 19 | 32 | 30 |
| Kirkcaldy | KY8.3 | 6091 | 1.75 | 5 | 53 | 18 | 22 | 31 |
| Kirkcaldy | KY8.4 | 5864 | -0.69 | 4 | 43 | 13 | 20 | 21 |
| Kirkcaldy | KY8.5P | 9573 | 0.63 | 4 | 38 | 13 | 25 | 32 |
| North East Fife | DD6.8 | 4522 | -5.28 | 1 | 16 | 6 | 8 | 9 |
| North East Fife | DD6.9 | 3118 | -0.91 | 4 | 40 | 11 | 20 | 22 |
| North East Fife | KY10.2 | 3189 | -0.53 | 4 | 28 | 7 | 19 | 40 |
| North East Fife | KY10.3 | 4370 | -1.11 | 3 | 30 | 9 | 17 | 32 |
| North East Fife | KY13.7P | 34 | 1.14 | 5 | 0 | 0 | 0 | 0 |
| North East Fife | KY14.6P | 2542 | -0.24 | 4 | 30 | 11 | 21 | 34 |
| North East Fife | KY14.7P | 3389 | -1.89 | 3 | 26 | 8 | 24 | 21 |
| North East Fife | KY15.4 | 5143 | -1.93 | 3 | 29 | 7 | 20 | 24 |
| North East Fife | KY15.5 | 6842 | -4.15 | 2 | 20 | 6 | 15 | 11 |
| North East Fife | KY16.0 | 4362 | -4.07 | 2 | 26 | 3 | 14 | 14 |
| North East Fife | KY16.8 | 9170 | -2.06 | 3 | 29 | 7 | 19 | 23 |

| L. A. District | Sector | Pop | Dep | DEPCAT | NOCAR* | MUNP* | OVERC* | SC45* |
|---|---|---|---|---|---|---|---|---|
| North East Fife | KY16.9 | 3385 | -3.98 | 2 | 27 | 6 | 7 | 17 |
| North East Fife | KY6.3P | 24 | n/a | - | 0 | 0 | 0 | 0 |
| North East Fife | KY7.6P | 23 | n/a | - | 4 | 0 | 0 | 0 |
| North East Fife | KY7.7 | 5927 | -2.79 | 3 | 19 | 7 | 19 | 21 |
| North East Fife | KY8.5P | 436 | -4.51 | 2 | 9 | 14 | 13 | 3 |
| North East Fife | KY8.6 | 2031 | -3.82 | 2 | 23 | 7 | 8 | 18 |
| North East Fife | KY9.1 | 1756 | -2.33 | 3 | 22 | 9 | 11 | 29 |

Deprivation Scores. Health Board: Forth Valley

| L. A. District | Sector | Pop | Dep | DEPCAT | NOCAR* | MUNP* | OVERC* | SC45* |
|---|---|---|---|---|---|---|---|---|
| Clackmannan | FK10.1 | 5312 | 2.57 | 5 | 54 | 20 | 34 | 25 |
| Clackmannan | FK10.2 | 13047 | -0.58 | 4 | 38 | 10 | 26 | 22 |
| Clackmannan | FK10.3P | 8933 | -0.82 | 4 | 35 | 10 | 23 | 25 |
| Clackmannan | FK10.4P | 3399 | -1.30 | 3 | 33 | 11 | 25 | 18 |
| Clackmannan | FK11.7 | 2207 | -3.14 | 2 | 20 | 5 | 16 | 22 |
| Clackmannan | FK12.5 | 4872 | -1.38 | 3 | 32 | 8 | 23 | 23 |
| Clackmannan | FK13.6 | 6185 | -1.83 | 3 | 32 | 10 | 19 | 19 |
| Clackmannan | FK14.7P | 3213 | -5.74 | 1 | 11 | 7 | 7 | 5 |
| Clackmannan | FK7.7P | 0 | n/a | - | 0 | 0 | 0 | 0 |
| Clackmannan | FK9.5P | 7 | n/a | - | 0 | 0 | 0 | 0 |
| Clackmannan | KY13.7P | 181 | -4.44 | 2 | 7 | 7 | 18 | 12 |
| Falkirk | EH49.6P | 1040 | 3.34 | 6 | 40 | 21 | 28 | 45 |
| Falkirk | EH49.7P | 452 | -1.25 | 3 | 17 | 9 | 23 | 32 |
| Falkirk | EH51.0 | 7327 | -0.77 | 4 | 36 | 11 | 20 | 25 |
| Falkirk | EH51.9 | 7489 | -0.07 | 4 | 41 | 12 | 22 | 27 |
| Falkirk | FK1.1 | 3361 | -1.58 | 3 | 51 | 9 | 8 | 22 |
| Falkirk | FK1.2P | 7658 | -0.48 | 4 | 33 | 13 | 21 | 26 |
| Falkirk | FK1.3P | 2140 | 0.33 | 4 | 37 | 16 | 27 | 24 |
| Falkirk | FK1.4 | 8770 | 0.93 | 4 | 50 | 15 | 24 | 26 |
| Falkirk | FK1.5 | 7083 | -3.90 | 2 | 22 | 6 | 11 | 16 |
| Falkirk | FK2.0 | 11245 | -3.19 | 2 | 21 | 8 | 16 | 17 |
| Falkirk | FK2.7 | 7827 | 1.84 | 5 | 54 | 19 | 21 | 31 |
| Falkirk | FK2.8P | 5556 | 0.05 | 4 | 40 | 14 | 24 | 24 |
| Falkirk | FK2.9 | 11576 | 1.49 | 5 | 45 | 14 | 27 | 33 |
| Falkirk | FK3.0 | 7582 | 1.28 | 5 | 35 | 12 | 35 | 33 |
| Falkirk | FK3.8 | 8584 | 1.12 | 5 | 43 | 15 | 26 | 31 |
| Falkirk | FK3.9 | 5578 | 0.23 | 4 | 37 | 13 | 23 | 30 |
| Falkirk | FK4.1 | 8544 | -0.22 | 4 | 40 | 13 | 22 | 25 |
| Falkirk | FK4.2P | 2167 | 1.03 | 5 | 51 | 17 | 28 | 20 |
| Falkirk | FK5.3 | 5080 | -1.82 | 3 | 34 | 10 | 17 | 20 |
| Falkirk | FK5.4P | 11236 | -2.95 | 3 | 27 | 8 | 14 | 19 |
| Falkirk | FK6.5P | 7638 | -1.38 | 3 | 31 | 12 | 24 | 18 |
| Falkirk | FK6.6P | 5759 | 1.75 | 5 | 46 | 17 | 25 | 34 |
| Falkirk | FK7.7P | 67 | -2.65 | 3 | 30 | 17 | 21 | 0 |
| Falkirk | G67.3P | 7 | n/a | - | 0 | 0 | 0 | 0 |
| Falkirk | G68.0P | 5 | n/a | - | 0 | 0 | 0 | 0 |
| Stirling | FK15.0P | 3022 | -5.21 | 1 | 16 | 6 | 10 | 8 |
| Stirling | FK15.9P | 4393 | -4.93 | 2 | 16 | 6 | 13 | 8 |
| Stirling | FK16.6 | 1702 | -2.08 | 3 | 24 | 8 | 18 | 25 |
| Stirling | FK17.8 | 2877 | -3.48 | 2 | 18 | 6 | 14 | 20 |
| Stirling | FK18.8 | 172 | 4.45 | 6 | 15 | 12 | 20 | 90 |
| Stirling | EK19.8P | 409 | -4.97 | 2 | 17 | 8 | 17 | 0 |
| Stirliny | FK2.8P | 69 | -8.40 | 1 | 1 | 0 | 0 | 0 |
| Stirling | FK20.8P | 345 | -4.59 | 2 | 24 | 8 | 16 | 0 |
| Stirling | FK21.8P | 724 | -2.55 | 3 | 20 | 7 | 20 | 22 |
| Stirling | FK5.4P | 2 | n/a | - | 0 | 0 | 0 | 0 |
| Stirling | FK6.5P | 87 | -0.92 | 4 | 6 | 13 | 19 | 40 |
| Stirling | FK6.6P | 20 | n/a | - | 0 | 0 | 0 | 0 |
| Stirling | FK7.0 | 7317 | -0.54 | 4 | 42 | 10 | 25 | 21 |
| Stirling | FK7.7P | 8757 | 1.54 | 5 | 43 | 13 | 32 | 33 |
| Stirling | FK7.8 | 4453 | -0.23 | 4 | 40 | 11 | 25 | 24 |
| Stirling | FK7.9 | 7089 | -0.83 | 4 | 35 | 11 | 26 | 21 |
| Stirling | FK8.1 | 8509 | 3.60 | 6 | 62 | 22 | 29 | 33 |
| Stirling | FK8.2 | 3320 | -5.62 | 1 | 15 | 5 | 6 | 9 |
| Stirling | FK8.3 | 5092 | -3.95 | 2 | 14 | 5 | 17 | 16 |
| Stirling | FK9.4 | 5362 | -4.28 | 2 | 19 | 6 | 8 | 16 |
| Stirling | FK9.5P | 5210 | -1.91 | 3 | 32 | 10 | 21 | 18 |
| Stirling | G62.8P | 81 | -7.78 | 1 | 4 | 4 | 0 | 0 |
| Stirling | G63.0P | 3740 | -4.05 | 2 | 15 | 6 | 11 | 19 |
| Stirling | G63.9P | 4148 | -6.61 | 1 | 10 | 3 | 8 | 2 |
| Stirling | G83.7P | 16 | n/a | - | 0 | 0 | 0 | 0 |
| Stirling | G83.8P | 7 | n/a | - | 0 | 0 | 0 | 0 |
| Stirling | G83.9P | 6 | n/a | - | 0 | 0 | 0 | 0 |

Deprivation Scores. Health Board: Grampian

| L. A. District | Sector | Pop | Dep | DEPCAT | NOCAR* | MUNP* | OVERC* | SC45* |
|---|---|---|---|---|---|---|---|---|
| Aberdeen City | AB1.0P | 6313 | -3.99 | 2 | 14 | 6 | 17 | 15 |
| Aberdeen City | AB1.1 | 4681 | 0.12 | 4 | 57 | 7 | 20 | 29 |
| Aberdeen City | AB1.2 | 5851 | -2.88 | 3 | 38 | 9 | 12 | 14 |
| Aberdeen City | AB1.3 | 10882 | 0.83 | 4 | 59 | 8 | 26 | 29 |
| Aberdeen City | AB1.4P | 5175 | -0.04 | 4 | 35 | 8 | 29 | 31 |
| Aberdeen City | AB1.5P | 10048 | -0. 02 | 4 | 40 | 6 | 35 | 25 |
| Aberdeen City | AB1.6 | 12582 | -4.93 | 2 | 32 | 4 | 7 | 8 |
| Aberdeen City | AB1.7 | 12913 | -3.41 | 2 | 29 | 5 | 16 | 15 |
| Aberdeen City | AB1.8P | 4458 | -5.44 | 1 | 16 | 2 | 12 | 9 |
| Aberdeen City | AB1.9 | 5679 | -7.17 | 1 | 7 | 2 | 5 | 2 |
| Aberdeen City | AB2.0P | 7095 | -3.08 | 2 | 16 | 3 | 24 | 21 |
| Aberdeen City | AB2.1 | 9763 | 1.44 | 5 | 64 | 12 | 23 | 29 |
| Aberdeen City | AB2.2 | 14445 | 0.96 | 4 | 57 | 11 | 26 | 26 |
| Aberdeen City | AB2.3 | 9887 | -0.48 | 4 | 53 | 10 | 16 | 24 |
| Aberdeen City | AB2.4 | 11748 | -4.61 | 2 | 32 | 4 | 8 | 9 |
| Aberdeen City | AB2.5 | 15733 | 0.44 | 4 | 45 | 6 | 31 | 31 |
| Aberdeen City | AB2.6 | 15858 | -0.67 | 4 | 40 | 6 | 32 | 21 |
| Aberdeen City | AB2 .7 | 13677 | 3.46 | 6 | 51 | 12 | 45 | 37 |
| Aberdeen City | AB2.8P | 14103 | -3.46 | 2 | 20 | 3 | 20 | 18 |
| Aberdeen City | AB2.9 | 8661 | -2.20 | 3 | 26 | 4 | 26 | 22 |
| Aberdeen City | AB3.3P | 23 | n/a | - | 0 | 0 | 0 | 0 |
| Aberdeen City | AB3.6P | 22 | n/a | - | 0 | 0 | 0 | 0 |
| Aberdeen City | AB4.0P | 2 | n/a | - | 0 | 0 | 0 | 0 |
| Aberdeen City | AB5.0P | 225 | -0.80 | 4 | 2 | 10 | 16 | 50 |
| Banff & Buchan | AB4.0P | 99 | -6.39 | 1 | 6 | 3 | 15 | 0 |
| Banff & Buchan | AB4.1 | 7728 | 0.12 | 4 | 35 | 10 | 22 | 36 |
| Banff & Buchan | AB4.2P | 4921 | -1.89 | 3 | 24 | 7 | 19 | 28 |
| Banff & Buchan | AB4.3 | 2357 | -1.26 | 3 | 11 | 8 | 15 | 43 |
| Banff & Buchan | AB4.4 | 7734 | -0.80 | 4 | 26 | 8 | 24 | 32 |
| Banff & Buchan | AB4.5 | 15170 | 0.84 | 4 | 37 | 9 | 28 | 37 |
| Banff & Buchan | AB4.6 | 16669 | 0.76 | 4 | 37 | 7 | 23 | 43 |
| Banff & Buchan | AB4.7P | 7173 | -2.13 | 3 | 19 | 6 | 19 | 29 |
| Banff & Buchan | AB4.8P | 6558 | -2.52 | 3 | 16 | 5 | 20 | 27 |
| Banff & Buchan | AB4.9P | 462 | -5.74 | 1 | 12 | 1 | 7 | 14 |
| Banff & Buchan | AB5.0P | 55 | 0.44 | 4 | 11 | 6 | 24 | 57 |
| Banff & Buchan | AB5.2P | 34 | n/a | - | 6 | 0 | 15 | 0 |
| Banff & Buchan | AB5.5P | 1618 | -1.93 | 3 | 18 | 8 | 24 | 25 |
| Banff & Buchan | AB5.6P | 101 | 1.67 | 5 | 2 | 6 | 27 | 71 |
| Banff & Buchan | AB5.7 | 6135 | -3.37 | 2 | 18 | 4 | 21 | 17 |
| Banff & Buchan | AB5.8P | 3268 | -4.04 | 2 | 11 | 4 | 18 | 19 |
| Banff & Buchan | AB5.9P | 30 | -6.36 | 1 | 0 | 0 | 24 | 0 |
| Gordon | AB1.8P | 65 | -6.25 | 1 | 8 | 4 | 14 | 0 |
| Gordon | AB2.0P | 531 | -5.16 | 1 | 7 | 6 | 12 | 12 |
| Gordon | AB2.8P | 81 | -7.63 | 1 | 8 | 0 | 5 | 0 |
| Gordon | AB3.3P | 0 | n/a | - | 0 | 0 | 0 | 0 |
| Gordon | AB3.4P | 27 | -2.60 | 3 | 7 | 0 | 26 | 33 |
| Gordon | AB3.6P | 6616 | -5.93 | 1 | 3 | 3 | 12 | 10 |
| Gordon | AB3.7P | 2266 | -4.29 | 2 | 9 | 2 | 15 | 22 |
| Gordon | AB3.8P | 3200 | -4.08 | 2 | 10 | 3 | 12 | 25 |
| Gordon | AB4.0P | 8299 | -4.00 | 2 | 9 | 3 | 17 | 22 |
| Gordon | AB4.7P | 25 | n/a | - | 0 | 10 | 0 | 0 |
| Gordon | AB4.8P | 3 | n/a | - | 0 | 0 | 0 | 0 |
| Gordon | AB4.9P | 7960 | -4.21 | 2 | 12 | 3 | 21 | 14 |
| Gordon | AB5.0P | 9132 | -4.80 | 2 | 10 | 2 | 15 | 16 |
| Gordon | AB5.3P | 34 | -8.48 | 1 | 0 | 0 | 0 | 0 |
| Gordon | AB5.4P | 2628 | -3.10 | 2 | 14 | 6 | 17 | 24 |
| Gordon | AB5.5P | 4327 | -1.49 | 3 | 34 | 6 | 22 | 25 |
| Gordon | AB5.6P | 3599 | -4.26 | 2 | 14 | 4 | 15 | 17 |
| Gordon | AB5.8P | 233 | -6.03 | 1 | 6 | 5 | 16 | 0 |
| Gordon | AB5.9P | 12766 | -3.37 | 2 | 19 | 3 | 22 | 17 |
| Kincardine & Deeside | AB1.0P | 345 | -5.92 | 1 | 4 | 6 | 9 | 7 |
| Kincardine & Deeside | AB1.4P | 3456 | -4.56 | 2 | 13 | 4 | 14 | 15 |
| Kincardine & Deeside | AB1.5P | 598 | -6.31 | 1 | 8 | 2 | 14 | 3 |
| Kincardine & Deeside | AB3.1P | 4821 | -2.42 | 3 | 17 | 6 | 17 | 30 |
| Kincardine & Deeside | AB3.2 | 11889 | -4.34 | 2 | 17 | 4 | 15 | 14 |
| Kincardine & Deeside | AB3.3P | 6693 | -4.73 | 2 | 12 | 3 | 15 | 15 |
| Kincardine & Deeside | AB3.4P | 3698 | -4.50 | 2 | 10 | 3 | 15 | 18 |
| Kincardine & Deeside | AB3.5 | 4795 | -2.82 | 3 | 20 | 5 | 14 | 29 |
| Kincardine & Deeside | AB3.7P | 8 | n/a | - | 0 | 0 | 0 | 0 |
| Kincardine & Deeside | AB3.8P | 66 | 2.09 | 5 | 3 | 0 | 9 | 0 |
| Kincardine & Deeside | DDl0.0P | 3925 | -1.15 | 3 | 29 | 6 | 18 | 36 |
| Kincardine & Deeside | DD9.7P | 715 | -7.37 | 1 | 7 | 1 | 7 | 0 |
| Moray | AB3.9P | 3114 | -3.06 | 2 | 18 | 5 | 16 | 24 |
| Moray | AB4.2P | 7 | n/a | - | 0 | 0 | 0 | 0 |
| Moray | AB5.1 | 7807 | 0.36 | 4 | 38 | 12 | 24 | 31 |

# DEPRIVATION AND HEALTH IN SCOTLAND

| L. A. District | Sector | Pop | Dep | DEPCAT | NOCAR* | MUNP* | OVERC* | SC45* |
|---|---|---|---|---|---|---|---|---|
| Moray | AB5.2P | 5810 | -0.57 | 4 | 28 | 10 | 14 | 40 |
| Moray | AB5.3P | 6525 | -0.62 | 4 | 31 | 8 | 20 | 34 |
| Moray | AB5.4P | 2262 | -2.08 | 3 | 24 | 6 | 21 | 25 |
| Moray | AB5.5P | 562 | -1.57 | 3 | 10 | 4 | 15 | 47 |
| Moray | IV30.1 | 4587 | -4.60 | 2 | 29 | 5 | 8 | 9 |
| Moray | IV30.2 | 10559 | -1.62 | 3 | 32 | 9 | 21 | 21 |
| Moray | IV30.3 | 11616 | -1.88 | 3 | 25 | 8 | 26 | 20 |
| Moray | IV31.6 | 6716 | -1.64 | 3 | 39 | 6 | 17 | 25 |
| Moray | IV32.7 | 4082 | -3.04 | 2 | 21 | 7 | 18 | 18 |
| Moray | IV33.7 | 1512 | -0.09 | 4 | 33 | 12 | 25 | 30 |
| Moray | IV34.7 | 373 | -2.29 | 3 | 17 | 4 | 12 | 38 |
| Moray | IV35.7 | 313 | -1.96 | 3 | 9 | 6 | 18 | 37 |
| Moray | IV36.0P | 14295 | -2.97 | 3 | 25 | 7 | 16 | 18 |
| Moray | PH26.3P | 11 | n/a | - | 0 | 0 | 0 | 0 |

Deprivation Scores. Health Board: Greater Glasgow

| L. A. District | Sector | Pop | Dep | DEPCAT | NOCAR* | MUNP* | OVERC* | SC45* |
|---|---|---|---|---|---|---|---|---|
| Bearsden & Milngavie | G61.1P | 6554 | -5.18 | 1 | 16 | 5 | 14 | 6 |
| Bearsden & Milngavie | G61.2 | 6417 | -6.63 | 1 | 8 | 4 | 5 | 5 |
| Bearsden & Milngavie | G61.3 | 6678 | -6.96 | 1 | 7 | 4 | 5 | 5 |
| Bearsden & Milngavie | G61.4 | 7502 | -5.91 | 1 | 9 | 4 | 12 | 5 |
| Bearsden & Milngavie | G62.6P | 3351 | -5.67 | 1 | 19 | 5 | 7 | 5 |
| Bearsden & Milngavie | G62.7 | 6207 | -2.61 | 3 | 29 | 8 | 21 | 13 |
| Bearsden & Milngavie | G62.8P | 2626 | -5.43 | 1 | 17 | 3 | 8 | 9 |
| Bearsden & Milngavie | G63.9P | 2 | n/a | - | 0 | 0 | 0 | 0 |
| Bearsden & Milngavie | G81.5P | 14 | n/a | - | 0 | 0 | 0 | 0 |
| Clydebank | G13.4P | 4 | n/a | - | 0 | 0 | 0 | 0 |
| Clydebank | G15.8P | 0 | n/a | - | 0 | 0 | 0 | 0 |
| Clydebank | G60.5P | 2997 | -1.37 | 3 | 43 | 12 | 21 | 14 |
| Clydebank | G81.1P | 7049 | 3.68 | 6 | 64 | 19 | 40 | 28 |
| Clydebank | G81.2 | 9150 | 3.65 | 6 | 58 | 20 | 37 | 30 |
| Clydebank | G81.3 | 9301 | 1.79 | 5 | 55 | 17 | 32 | 22 |
| Clydebank | G81.4 | 7483 | 2.66 | 5 | 60 | 18 | 26 | 31 |
| Clydebank | G81.5 | 8501 | 3.97 | 6 | 58 | 21 | 43 | 27 |
| Clydebank | G81.6 | 7514 | -1.15 | 3 | 33 | 13 | 28 | 14 |
| Eastwood | G44.3P | 4003 | -6.75 | 1 | 14 | 3 | 4 | 2 |
| Eastwood | G46.6 | 8307 | -6.79 | 1 | 11 | 3 | 5 | 2 |
| Eastwood | G46.7P | 6374 | -4.60 | 2 | 20 | 6 | 12 | 10 |
| Eastwood | G46.8P | 539 | 0.63 | 4 | 51 | 11 | 22 | 31 |
| Eastwood | G76.0 | 4739 | -5.11 | 1 | 12 | 5 | 16 | 7 |
| Eastwood | G76.7 | 8521 | -6.36 | 1 | 11 | 4 | 6 | 4 |
| Eastwood | G76.8P | 5678 | -2.81 | 3 | 28 | 6 | 22 | 15 |
| Eastwood | G77.5 | 8189 | -7.31 | 1 | 4 | 3 | 2 | 3 |
| Eastwood | G77.6P | 7039 | -4.99 | 2 | 14 | 6 | 12 | 9 |
| Eastwood | G78.2P | 6 | n/a | - | 0 | 0 | 0 | 0 |
| Eastwood | G78.3P | 0 | n/a | - | 0 | 0 | 0 | 0 |
| Glasgow City | G1.1 | 212 | 1.73 | 5 | 55 | 14 | 50 | 10 |
| Glasgow City | G1.2 | 347 | 4.17 | 6 | 89 | 13 | 11 | 53 |
| Glasgow City | G1.3 | 42 | n/a | - | 0 | 0 | 0 | 0 |
| Glasgow City | G1.4 | 77 | -1.23 | 3 | 46 | 26 | 13 | 0 |
| Glasgow City | G1.5 | 934 | 11.66 | 7 | 93 | 45 | 24 | 71 |
| Glasgow City | G11.5 | 6507 | 1.84 | 5 | 63 | 14 | 28 | 27 |
| Glasgow City | G11.6 | 2516 | 4.62 | 6 | 77 | 19 | 40 | 28 |
| Glasgow City | G11.7 | 9268 | -1.38 | 3 | 52 | 9 | 19 | 14 |
| Glasgow City | G12.0 | 8127 | -5.20 | 1 | 26 | 5 | 7 | 6 |
| Glasgow City | G12.8 | 5801 | 0.11 | 4 | 55 | 17 | 22 | 13 |
| Glasgow City | G12.9 | 7811 | -4.09 | 2 | 41 | 7 | 9 | 4 |
| Glasgow City | G13.1 | 6933 | -0.53 | 4 | 45 | 13 | 22 | 18 |
| Glasgow City | G13.2 | 8696 | 3.50 | 6 | 63 | 18 | 30 | 36 |
| Glasgow City | G13.3 | 11060 | 0.55 | 4 | 59 | 14 | 24 | 20 |
| Glasgow City | G13.4P | 7037 | 4.56 | 6 | 62 | 20 | 42 | 34 |
| Glasgow City | G14.0 | 8796 | 5.83 | 6 | 75 | 21 | 41 | 38 |
| Glasgow City | G14.9 | 9988 | -0.81 | 4 | 48 | 12 | 21 | 16 |
| Glasgow City | G15.6 | 7103 | 0.94 | 4 | 52 | 13 | 26 | 26 |
| Glasgow City | G15.7 | 14644 | 8.46 | 7 | 78 | 30 | 53 | 41 |
| Glasgow City | G15.8 | 10016 | 9.67 | 7 | 85 | 39 | 54 | 37 |
| Glasgow City | G2.1 | 26 | n/a | - | 0 | 0 | 0 | 0 |
| Glasgow City | G2.2 | 32 | 8.46 | 7 | 50 | 8 | 41 | 0 |
| Glasgow City | G2.3 | 187 | -1.29 | 3 | 63 | 8 | 18 | 11 |
| Glasgow City | G2.4 | 200 | 5.83 | 6 | 64 | 15 | 32 | 63 |
| Glasgow City | G2.5 | 36 | n/a | - | 61 | 17 | 29 | 0 |
| Glaggow C~ty | G2.6 | 53 | 12.82 | 7 | 63 | 25 | 55 | 0 |
| Glasgow City | G2.7 | 451 | 5.52 | 6 | 98 | 27 | 5 | 47 |

| | | | | | | | | |
|---|---|---|---|---|---|---|---|---|
| Glasgow City | G2.8 | 39 | 11.39 | 7 | 96 | 25 | 19 | 0 |
| Glasgow City | G20.0 | 7339 | 5.56 | 6 | 72 | 22 | 39 | 39 |
| Glasgow City | G20.6 | 4999 | 0.94 | 4 | 57 | 17 | 23 | 21 |
| Glasgow City | G20.7 | 3268 | 7.36 | 7 | 83 | 26 | 40 | 44 |
| Glasgow City | G20.8 | 8526 | 4.70 | 6 | 75 | 21 | 32 | 35 |
| Glasgow City | G20.9 | 5762 | 9.29 | 7 | 86 | 34 | 49 | 44 |
| Glasgow City | G21.1 | 9138 | 5.83 | 6 | 81 | 22 | 41 | 35 |
| Glasgow City | G21.2 | 9321 | 9.15 | 7 | 88 | 31 | 45 | 48 |
| Glasgow City | G21.3 | 15056 | 5.55 | 6 | 74 | 22 | 44 | 33 |
| Glasgow City | G21.4 | 8987 | 6.84 | 7 | 80 | 24 | 45 | 39 |
| Glasgow City | G22.5 | 11172 | 10.88 | 7 | 89 | 38 | 53 | 49 |
| Glasgow City | G22.6 | 8852 | 5.54 | 6 | 77 | 23 | 38 | 35 |
| Glasgow City | G22.7 | 11337 | 6.38 | 7 | 73 | 23 | 50 | 35 |
| Glasgow City | G23.5P | 6940 | 3.14 | 6 | 66 | 18 | 33 | 28 |
| Glasgow City | G3.6 | 4154 | 4.89 | 6 | 65 | 23 | 49 | 25 |
| Glasgow City | G3.7 | 2724 | 4.10 | 6 | 70 | 20 | 41 | 26 |
| Glasgow City | G3.8 | 4556 | 4.57 | 6 | 75 | 23 | 34 | 30 |
| Glasgow City | G31.1 | 4384 | 5.82 | 6 | 78 | 23 | 41 | 35 |
| Glasgow City | G31.2 | 7889 | 2.14 | 5 | 63 | 14 | 35 | 23 |
| Glasgow City | G31.3 | 8323 | 5.62 | 6 | 81 | 23 | 40 | 32 |
| Glasgow City | G31.4 | 6699 | 9.48 | 7 | 87 | 35 | 46 | 45 |
| Glasgow City | G31.5 | 2732 | 8.51 | 7 | 80 | 32 | 46 | 44 |
| Glasgow City | G32.0 | 6086 | -0.14 | 4 | 46 | 14 | 30 | 14 |
| Glasgow City | G32.6 | 9113 | 5.40 | 6 | 75 | 24 | 37 | 34 |
| Glasgow City | G32.7 | 7225 | 6.57 | 7 | 75 | 24 | 41 | 43 |
| Glasgow City | G32.8 | 8030 | 4.48 | 6 | 64 | 22 | 41 | 30 |
| Glasgow City | G32.9 | 6784 | -1.96 | 3 | 43 | 9 | 20 | 12 |
| Glasgow City | G33.1 | 6013 | 10.63 | 7 | 83 | 36 | 59 | 47 |
| Glasgow City | G33.2 | 6504 | 2.21 | 5 | 58 | 13 | 24 | 38 |
| Glasgow City | G33.3 | 14641 | 7.82 | 7 | 77 | 29 | 51 | 38 |
| Glasgow City | G33.4 | 15033 | 9.00 | 7 | 82 | 32 | 55 | 41 |
| Glasgow City | G33.5 | 8617 | 7.83 | 7 | 76 | 30 | 57 | 32 |
| Glasgow City | G33.6P | 318 | -4.67 | 2 | 29 | 1 | 11 | 12 |
| Glasgow City | G34.0 | 9387 | 10.16 | 7 | 84 | 35 | 59 | 43 |
| Glasgow City | G34.9 | 11831 | 10.18 | 7 | 84 | 36 | 60 | 41 |
| Glasgow City | G4.0 | 6012 | 6.92 | 7 | 85 | 34 | 21 | 44 |
| Glasgow City | G4.9 | 4301 | 3.09 | 6 | 65 | 16 | 39 | 25 |
| Glasgow City | G40.1 | 1397 | 8.26 | 7 | 77 | 29 | 44 | 49 |
| Glasgow City | G40.2 | 1659 | 11.97 | 7 | 86 | 53 | 35 | 58 |
| Glasgow City | G40.3 | 4797 | 10.23 | 7 | 88 | 33 | 48 | 54 |
| Glasgow City | G40.4 | 3614 | 9.57 | 7 | 83 | 32 | 44 | 55 |
| Glasgow City | G41.1 | 1437 | 6.57 | 7 | 62 | 22 | 58 | 36 |
| Glasgow City | G41.2 | 8411 | 0.03 | 4 | 48 | 13 | 35 | 11 |
| Glasgow City | G41.3 | 9955 | -2.22 | 3 | 51 | 8 | 15 | 11 |
| Glasgow City | G41.4 | 4341 | -6.43 | 1 | 12 | 5 | 5 | 2 |
| Glasgow City | G41.5 | 5730 | -3.51 | 2 | 34 | 7 | 13 | 10 |
| Glasgow City | G42.0 | 8119 | 4.57 | 6 | 71 | 19 | 39 | 32 |
| Glasgow City | G42.7 | 4694 | 5.38 | 6 | 79 | 21 | 36 | 38 |
| Glasgow City | G42.8 | 12257 | 2.45 | 5 | 61 | 15 | 37 | 24 |
| Glasgow City | G42.9 | 9308 | -0.75 | 4 | 55 | 11 | 21 | 14 |
| Glasgow City | G43.1 | 7960 | 2.05 | 5 | 64 | 15 | 23 | 31 |
| Glasgow City | G43.2 | 10992 | -3.81 | 2 | 30 | 7 | 13 | 9 |
| Glasgow City | G44.3P | 3896 | -4.57 | 2 | 28 | 6 | 14 | 4 |
| Glasgow City | G44.4 | 9969 | -2.46 | 3 | 44 | 6 | 17 | 14 |
| Glasgow City | G44.5 | 10980 | -3.80 | 2 | 32 | 5 | 17 | 8 |
| Glasgow City | G45.0 | 11926 | 10.17 | 7 | 85 | 34 | 56 | 47 |
| Glasgow City | G45.9 | 16932 | 7.89 | 7 | 80 | 27 | 49 | 41 |
| Glasgow City | G46.7P | 91 | -0.54 | 4 | 44 | 14 | 26 | 14 |
| Glasgow City | G46.8P | 11782 | 5.55 | 6 | 69 | 23 | 46 | 32 |
| Glasgow City | G5.0 | 9179 | 7.91 | 7 | 86 | 27 | 40 | 47 |
| Glasgow City | G5.8 | 473 | 7.02 | 7 | 68 | 48 | 50 | 8 |
| Glasgow City | G5.9 | 3382 | 7.25 | 7 | 87 | 24 | 39 | 45 |
| Glasgow City | G51.1 | 6173 | 5.90 | 6 | 70 | 23 | 43 | 38 |
| Glasaow City | G51.2 | 9742 | 8.79 | 7 | 81 | 30 | 44 | 5 |
| Glasgow City | G51.3 | 4880 | 9.53 | 7 | 87 | 34 | 42 | 51 |
| Glasgow City | G51.4 | 9268 | 5.23 | 6 | 73 | 22 | 36 | 37 |
| Glasgow City | G52.1 | 9103 | 1.61 | 5 | 59 | 14 | 24 | 30 |
| Glasgow City | G52.2 | 11738 | 1.44 | 5 | 57 | 15 | 25 | 27 |
| Glasgow City | G52.3P | 8744 | -1.42 | 3 | 46 | 9 | 17 | 20 |
| Glasgow City | G52.4P | 5419 | 5.42 | 6 | 66 | 22 | 44 | 36 |
| Glasgow City | G53.5 | 16557 | 6.94 | 7 | 70 | 26 | 49 | 40 |
| Glasgow City | G53.6 | 12663 | 8.90 | 7 | 77 | 31 | 59 | 39 |
| Glasgow City | G53.7P | 11981 | 5.45 | 6 | 71 | 23 | 41 | 35 |
| Glasgow City | G61.1P | 173 | -5.63 | 1 | 23 | 8 | 6 | 0 |
| Glasgow City | G62.6P | 12 | n/a | - | 0 | 0 | 0 | 0 |
| Glasgow City | G64.1P | 133 | 0.56 | 4 | 56 | 11 | 50 | 0 |
| Glasgow City | G64.2P | 105 | -4.00 | 2 | 41 | 10 | 10 | 0 |
| Glasgow City | G69.6P | 6791 | -2.64 | 3 | 30 | 8 | 24 | 10 |
| Glasgow City | G69.7P | 7898 | 1.83 | 5 | 46 | 16 | 43 | 20 |

# DEPRIVATION AND HEALTH IN SCOTLAND

| L. A. District | Sector | Pop | Dep | DEPCAT | NOCAR* | MUNP* | OVERC* | SC45* |
|---|---|---|---|---|---|---|---|---|
| Glasgow City | G69.8P | 803 | 2.21 | 5 | 42 | 6 | 42 | 40 |
| Glasgow City | G71.7P | 413 | 3.52 | 6 | 53 | 9 | 43 | 43 |
| Glasgow City | G72.7 | 8626 | 3.68 | 6 | 59 | 21 | 37 | 28 |
| Glasgow City | G72.8P | 13162 | 0.55 | 4 | 43 | 14 | 29 | 23 |
| Glasgow City | G72.9P | 4 | n/a | - | 0 | 0 | 0 | 0 |
| Glasgow City | G73.1 | 4140 | 5.87 | 6 | 76 | 25 | 41 | 34 |
| Glasgow City | G73.2 | 7868 | -1.27 | 3 | 49 | 10 | 19 | 15 |
| Glasgow City | G73.3 | 8458 | -2.45 | 3 | 37 | 10 | 17 | 13 |
| Glasgow City | G73.4P | 10022 | 1.34 | 5 | 50 | 14 | 33 | 23 |
| Glasgow City | G73.5P | 6931 | 1.75 | 5 | 50 | 17 | 33 | 25 |
| Glasgow City | G76.9P | 1163 | -5.80 | 1 | 16 | 4 | 12 | 2 |
| Glasgow City | G77.6P | 3 | n/a | - | 0 | 0 | 0 | 0 |
| Glasgow City | G78.1P | 37 | -3.73 | 2 | 19 | 0 | 42 | 0 |
| Glasgow City | G78.2P | 19 | n/a | - | 0 | 0 | 0 | 0 |
| Glasgow City | G81.1P | 114 | -4.06 | 2 | 25 | 6 | 25 | 0 |
| Glasgow City | PA1.3P | 8 | n/a | - | 0 | 0 | 0 | 0 |
| Glasgow City | PA4.8P | 5 | n/a | - | 0 | 0 | 0 | 0 |
| Strathkelvin | G23.5P | 6 | n/a | - | 0 | 0 | 0 | 0 |
| Strathkelvin | G33.6P | 4363 | -2.02 | 3 | 31 | 9 | 25 | 14 |
| Strathkelvin | G62.6P | 262 | -6.68 | 1 | 7 | 4 | 10 | 0 |
| Strathkelvin | G62.8P | 39 | -1.27 | 3 | 5 | 24 | 42 | 0 |
| Strathkelvin | G63.0P | 4 | n/a | - | 0 | 0 | 0 | 0 |
| Strathkelvin | G64.1P | 11776 | -2.72 | 3 | 26 | 7 | 23 | 14 |
| Strathkelvin | G64.2P | 5277 | -4.37 | 2 | 18 | 7 | 20 | 4 |
| Strathkelvin | G64.3 | 6242 | -5.72 | 1 | 11 | 5 | 12 | 5 |
| Strathkelvin | G64.4 | 2568 | -5.09 | 1 | 15 | 6 | 12 | 8 |
| Strathkelvin | G65.0P | 8 | n/a | - | 0 | 0 | 0 | 0 |
| Strathkelvin | G65.7 | 5087 | 0.07 | 4 | 43 | 11 | 28 | 23 |
| Strathkelvin | G65.8 | 3652 | -4.41 | 2 | 19 | 7 | 17 | 7 |
| Strathkelvin | G65.9P | 1738 | 3.48 | 6 | 61 | 16 | 44 | 27 |
| Strathkelvin | G66.1 | 3324 | -4.84 | 2 | 26 | 6 | 12 | 3 |
| Strathkelvin | G66.2 | 9989 | 1.41 | 5 | 49 | 14 | 36 | 23 |
| Strathkelvin | G66.3 | 9111 | -3.45 | 2 | 23 | 6 | 19 | 14 |
| Strathkelvin | G66.4 | 6696 | -3.88 | 2 | 21 | 7 | 19 | 8 |
| Strathkelvin | G66.5 | 4283 | -5.68 | 1 | 12 | 4 | 10 | 8 |
| Strathkelvin | G67.4P | 120 | -2.92 | 3 | 13 | 15 | 32 | 0 |
| Strathkelvin | G68.9P | 15 | n/a | - | 0 | 0 | 0 | 0 |
| Strathkelvin | G69.0 | 6776 | 1.07 | 5 | 39 | 13 | 35 | 26 |
| Strathkelvin | G69.8P | 1682 | 2.06 | 5 | 47 | 14 | 31 | 35 |
| Strathkelvin | G69.9 | 3626 | -0.71 | 4 | 32 | 12 | 27 | 21 |

Deprivation Scores. Health Board: Highland

| L. A. District | Sector | Pop | Dep | DEPCAT | NOCAR* | MUNP* | OVERC* | SC45* |
|---|---|---|---|---|---|---|---|---|
| Badenoch & Strathspey | AB3.9P | 1 | n/a | - | 0 | 0 | 0 | 0 |
| Badenoch & Strathspey | PH19.1 | 105 | -4.11 | 2 | 31 | 5 | 23 | 0 |
| Badenoch & Strathspey | PH20.1 | 1228 | -3.24 | 2 | 27 | 6 | 15 | 17 |
| Badenoch & Strathspey | PH21.1 | 1680 | -2.30 | 3 | 22 | 8 | 15 | 27 |
| Badenoch & Strathspey | PH22.1 | 1994 | -0.90 | 4 | 30 | 9 | 25 | 26 |
| Badenoch & Strathspey | PH23.3 | 443 | -0.54 | 4 | 20 | 8 | 22 | 40 |
| Badenoch & Strathspey | PH24.3 | 444 | -1.65 | 3 | 17 | 8 | 13 | 38 |
| Badenoch & Strathspey | PH25.3 | 556 | -2.37 | 3 | 18 | 13 | 13 | 23 |
| Badenoch & Strathspey | PH26.3P | 2908 | -3.48 | 2 | 23 | 6 | 9 | 21 |
| Badenoch & Strathspey | PH31.4P | 4 | n/a | - | 0 | 0 | 0 | 0 |
| Caithness | KW1.4 | 5502 | 0.33 | 4 | 31 | 10 | 27 | 36 |
| Caithness | KW1.5 | 5802 | -0.73 | 4 | 35 | 10 | 25 | 23 |
| Caithness | KW12.6 | 1428 | -2.71 | 3 | 16 | 7 | 19 | 24 |
| Caithness | KW14.7P | 6796 | -3.16 | 2 | 26 | 6 | 16 | 18 |
| Caithness | KW14.8 | 5671 | -1.07 | 3 | 34 | 7 | 27 | 23 |
| Caithness | KW2.6 | 59 | 6.19 | 7 | 31 | 13 | 19 | 0 |
| Caithness | KW3.6 | 877 | -0.72 | 4 | 34 | 20 | 20 | 15 |
| Caithness | KW5.6 | 293 | 2.32 | 5 | 22 | 16 | 22 | 57 |
| Caithness | KW6.6 | 386 | 1.89 | 5 | 26 | 9 | 21 | 61 |
| Caithness | KW7.6 | 130 | -5.03 | 1 | 12 | 13 | 12 | 0 |
| Inverness | IV1.1P | 614 | -1.51 | 3 | 55 | 9 | 13 | 16 |
| Inverness | IV1.2P | 9412 | -2.86 | 3 | 20 | 8 | 21 | 16 |
| Inverness | IV13.7 | 434 | -2.32 | 3 | 14 | 3 | 17 | 37 |
| Inverness | IV2.3 | 9906 | -3.78 | 2 | 25 | 5 | 14 | 14 |
| Inverness | IV2.4 | 10884 | -2.85 | 3 | 27 | 6 | 20 | 16 |
| Inverness | IV3.5 | 7722 | -0.13 | 4 | 47 | 10 | 21 | 27 |
| Inverness | IV3.6P | 11223 | -0.36 | 4 | 40 | 12 | 25 | 22 |
| Inverness | IV4.7P | 2845 | -2.22 | 3 | 23 | 8 | 20 | 23 |
| Inverness | IV5.7 | 607 | -4.20 | 2 | 16 | 6 | 16 | 12 |
| Inverness | PH32.4 | 608 | -2.45 | 3 | 26 | 8 | 17 | 21 |

| Region | Code | | | | | | | |
|---|---|---|---|---|---|---|---|---|
| Inverness | PH35.4P | 30 | n/a | - | 4 | 0 | 0 | 0 |
| Lochaber | IV40.8P | 0 | n/a | - | 0 | 0 | 0 | 0 |
| Lochaber | PA34.5P | 336 | -0.93 | 4 | 34 | 15 | 16 | 23 |
| Lochaber | PA38.4P | 193 | -4.30 | 2 | 18 | 12 | 18 | 0 |
| Lochaber | PA39.4 | 912 | -0.45 | 4 | 32 | 12 | 22 | 29 |
| Lochaber | PA40.4 | 1047 | -1.28 | 3 | 42 | 9 | 23 | 18 |
| Lochaber | PH30.4 | 17 | n/a | - | 0 | 0 | 0 | 0 |
| Lochaber | PH31.4P | 422 | -0.98 | 4 | 24 | 11 | 22 | 29 |
| Lochaber | PH33.6 | 6428 | -1.06 | 3 | 35 | 11 | 25 | 19 |
| Lochaber | PH33.7 | 5716 | 1.00 | 5 | 33 | 13 | 31 | 32 |
| Lochaber | PH34.4 | 818 | -3.05 | 2 | 18 | 7 | 18 | 20 |
| Lochaber | PH35.4P | 286 | 0.49 | 4 | 17 | 10 | 21 | 50 |
| Lochaber | PH36.4 | 885 | -3.33 | 2 | 23 | 9 | 16 | 13 |
| Lochaber | PH37.4 | 88 | 3.91 | 6 | 16 | 10 | 6 | 0 |
| Lochaber | PH38.4 | 143 | -3.33 | 2 | 19 | 19 | 18 | 0 |
| Lochaber | PH39.4 | 331 | 2.24 | 5 | 38 | 18 | 20 | 46 |
| Lochaber | PH40.4 | 276 | 0.23 | 4 | 21 | 10 | 29 | 38 |
| Lochaber | PH41.4P | 1007 | 0.45 | 4 | 37 | 10 | 35 | 26 |
| Lochaber | PH42.4 | 84 | 1.31 | 5 | 49 | 15 | 9 | 45 |
| Lochaber | PH43.4 | 17 | -5.59 | 1 | 53 | 0 | 0 | 0 |
| Lochaber | PH44.4 | 18 | n/a | - | 0 | 0 | 0 | 0 |
| Nairn | IV1.2P | 132 | -2.22 | 3 | 11 | 7 | 13 | 36 |
| Nairn | IV12.4 | 4532 | -3.72 | 2 | 24 | 8 | 14 | 12 |
| Nairn | IV12.5 | 4956 | -1.22 | 3 | 32 | 10 | 20 | 25 |
| Nairn | IV36.0P | 20 | n/a | - | 0 | 0 | 0 | 0 |
| Nairn | PH26.3P | 0 | n/a | - | 0 | 0 | 0 | 0 |
| Ross & Cromarty | IV1.1P | 932 | -4.30 | 2 | 20 | 6 | 9 | 15 |
| Ross & Cromarty | IV10.8 | 1460 | -4.51 | 2 | 20 | 7 | 13 | 8 |
| Ross & Cromarty | IV11.8 | 792 | -3.99 | 2 | 36 | 9 | 16 | 0 |
| Ross & Cromarty | IV14. 9 | 1699 | -2.74 | 3 | 20 | 7 | 15 | 24 |
| Ross & Cromarty | IV15.9 | 4995 | -2.54 | 3 | 28 | 6 | 19 | 20 |
| Ross & Cromarty | IV16.9 | 1245 | -4.04 | 2 | 19 | 5 | 15 | 15 |
| Ross & Cromarty | IV17.0 | 6647 | -0.52 | 4 | 35 | 7 | 30 | 25 |
| Ross & Cromarty | IV18.0 | 5615 | -1.76 | 3 | 29 | 5 | 20 | 29 |
| Ross & Cromarty | IV19.1 | 4426 | -2.74 | 3 | 25 | 4 | 20 | 21 |
| Ross & Cromarty | IV20.1 | 2997 | -2.91 | 3 | 26 | 6 | 22 | 16 |
| Ross & Cromarty | IV21.2 | 869 | -0.85 | 4 | 21 | 9 | 19 | 38 |
| Ross & Cromarty | IV22.2 | 1218 | -2.31 | 3 | 18 | 9 | 13 | 29 |
| Ross & Cromarty | IV23.2 | 589 | -2.04 | 3 | 14 | 9 | 17 | 31 |
| Ross & Cromarty | IV24.3P | 33 | n/a | - | 0 | 0 | 36 | 0 |
| Ross & Cromarty | IV26.2 | 1372 | -1.23 | 3 | 23 | 14 | 19 | 26 |
| Ross & Cromarty | IV27.4P | 4 | n/a | - | 0 | 0 | 0 | 0 |
| Ross & Cromarty | IV4.7P | 211 | -2.88 | 3 | 17 | 13 | 34 | 0 |
| Ross & Cromarty | IV54.8 | 1239 | -2.56 | 3 | 19 | 6 | 14 | 29 |
| Ross & Cromarty | IV6.7 | 3132 | -1.75 | 3 | 23 | 7 | 27 | 22 |
| Ross & Cromarty | IV7.8 | 3799 | -3.93 | 2 | 18 | 4 | 19 | 14 |
| Ross & Cromarty | IV8.8 | 546 | -3.08 | 2 | 23 | 4 | 14 | 25 |
| Ross & Cromarty | IV9.8 | 1052 | -0.79 | 4 | 23 | 6 | 16 | 44 |
| Skye & Lochalsh | IV3.6P | 6 | n/a | - | 0 | 0 | 0 | 0 |
| Skye & Lochalsh | IV4.7P | 0 | n/a | - | 0 | 0 | 0 | 0 |
| Skye & Lochalsh | IV40.8P | 2277 | -1.54 | 3 | 22 | 8 | 22 | 27 |
| Skye & Lochalsh | IV41.8 | 386 | -3.12 | 2 | 24 | 8 | 33 | 0 |
| Skye & Lochalsh | IV42.8 | 322 | -3.62 | 2 | 22 | 21 | 9 | 0 |
| Skye & Lochalsh | IV43.8 | 173 | 0.52 | 4 | 34 | 25 | 26 | 15 |
| Skye & Lochalsh | IV44.8 | 126 | -2.42 | 3 | 19 | 16 | 8 | 22 |
| Skye & Lochalsh | IV45.8 | 175 | -1.70 | 3 | 23 | 8 | 16 | 32 |
| Skye & Lochalsh | IV46.8 | 66 | -2.73 | 3 | 44 | 19 | 9 | 0 |
| Skye & Lochalsh | IV47.8 | 416 | 0.73 | 4 | 24 | 6 | 20 | 56 |
| Skye & Lochalsh | IV48.8 | 60 | 0.09 | 4 | 17 | 19 | 8 | 44 |
| Skye & Lochalsh | IV49.9 | 683 | 1.39 | 5 | 30 | 17 | 18 | 44 |
| Skye & Lochalsh | IV51.9 | 3716 | 0.02 | 4 | 28 | 15 | 23 | 31 |
| Skye & Lochalsh | IV52.8 | 294 | -2.61 | 3 | 26 | 6 | 14 | 25 |
| Skye & Lochalsh | IV53.8 | 81 | -4.65 | 2 | 18 | 4 | 9 | 17 |
| Skye & Lochalsh | IV55.8 | 927 | -1.75 | 3 | 22 | 22 | 17 | 11 |
| Skye & Lochalsh | IV56.8 | 226 | -1.40 | 3 | 22 | 21 | 23 | 11 |
| Skye & Lochalsh | PH35.4P | 0 | n/a | - | 0 | 0 | 0 | 0 |
| Skye & Lochalsh | PH41.4P | 8 | n/a | - | 0 | 0 | 0 | 0 |
| Sutherland | IV24.3P | 1385 | -2.23 | 3 | 21 | 7 | 24 | 22 |
| Sutherland | IV25.3 | 1982 | -3.62 | 2 | 21 | 5 | 14 | 18 |
| Sutherland | IV27.4P | 3476 | -2.49 | 3 | 22 | 11 | 15 | 21 |
| Sutherland | IV28.3 | 366 | -3.56 | 2 | 19 | 5 | 9 | 26 |
| Sutherland | KW10.6 | 1625 | -1.86 | 3 | 27 | 4 | 21 | 29 |
| Sutherland | KW11.6 | 121 | -3.01 | 2 | 13 | 11 | 10 | 25 |
| Sutherland | KW13.6 | 112 | -4.18 | 2 | 20 | 9 | 9 | 13 |
| Sutherland | KW14.7P | 999 | -1.32 | 3 | 31 | 16 | 17 | 19 |
| Sutherland | KW8.6 | 943 | -1.00 | 4 | 36 | 9 | 12 | 34 |
| Sutherland | KW9.6 | 1918 | -0.95 | 4 | 31 | 9 | 14 | 35 |

Deprivation Scores. Health Board: Lanarkshire

| L. A. District | Sector | Pop | Dep | DEPCAT | NOCAR* | MUNP* | OVERC* | SC45* |
|---|---|---|---|---|---|---|---|---|
| Cumbernauld & Kilsyth | FK1.3P | 13 | n/a | - | 0 | 0 | 0 | 0 |
| Cumbernauld & Kilsyth | FK4.2P | 15 | n/a | - | 0 | 0 | 0 | 0 |
| Cumbernauld & Kilsyth | FK6.5P | 3 | n/a | - | 0 | 0 | 0 | 0 |
| Cumbernauld & Kilsyth | G65.0P | 6159 | 1.60 | 5 | 47 | 15 | 32 | 28 |
| Cumbernauld & Kilsyth | G65.8P | 16 | n/a | - | 0 | 0 | 0 | 0 |
| Cumbernauld & Kilsyth | G65.9P | 7242 | 1.05 | 5 | 44 | 14 | 35 | 23 |
| Cumbernauld & Kilsyth | G67.1 | 6131 | -1.27 | 3 | 36 | 11 | 20 | 21 |
| Cumbernauld & Kilsyth | G67.2 | 16204 | 0.17 | 4 | 49 | 15 | 22 | 21 |
| Cumbernauld & Kilsyth | G67.3P | 10869 | -1.80 | 3 | 36 | 11 | 17 | 18 |
| Cumbernauld & Kilsyth | G67.4P | 11360 | -2.49 | 3 | 27 | 11 | 15 | 18 |
| Cumbernauld & Kilsyth | G68.0 | 372 | -4.18 | 2 | 18 | 8 | 25 | 0 |
| Cumbernauld & Kilsyth | G68.9P | 3147 | -1.58 | 3 | 38 | 13 | 19 | 15 |
| Cumbernauld & Kilsyth | ML6.7P | 3 | n/a | - | 0 | 0 | 0 | 0 |
| East Kilbride | G72.0P | 17 | n/a | - | 0 | 0 | 0 | 0 |
| East Kilbride | G72.8P | 51 | -8.26 | 1 | 4 | 0 | 0 | 0 |
| East Kilbride | G72.9P | 40 | 4.29 | 6 | 8 | 7 | 33 | 88 |
| East Kilbride | G73.4P | 4 | n/a | - | 0 | 0 | 0 | 0 |
| East Kilbride | G73.5P | 23 | n/a | - | 0 | 0 | 0 | 0 |
| East Kilbride | G74.1 | 4567 | -0.09 | 4 | 42 | 16 | 30 | 14 |
| East Kilbride | G74.2P | 10111 | -3.68 | 2 | 20 | 7 | 19 | 12 |
| East Kilbride | G74.3 | 15723 | -1.08 | 3 | 34 | 11 | 29 | 16 |
| East Kilbride | G74.4 | 5101 | 0.65 | 4 | 40 | 13 | 26 | 31 |
| East Kilbride | G74.5 | 432 | -7.02 | 1 | 5 | 4 | 7 | 0 |
| East Kilbride | G75.0 | 8106 | -0.45 | 4 | 41 | 11 | 28 | 19 |
| East Kilbride | G75.8 | 17558 | -1.24 | 3 | 30 | 11 | 28 | 17 |
| East Kilbride | G75.9 | 10211 | 0.13 | 4 | 37 | 14 | 36 | 16 |
| East Kilbride | G76.8P | 1253 | -3.57 | 2 | 26 | 7 | 16 | 11 |
| East Kilbride | G76.9P | 143 | 0.50 | 4 | 9 | 9 | 2 | 74 |
| East Kilbride | KA17.0P | 5 | n/a | - | 0 | 0 | 0 | 0 |
| East Kilbride | ML10.6P | 9235 | -3.41 | 2 | 20 | 9 | 17 | 13 |
| East Kilbride | ML3.7P | 15 | n/a | - | 0 | 0 | 0 | 0 |
| East Kilbride | ML3.8P | 5 | n/a | - | 0 | 0 | 0 | 0 |
| Hamilton | G71.6P | 0 | n/a | - | 0 | 0 | 0 | 0 |
| Hamilton | G71.7P | 4804 | -2.57 | 3 | 30 | 10 | 20 | 12 |
| Hamilton | G71.8P | 6197 | -2.64 | 3 | 28 | 8 | 23 | 12 |
| Hamilton | G72.0P | 9190 | 5.52 | 6 | 60 | 26 | 42 | 36 |
| Hamilton | G72.9P | 10866 | 0.20 | 4 | 43 | 15 | 30 | 18 |
| Hamilton | G74.2P | 9 | n/a | - | 0 | 0 | 0 | 0 |
| Hamilton | ML10.6P | 51 | 2.42 | 5 | 8 | 0 | 10 | 0 |
| Hamilton | ML3.0 | 5754 | 3.67 | 6 | 59 | 22 | 36 | 29 |
| Hamilton | ML3.6 | 5625 | 0.39 | 4 | 50 | 15 | 21 | 23 |
| Hamilton | ML3.7P | 12261 | -1.97 | 3 | 30 | 10 | 22 | 16 |
| Hamilton | ML3.8P | 15389 | 0.24 | 4 | 38 | 17 | 30 | 18 |
| Hamilton | ML3.9 | 14005 | 2.31 | 5 | 49 | 18 | 34 | 28 |
| Hamilton | ML8.5P | 91 | -6.65 | 1 | 11 | 7 | 3 | 0 |
| Hamilton | ML9.1 | 7393 | 1.84 | 5 | 50 | 15 | 27 | 33 |
| Hamilton | ML9.2 | 9061 | -1.06 | 3 | 35 | 12 | 25 | 17 |
| Hamilton | ML9.3P | 7239 | -1.01 | 3 | 34 | 11 | 25 | 20 |
| Lanark (Clydesdale) | DG10.9P | 7 | n/a | - | 0 | 0 | 0 | 0 |
| Lanark (Clydesdale) | EH46.7P | 136 | -4.97 | 2 | 12 | 10 | 17 | 0 |
| Lanark (Clydesdale) | EH55.8P | 311 | -1.60 | 3 | 14 | 2 | 22 | 41 |
| Lanark (Clydesdale) | ML11.0 | 7975 | 0.72 | 4 | 41 | 14 | 29 | 27 |
| Lanark (Clydesdale) | ML11.7 | 7431 | -1.81 | 3 | 33 | 10 | 22 | 16 |
| Lanark (Clydesdale) | ML11.8 | 8473 | -0.46 | 4 | 33 | 10 | 26 | 27 |
| Lanark (Clydesdale) | ML11.9 | 9495 | -1.98 | 3 | 27 | 10 | 23 | 17 |
| Lanark (Clydesdale) | ML12.6P | 6042 | -2.33 | 3 | 18 | 8 | 17 | 27 |
| Lanark (Clydesdale) | ML2.9P | 0 | n/a | - | 0 | 0 | 0 | 0 |
| Lanark (Clydesdale) | ML8.4 | 7055 | -0.59 | 4 | 32 | 10 | 28 | 24 |
| Lanark (Clydesdale) | ML8.5P | 9667 | -2.89 | 3 | 22 | 7 | 20 | 18 |
| Lanark (Clydesdale) | ML9.3P | 16 | n/a | - | 0 | 0 | 0 | 0 |
| Monklands | EH48.3P | 4 | n/a | - | 0 | 0 | 0 | 0 |
| Monklands | FK1.3P | 24 | n/a | - | 0 | 0 | 0 | 0 |
| Monklands | G67.4P | 104 | -1.77 | 3 | 5 | 0 | 32 | 38 |
| Monklands | G69.6P | 9 | n/a | - | 0 | 0 | 0 | 0 |
| Monklands | G69.7P | 2639 | 3.95 | 6 | 59 | 19 | 51 | 22 |
| Monklands | G69.8P | 44 | -4.43 | 2 | 27 | 13 | 9 | 0 |
| Monklands | ML1.5P | 61 | -7.60 | 1 | 8 | 0 | 5 | 0 |
| Monklands | ML4.1P | 0 | n/a | - | 0 | 0 | 0 | 0 |
| Monklands | ML5.1 | 6926 | 0.98 | 4 | 46 | 13 | 33 | 24 |
| Monklands | ML5.2P | 11072 | 3.36 | 6 | 53 | 20 | 41 | 28 |
| Monklands | ML5.3 | 4821 | 1.50 | 5 | 50 | 14 | 29 | 29 |
| Monklands | ML5.4P | 12945 | 3.23 | 6 | 54 | 17 | 41 | 30 |
| Monklands | ML5.5 | 15044 | 5.40 | 6 | 61 | 22 | 49 | 35 |
| Monklands | ML6.0 | 8674 | 2.92 | 5 | 50 | 19 | 39 | 29 |
| Monklands | ML6.6 | 9848 | 3.54 | 6 | 54 | 22 | 39 | 27 |

| | | | | | | | | |
|---|---|---|---|---|---|---|---|---|
| onklands | ML6.7P | 10697 | 3.25 | 6 | 46 | 18 | 37 | 36 |
| Monklands | ML6.8 | 13115 | 2.91 | 5 | 43 | 18 | 38 | 34 |
| Monklands | ML6.9 | 12082 | -0.18 | 4 | 39 | 13 | 26 | 22 |
| Monklands | ML7.4P | 1734 | 4.53 | 6 | 52 | 19 | 40 | 43 |
| Monklands | ML7.5P | 19 | n/a | - | 0 | 0 | 0 | 0 |
| Motherwell | EH47.9P | 20 | n/a | - | 0 | 0 | 0 | 0 |
| Motherwell | EH48.3P | 184 | 2.84 | 5 | 41 | 31 | 46 | 9 |
| Motherwell | G71.5 | 8332 | 5.92 | 6 | 58 | 20 | 49 | 44 |
| Motherwell | G71.6P | 7017 | -0.51 | 4 | 38 | 11 | 29 | 20 |
| Motherwell | G71.7P | 59 | -6.65 | 1 | 2 | 7 | 9 | 0 |
| Motherwell | G71.8P | 3 | n/a | - | 0 | 0 | 0 | 0 |
| Motherwell | ML1.1 | 6233 | 1.86 | 5 | 59 | 15 | 27 | 28 |
| Motherwell | ML1.2 | 9275 | 0.38 | 4 | 47 | 13 | 26 | 24 |
| Motherwell | ML1.3 | 14765 | 2.05 | 5 | 51 | 18 | 33 | 26 |
| Motherwell | ML1.4 | 11551 | 3.29 | 6 | 54 | 15 | 40 | 34 |
| Motherwell | ML1.5P | 10308 | 3.05 | 6 | 45 | 15 | 43 | 34 |
| Motherwell | ML2.0 | 12296 | 2.25 | 5 | 44 | 15 | 37 | 31 |
| Motherwell | ML2.7 | 11624 | 2.92 | 5 | 52 | 21 | 38 | 25 |
| Motherwell | ML2.8 | 13454 | 0.77 | 4 | 41 | 15 | 30 | 24 |
| Motherwell | ML2.9P | 6932 | 2.49 | 5 | 46 | 17 | 40 | 27 |
| Motherwell | ML4.1P | 6758 | 0.84 | 4 | 46 | 14 | 33 | 21 |
| Motherwell | ML4.2 | 11462 | 3.69 | 6 | 57 | 20 | 37 | 32 |
| Motherwell | ML4.3 | 3656 | 2.81 | 5 | 58 | 17 | 28 | 35 |
| Motherwell | ML5.4P | 0 | n/a | - | 0 | 0 | 0 | 0 |
| Motherwell | ML7.4P | 7055 | 2.65 | 5 | 44 | 11 | 39 | 39 |
| Motherwell | ML7.5P | 8494 | 2.55 | 5 | 49 | 14 | 37 | 32 |

Deprivation Scores. Health Board: Lothian

| L. A. District | Sector | Pop | Dep | DEPCAT | NOCAR* | MUNP* | OVERC* | SC45* |
|---|---|---|---|---|---|---|---|---|
| East Lothian | EH21.6P | 7309 | -2.99 | 3 | 39 | 5 | 17 | 13 |
| East Lothian | EH21.7 | 6862 | -0.26 | 4 | 44 | 10 | 25 | 24 |
| East Lothian | EH21.8P | 6324 | 1.29 | 5 | 50 | 12 | 30 | 29 |
| East Lothian | EH22.2P | 67 | -5.32 | 1 | 7 | 11 | 15 | 0 |
| East Lothian | EH31.2 | 2124 | -5.91 | 1 | 18 | 5 | 9 | 1 |
| East Lothian | EH32.0 | 7981 | -3.83 | 2 | 22 | 5 | 14 | 16 |
| East Lothian | EH32.9 | 7577 | 1.46 | 5 | 49 | 13 | 31 | 28 |
| East Lothian | EH33.1 | 4717 | 0.23 | 4 | 39 | 12 | 25 | 29 |
| East Lothian | EH33.2 | 5746 | -0.86 | 4 | 40 | 9 | 24 | 21 |
| East Lothian | EH34.5 | 1766 | -4.28 | 2 | 15 | 5 | 19 | 11 |
| East Lothian | EH35.5 | 2241 | -2.70 | 3 | 36 | 8 | 23 | 8 |
| East Lothian | EH36.5 | 304 | -4.58 | 2 | 14 | 4 | 7 | 21 |
| East Lothian | EH37.5P | 40 | -7.35 | 1 | 5 | 6 | 0 | 0 |
| East Lothian | EH39.4 | 4543 | -3.34 | 2 | 25 | 8 | 12 | 18 |
| East Lothian | EH39.5 | 2218 | -4.06 | 2 | 18 | 4 | 15 | 16 |
| East Lothian | EH40.3 | 1337 | -3.11 | 2 | 23 | 3 | 17 | 23 |
| East Lothian | EH41.3 | 4974 | -1.87 | 3 | 27 | 8 | 22 | 23 |
| East Lothian | EH41.4 | 5432 | -2.75 | 3 | 21 | 8 | 16 | 23 |
| East Lothian | EH42.1 | 7176 | -0.56 | 4 | 37 | 7 | 26 | 28 |
| East Lothian | TD11.3P | 60 | 1.9 | 5 | 0 | 9 | 8 | 80 |
| East Lothian | TD13.5P | 154 | -4.98 | 2 | 16 | 6 | 7 | 13 |
| Edinburgh City | EH1.1 | 815 | 4.17 | 6 | 71 | 33 | 18 | 28 |
| Edinburgh City | EH1.2 | 1291 | 0.14 | 4 | 62 | 19 | 11 | 17 |
| Edinburgh City | EH1.3 | 1111 | 1.07 | 5 | 59 | 17 | 15 | 27 |
| Edinburgh City | EH10.4 | 8042 | -4.07 | 2 | 45 | 6 | 6 | 7 |
| Edinburgh City | EH10.5 | 8462 | -5.17 | 1 | 28 | 5 | 5 | 6 |
| Edinburgh City | EH10.6 | 7825 | -6.97 | 1 | 11 | 2 | 6 | 0 |
| Edinburgh City | EH10.7P | 2434 | -7.16 | 1 | 5 | 3 | 2 | 5 |
| Edinburgh City | EH11.1 | 10651 | -1.38 | 3 | 57 | 8 | 15 | 16 |
| Edinburgh City | EH11.2 | 6646 | 0.71 | 4 | 67 | 10 | 19 | 26 |
| Edinburgh City | EH11.3 | 10964 | 3.19 | 6 | 67 | 13 | 32 | 35 |
| Edinburgh City | EH11.4 | 9092 | 0.74 | 4 | 55 | 9 | 32 | 23 |
| Edinburgh City | EH12.0 | 251 | 0.51 | 4 | 33 | 2 | 11 | 62 |
| Edinburgh City | EH12.5 | 5775 | -3.63 | 2 | 40 | 6 | 10 | 10 |
| Edinburgh City | EH12.6 | 4796 | -6.96 | 1 | 13 | 3 | 4 | 1 |
| Edinburgh City | EH12.7 | 10129 | -3.89 | 2 | 30 | 4 | 18 | 9 |
| Edinburgh City | EH12.8 | 11360 | -5.85 | 1 | 19 | 3 | 7 | 6 |
| Edinburgh City | EH12.9 | 1868 | -2.88 | 3 | 34 | 3 | 20 | 16 |
| Edinburgh City | EH13.0 | 5499 | -6.89 | 1 | 12 | 3 | 4 | 1 |
| Edinburgh City | EH13.9 | 8713 | 0.16 | 4 | 53 | 7 | 29 | 24 |
| Edinburgh City | EH14.1 | 6812 | -3.01 | 2 | 40 | 5 | 13 | 15 |
| Edinburgh City | EH14.2 | 11869 | 1.48 | 5 | 53 | 11 | 32 | 29 |
| Edinburgh City | EH14.3 | 8553 | 0.14 | 4 | 47 | 12 | 29 | 20 |
| Edinburgh City | EH14.4 | 178 | -4.50 | 2 | 10 | 2 | 23 | 12 |
| Edinburgh City | EH14.5 | 9674 | -5.65 | 1 | 15 | 3 | 12 | 6 |
| Edinburgh City | EH14.6 | 237 | -2.61 | 3 | 15 | 4 | 26 | 24 |
| Edinburgh City | EH14.7 | 4533 | -5.77 | 1 | 12 | 3 | 13 | 5 |

| L. A. District | Sector | Pop | Dep | DEPCAT | NOCAR* | MUNP* | OVERC* | SC45* |
|---|---|---|---|---|---|---|---|---|
| Edinburgh City | EH15.1 | 5797 | -3.50 | 2 | 31 | 7 | 10 | 14 |
| Edinburgh City | EH15.2 | 5338 | -3.93 | 2 | 31 | 7 | 10 | 11 |
| Edinburgh City | EH15.3 | 8262 | 3.46 | 6 | 60 | 17 | 38 | 32 |
| Edinburgh City | EH16.4 | 12460 | 7.62 | 7 | 78 | 32 | 41 | 41 |
| Edinburgh City | EH16.5 | 8345 | -1.30 | 3 | 47 | 9 | 18 | 18 |
| Edinburgh City | EH16.6 | 10544 | -0.83 | 4 | 44 | 9 | 25 | 19 |
| Edinburgh City | EH17.7 | 8527 | 1.62 | 5 | 50 | 12 | 37 | 26 |
| Edinburgh City | EH17.8P | 9802 | 2.52 | 5 | 53 | 13 | 37 | 32 |
| Edinburgh City | EH18.1P | 16 | n/a | - | 0 | 0 | 0 | 0 |
| Edinburgh City | EH2.1 | 140 | -2.00 | 3 | 63 | 6 | 8 | 17 |
| Edinburgh City | EH2.2 | 132 | 1.09 | 5 | 47 | 9 | 11 | 50 |
| Edinburgh City | EH2.3 | 108 | -0.06 | 4 | 53 | 7 | 6 | 42 |
| Edinburgh City | EH2.4 | 319 | -0.55 | 4 | 53 | 9 | 11 | 30 |
| Edinburgh City | EH20.9P | 240 | -1.53 | 3 | 28 | 11 | 34 | 10 |
| Edinburgh City | EH21.6P | 4 | n/a | - | 0 | 0 | 0 | 0 |
| Edinburgh City | EH21.8P | 280 | 3.45 | 6 | 66 | 20 | 22 | 38 |
| Edinburgh City | EH22.1P | 19 | n/a | - | 0 | 0 | 0 | 0 |
| Edinburgh City | EH27.8P | 170 | -5.69 | 1 | 9 | 6 | 16 | 0 |
| Edinburgh City | EH28.8 | 3283 | -2.18 | 3 | 23 | 7 | 27 | 18 |
| Edinburgh City | EH29.9 | 3135 | -3.30 | 2 | 25 | 5 | 15 | 19 |
| Edinburgh City | EH3.5 | 5501 | -2.88 | 3 | 44 | 8 | 10 | 13 |
| Edinburgh City | EH3.6 | 5004 | -3.01 | 2 | 43 | 8 | 9 | 12 |
| Edinburgh City | EH3.7 | 801 | -1.72 | 3 | 39 | 11 | 5 | 28 |
| Edinburgh City | EH3.8 | 1555 | 2.30 | 5 | 71 | 23 | 19 | 22 |
| Edinburgh City | EH3.9 | 5067 | -0.27 | 4 | 64 | 14 | 15 | 16 |
| Edinburgh City | EH30.9P | 8005 | -2.62 | 3 | 27 | 5 | 17 | 22 |
| Edinburgh Clty | EH4.1 | 5507 | -3.64 | 2 | 42 | 8 | 8 | 8 |
| Edinburgh City | EH4.2 | 9953 | -0.66 | 4 | 43 | 8 | 22 | 26 |
| Edinburgh City | EH4.3 | 4728 | -6.68 | 1 | 17 | 3 | 2 | 2 |
| Edinburgh City | EH4.4 | 15099 | 7.38 | 7 | 79 | 26 | 47 | 41 |
| Edinburgh City | EH4.5 | 4876 | -4.69 | 2 | 22 | 5 | 11 | 9 |
| Edinburgh City | EH4.6 | 5335 | -7.10 | 1 | 7 | 3 | 4 | 2 |
| Edinburgh City | EH4.7 | 8327 | 0.02 | 4 | 44 | 9 | 31 | 23 |
| Edinburgh City | EH4.8 | 2819 | -7.06 | 1 | 9 | 3 | 3 | 2 |
| Edinburgh City | EH5.1 | 5654 | 5.13 | 6 | 76 | 19 | 36 | 39 |
| Edinburgh City | EH5.2 | 5594 | -0.45 | 4 | 48 | 7 | 26 | 23 |
| Edinburgh City | EH5.3 | 5365 | -4.78 | 2 | 28 | 4 | 8 | 9 |
| Edinburgh City | EH52.5P | 11 | n/a | - | 0 | 0 | 0 | 0 |
| Edinburgh City | EH52.6P | 21 | n/a | - | 0 | 0 | 0 | 0 |
| Edinburgh City | EH53.0P | 35 | -3.72 | 2 | 12 | 0 | 0 | 43 |
| Edinburgh City | EH6.4 | 7883 | -0.77 | 4 | 50 | 11 | 18 | 20 |
| Edinburgh City | EH6.5 | 3437 | 0.17 | 4 | 61 | 12 | 20 | 20 |
| Edinburgh City | EH6.6 | 3617 | 4.70 | 6 | 76 | 18 | 33 | 39 |
| Edinburgh City | EH6.7 | 2917 | -1.67 | 3 | 45 | 11 | 17 | 13 |
| Edinburgh City | EH6.8 | 8966 | 0.48 | 4 | 62 | 9 | 22 | 25 |
| Edinburgh City | EH7.4 | 6429 | -0.62 | 4 | 58 | 10 | 16 | 20 |
| Edinburgh City | EH7.5 | 9508 | 0.65 | 4 | 65 | 11 | 20 | 25 |
| Edinburgh City | EH7.6 | 11412 | 0.67 | 4 | 58 | 9 | 22 | 29 |
| Edinburgh City | EH8.7 | 11479 | -2.62 | 3 | 42 | 6 | 18 | 13 |
| Edinburgh City | EH8.8 | 2867 | 0.07 | 4 | 65 | 11 | 18 | 20 |
| Edinburgh City | EH8.9 | 5676 | 1.86 | 5 | 68 | 16 | 19 | 29 |
| Edinburgh City | EH9.1 | 9098 | -3.40 | 2 | 44 | 9 | 7 | 9 |
| Edinburgh City | EH9.2 | 5237 | -5.89 | 1 | 21 | 6 | 4 | 4 |
| Edinburgh City | EH9.3 | 2972 | -5.02 | 1 | 32 | 4 | 6 | 6 |
| Midlothian | EH10.7P | 181 | 0.84 | 4 | 16 | 0 | 17 | 73 |
| Midlothian | EH16.4P | 2 | n/a | - | 0 | 0 | 0 | 0 |
| Midlothian | EH17.8P | 8 | n/a | - | 0 | 0 | 0 | 0 |
| Midlothian | EH18.1P | 2262 | -5.03 | 1 | 16 | 4 | 15 | 8 |
| Midlothian | EH19.2 | 6609 | -0.98 | 4 | 35 | 6 | 26 | 26 |
| Midlothian | EH19.3 | 5656 | -2.04 | 3 | 32 | 6 | 25 | 18 |
| Midlothian | EH20.9P | 6686 | -1.32 | 3 | 35 | 8 | 21 | 24 |
| Midlothian | EH21.8P | 7 | n/a | - | 0 | 0 | 0 | 0 |
| Midlothian | EH22.1P | 5727 | 0.04 | 4 | 44 | 9 | 27 | 26 |
| Midlothian | EH22.2P | 6624 | 0.99 | 4 | 45 | 10 | 31 | 31 |
| Midlothian | EH22.3 | 2876 | -6.66 | 1 | 10 | 3 | 6 | 3 |
| Midlothian | EH22.4 | 5551 | 0.24 | 4 | 49 | 9 | 27 | 26 |
| Midlothian | EH22.5 | 7739 | 0.59 | 4 | 43 | 10 | 36 | 23 |
| Midlothian | EH23.4 | 7080 | -0.24 | 4 | 43 | 8 | 25 | 28 |
| Midlothian | EH24.9 | 1432 | 2.05 | 5 | 50 | 13 | 31 | 34 |
| Midlothian | EH25.9 | 3483 | -2.61 | 3 | 27 | 6 | 21 | 18 |
| Midlothian | EH26.0 | 7012 | -3.17 | 2 | 26 | 5 | 19 | 16 |
| Midlothian | EH26.8P | 6441 | -1.62 | 3 | 33 | 7 | 24 | 21 |
| Midlothian | EH26.9P | 4818 | -6.82 | 1 | 7 | 2 | 8 | 3 |
| Midlothian | EH37.5P | 1442 | -3.61 | 2 | 22 | 8 | 18 | 10 |
| Midlothian | EH38.5P | 19 | n/a | - | 0 | 0 | 0 | 0 |
| Midlothian | EH46.7P | 25 | n/a | - | 0 | 0 | 0 | 0 |

| L. A. District | Sector | Pop | Dep | DEPCAT | NOCAR* | MUNP* | OVERC* | SC45* |
|---|---|---|---|---|---|---|---|---|
| West Lothian | EH27.8P | 1837 | -2.51 | 3 | 40 | 2 | 26 | 12 |
| West Lothian | EH30.9P | 104 | -3.05 | 2 | 15 | 6 | 10 | 30 |
| West Lothian | EH47.0 | 7845 | 2.44 | 5 | 47 | 15 | 33 | 36 |
| West Lothian | EH47.7 | 6676 | 4.44 | 6 | 53 | 22 | 38 | 39 |
| West Lothian | EH47.8 | 7490 | 1.75 | 5 | 41 | 14 | 30 | 36 |
| West Lothian | EH47.9P | 5147 | 5.09 | 6 | 53 | 17 | 38 | 53 |
| West Lothian | EH48.1 | 6799 | -0.15 | 4 | 34 | 12 | 27 | 26 |
| West Lothian | EH48.2 | 7240 | 1.84 | 5 | 47 | 16 | 30 | 32 |
| West Lothian | EH48.3P | 8621 | 0.28 | 4 | 40 | 15 | 24 | 25 |
| West Lothian | EH48.4 | 4707 | 1.02 | 5 | 44 | 14 | 24 | 33 |
| West Lothian | EH49.6P | 6439 | -3.02 | 2 | 25 | 8 | 18 | 15 |
| West Lothian | EH49.7P | 5108 | -4.47 | 2 | 19 | 6 | 13 | 11 |
| West Lothian | EH52.5P | 6257 | -1.83 | 3 | 34 | 8 | 21 | 20 |
| West Lothian | EH52.6 | 10479 | -0.43 | 4 | 39 | 11 | 24 | 24 |
| West Lothian | EH53.0P | 6486 | -1.81 | 3 | 30 | 9 | 24 | 17 |
| West Lothian | EH54.5 | 8216 | 1.14 | 5 | 43 | 20 | 23 | 27 |
| West Lothian | EH54.6 | 15756 | 0.02 | 4 | 35 | 14 | 24 | 27 |
| West Lothian | EH54.7 | 621 | -5.93 | 1 | 11 | 5 | 10 | 4 |
| West Lothian | EH54.8 | 11785 | -0.13 | 4 | 34 | 14 | 19 | 30 |
| West Lothian | EH54.9 | 1264 | -6.39 | 1 | 4 | 3 | 12 | 4 |
| West Lothian | EH55.8P | 7263 | 0.89 | 4 | 42 | 15 | 29 | 25 |
| West Lothian | FK1.2P | 62 | -3.28 | 2 | 17 | 16 | 24 | 0 |
| West Lothian | ML6.7P | 4 | n/a | - | 0 | 0 | 0 | 0 |
| West Lothian | ML7.5P | 1014 | 0.52 | 4 | 45 | 12 | 27 | 27 |

Deprivation Scores. Health Board: Tayside

| L. A. District | Sector | Pop | Dep | DEPCAT | NOCAR* | MUNP* | OVERC* | SC45* |
|---|---|---|---|---|---|---|---|---|
| Angus | AB3.1P | 88 | -2.19 | 3 | 12 | 0 | 28 | 33 |
| Angus | DD10.0P | 10 | n/a | - | 0 | 0 | 0 | 0 |
| Angus | DD10.8 | 6583 | -0.47 | 4 | 47 | 12 | 17 | 24 |
| Angus | DD10.9 | 8277 | -1.40 | 3 | 32 | 8 | 22 | 24 |
| Angus | DD11.1 | 5267 | 2.37 | 5 | 58 | 16 | 23 | 37 |
| Angus | DD11.2 | 5275 | -2.96 | 3 | 23 | 5 | 22 | 17 |
| Angus | DD11.3 | 4197 | -1.80 | 3 | 37 | 6 | 22 | 20 |
| Angus | DD11.4 | 6818 | -0.67 | 4 | 37 | 7 | 26 | 26 |
| Angus | DD11.5 | 6336 | 0.38 | 4 | 44 | 11 | 30 | 24 |
| Angus | DD4.0P | 0 | na | - | 0 | 0 | 0 | 0 |
| Angus | DD5.3P | 955 | -5.89 | 1 | 8 | 3 | 16 | 4 |
| Angus | DD5.4P | 52 | -4.45 | 2 | 8 | 7 | 31 | 0 |
| Angus | DD7.6 | 3847 | -5.44 | 1 | 15 | 4 | 10 | 8 |
| Angus | DD7.7 | 6101 | -2.30 | 3 | 31 | 8 | 22 | 16 |
| Angus | DD8.1P | 8173 | -0.36 | 4 | 34 | 9 | 28 | 28 |
| Angus | DD8.2 | 6099 | -1.48 | 3 | 28 | 8 | 23 | 25 |
| Angus | DD8.3 | 4477 | -2.60 | 3 | 22 | 8 | 15 | 23 |
| Angus | DD8.4 | 3371 | -3.53 | 2 | 20 | 8 | 14 | 16 |
| Angus | DD8.5 | 3542 | -1.67 | 3 | 24 | 10 | 22 | 23 |
| Angus | DD9.6 | 5105 | -3.04 | 2 | 25 | 6 | 13 | 22 |
| Angus | DD9.7P | 5550 | -0.76 | 4 | 35 | 11 | 20 | 27 |
| Angus | PH11.8P | 366 | -3.03 | 2 | 8 | 5 | 16 | 31 |
| Angus | PH12.8P | 954 | -2.84 | 3 | 20 | 7 | 20 | 19 |
| Angus | PH13.9P | 11 | n/a | - | 0 | 0 | 0 | 0 |
| Dundee City | DD1.1 | 565 | 1.58 | 5 | 62 | 25 | 12 | 24 |
| Dundee City | DD1.2 | 1297 | 1.95 | 5 | 62 | 16 | 16 | 37 |
| Dundee City | DD1.3 | 146 | -1.84 | 3 | 48 | 22 | 12 | 0 |
| Dundee City | DD1.4 | 1276 | -3.19 | 2 | 48 | 11 | 11 | 2 |
| Dundee City | DD1.5 | 1573 | 3.68 | 6 | 71 | 17 | 21 | 43 |
| Dundee City | DD2.1 | 6818 | -4.52 | 2 | 31 | 7 | 7 | 8 |
| Dundee City | DD2.2 | 8857 | -0.60 | 4 | 47 | 14 | 21 | 17 |
| Dundee City | DD2.3 | 14237 | 3.27 | 6 | 62 | 18 | 33 | 32 |
| Dundee City | DD2.4 | 14985 | 2.27 | 5 | 55 | 14 | 34 | 29 |
| Dundee City | DD2.5 | 5326 | -3.87 | 2 | 16 | 5 | 17 | 16 |
| Dundee City | DD3.0 | 9870 | 4.11 | 6 | 54 | 23 | 41 | 30 |
| Dundee City | DD3.6 | 7629 | 1.26 | 5 | 60 | 16 | 19 | 28 |
| Dundee City | DD3.7 | 6883 | 4.20 | 6 | 74 | 20 | 24 | 39 |
| Dundee City | DD3.8 | 6952 | -2.16 | 3 | 39 | 10 | 14 | 17 |
| Dundee City | DD3.9 | 9871 | 0.70 | 4 | 42 | 14 | 30 | 24 |
| Dundee City | DD4.0P | 12168 | 6.04 | 7 | 67 | 31 | 37 | 35 |
| Dundee City | DD4.6 | 5647 | 1.35 | 5 | 62 | 15 | 19 | 29 |
| Dundee City | DD4.7 | 7717 | -3.33 | 2 | 36 | 8 | 11 | 12 |
| Dundee City | DD4.8 | 15716 | 6.19 | 7 | 66 | 27 | 39 | 42 |
| Dundee City | DD4.9 | 14311 | 2.72 | 5 | 55 | 19 | 33 | 28 |
| Dundee City | DD5.1 | 4483 | -5.62 | 1 | 15 | 6 | 6 | 6 |
| Dundee City | DD5.2 | 6099 | -4.44 | 2 | 26 | 7 | 9 | 10 |
| Dundee City | DD5.3P | 7708 | -5.94 | 1 | 11 | 4 | 10 | 6 |
| Dundee City | DD5.4P | 7245 | -4.79 | 2 | 18 | 4 | 14 | 9 |
| Dundee City | DD8.1P | 15 | n/a | - | 0 | 0 | 0 | 0 |

| L. A. District | Sector | Pop | Dep | DEPCAT NOCAR* | MUNP* | OVERC* | SC45* |
|---|---|---|---|---|---|---|---|
| Dundee City | PH13.9P | 8 | n/a | - | 0 | 0 | 0 | 0 |
| Dundee City | PH14.9P | 143 | -5.64 | 1 | 6 | 8 | 16 | 0 |
| Perth & Kinross | DD8.1P | 7 | na | - | 0 | 0 | 0 | 0 |
| Perth & Kinross | FK14.7P | 436 | -4.72 | 2 | 8 | 7 | 10 | 15 |
| Perth & Kinross | FK15.0P | 92 | -6.74 | 1 | 18 | 3 | 3 | 0 |
| Perth & Kinross | FK15.9P | 729 | -5.37 | 1 | 11 | 5 | 13 | 7 |
| Perth & Kinross | FK19.8P | 12 | n/a | - | 15 | 0 | 0 | 0 |
| Perth & Kinross | FK21.8P | 38 | -8.07 | 1 | 8 | 0 | 0 | 0 |
| Perth & Kinross | KY13.7P | 7073 | -3.57 | 2 | 19 | 7 | 16 | 16 |
| Perth & Kinross | KY14.6P | 48 | -4.47 | 2 | 8 | 14 | 18 | 0 |
| Perth & Kinross | KY14.7P | 76 | -7.05 | 1 | 3 | 4 | 8 | 0 |
| Perth & Kinross | KY4.0P | 195 | -6.44 | 1 | 9 | 2 | 15 | 0 |
| Perth & Kinross | KY5.0P | 32 | na | - | 3 | 0 | 16 | 0 |
| Perth & Kinross | KY6.3P | 65 | 4.89 | 6 | 11 | 14 | 14 | 0 |
| Perth & Kinross | PH1.1 | 6421 | -6.14 | 1 | 11 | 2 | 6 | 9 |
| Perth & Kinross | PH1.2 | 12668 | 1.72 | 5 | 50 | 13 | 30 | 32 |
| Perth & Kinross | PH1.3 | 8369 | -0.95 | 4 | 33 | 7 | 30 | 23 |
| Perth & Kinross | PH1.4 | 3727 | -2.09 | 3 | 23 | 8 | 20 | 24 |
| Perth & Kinross | PH1.5 | 6640 | 1.75 | 5 | 62 | 18 | 22 | 26 |
| Perth & Kinross | PH10.6 | 4817 | -3.07 | 2 | 23 | 9 | 11 | 20 |
| Perth & Kinross | PH10.7 | 3732 | 0.71 | 4 | 31 | 17 | 29 | 27 |
| Perth & Kinross | PH11.8P | 2717 | -1.28 | 3 | 25 | 10 | 23 | 26 |
| Perth & Kinross | PH12.8P | 906 | -1.85 | 3 | 14 | 5 | 22 | 34 |
| Perth & Kinross | PH13.9P | 3705 | -2.07 | 3 | 27 | 6 | 21 | 24 |
| Perth & Kinross | PH14.9P | 1078 | -4.61 | 2 | 8 | 3 | 17 | 15 |
| Perth & Kinross | PH15.2 | 2740 | -2.59 | 3 | 22 | 6 | 16 | 26 |
| Perth & Kinross | PH16.5 | 3291 | -2.62 | 3 | 22 | 8 | 14 | 25 |
| Perth & Kinross | PH17.2 | 186 | 0.50 | 4 | 11 | 8 | 16 | 62 |
| Perth & Kinross | PH18.5 | 805 | -1.44 | 3 | 22 | 8 | 19 | 32 |
| Perth & Kinross | PH2.0 | 6982 | -3.02 | 2 | 33 | 6 | 15 | 15 |
| Perth & Kinross | PH2.6 | 6132 | -4.21 | 2 | 19 | 5 | 15 | 13 |
| Perth & Kinross | PH2.7 | 6607 | -4.51 | 2 | 21 | 5 | 12 | 12 |
| Perth & Kinross | PH2.8 | 2799 | -0.37 | 4 | 47 | 8 | 12 | 36 |
| Perth & Kinross | PH2.9 | 4427 | -3.95 | 2 | 17 | 6 | 15 | 16 |
| Perth & Kinross | PH3.1 | 3827 | -2.27 | 3 | 24 | 9 | 21 | 19 |
| Perth & Kinross | PH4.1 | 630 | 0.96 | 4 | 33 | 8 | 24 | 48 |
| Perth & Kinross | PH5.2 | 779 | -3.28 | 2 | 27 | 9 | 25 | 3 |
| Perth & Kinross | PH6.2 | 1868 | -2.36 | 3 | 21 | 10 | 14 | 25 |
| Perth & Kinross | PH7.3 | 4799 | -1.57 | 3 | 28 | 8 | 20 | 27 |
| Perth & Kinross | PH7.4 | 1812 | -3.31 | 2 | 20 | 9 | 14 | 18 |
| Perth & Kinross | PH8.0 | 1599 | -3.42 | 2 | 19 | 7 | 18 | 15 |
| Perth & Kinross | PH9.0 | 842 | -1.61 | 3 | 20 | 6 | 14 | 38 |

Deprivation Scores. Health Board: The Islands

| L. A. District | Sector | Pop | Dep | DEPCAT NOCAR* | MUNP* | OVERC* | SC45* |
|---|---|---|---|---|---|---|---|
| Orkney | KW15.1 | 6734 | -1.77 | 3 | 27 | 7 | 18 | 28 |
| Orkney | KW16.3 | 3685 | -1.30 | 3 | 26 | 10 | 14 | 33 |
| Orkney | KW17.2 | 8000 | -3.21 | 2 | 14 | 6 | 13 | 27 |
| Shetland | ZE1.0 | 8402 | -1.60 | 3 | 31 | 4 | 20 | 30 |
| Shetland | ZE2.9 | 13772 | -2.92 | 3 | 18 | 4 | 16 | 27 |
| Shetland | ZE3.9 | 594 | -4.04 | 2 | 17 | 0 | 15 | 22 |
| Western Isles | PA80.5 | 1371 | 3.94 | 6 | 40 | 22 | 39 | 40 |
| Western Isles | PA81.5 | 2432 | 4.09 | 6 | 32 | 23 | 44 | 40 |
| Western Isles | PA82.5 | 1803 | 0.80 | 4 | 28 | 21 | 23 | 30 |
| Western Isles | PA83.3 | 352 | -1.23 | 3 | 34 | 26 | 20 | 0 |
| Western Isles | PA84.3 | 455 | 0.61 | 4 | 51 | 22 | 18 | 19 |
| Western Isles | PA85.3 | 1685 | 1.83 | 5 | 38 | 24 | 18 | 35 |
| Western Isles | PA86.0 | 9707 | -0.53 | 4 | 31 | 13 | 22 | 26 |
| Western Isles | PA86.9 | 5075 | 0.01 | 4 | 31 | 16 | 21 | 29 |
| Western Isles | PA87.2 | 5944 | -0.63 | 4 | 36 | 9 | 27 | 24 |
| Western Isles | PA88.5 | 1887 | -1.55 | 3 | 31 | 5 | 30 | 19 |

TABLE B3.1  STANDARDISED MORTALITY RATIOS. HEALTH BOARD: ARGYLL & CLYDE

| L. A. District | Sector | DEPCAT | SMR | S64 | S65 | Obs | O64 | O65 |
|---|---|---|---|---|---|---|---|---|
| Argyll & Bute | FK20.8P | n/a | - | - | - | 0 | 0 | 0 |
| Argyll & Bute | G83.7P | 4 | 81 | 46 | 99 | 5 | 1 | 4 |
| Argyll & Bute | PA20.0 | 4 | 117* | 138* | 112 | 278 | 53 | 225 |
| Argyll & Bute | PA20.9 | 3 | 92 | 81 | 94 | 195 | 27 | 168 |
| Argyll & Bute | PA21.2 | 3 | 81 | 100 | 78 | 51 | 9 | 42 |
| Argyll & Bute | PA22.3 | 3 | 116 | 87 | 122 | 21 | 3 | 18 |

| | | | | | | | | |
|---|---|---|---|---|---|---|---|---|
| Argyll & Bute | PA23.7 | 3 | 119* | 123 | 119* | 339 | 61 | 278 |
| Argyll & Bute | PA23.8 | 3 | 102 | 99 | 103 | 377 | 64 | 313 |
| Argyll & Bute | PA24.8 | 3 | 78 | 64 | 81 | 18 | 3 | 15 |
| Argyll & Bute | PA25.8 | 1 | 128 | 186 | 114 | 7 | 2 | 5 |
| Argyll & Bute | PA26.8 | 1 | 93 | - | 134 | 4 | 0 | 4 |
| Argyl' & Bute | PA27.8 | 3 | 91 | 40 | 107 | 29 | 3 | 26 |
| Argyll & Bute | PA28.6 | 4 | 107 | 109 | 106 | 382 | 94 | 288 |
| Argyll & Bute | PA29.6 | 4 | 97 | 72 | 104 | 112 | 18 | 94 |
| Argyll & Bute | PA30.8 | 3 | 127* | 118 | 129* | 79 | 16 | 63 |
| Argyll & Bute | PA31.8 | 3 | 97 | 89 | 98 | 204 | 38 | 166 |
| Argyll & Bute | PA32.8 | 4 | 82 | 88 | 80 | 49 | 11 | 38 |
| Argyll & Bute | PA33.1 | 3 | 97 | 109 | 93 | 26 | 8 | 18 |
| Argyll & Bute | PA34.4 | 4 | 104 | 101 | 104 | 204 | 52 | 152 |
| Argyll & Bute | PA34.5P | 3 | 89 | 72 | 93 | 133 | 24 | 109 |
| Argyll & Bute | PA35.1 | 2 | 101 | 81 | 107 | 47 | 8 | 39 |
| Argyll & Bute | PA36.4 | 1 | 208 | 411 | 105 | 3 | 2 | 1 |
| Argyll & Bute | PA37.1 | 4 | 90 | 124 | 79 | 91 | 30 | 61 |
| Argyll & Bute | PA38.4P | 4 | 76 | - | 94 | 16 | 0 | 16 |
| Argyll & Bute | PA41.7 | 2 | 111 | 127 | 106 | 7 | 2 | 5 |
| Argyll & Bute | PA42.7 | 4 | 143* | 123 | 150* | 60 | 14 | 46 |
| Argyll & Bute | PA43.7 | 4 | 108 | 93 | 113 | 44 | 9 | 35 |
| Argyll & Bute | PA44.7 | 3 | 96 | 105 | 93 | 12 | 3 | 9 |
| Argyll & Bute | PA45.7 | 5 | 131 | 114 | 135 | 13 | 2 | 11 |
| Argyll & Bute | PA46.7 | 4 | 121 | 97 | 130 | 13 | 3 | 10 |
| Argyll & Bute | PA47.7 | 6 | 120 | 172 | 109 | 12 | 3 | 9 |
| Argyll & Bute | PA48.7 | 3 | 74 | 64 | 76 | 12 | 2 | 10 |
| Argyll & Bute | PA49.7 | 4 | 133 | 98 | 142 | 13 | 2 | 11 |
| Argyll & Bute | PA60.7 | 4 | 148 | 105 | 161 | 12 | 2 | 10 |
| Argyll & Bute | PA61.7 | 6 | 80 | 266 | 39 | 5 | 3 | 2 |
| Argyll & Bute | PA62.6 | 1 | - | - | - | 0 | 0 | 0 |
| Argyll & Bute | PA63.6 | n/a | - | - | - | 0 | 0 | 0 |
| Argyll & Bute | PA64.6 | 2 | 159 | - | 194 | 6 | 0 | 6 |
| Argyll & Bute | PA65.6 | 1 | 76 | 140 | 64 | 7 | 2 | 5 |
| Argyll & Bute | PA66.6 | 3 | 76 | 74 | 76 | 6 | 1 | 5 |
| Argyll & Bute | PA67.6 | 4 | 92 | 130 | 83 | 11 | 3 | 8 |
| Argyll & Bute | PA68.6 | n/a | - | - | - | 0 | 0 | 0 |
| Argyll & Bute | PA69.6 | n/a | 114 | - | 146 | 1 | 0 | 1 |
| Argyll & Bute | PA70.6 | 1 | 39 | - | 64 | 1 | 0 | 1 |
| Argyll & Bute | PA71.6 | n/a | 179 | - | 244 | 2 | 0 | 2 |
| Argyll & Bute | PA72.6 | 2 | 106 | 108 | 105 | 20 | 4 | 16 |
| Argyll & Bute | PA73.6 | 6 | - | - | - | 0 | 0 | 0 |
| Argyll & Bute | PA74.6 | 3 | - | - | - | 0 | 0 | 0 |
| Argyll & Bute | PA75.6 | 3 | 87 | 29 | 107 | 35 | 3 | 32 |
| Argyll & Bute | PA76.6 | 2 | 54 | 100 | 46 | 4 | 1 | 3 |
| Argyll & Bute | PA77.6 | 2 | 96 | 65 | 105 | 43 | 6 | 37 |
| Argyll & Bute | PA78.6 | 3 | 134 | 71 | 149 | 10 | 1 | 9 |
| Dumbarton | G60.5P | 5 | 46 | 85 | 34 | 9 | 4 | 5 |
| Dumbarton | G63.0P | 2 | 91 | 113 | 77 | 6 | 3 | 3 |
| Dumbarton | G82.1 | 3 | 98 | 98 | 98 | 148 | 30 | 118 |
| Dumbarton | G82.2 | 4 | 116* | 107 | 118* | 340 | 69 | 271 |
| Dumbarton | G82.3 | 5 | 99 | 94 | 103 | 157 | 69 | 88 |
| Dumbarton | G82.4 | 6 | 133* | 140* | 131* | 275 | 76 | 199 |
| Dumbarton | G82.5 | 5 | 89 | 113 | 78* | 171 | 71 | 100 |
| Dumbarton | G83.0 | 4 | 111 | 107 | 112 | 363 | 78 | 285 |
| Dumbarton | G83.7P | 2 | 66 | 46 | 73 | 15 | 3 | 12 |
| Dumbarton | G83.8P | 4 | 105 | 114 | 101 | 289 | 92 | 197 |
| Dumbarton | G83.9P | 5 | 96 | 80 | 108 | 152 | 56 | 96 |
| Dumbarton | G84.0 | 2 | 94 | 77 | 101 | 157 | 37 | 120 |
| Dumbarton | G84.7 | 4 | 98 | 100 | 97 | 265 | 58 | 207 |
| Dumbarton | G84.8 | 2 | 103 | 88 | 107 | 261 | 45 | 216 |
| Dumbarton | G84.9 | 1 | 69* | 52* | 80 | 63 | 19 | 44 |
| Inverclyde | PA10.2P | n/a | - | - | - | 0 | 0 | 0 |
| Inverclyde | PA11.3P | 2 | 57* | 110 | 49* | 20 | 5 | 15 |
| Inverclyde | PA13.4P | 1 | 88 | 57* | 97 | 147 | 22 | 125 |
| Inverclyde | PA14.5 | 4 | 118* | 122* | 116* | 408 | 118 | 290 |
| Inverclyde | PA14.6P | 6 | 122* | 162* | 95 | 340 | 180 | 160 |
| Inverclyde | PA15.1 | 6 | 124* | 174* | 115 | 235 | 49 | 186 |
| Inverclyde | PA15.2 | 7 | 148* | 175* | 137* | 386 | 136 | 250 |
| Inverclyde | PA15.3 | 7 | 132* | 143* | 124 | 144 | 68 | 76 |
| Inverclyde | PA15.4 | 5 | 112* | 132* | 107 | 568 | 143 | 425 |
| Inverclyde | PA16.0 | 6 | 112 | 125* | 102 | 274 | 137 | 137 |
| Inverclyde | PA16.7 | 6 | 111* | 112 | 110 | 395 | 123 | 272 |
| Inverclyde | PA16.8 | 2 | 101 | 72* | 108 | 321 | 47 | 274 |
| Inverclyde | PA16.9 | 4 | 86* | 91 | 85* | 225 | 53 | 172 |
| Inverclyde | PA18.6 | 2 | 103 | 59 | 135 | 29 | 7 | 22 |
| Inverclyde | PA19.1 | 3 | 104 | 102 | 105 | 470 | 115 | 355 |
| Renfrew | G52.3P | n/a | - | - | - | 0 | 0 | 0 |
| Renfrew | G52.4P | n/a | - | - | - | 0 | 0 | 0 |
| Renfrew | G53.7P | 3 | 166 | - | 237 | 2 | 0 | 2 |

# DEPRIVATION AND HEALTH IN SCOTLAND

| L. A. District | Sector | DEPCAT | SMR | S64 | S65 | Obs | O64 | O65 |
|---|---|---|---|---|---|---|---|---|
| Renfrew | G77.6P | n/a | - | - | - | 0 | 0 | 0 |
| Renfrew | G78.1P | 4 | 108 | 103 | 111 | 260 | 79 | 181 |
| Renfrew | G78.2P | 5 | 112* | 103 | 117* | 324 | 101 | 223 |
| Renfrew | G78.3 | 3 | 111 | 77 | 124* | 163 | 33 | 130 |
| Renfrew | G78.4P | 1 | 58 | 74 | 53 | 15 | 5 | 10 |
| Renfrew | PA1.1 | 6 | 123* | 139* | 118* | 254 | 65 | 189 |
| Rertrew | PA1.2 | 5 | 122* | 129* | 120* | 394 | 84 | 310 |
| Renfrew | PA1.3P | 1 | 95 | 74* | 100 | 442 | 69 | 373 |
| Renfrew | PA10.2P | 2 | 106 | 88 | 114 | 155 | 36 | 119 |
| Renfrew | PA11.3P | 2 | 88 | 99 | 82 | 133 | 48 | 85 |
| Renfrew | PA12.4 | 3 | 100 | 68 | 112 | 96 | 19 | 77 |
| Renfrew | PA13.4P | n/a | - | - | - | 0 | 0 | 0 |
| Renfrew | PA14.6P | 1 | 92 | 88 | 95 | 19 | 7 | 12 |
| Renfrew | PA2.0 | 5 | 109 | 105 | 111 | 257 | 102 | 155 |
| Renfrew | PA2.6 | 4 | 102 | 118 | 98 | 558 | 122 | 436 |
| Renfrew | PA2.7 | 4 | 88* | 81 | 90 | 259 | 60 | 199 |
| Renfrew | PA2.8 | 5 | 109 | 106 | 111 | 300 | 112 | 188 |
| Renfrew | PA2.9 | 3 | 115* | 86 | 125* | 275 | 54 | 221 |
| Renfrew | PA3.1 | 7 | 128* | 166* | 111 | 262 | 105 | 157 |
| Renfrew | PA3.2 | 6 | 136* | 147* | 132* | 264 | 68 | 196 |
| Renfrew | PA3.3 | 5 | 106 | 98 | 112 | 245 | 107 | 138 |
| Renfrew | PA3.4 | 6 | 126* | 122 | 127* | 392 | 99 | 293 |
| Renfrew | PA4.0 | 3 | 105 | 99 | 108 | 329 | 99 | 230 |
| Renfrew | PA4.8P | 5 | 118* | 136* | 112 | 320 | 95 | 225 |
| Renfrew | PA4.9 | 4 | 97 | 108 | 90 | 133 | 57 | 76 |
| Renfrew | PA5.0 | 5 | 109 | 116 | 104 | 241 | 117 | 124 |
| Renfrew | PA5.8 | 5 | 126* | 139* | 121* | 448 | 114 | 334 |
| Renfrew | PA5.9 | 4 | 99 | 103 | 96 | 213 | 84 | 159 |
| Renfrew | PA6.7 | 1 | 90 | 85 | 92 | 67 | 24 | 43 |
| Renfrew | PA7.5 | 1 | 85 | 78 | 89 | 160 | 45 | 115 |
| Renfrew | PA8.6 | 2 | 87 | 105 | 74* | 130 | 64 | 66 |
| Renfrew | PA8.7 | 2 | 90 | 90 | 89 | 81 | 35 | 46 |
| Renfrew | PA9.1 | 3 | 88 | 48 | 104 | 39 | 6 | 33 |

Standardised Mortality Ratios. Health Board: Ayrshire & Arran

| L. A. District | Sector | DEPCAT | SMR | S64 | S65 | Obs | O64 | O65 |
|---|---|---|---|---|---|---|---|---|
| Cumnock & Doon Valley | DG4.6P | n/a | - | - | - | 0 | 0 | 0 |
| Cumnock & Doon Valley | DG7.3P | n/a | - | - | - | 0 | 0 | 0 |
| Cumnock & Doon Valley | KA1.5P | n/a | - | - | - | 0 | 0 | 0 |
| Cumnock & Doon Valley | KA18.1 | 4 | 113* | 94 | 121* | 273 | 66 | 207 |
| Cumnock & Doon Valley | KA18.2 | 5 | 106 | 110 | 104 | 210 | 65 | 145 |
| Cumnock & Doon Valley | KA18.3 | 5 | 115* | 93 | 126* | 257 | 67 | 190 |
| Cumnock & Doon Valley | KA18.4P | 5 | 116* | 142* | 104 | 206 | 78 | 128 |
| Cumnock & Doon Valley | KA4.8P | 1 | 211 | - | 516 | 2 | 0 | 2 |
| Cumnock & Doon Valley | KA5.5P | 1 | 95 | 96 | 94 | 60 | 15 | 45 |
| Cumnock & Doon Valley | KA5.6 | 4 | 109 | 121 | 104 | 229 | 70 | 159 |
| Cumnock & Doon Valley | KA6.6P | 4 | 122 | 145 | 112 | 59 | 22 | 37 |
| Cumnock & Doon Valley | KA6.7P | 6 | 105 | 102 | 106 | 359 | 112 | 247 |
| Cunninghame | G78.4P | n/a | 435 | 541 | - | 2 | 2 | 0 |
| Cunninghame | KA11.1 | 4 | 96 | 97 | 96 | 144 | 62 | 82 |
| Cunninghame | KA11.2P | 2 | 153 | 187 | 136 | 10 | 4 | 6 |
| Cunninghame | KA11.3 | 7 | 128* | 133 | 126 | 68 | 19 | 49 |
| Cunninghame | KA11.4 | 4 | 89 | 89 | 89 | 93 | 30 | 63 |
| Cunninghame | KA11.5P | 4 | 162 | 190 | 144 | 13 | 6 | 7 |
| Cunninghame | KA12.0 | 5 | 115* | 139* | 106 | 425 | 141 | 284 |
| Cunninghame | KA12.8 | 5 | 101 | 115 | 97 | 214 | 49 | 165 |
| Cunninghame | KA12.9 | 5 | 99 | 101 | 97 | 189 | 78 | 111 |
| Cunninghame | KA13.6 | 4 | 102 | 101 | 103 | 221 | 78 | 143 |
| Cunninghame | KA13.7P | 5 | 115* | 140* | 103 | 249 | 96 | 153 |
| Cunninghame | KA14.3 | 5 | 134 | 153 | 126 | 34 | 12 | 22 |
| ·Cunninghame | KA15.1 | 3 | 100 | 98 | 101 | 118 | 31 | 87 |
| Cunninghame | KA15.2 | 3 | 103 | 130 | 93 | 121 | 44 | 77 |
| Cunninghame | KA2.0P | n/a | 178 | - | 203 | 2 | 0 | 2 |
| Cunninghame | KA20.3 | 5 | 121* | 115 | 124* | 240 | 60 | 180 |
| Cunninghame | KA20.4 | 6 | 119* | 127 | 115 | 181 | 65 | 116 |
| Cunninghame | KA21.5 | 5 | 108 | 135* | 102 | 373 | 89 | 284 |
| Cunninghame | KA21.6 | 6 | 105 | 107 | 103 | 149 | 65 | 84 |
| Cunninghame | KA22.7 | 6 | 121* | 124 | 119* | 220 | 84 | 136 |
| Cunninghame | KA22.8 | 4 | 110 | 92 | 115 | 183 | 33 | 150 |
| Cunninghame | KA23.9 | 2 | 92 | 85 | 93 | 188 | 36 | 152 |
| Cunninghame | KA24.4 | 5 | 106 | 117 | 102 | 153 | 49 | 104 |
| Cunninghame | KA24.5 | 3 | 108 | 93 | 113 | 84 | 20 | 64 |
| Cunninghame | KA25.6 | 6 | 114 | 112 | 115 | 193 | 53 | 140 |

| | | | | | | | | |
|---|---|---|---|---|---|---|---|---|
| Cunninghame | KA25.7 | 4 | 104 | 76 | 114 | 127 | 24 | 103 |
| Cunninghame | KA27.8 | 3 | 100 | 120 | 96 | 214 | 45 | 169 |
| Cunninghame | KA28.0 | 3 | 75* | 55 | 77 | 73 | 7 | 66 |
| Cunninghame | KA29.0 | 2 | 99 | 90 | 102 | 61 | 12 | 49 |
| Cunninghame | KA3.2P | 2 | 96 | - | 190 | 4 | 0 | 4 |
| Cunninghame | KA3.3P | n/a | - | - | - | 0 | 0 | 0 |
| Cunninghame | KA3.4P | n/a | - | - | - | 0 | 0 | 0 |
| Cunninghame | KA30.8 | 2 | 102 | 78 | 106 | 271 | 30 | 241 |
| Cunninghame | KA30.9 | 3 | 104 | 119 | 101 | 334 | 66 | 268 |
| Cunninghame | PA17.5 | 2 | 66* | 100 | 59* | 58 | 15 | 43 |
| Kilmarnock & Loudoun | G77.6P | n/a | - | - | - | 0 | 0 | 0 |
| Kilmarnock & Loudoun | G78.4P | n/a | - | - | - | 0 | 0 | 0 |
| Kilmarnock & Loudoun | KA1.1 | 1 | 94 | 76 | 98 | 111 | 18 | 93 |
| Kilmarnock & Loudoun | KA1.2 | 3 | 111 | 83 | 117* | 322 | 42 | 280 |
| Kilmarnock & Loudoun | KA1.3 | 4 | 103 | 108 | 101 | 327 | 103 | 224 |
| Kilmarnock & Loudoun | KA1.4 | 6 | 103 | 102 | 103 | 311 | 89 | 222 |
| Kilmarnock ~ Loudoun | KA1.5P | 5 | 91 | 85 | 93 | 166 | 40 | 126 |
| Kilmarnock & Loudoun | KA11.2P | n/a | - | - | - | 0 | 0 | 0 |
| Kilmarnock & Loudoun | KA13.7P | 1 | - | - | - | 0 | 0 | 0 |
| Kilmarnock & Loudoun | KA16.9 | 3 | 110 | 116 | 108 | 164 | 40 | 124 |
| Kilmarnock & Loudoun | KA17.0P | 3 | 97 | 101 | 95 | 160 | 35 | 125 |
| Kilmarnock & Loudoun | KA2.0P | 4 | 124* | 97 | 135* | 140 | 33 | 107 |
| Kilmarnock & Loudoun | KA2.9P | 5 | 38 | - | 46 | 1 | 0 | 1 |
| Kilmarnock & Loudoun | KA3.1 | 6 | 122* | 137* | 117* | 310 | 84 | 226 |
| Kilmarnock & Loudoun | KA3.2P | 5 | 122* | 126* | 119* | 270 | 113 | 157 |
| Kilmarnock & Loudoun | KA3.3P | 4 | 118 | 91 | 134* | 97 | 28 | 69 |
| Kilmarnock & Loudoun | KA3.4P | 3 | 82 | 48 | 92 | 44 | 6 | 38 |
| Kilmarnock & Loudoun | KA3.5 | 2 | 107 | 120 | 102 | 126 | 37 | 89 |
| Kilmarnock & Loudoun | KA3.6 | 3 | 105 | 119 | 99 | 108 | 33 | 75 |
| Kilmarnock & Loudoun | KA3.7 | 4 | 113 | 96 | 122* | 247 | 76 | 171 |
| Kilmarnock & Loudoun | KA4.8P | 4 | 108 | 80 | 117* | 229 | 42 | 187 |
| Kyle & Carrick | DG8.0P | n/a | - | - | - | 0 | 0 | 0 |
| Kyle & Carrick | DG8.6P | n/a | - | - | - | 0 | 0 | 0 |
| Kyle & Carrick | KA1.5P | 3 | 103 | 78 | 116 | 60 | 15 | 45 |
| Kyle & Carrick | KA10.6 | 2 | 92 | 59* | 100 | 436 | 55 | 381 |
| Kyle & Carrick | KA10.7 | 2 | 95 | 85 | 100 | 110 | 34 | 76 |
| Kyle & Carrick | KA11.5P | n/a | - | - | - | 0 | 0 | 0 |
| Kyle & Carrick | KA19.7P | 4 | 115* | 123 | 113 | 219 | 57 | 162 |
| Kyle & Carrick | KA19.8 | 4 | 105 | 74 | 117 | 106 | 21 | 85 |
| Kyle & Carrick | KA2.9P | 4 | 120 | 100 | 131* | 88 | 26 | 62 |
| Kyle & Carrick | KA26.0P | 5 | 100 | 76 | 109 | 242 | 50 | 192 |
| Kyle & Carrick | KA26.9 | 3 | 99 | 115 | 95 | 275 | 65 | 210 |
| Kyle & Carrick | KA5.5P | 4 | 106 | 105 | 107 | 88 | 27 | 61 |
| Kyle & Carrick | KA6.5 | 5 | 124* | 137* | 119 | 173 | 54 | 119 |
| Kyle & Carrick | KA6.6P | 3 | 74* | 76 | 73* | 112 | 22 | 90 |
| Kyle & Carrick | KA6.7P | 6 | 29 | - | 43 | 1 | 0 | 1 |
| Kyle & Carrick | KA7.1 | 3 | 110 | 90 | 115 | 116 | 17 | 99 |
| Kyle & Carrick | KA7.2 | 2 | 95 | 86 | 97 | 362 | 49 | 313 |
| Kyle & Carrick | KA7.3 | 4 | 100 | 96 | 102 | 351 | 118 | 233 |
| Kyle & Carrick | KA7.4 | 1 | 79* | 59* | 86* | 261 | 49 | 212 |
| Kyle & Carrick | KA8.0 | 5 | 115* | 106 | 118* | 419 | 101 | 318 |
| Kyle & Carrick | KA8.8 | 4 | 111 | 119 | 109 | 225 | 51 | 174 |
| Ky'e & Carrick | KA8.9 | 5 | 116* | 128* | 112 | 381 | 107 | 274 |
| Kyle & Carrick | KA9.1 | 3 | 92 | 77 | 96 | 361 | 62 | 299 |
| Kyle & Carrick | KA9.2 | 2 | 95 | 94 | 95 | 302 | 72 | 230 |

Standardised Mortality Ratios. Health Board: Borders

| L. A. District | Sector | DEPCAT | SMR | S64 | S65 | Obs | O64 | O65 |
|---|---|---|---|---|---|---|---|---|
| Berwickshire | TD10.6 | 3 | 80 | 89 | 78 | 34 | 9 | 25 |
| Berwickshire | TD11.3P | 3 | 83* | 70* | 86* | 237 | 43 | 194 |
| Berwickshire | TD12.4 | 3 | 115 | 111 | 115 | 163 | 29 | 134 |
| Berwickshire | TD13.5P | 2 | 113 | 62 | 124 | 30 | 3 | 27 |
| Berwickshire | TD14.5 | 4 | 84* | 74 | 87 | 221 | 42 | 182 |
| Berwickshire | TD15.1 | 3 | 49* | 64 | 45* | 26 | 7 | 19 |
| Berwickshire | TD2.6P | n/a | 2761 | 2761 | - | 1 | 1 | 0 |
| Berwickshire | TD3.6P | 2 | 89 | 85 | 90 | 31 | 6 | 25 |
| Berwickshire | TD4.6P | 1 | - | - | - | 0 | 0 | 0 |
| Berwickshire | TD5.7P | 2 | 65 | 110 | 54 | 6 | 2 | 4 |
| Ettrick & Lauderdale | EH37.5P | n/a | - | - | - | 0 | 0 | 0 |
| Ettrick & Lauderdale | EH38.5P | 6 | 75 | 82 | 72 | 8 | 2 | 6 |
| Ettrick & Lauderdale | EH43.6P | n/a | - | - | - | 0 | 0 | 0 |
| Ettrick & Lauderdale | EH44.6P | n/a | - | - | - | 0 | 0 | 0 |
| Ettrick & Lauderdale | TD1.1 | 4 | 126* | 105 | 131* | 315 | 52 | 263 |
| Ettrick & Lauderdale | TD1.2 | 4 | 98 | 95 | 99 | 183 | 54 | 129 |
| Ettrick & Lauderdale | TD1.3P | 2 | 99 | 78 | 104 | 180 | 26 | 154 |
| Ettrick & Lauderdale | TD2.6P | 2 | 101 | 92 | 104 | 68 | 13 | 55 |

| L. A. District | Sector | DEPCAT | SMR | S64 | S65 | Obs | O64 | O65 |
|---|---|---|---|---|---|---|---|---|
| Ettrick & Lauderdale | TD3.6P | 1 | 30 | 173 | - | 1 | 1 | 0 |
| Ettrick & Lauderdale | TD4.6P | 3 | 83 | 72 | 87 | 72 | 14 | 58 |
| Ettrick & Lauderdale | TD5.7P | 3 | 111 | - | 124 | 2 | 0 | 2 |
| Ettrick & Lauderdale | TD5.8P | 1 | 32 | - | 42 | 1 | 0 | 1 |
| Ettrick & Lauderdale | TD6.0 | 3 | 91 | 85 | 93 | 130 | 26 | 104 |
| Ettrick & Lauderdale | TD6.9P | 2 | 73* | 110 | 65* | 156 | 38 | 118 |
| Ettrick & Lauderdale | TD7.4 | 3 | 93 | 68 | 98 | 197 | 28 | 169 |
| Ettrick & Lauderdale | TD7.5P | 4 | 70* | 86 | 64* | 71 | 23 | 48 |
| Ettrick & Lauderdale | TD9.7P | n/a | - | - | - | 0 | 0 | 0 |
| Roxburgh | DG14.0P | n/a | - | - | - | 0 | 0 | 0 |
| Roxburgh | TD3.6P | n/a | - | - | - | 0 | 0 | 0 |
| Roxburgh | TD5.7P | 3 | 99 | 90 | 101 | 257 | 48 | 209 |
| Roxburgh | TD5.8P | 2 | 98 | 54* | 110 | 152 | 18 | 134 |
| Roxburgh | TD6.9P | 2 | 123 | 497 | 49 | 3 | 2 | 1 |
| Roxburgh | TD8.6 | 3 | 91 | 77 | 96 | 233 | 45 | 188 |
| Roxburgh | TD9.0P | 4 | 96 | 61* | 102 | 300 | 31 | 269 |
| Roxburgh | TD9.7P | 3 | 105 | 87 | 112 | 172 | 37 | 135 |
| Roxburgh | TD9.8 | 4 | 94 | 94 | 94 | 209 | 56 | 153 |
| Roxburgh | TD9.9 | 3 | 93 | 80 | 96 | 235 | 38 | 197 |
| Tweeddale | EH26.8P | n/a | - | - | - | 0 | 0 | 0 |
| Tweeddale | EH26.9P | 5 | 86 | - | 105 | 4 | 0 | 4 |
| Tweeddale | EH43.6P | 4 | 66* | 92 | 61* | 31 | 7 | 24 |
| Tweeddale | EH44.6P | 3 | 88 | 54* | 97 | 117 | 14 | 103 |
| Tweeddale | EH45.8 | 3 | 93 | 81 | 95 | 251 | 35 | 216 |
| Tweeddale | EH45.9 | 3 | 95 | 50* | 108 | 122 | 14 | 108 |
| Tweeddale | EH46.7P | 3 | 107 | 91 | 112 | 81 | 16 | 65 |
| Tweeddale | ML12.6P | 2 | 85 | 105 | 80 | 32 | 8 | 24 |
| Tweeddale | TD1.3P | n/a | - | - | - | 0 | 0 | 0 |

Standardised Mortality Ratios. Health Board: Dumfries & Galloway

| L. A. District | Sector | DEPCAT | SMR | S64 | S65 | Obs | O64 | O65 |
|---|---|---|---|---|---|---|---|---|
| Annandale & Eskdale | CA6.5 | 4 | 59* | 54* | 61* | 62 | 18 | 44 |
| Annandale & Eskdale | DG1.3P | n/a | - | - | - | 0 | 0 | 0 |
| Annandale & Eskdale | DG1.4P | 3 | 137 | 201 | 103 | 12 | 6 | 6 |
| Annandale & Eskdale | DG10.9P | 3 | 86 | 106 | 81* | 140 | 34 | 106 |
| Annandale & Eskdale | DG11.1P | 2 | 87 | 81 | 89 | 151 | 34 | 117 |
| Annandale & Eskdale | DG11.2 | 3 | 97 | 91 | 98 | 194 | 44 | 150 |
| Annandale & Eskdale | DG11.3 | 3 | 104 | 104 | 104 | 126 | 32 | 94 |
| Annandale & Eskdale | DG12.5P | 4 | 91 | 101 | 88 | 226 | 63 | 163 |
| Annandale & Eskdale | DG12.6 | 3 | 93 | 96 | 92 | 200 | 57 | 143 |
| Annandale & Eskdale | DG13.0 | 3 | 77* | 87 | 75* | 125 | 28 | 97 |
| Annandale & Eskdale | DG14.0P | 2 | 48* | 41 | 51* | 28 | 6 | 22 |
| Annandale & Eskdale | TD7.5P | n/a | - | - | - | 0 | 0 | 0 |
| Annandale & Eskdale | TD9.0P | n/a | - | - | - | 0 | 0 | 0 |
| Nithsdale | DG1.1 | 3 | 96 | 85 | 100 | 210 | 50 | 160 |
| Nithsdale | DG1.2 | 3 | 102 | 118 | 99 | 169 | 27 | 142 |
| Nithsdale | DG1.3P | 2 | 92 | 104 | 89 | 164 | 47 | 117 |
| Nithsdale | DG1.4P | 2 | 83* | 82 | 84* | 264 | 69 | 195 |
| Nithsdale | DG11.1P | 2 | 91 | 92 | 91 | 7 | 3 | 4 |
| Nithsdale | DG12.5P | 1 | 139 | - | 205 | 2 | 0 | 2 |
| Nithsdale | DG2.0P | 5 | 97 | 98 | 97 | 293 | 85 | 208 |
| Nithsdale | DG2.7 | 3 | 107 | 101 | 109 | 259 | 52 | 207 |
| Nithsdale | DG2.8P | 3 | 100 | 119 | 94 | 91 | 26 | 65 |
| Nithsdale | DG2.9P | 4 | 107 | 105 | 108 | 220 | 76 | 144 |
| Nithsdale | DG3.4P | 3 | 75* | 97 | 69* | 81 | 23 | 58 |
| Nithsdale | DG3.5 | 3 | 101 | 122 | 96 | 126 | 29 | 97 |
| Nithsdale | DG4.6P | 5 | 102 | 114 | 97 | 218 | 62 | 156 |
| Nithsdale | KA18.4P | n/a | - | - | - | 0 | 0 | 0 |
| Nithsdale | ML12.6P | 2 | 124 | 156 | 115 | 11 | 3 | 8 |
| Stewartry | DG2.0P | n/a | - | - | - | 0 | 0 | 0 |
| Stewartry | DG2.8P | 2 | 77 | 88 | 74 | 33 | 10 | 23 |
| Stewartry | DG2.9P | n/a | - | - | - | 0 | 0 | 0 |
| Stewartry | DG3.4P | n/a | - | - | - | 0 | 0 | 0 |
| Stewartry | DG5.4 | 4 | 88 | 75 | 92 | 194 | 37 | 157 |
| Stewartry | DG6.4 | 3 | 90 | 79 | 93 | 230 | 41 | 189 |
| Stewartry | DG7.1 | 3 | 93 | 86 | 94 | 230 | 44 | 186 |
| Stewartry | DG7.2P | 3 | 93 | 114 | 87 | 94 | 26 | 68 |
| Stewartry | DG7.3P | 3 | 78* | 83 | 76* | 152 | 35 | 117 |
| Stewartry | KA6.7P | n/a | - | - | - | 0 | 0 | 0 |
| Wigtown | DG7.2P | n/a | - | - | - | 0 | 0 | 0 |
| Wigtown | DG7.3P | n/a | - | - | - | 0 | 0 | 0 |
| Wigtown | DG8.0P | 3 | 114 | 100 | 119 | 94 | 21 | 73 |
| Wigtown | DG8.6P | 3 | 100 | 93 | 101 | 182 | 36 | 146 |

| L. A. District | Sector | DEPCAT | SMR | S64 | S65 | Obs | O64 | O65 |
|---|---|---|---|---|---|---|---|---|
| Wigtown | DG8.7 | 4 | 138* | 85 | 152* | 91 | 12 | 79 |
| Wigtown | DG8.8 | 4 | 100 | 132 | 91 | 103 | 31 | 72 |
| Wigtown | DG8.9 | 3 | 99 | 116 | 94 | 140 | 37 | 103 |
| Wigtown | DG9.0 | 3 | 96 | 90 | 98 | 144 | 37 | 107 |
| Wigtown | DG9.7 | 6 | 121* | 147* | 112 | 262 | 80 | 182 |
| Wigtown | DG9.8 | 3 | 110 | 97 | 115 | 182 | 46 | 136 |
| Wigtown | DG9.9 | 4 | 92 | 69 | 100 | 93 | 17 | 76 |
| Wigtown | KA26.0P | n/a | - | - | - | 0 | 0 | 0 |

Standardised Mortality Ratios. Health Board: Fife

| L. A. District | Sector | DEPCAT | SMR | S64 | S65 | Obs | O64 | O65 |
|---|---|---|---|---|---|---|---|---|
| Dunfermline | FK10.3P | 3 | 183 | - | 400 | 1 | 0 | 1 |
| Dunfermline | FK10.4P | 3 | 87 | 99 | 81 | 93 | 36 | 57 |
| Dunfermline | FK14.7P | n/a | - | - | - | 0 | 0 | 0 |
| Dunfermline | KY11.1 | 4 | 106 | 100 | 108 | 221 | 63 | 158 |
| Dunfermline | KY11.2 | 3 | 109 | 105 | 110 | 401 | 115 | 286 |
| Dunfermline | KY11.3 | 3 | 90 | 91 | 90 | 127 | 32 | 95 |
| Dunfermline | KY11.4 | 4 | 101 | 105 | 100 | 491 | 170 | 321 |
| Dunfermline | KY11.5 | 1 | 81* | 53* | 110 | 126 | 41 | 85 |
| Dunfermline | KY12.0 | 3 | 89* | 96 | 87* | 369 | 78 | 291 |
| Dunfermline | KY12.7 | 1 | 99 | 76 | 107 | 159 | 29 | 130 |
| Dunfermline | KY12.8 | 3 | 95 | 90 | 97 | 295 | 79 | 216 |
| Dunfermline | KY12.9 | 3 | 107 | 111 | 106 | 380 | 107 | 273 |
| Dunfermline | KY13.7P | n/a | - | - | - | 0 | 0 | 0 |
| Dunfermline | KY2.5P | n/a | 151 | 600 | - | 1 | 1 | 0 |
| Dunfermline | KY3.0P | 1 | 82 | 57 | 88 | 69 | 10 | 59 |
| Dunfermline | KY4.0P | 1 | 109 | 115 | 107 | 252 | 71 | 181 |
| Dunfermline | KY4.8 | 4 | 102 | 90 | 107 | 252 | 56 | 196 |
| Dunfermline | KY4.9 | 4 | 105 | 122* | 98 | 331 | 107 | 224 |
| Dunfermline | KY5.0P | n/a | - | - | - | 0 | 0 | 0 |
| Dunfermline | KY5.8P | 6 | 113* | 126* | 107 | 264 | 91 | 173 |
| Dunfermline | KY5.9 | 4 | 106 | 98 | 109 | 328 | 78 | 250 |
| Kirkcaldy | KY1.1 | 3 | 103 | 116 | 100 | 312 | 65 | 247 |
| Kirkcaldy | KY1.2 | 4 | 99 | 111 | 96 | 358 | 74 | 284 |
| Kirkcaldy | KY1.3 | 5 | 106 | 102 | 108 | 298 | 62 | 236 |
| Kirkcaldy | KY1.4 | 4 | 102 | 115 | 99 | 256 | 59 | 197 |
| Kirkcaldy | KY2.5P | 3 | 93 | 91 | 93 | 496 | 94 | 402 |
| Kirkcaldy | KY2.6 | 3 | 92 | 81* | 99 | 444 | 153 | 291 |
| Kirkcaldy | KY3.0P | 4 | 105 | 107 | 105 | 129 | 33 | 96 |
| Kirkcaldy | KY3.9 | 3 | 95 | 95 | 95 | 246 | 52 | 194 |
| Kirkcaldy | KY5.0P | 4 | 97 | 81 | 103 | 317 | 64 | 253 |
| Kirkcaldy | KY5.8P | n/a | - | - | - | 0 | 0 | 0 |
| Kirkcaldy | KY6.1 | 4 | 119* | 94 | 132* | 159 | 44 | 115 |
| Kirkcaldy | KY6.2 | 3 | 90 | 93 | 87 | 155 | 66 | 89 |
| Kirkcaldy | KY6.3P | 3 | 101 | 103 | 100 | 161 | 37 | 124 |
| Kirkcaldy | KY7.4 | 4 | 101 | 117 | 91 | 187 | 84 | 103 |
| Kirkcaldy | KY7.5 | 4 | 95 | 102 | 91 | 125 | 49 | 76 |
| Kirkcaldy | KY7.6P | 3 | 100 | 100 | 100 | 228 | 63 | 165 |
| Kirkcaldy | KY8.1 | 5 | 127* | 141* | 123* | 322 | 84 | 238 |
| Kirkcaldy | KY8.2 | 5 | 119* | 108 | 126* | 224 | 77 | 147 |
| Kirkcaldy | KY8.3 | 5 | 110 | 137* | 104 | 352 | 88 | 264 |
| Kirkcaldy | KY8.4 | 4 | 100 | 87 | 103 | 357 | 53 | 304 |
| Kirkcaldy | KY8.5P | 4 | 108 | 112 | 106 | 343 | 101 | 242 |
| North East Fife | DD6.8 | 1 | 94 | 89 | 95 | 193 | 38 | 155 |
| North East Fife | DD6.9 | 4 | 93 | 67 | 101 | 125 | 21 | 104 |
| North East Fife | KY10.2 | 4 | 85 | 72 | 88 | 143 | 24 | 119 |
| North East Fife | KY10.3 | 3 | 89 | 102 | 86 | 208 | 42 | 166 |
| North East Fife | KY13.7P | 5 | - | - | - | 0 | 0 | 0 |
| North East Fife | KY14.6P | 4 | 84 | 71 | 87 | 104 | 18 | 86 |
| North East Fife | KY14.7P | 3 | 97 | 62 | 106 | 154 | 21 | 133 |
| North East Fife | KY15.4 | 3 | 78* | 87 | 76* | 196 | 44 | 152 |
| North East Fife | KY15.5 | 2 | 72* | 79 | 70* | 257 | 54 | 203 |
| North East Fife | KY16.0 | 2 | 86 | 78 | 89 | 93 | 25 | 68 |
| North East Fife | KY16.8 | 3 | 77* | 77* | 78* | 304 | 71 | 233 |
| North East Fife | KY16.9 | 2 | 89 | 98 | 88 | 234 | 33 | 201 |
| North East Fife | KY6.3P | n/a | 327 | - | - | 1 | 0 | 0 |
| North East Fife | KY7.6P | n/a | - | - | - | 0 | 0 | 0 |
| North East Fife | KY7.7 | 3 | 92 | 86 | 94 | 262 | 49 | 213 |
| North East Fife | KY8.5P | 2 | 58 | 55 | 60 | 8 | 3 | 5 |
| North East Fife | KY8.6 | 2 | 89 | 74 | 91 | 125 | 15 | 110 |
| North East Fife | KY9.1 | 3 | 70* | 65 | 71* | 83 | 12 | 71 |

Standardised Mortality Ratios. Health Board: Forth Valley

| L. A. District | Sector | DEPCAT | SMR | S64 | S65 | Obs | O64 | O65 |
|---|---|---|---|---|---|---|---|---|
| Clackmannan | FK10.1 | 5 | 122* | 124 | 121* | 165 | 56 | 109 |
| Clackmannan | FK10.2 | 4 | 111* | 106 | 113* | 484 | 141 | 343 |
| Clackmannan | FK10.3P | 4 | 98 | 109 | 93 | 294 | 91 | 203 |
| Clackmannan | FK10.4P | 3 | 122* | 123 | 122 | 125 | 38 | 87 |
| Clackmannan | FK11.7 | 2 | 91 | 75 | 100 | 50 | 15 | 35 |
| Clackmannan | FK12.5 | 3 | 108 | 112 | 106 | 179 | 50 | 129 |
| Clackmannan | FK13.6 | 3 | 91 | 83 | 94 | 183 | 49 | 134 |
| Clackmannan | FK14.7P | 1 | 81 | 61 | 88 | 95 | 19 | 76 |
| Clackmannan | FK7.7P | n/a | - | - | - | 0 | 0 | 0 |
| Clackmannan | FK9.5P | n/a | - | - | - | 0 | 0 | 0 |
| Clackmannan | KY13.7P | 2 | 85 | - | 124 | 4 | 0 | 4 |
| Falkirk | EH49.6P | 6 | 88 | 64 | 103 | 29 | 8 | 21 |
| Falkirk | EH49.7P | 3 | 109 | 67 | 122 | 21 | 3 | 18 |
| Falkirk | EH51.0 | 4 | 99 | 95 | 100 | 227 | 66 | 161 |
| Falkirk | EH51.9 | 4 | 104 | 117 | 99 | 302 | 84 | 218 |
| Falkirk | FK1.1 | 3 | 86* | 95 | 85* | 240 | 39 | 201 |
| Falkirk | FK1.2P | 4 | 104 | 84 | 115 | 192 | 57 | 135 |
| Falkirk | FK1.3P | 4 | 126* | 143* | 117 | 83 | 30 | 53 |
| Falkirk | FK1.4 | 4 | 106 | 104 | 107 | 318 | 87 | 231 |
| Falkirk | FK1.5 | 2 | 80* | 73* | 82* | 260 | 58 | 202 |
| Falkirk | FK2.0 | 2 | 92 | 87 | 95 | 284 | 85 | 199 |
| Falkirk | FK2.7 | 5 | 104 | 123* | 98 | 363 | 102 | 261 |
| Falkirk | FK2.8P | 4 | 99 | 101 | 98 | 174 | 56 | 118 |
| Falkirk | FK2.9 | 5 | 98 | 88 | 102 | 396 | 104 | 292 |
| Falkirk | FK3.0 | 5 | 83* | 70* | 92 | 125 | 45 | 80 |
| Falkirk | FK3.8 | 5 | 101 | 118 | 95 | 377 | 114 | 263 |
| Falkirk | FK3.9 | 4 | 105 | 101 | 107 | 186 | 54 | 132 |
| Falkirk | FK4.1 | 4 | 102 | 103 | 102 | 287 | 84 | 203 |
| Falkirk | FK4.2P | 5 | 97 | 129 | 83 | 69 | 29 | 40 |
| Falkirk | FK5.3 | 3 | 96 | 62* | 109 | 173 | 32 | 141 |
| Falkirk | FK5.4P | 3 | 87* | 104 | 82* | 427 | 118 | 309 |
| Falkirk | FK6.5P | 3 | 101 | 104 | 100 | 175 | 63 | 112 |
| Falkirk | FK6.6P | 5 | 89 | 102 | 84 | 185 | 58 | 127 |
| Falkirk | FK7.7P | 3 | 190 | 215 | 177 | 5 | 2 | 3 |
| Falkirk | G67.3P | n/a | - | - | - | 0 | 0 | 0 |
| Falkirk | G68.0P | n/a | - | - | - | 0 | 0 | 0 |
| Stirling | FK15.0P | 1 | 106 | 50* | 122* | 125 | 13 | 112 |
| Stirling | FK15.9P | 2 | 93 | 68 | 101 | 131 | 25 | 106 |
| Stirling | FK16.6 | 3 | 82 | 87 | 80 | 54 | 15 | 39 |
| Stirling | FK17.8 | 2 | 82* | 89 | 80 | 112 | 26 | 86 |
| Stirling | FK18.8 | 6 | 95 | 133 | 74 | 6 | 3 | 3 |
| Stirling | FK19.8P | 2 | 77 | 70 | 79 | 18 | 3 | 15 |
| Stirling | FK2.8P | 1 | 96 | - | 133 | 3 | 0 | 3 |
| Stirling | FK20.8P | 2 | 89 | 57 | 103 | 10 | 2 | 8 |
| Stirling | FK21.8P | 3 | 77 | 50 | 84 | 29 | 4 | 25 |
| Stirling | FK5.4P | n/a | - | - | - | 0 | 0 | 0 |
| Stirling | FK6.5P | 4 | 42 | - | 62 | 1 | 0 | 1 |
| Stirling | FK6.6P | n/a | - | - | - | 0 | 0 | 0 |
| Stirling | FK7.0 | 4 | 98 | 90 | 101 | 298 | 73 | 225 |
| Stirling | FK7.7P | 5 | 122* | 110 | 127* | 293 | 86 | 207 |
| Stirling | FK7.8 | 4 | 97 | 101 | 95 | 167 | 45 | 122 |
| Stirling | FK7.9 | 4 | 97 | 90 | 101 | 203 | 61 | 142 |
| Stirling | FK8.1 | 6 | 106 | 129* | 99 | 374 | 97 | 277 |
| Stirling | FK8.2 | 1 | 88 | 63 | 95 | 120 | 20 | 100 |
| Stirling | FK8.3 | 2 | 101 | 72 | 110 | 223 | 37 | 186 |
| Stirling | FK9.4 | 2 | 93 | 76 | 98 | 209 | 40 | 169 |
| Stirling | FK9.5P | 3 | 92 | 91 | 92 | 140 | 43 | 97 |
| Stirling | G62.8P | 1 | 32 | - | 51 | 1 | 0 | 1 |
| Stirling | G63.0P | 2 | 95 | 102 | 93 | 156 | 39 | 117 |
| Stirling | G63.9P | 1 | 74* | 61* | 79 | 98 | 24 | 74 |
| Stirling | G83.7P | n/a | - | - | - | 0 | 0 | 0 |
| Stirling | G83.8P | n/a | - | - | - | 0 | 0 | 0 |
| Stirling | G83.9P | n/a | - | - | - | 0 | 0 | 0 |

Standardised Mortality Ratios. Health Board: Grampian

| L. A. District | Sector | DEPCAT | SMR | S64 | S65 | Obs | O64 | O65 |
|---|---|---|---|---|---|---|---|---|
| Aberdeen City | AB1.0P | 2 | 86* | 54* | 98 | 193 | 32 | 161 |
| Aberdeen City | AB1.1 | 4 | 96 | 81 | 102 | 204 | 42 | 162 |
| Aberdeen City | AB1.2 | 3 | 108 | 92 | 112 | 277 | 47 | 230 |
| Aberdeen City | AB1.3 | 4 | 104 | 108 | 103 | 491 | 115 | 376 |
| Aberdeen City | AB1.4P | 4 | 104 | 131* | 88 | 114 | 54 | 60 |
| Aberdeen City | AB1.5P | 4 | 89 | 79* | 95 | 273 | 93 | 180 |

| | | | | | | | | |
|---|---|---|---|---|---|---|---|---|
| Aberdeen City | AB1.6 | 2 | 91* | 86 | 92 | 677 | 98 | 579 |
| Aberdeen City | AB1.7 | 2 | 94 | 83 | 97 | 629 | 117 | 512 |
| Aberdeen City | AB1.8P | 1 | 84* | 66* | 91 | 180 | 35 | 145 |
| Aberdeen City | AB1.9 | 1 | 82* | 56* | 92 | 167 | 31 | 136 |
| Aberdeen City | AB2.0P | 2 | 92 | 66* | 106 | 142 | 36 | 106 |
| Aberdeen City | AB2.1 | 5 | 109* | 116 | 107 | 607 | 125 | 482 |
| Aberdeen City | AB2.2 | 4 | 110* | 116 | 109* | 809 | 161 | 648 |
| Aberdeen City | AB2.3 | 4 | 100 | 95 | 101 | 446 | 85 | 361 |
| Aberdeen City | AB2.4 | 2 | 87* | 77 | 89* | 569 | 81 | 488 |
| Aberdeen City | AB2.5 | 4 | 91* | 84* | 94 | 611 | 158 | 453 |
| Aberdeen City | AB2.6 | 4 | 101 | 86 | 107 | 559 | 142 | 417 |
| Aberdeen City | AB2.7 | 6 | 103 | 85 | 114* | 343 | 107 | 236 |
| Aberdeen City | AB2.8P | 2 | 84* | 77* | 89 | 243 | 81 | 162 |
| Aberdeen City | AB2.9 | 3 | 94 | 75* | 101 | 303 | 65 | 238 |
| Aberdeen City | AB3.3P | n/a | - | - | - | 0 | 0 | 0 |
| Aberdeen City | AB3.6P | n/a | - | - | - | 0 | 0 | 0 |
| Aberdeen City | AB4.0P | n/a | - | - | - | 0 | 0 | 0 |
| Aberdeen City | AB5.0P | 4 | 17 | - | 25 | 1 | 0 | 1 |
| Banff & Buchan | AB4.0P | 1 | 83 | - | 120 | 2 | 0 | 2 |
| Banff & Buchan | AB4.1 | 4 | 93 | 81 | 96 | 321 | 59 | 262 |
| Banff & Buchan | AB4.2P | 3 | 87 | 87 | 88 | 203 | 43 | 160 |
| Banff & Buchan | AB4.3 | 3 | 85 | 70 | 91 | 77 | 17 | 60 |
| Banff & Buchan | AB4.4 | 4 | 84* | 79 | 85* | 252 | 59 | 193 |
| Banff & Buchan | AB4.5 | 4 | 93 | 81* | 97 | 507 | 118 | 389 |
| Banff & Buchan | AB4.6 | 4 | 107 | 103 | 109 | 539 | 152 | 387 |
| Banff & Buchan | AB4.7P | 3 | 99 | 83 | 107 | 213 | 53 | 160 |
| Banff & Buchan | AB4.8P | 3 | 82* | 77 | 83* | 216 | 44 | 172 |
| Banff & Buchan | AB4.9P | 1 | 80 | 89 | 74 | 9 | 4 | 5 |
| Banff & Buchan | AB5.0P | 4 | 261 | 561 | 126 | 3 | 2 | 1 |
| Banff & Buchan | AB5.2P | n/a | 157 | - | 205 | 2 | 0 | 2 |
| Banff & Buchan | AB5.5P | 3 | 87 | 81 | 88 | 73 | 12 | 61 |
| Banff & Buchan | AB5.6P | 5 | 66 | 85 | 59 | 3 | 1 | 2 |
| Banff & Buchan | AB5.7 | 2 | 85* | 86 | 85* | 240 | 51 | 189 |
| Banff & Buchan | AB5.8P | 2 | 75 | 76 | 74* | 86 | 23 | 63 |
| Banff & Buchan | AB5.9P | 1 | - | - | - | 0 | 0 | 0 |
| Gordon | AB1.8P | 1 | 59 | 153 | 36 | 2 | 1 | 1 |
| Gordon | AB2.0P | 1 | 54 | 59 | 53 | 10 | 3 | 7 |
| Gordon | AB2.8P | 1 | 142 | - | 181 | 4 | 0 | 4 |
| Gordon | AB3.3P | n/a | - | - | - | 0 | 0 | 0 |
| Gordon | AB3.4P | 3 | - | - | - | 0 | 0 | 0 |
| Gordon | AB3.6P | 1 | 64* | 47* | 77 | 65 | 20 | 45 |
| Gordon | AB3.7P | 2 | 81 | 82 | 81 | 73 | 18 | 55 |
| Gordon | AB3.8P | 2 | 89 | 73 | 94 | 132 | 24 | 108 |
| Gordon | AB4.0P | 2 | 87 | 76 | 91 | 210 | 52 | 158 |
| Gordon | AB4.7P | n/a | 180 | - | 336 | 1 | 0 | 1 |
| Gordon | AB4.8P | n/a | - | - | - | 0 | 0 | 0 |
| Gordon | AB4.9P | 2 | 86 | 62* | 95 | 176 | 37 | 139 |
| Gordon | AB5.0P | 2 | 80* | 80 | 81* | 309 | 63 | 246 |
| Gordon | AB5.3P | 1 | 70 | - | 96 | 1 | 0 | 1 |
| Gordon | AB5.4P | 2 | 92 | 71 | 99 | 107 | 19 | 88 |
| Gordon | AB5.5P | 3 | 87* | 93 | 85 | 206 | 40 | 166 |
| Gordon | AB5.6P | 2 | 73* | 71 | 73* | 115 | 23 | 92 |
| Gordon | AB5.8P | 1 | 70 | 87 | 62 | 5 | 2 | 3 |
| Gordon | AB5.9P | 2 | 80* | 63* | 85* | 391 | 68 | 323 |
| Kincardine & Deeside | AB1.0P | 1 | 136 | 151 | 130 | 15 | 5 | 10 |
| Kincardine & Deeside | AB1.4P | 2 | 75 | 71 | 79 | 39 | 17 | 22 |
| Kincardine & Deeside | AB1.5P | 1 | 81 | 34 | 99 | 17 | 2 | 15 |
| Kincardine & Deeside | AB3.1P | 3 | 81* | 75 | 83 | 160 | 36 | 124 |
| Kincardine & Deeside | AB3.2 | 2 | 86* | 71* | 91 | 373 | 73 | 300 |
| Kincardine & Deeside | AB3.3P | 2 | 90 | 77 | 93 | 250 | 47 | 203 |
| Kincardine & Deeside | AB3.4P | 2 | 84 | 51* | 93 | 141 | 18 | 123 |
| Kincardine & Deeside | AB3.5 | 3 | 87* | 69 | 90 | 234 | 33 | 201 |
| Kincardine & Deeside | AB3.7P | n/a | - | - | - | 0 | 0 | 0 |
| Kincardine & Deeside | AB3.8P | 5 | - | - | - | 0 | 0 | 0 |
| Kincardine & Deeside | DD10.0P | 3 | 93 | 93 | 93 | 163 | 37 | 126 |
| Kincardine & Deeside | DD9.7P | 1 | - | - | - | 0 | 0 | 0 |
| Moray | AB3.9P | 2 | 82* | 76 | 83 | 111 | 24 | 87 |
| Moray | AB4.2P | n/a | - | - | - | 0 | 0 | 0 |
| Moray | AB5.1 | 4 | 97 | 89 | 100 | 309 | 68 | 241 |
| Moray | AB5.2P | 4 | 78* | 91 | 75* | 240 | 54 | 186 |
| Moray | AB5.3P | 4 | 95 | 66 | 104 | 254 | 43 | 211 |
| Moray | AB5.4P | 3 | 90 | 76 | 93 | 92 | 16 | 76 |
| Moray | AB5.5P | 3 | 86 | 75 | 90 | 19 | 5 | 14 |
| Moray | IV30.1 | 2 | 92 | 95 | 92 | 288 | 45 | 243 |
| Moray | IV30.2 | 3 | 85* | 85 | 85* | 306 | 87 | 219 |
| Moray | IV30.3 | 3 | 91 | 99 | 87 | 283 | 98 | 185 |
| Moray | IV31.6 | 3 | 100 | 75 | 110 | 203 | 43 | 160 |
| Moray | IV32.7 | 2 | 87 | 104 | 82* | 160 | 42 | 118 |
| Moray | IV33.7 | 4 | 86 | 53 | 97 | 52 | 8 | 44 |

| L. A. District | Sector | DEPCAT | SMR | S64 | S65 | Obs | O64 | O65 |
|---|---|---|---|---|---|---|---|---|
| Moray | IV34.7 | 3 | 127 | 143 | 121 | 23 | 7 | 16 |
| Moray | IV35.7 | 3 | 100 | 59 | 130 | 8 | 2 | 6 |
| Moray | IV36.0P | 3 | 101 | 95 | 104 | 443 | 113 | 330 |
| Moray | PH26.3P | n/a | - | - | - | 0 | 0 | 0 |

Standardised Mortality Ratios. Health Board: Greater Glasgow

| L. A. District | Sector | DEPCAT | SMR | S64 | S65 | Obs | O64 | O65 |
|---|---|---|---|---|---|---|---|---|
| Bearsden & Milngavie | G61.1P | 1 | 67* | 67* | 66* | 156 | 43 | 113 |
| Bearsden & Milngavie | G61.2 | 1 | 85* | 78 | 87 | 218 | 51 | 167 |
| Bearsden & Milngavie | G61.3 | 1 | 80* | 62* | 87 | 185 | 40 | 145 |
| Bearsden & Milngavie | G61.4 | 1 | 78* | 59* | 91 | 133 | 42 | 91 |
| Bearsden & Milngavie | G62.6P | 1 | 76* | 62* | 79* | 128 | 22 | 106 |
| Bearsden & Milngavie | G62.7 | 3 | 87 | 83 | 90 | 152 | 52 | 100 |
| Bearsden & Milngavie | G62.8P | 1 | 92 | 59 | 103 | 106 | 17 | 89 |
| Bearsden & Milngavie | G63.9P | n/a | - | - | - | 0 | 0 | 0 |
| Bearsden & Milngavie | G81.5P | n/a | - | - | - | 0 | 0 | 0 |
| Clydebank | G13.4P | n/a | - | - | - | 0 | 0 | 0 |
| Clydebank | G15.8P | n/a | - | - | - | 0 | 0 | 0 |
| Clydebank | G60.5P | 3 | 94 | 108 | 89 | 118 | 33 | 85 |
| Clydebank | G81.1P | 6 | 116* | 116 | 116* | 318 | 81 | 237 |
| Clydebank | G81.2 | 6 | 105 | 118 | 100 | 344 | 110 | 234 |
| Clydebank | G81.3 | 5 | 101 | 91 | 105 | 396 | 98 | 298 |
| Clydebank | G81.4 | 5 | 118* | 141* | 109 | 395 | 127 | 268 |
| Clydebank | G81.5 | 6 | 92 | 84 | 98 | 172 | 69 | 103 |
| Clydebank | G81.6 | 3 | 103 | 106 | 101 | 158 | 65 | 93 |
| Eastwood | G44.3P | 1 | 82* | 62* | 87 | 148 | 25 | 123 |
| Eastwood | G46.6 | 1 | 90 | 94 | 89 | 303 | 75 | 228 |
| Eastwood | G46.7P | 2 | 83* | 65* | 89 | 217 | 43 | 174 |
| Eastwood | G46.8P | 4 | 111 | 127 | 107 | 25 | 6 | 19 |
| Eastwood | G76.0 | 1 | 82* | 84 | 81 | 114 | 39 | 75 |
| Eastwood | G76.7 | 1 | 72* | 57* | 77* | 216 | 47 | 169 |
| Eastwood | G76.8P | 3 | 77* | 64* | 81* | 192 | 34 | 158 |
| Eastwood | G77.5 | 1 | 62* | 46* | 67* | 193 | 38 | 155 |
| Eastwood | G77.6P | 2 | 89 | 71* | 97 | 189 | 43 | 146 |
| Eastwood | G78.2P | n/a | - | - | - | 0 | 0 | 0 |
| Eastwood | G78.3P | n/a | - | - | - | 0 | 0 | 0 |
| Glasgow City | G1.1 | 5 | 140 | 159 | 125 | 6 | 3 | 3 |
| Glasgow City | G1.2 | 6 | 115 | 119 | 114 | 31 | 7 | 24 |
| Glasgow City | G1.3 | n/a | 314 | 338 | 293 | 2 | 1 | 1 |
| Glasgow City | G1.4 | 3 | 247* | 276 | 224 | 6 | 3 | 3 |
| Glasgow City | G1.5 | 7 | 146* | 257* | 120 | 118 | 39 | 79 |
| Glasgow City | G11.5 | 5 | 103 | 107 | 102 | 289 | 62 | 227 |
| Glasgow City | G11.6 | 6 | 121* | 147* | 114 | 135 | 35 | 100 |
| Glasgow City | G11.7 | 3 | 93 | 84 | 95 | 493 | 78 | 415 |
| Glasgow City | G12.0 | 1 | 116* | 85 | 122* | 565 | 68 | 497 |
| Glasgow City | G12.8 | 4 | 114 | 97 | 120* | 204 | 45 | 159 |
| Glasgow City | G12.9 | 2 | 87* | 77 | 89 | 321 | 47 | 274 |
| Glasgow City | G13.1 | 4 | 108 | 89 | 114* | 344 | 63 | 281 |
| Glasgow City | G13.2 | 6 | 96 | 121* | 90* | 542 | 134 | 408 |
| Glasgow City | G13.3 | 4 | 98 | 118* | 94 | 788 | 175 | 613 |
| Glasgow City | G13.4P | 6 | 106 | 117 | 102 | 319 | 96 | 223 |
| Glasgow City | G14.0 | 6 | 123* | 132* | 121* | 449 | 118 | 331 |
| Glasgow City | G14.9 | 4 | 103 | 95 | 105 | 524 | 109 | 415 |
| Glasgow City | G15.6 | 4 | 101 | 131* | 92 | 378 | 121 | 257 |
| Glasgow City | G15.7 | 7 | 140* | 130* | 147* | 439 | 181 | 258 |
| Glasgow City | G15.8 | 7 | 116* | 133* | 103 | 218 | 107 | 111 |
| Glasgow City | G2.1 | n/a | 177 | 319 | - | 1 | 1 | 0 |
| Glasgow City | G2.2 | 7 | 92 | - | 313 | 1 | 0 | 1 |
| Glasgow City | G2.3 | 3 | 151 | 87 | 191 | 9 | 2 | 7 |
| Glasgow City | G2.4 | 6 | 56 | 41 | 64 | 4 | 1 | 3 |
| Glasgow City | G2.5 | n/a | 116 | - | 313 | 1 | 0 | 1 |
| Glasgow City | G2.6 | 7 | - | - | - | 0 | 0 | 0 |
| Glasgow City | G2.7 | 6 | 122 | 151 | 116 | 58 | 11 | 47 |
| Glasgow City | G2.8 | 7 | 360* | 324 | 382 | 6 | 2 | 4 |
| Glasgow City | G20.0 | 6 | 115* | 148* | 106 | 379 | 108 | 271 |
| Glasgow City | G20.6 | 4 | 128* | 111 | 131* | 295 | 45 | 250 |
| Glasgow City | G20.7 | 7 | 123* | 138* | 117 | 160 | 53 | 107 |
| Glasgow City | G20.8 | 6 | 113* | 136* | 107 | 499 | 129 | 370 |
| Glasgow City | G20.9 | 7 | 131* | 158* | 120* | 266 | 89 | 177 |
| Glasgow City | G21.1 | 6 | 124* | 150* | 116* | 498 | 151 | 347 |
| Glasgow City | G21.2 | 7 | 143* | 170* | 134* | 529 | 162 | 367 |
| Glasgow City | G21.3 | 6 | 118* | 139* | 108 | 586 | 215 | 371 |
| Glasgow City | G21.4 | 7 | 123* | 137* | 119* | 496 | 125 | 371 |

| | | | | | | | | |
|---|---|---|---|---|---|---|---|---|
| Glasgow City | G22.5 | 7 | 147* | 164* | 139* | 493 | 168 | 325 |
| Glasgow City | G22.6 | 6 | 114* | 133* | 108 | 529 | 136 | 393 |
| Glasgow City | G22.7 | 7 | 109 | 122* | 103 | 391 | 135 | 256 |
| Glasgow City | G23.5P | 6 | 109 | 119 | 104 | 221 | 81 | 140 |
| Glasgow City | G3.6 | 6 | 121* | 141* | 114 | 170 | 53 | 117 |
| Glasgow City | G3.7 | 6 | 116 | 106 | 120 | 94 | 26 | 68 |
| Glasgow City | G3.8 | 6 | 134* | 177* | 119* | 273 | 91 | 182 |
| Glasgow City | G31.1 | 6 | 133* | 162* | 124* | 258 | 70 | 188 |
| Glasgow City | G31.2, | 5 | 114* | 140* | 105 | 306 | 97 | 209 |
| Glasgow City | G31.3 | 6 | 120* | 165* | 108 | 436 | 128 | 308 |
| Glasgow City | G31.4 | 7 | 119* | 154* | 109 | 373 | 108 | 265 |
| Glasgow City | G31.5 | 7 | 144* | 163* | 139* | 177 | 47 | 130 |
| Glasgow City | G32.0 | 4 | 89 | 63* | 100 | 191 | 41 | 150 |
| Glasgow City | G32.6 | 6 | 114* | 142* | 106 | 552 | 151 | 401 |
| Glasgow City | G32.7 | 7 | 117* | 130* | 113* | 410 | 101 | 309 |
| Glasgow City | G32.8 | 6 | 116* | 131* | 110 | 347 | 114 | 233 |
| Glasgow City | G32.9 | 3 | 98 | 94 | 99 | 382 | 77 | 305 |
| Glasgow City | G33.1 | 7 | 137* | 169* | 121* | 215 | 89 | 126 |
| Glasgow City | G33.2 | 5 | 103 | 99 | 104 | 420 | 80 | 340 |
| Glasgow City | G33.3 | 7 | 115* | 133* | 107 | 478 | 180 | 298 |
| Glasgow City | G33.4 | 7 | 123* | 132* | 116* | 361 | 175 | 186 |
| Glasgow City | G33.5 | 7 | 134* | 143* | 129* | 285 | 108 | 177 |
| Glasgow City | G33.6P | 2 | 95 | 57 | 293 | 2 | 1 | 1 |
| Glasgow City | G34.0 | 7 | 131* | 130* | 132* | 212 | 100 | 112 |
| Glasgow City | G34.9 | 7 | 141* | 146* | 136* | 284 | 141 | 143 |
| Glasgow City | G4.0 | 7 | 121* | 144* | 116* | 542 | 122 | 420 |
| Glasgow City | G4.9 | 6 | 120* | 120 | 119* | 185 | 49 | 136 |
| Glasgow City | G40.1 | 7 | 180* | 197* | 175* | 129 | 31 | 98 |
| Glasgow City | G40.2 | 7 | 163* | 250* | 138* | 196 | 67 | 129 |
| Glasgow City | G40.3 | 7 | 134* | 147* | 129* | 216 | 69 | 147 |
| Glasgow City | G40.4 | 7 | 142* | 195* | 124* | 234 | 83 | 151 |
| Glasgow City | G41.1 | 7 | 142* | 199* | 112 | 56 | 27 | 29 |
| Glasgow City | G41.2 | 4 | 103 | 98 | 104 | 310 | 67 | 243 |
| Glasgow City | G41.3 | 3 | 99 | 122* | 94 | 556 | 113 | 443 |
| Glasgow City | G41.4 | 1 | 96 | 57* | 105 | 232 | 26 | 206 |
| Glasgow City | G41.5 | 2 | 99 | 88 | 102 | 305 | 56 | 249 |
| Glasgow City | G42.0 | 6 | 104 | 114 | 99 | 377 | 113 | 264 |
| Glasgow City | G42.7 | 6 | 114* | 177* | 101 | 300 | 84 | 216 |
| Glasgow City | G42.8 | 5 | 105 | 101 | 105 | 556 | 109 | 447 |
| Glasgow City | G42.9 | 4 | 94 | 96 | 93 | 470 | 80 | 390 |
| Glasgow City | G43.1 | 5 | 103 | 117 | 100 | 523 | 111 | 412 |
| Glasgow City | G43.2 | 2 | 83* | 71* | 87* | 439 | 94 | 345 |
| Glasgow City | G44.3P | 2 | 96 | 81 | 101 | 165 | 33 | 132 |
| Glasgow City | G44.4 | 3 | 86* | 79 | 88* | 404 | 71 | 333 |
| Glasgow City | G44.5 | 2 | 78* | 66* | 82* | 303 | 61 | 242 |
| Glasgow City | G45.0 | 7 | 118* | 115 | 120* | 308 | 118 | 190 |
| Glasgow City | G45.9 | 7 | 116* | 137* | 106 | 587 | 236 | 351 |
| Glasgow City | G46.7P | 4 | 87 | 165 | 59 | 4 | 2 | 2 |
| Glasgow City | G46.8P | 6 | 124* | 136* | 116* | 349 | 139 | 210 |
| Glasgow City | G5.0 | 7 | 130* | 144* | 125* | 542 | 152 | 390 |
| Glasgow City | G5.8 | 7 | 223* | 376* | 102 | 35 | 26 | 9 |
| Glasgow City | G5.9 | 7 | 141* | 165* | 131* | 195 | 65 | 130 |
| Glasgow City | G51.1 | 6 | 132* | 149* | 127* | 306 | 84 | 222 |
| Glasgow City | G51.2 | 7 | 131* | 138* | 128* | 489 | 140 | 349 |
| Glasgow City | G51.3 | 7 | 124* | 151* | 115 | 232 | 68 | 164 |
| Glasgow City | G51.4 | 6 | 123* | 142* | 117* | 555 | 150 | 405 |
| Glasgow City | G52.1 | 5 | 111* | 122* | 108 | 648 | 147 | 501 |
| Glasgow City | G52.2 | 5 | 104 | 107 | 103 | 635 | 141 | 494 |
| Glasgow City | G52.3P | 3 | 102 | 115 | 99 | 513 | 104 | 409 |
| Glasgow City | G52.4P | 6 | 115* | 127* | 111 | 239 | 77 | 162 |
| Glasgow City | G53.5 | 7 | 108 | 115 | 105 | 509 | 172 | 337 |
| Glasgow City | G53.6 | 7 | 120* | 143* | 107 | 361 | 148 | 213 |
| Glasgow City | G53.7P | 6 | 112* | 142* | 104 | 598 | 158 | 440 |
| Glasgow City | G61.1P | 1 | 89 | - | 111 | 9 | 0 | 9 |
| Glasgow City | G62.6P | n/a | - | - | - | 0 | 0 | 0 |
| Glasgow City | G64.1P | 4 | 187 | 142 | 209 | 8 | 2 | 6 |
| Glasgow City | G64.2P | 2 | 123 | 116 | 124 | 9 | 1 | 8 |
| Glasgow City | G69.6P | 3 | 87 | 87 | 87 | 210 | 57 | 153 |
| Glasgow City | G69.7P | 5 | 115* | 117 | 114 | 239 | 86 | 153 |
| Glasgow City | G69.8P | 5 | 67* | 143 | 59* | 64 | 13 | 51 |
| Glasgow City | G71.7P | 6 | 80 | 93 | 76 | 13 | 4 | 9 |
| Glasgow City | G72.7 | 6 | 108 | 124* | 102 | 324 | 105 | 219 |
| Glasgow City | G72.8P | 4 | 103 | 91 | 109 | 382 | 109 | 273 |
| Glasgow City | G72.9P | n/a | - | - | - | 0 | 0 | 0 |
| Glasgow City | G73.1 | 6 | 127* | 159* | 116 | 193 | 61 | 132 |
| Glasgow City | G73.2 | 3 | 99 | 101 | 99 | 381 | 80 | 301 |
| Glasgow City | G73.3 | 3 | 101 | 108 | 99 | 435 | 95 | 340 |
| Glasgow City | G73.4P | 5 | 116* | 108 | 119* | 346 | 111 | 235 |
| Glasgow City | G73.5P | 5 | 101 | 95 | 103 | 254 | 68 | 186 |

| L. A. District | Sector | DEPCAT | SMR | S64 | S65 | Obs | O64 | O65 |
|---|---|---|---|---|---|---|---|---|
| Glasgow City | G76.9P | 1 | 83 | 77 | 84 | 42 | 9 | 33 |
| Glasgow City | G77.6P | n/a | - | - | - | 0 | 0 | 0 |
| Glasgow City | G78.IP | 2 | 415* | - | 600* | 6 | 0 | 6 |
| Glasgow City | G78.2P | n/a | - | - | - | 0 | 0 | 0 |
| Glasgow City | G81.IP | 2 | - | - | - | 0 | 0 | 0 |
| Glasgow City | PA1.3P | n/a | - | - | - | 0 | 0 | 0 |
| Glasgow City | PA4.8P | n/a | - | - | - | 0 | 0 | 0 |
| Strathkelvin | G23.5P | n/a | - | - | - | 0 | 0 | 0 |
| Strathkelvin | G33.6P | 3 | 100 | 86 | 105 | 146 | 36 | 110 |
| Strathkelvin | G62.6P | 1 | 88 | 109 | 79 | 8 | 3 | 5 |
| Strathkelvin | G62.8P | 3 | - | - | - | 0 | 0 | 0 |
| Strathkelvin | G63.0P | n/a | - | - | - | 0 | 0 | 0 |
| Strathkelvin | G64.1P | 3 | 96 | 81 | 107 | 219 | 79 | 140 |
| Strathkelvin | G64.2P | 2 | 79* | 64* | 87 | 120 | 36 | 84 |
| Strathkelvin | G64.3 | 1 | 76* | 55* | 95 | 102 | 35 | 67 |
| Strathkelvin | G64.4 | 1 | 95 | 81 | 102 | 67 | 18 | 49 |
| Strathkelvin | G65.0P | n/a | - | - | - | 0 | 0 | 0 |
| Strathkelvin | G65.7 | 4 | 113 | 152* | 97 | 203 | 78 | 125 |
| Strathkelvin | G65.8 | 2 | 124* | 98 | 138* | 104 | 29 | 75 |
| Strathkelvin | G65.9P | 6 | 123 | 137 | 117 | 69 | 23 | 46 |
| Strathkelvin | G66.1 | 2 | 101 | 87 | 107 | 138 | 31 | 107 |
| Strathkelvin | G66.2 | 5 | 103 | 100 | 105 | 271 | 93 | 178 |
| Strathkelvin | G66.3 | 2 | 75* | 83 | 72* | 268 | 64 | 204 |
| Strathkelvin | G66.4 | 2 | 98 | 72* | 112 | 187 | 48 | 139 |
| Strathkelvin | G66.5 | 1 | 77* | 47* | 94 | 71 | 16 | 55 |
| Strathkelvin | G67.4P | 3 | 121 | 78 | 136 | 6 | 1 | 5 |
| Strathkelvin | G68.9P | n/a | - | - | - | 0 | 0 | 0 |
| Strathkelvin | G69.0 | 5 | 120* | 115 | 123* | 181 | 64 | 117 |
| Strathkelvin | G69.8P | 5 | 101 | 98 | 102 | 60 | 15 | 45 |
| Strathkelvin | G69.9 | 4 | 100 | 97 | 100 | 137 | 31 | 106 |

Standardised Mortality Ratios. Health Board: Highland

| L. A. District | Sector | DEPCAT | SMR | S64 | S65 | Obs | O64 | O65 |
|---|---|---|---|---|---|---|---|---|
| Badenoch & Strathspey | AB3.9P | n/a | - | - | - | 0 | 0 | 0 |
| Badenoch & Strathspey | PHI9.1 | 2 | 135 | 181 | - | 3 | 3 | 0 |
| Badenoch & Strathspey | PH20.1 | 2 | 104 | 81 | 109 | 63 | 9 | 54 |
| Badenoch & Strathspey | PH21.1 | 3 | 99 | 95 | 100 | 78 | 15 | 63 |
| Badenoch & Strathspey | PH22.1 | 4 | 70 | 51 | 80 | 35 | 9 | 26 |
| Badenoch & Strathspey | PH23.3 | 4 | 68 | 165 | 33 | 11 | 7 | 4 |
| Badenoch & Strathspey | PH24.3 | 3 | 98 | 137 | 88 | 24 | 7 | 17 |
| Badenoch & Strathspey | PH25.3 | 3 | 88 | 61 | 96 | 26 | 4 | 22 |
| Badenoch & Strathspey | PH26.3P | 2 | 105 | 109 | 104 | 144 | 32 | 112 |
| Badenoch & Strathspey | PH31.4P | n/a | - | - | - | 0 | 0 | 0 |
| Caithness | KW1.4 | 4 | 110 | 123 | 105 | 209 | 64 | 145 |
| Caithness | KW1.5 | 4 | 106 | 119 | 102 | 263 | 65 | 198 |
| Caithness | KW12.6 | 3 | 145* | 140 | 147* | 79 | 18 | 61 |
| Caithness | KW14.7P | 2 | 107 | 85 | 119* | 196 | 54 | 142 |
| Caithness | KW14.8 | 3 | 97 | 103 | 94 | 202 | 58 | 144 |
| Caithness | KW2.6 | 7 | 83 | 94 | 78 | 3 | 1 | 2 |
| Caithness | KW3.6 | 4 | 133* | 214* | 112 | 54 | 18 | 36 |
| Caithness | KW5.6 | 5 | 131 | 81 | 146 | 21 | 3 | 18 |
| Caithness | KW6.6 | 5 | 126 | 156 | 118 | 23 | 6 | 17 |
| Caithness | KW7.6 | 1 | 63 | 158 | 45 | 5 | 2 | 3 |
| Inverness | IVI.IP | 3 | 130 | 204* | 108 | 36 | 13 | 23 |
| Inverness | IV1.2P | 3 | 94 | 90 | 96 | 233 | 73 | 160 |
| Inverness | IV13.7 | 3 | 100 | 89 | 104 | 17 | 4 | 13 |
| Inverness | IV2.3 | 2 | 82* | 76* | 84* | 248 | 65 | 183 |
| Inverness | IV2.4 | 3 | 91 | 88 | 92 | 371 | 96 | 275 |
| Inverness | IV3.5 | 4 | 109 | 113 | 108 | 457 | 100 | 357 |
| Inverness | IV3.6P | 4 | 105 | 113 | 103 | 405 | 112 | 293 |
| Inverness | IV4.7P | 3 | 96 | 80 | 102 | 102 | 24 | 78 |
| Inverness | IV5.7 | 2 | 89 | 114 | 81 | 22 | 7 | 15 |
| Inverness | PH32.4 | 3 | 135 | 210* | 115 | 40 | 13 | 27 |
| Inverness | PH35.4P | n/a | 68 | - | 92 | 1 | 0 | 1 |
| Lochaber | IV40.8P | n/a | - | - | - | 0 | 0 | 0 |
| Lochaber | PA34.5P | 4 | 66 | 83 | 57 | 7 | 3 | 4 |
| Lochaber | PA38.4P | 2 | 140 | 382* | 99 | 15 | 6 | 9 |
| Lochaber | PA39.4 | 4 | 82 | 91 | 79 | 36 | 9 | 27 |
| Lochaber | PA40.4 | 3 | 96 | 110 | 92 | 50 | 14 | 36 |
| Lochaber | PH30.4 | n/a | - | - | - | 0 | 0 | 0 |
| Lochaber | PH31.4P | 4 | 93 | 91 | 94 | 14 | 4 | 10 |
| Lochaber | PH33.6 | 3 | 116* | 100 | 123* | 223 | 57 | 166 |
| Lochaber | PH33.7 | 5 | 97 | 108 | 93 | 164 | 54 | 110 |

| L. A. District | Sector | DEPCAT | SMR | S64 | S65 | Obs | O64 | O65 |
|---|---|---|---|---|---|---|---|---|
| Lochaber | PH34.4 | 2 | 106 | 122 | 100 | 28 | 9 | 19 |
| Lochaber | PH35.4P | 4 | 106 | 76 | 114 | 13 | 2 | 11 |
| Lochaber | PH36.4 | 2 | 108 | 134 | 103 | 59 | 12 | 47 |
| Lochaber | PH37.4 | 6 | 96 | - | 130 | 3 | 0 | 3 |
| Lochaber | PH38.4 | 2 | 131 | 110 | 135 | 7 | 1 | 6 |
| Lochaber | PH39.4 | 5 | 82 | 33 | 94 | 13 | 1 | 12 |
| Lochaber | PH40.4 | 4 | 79 | 125 | 65 | 8 | 3 | 5 |
| Lochaber | PH41.4P | 4 | 99 | 104 | 97 | 30 | 9 | 21 |
| Lochaber | PH42.4 | 5 | 202 | 498 | 92 | 6 | 4 | 2 |
| Lochaber | PH43.4 | 1 | - | - | - | 0 | 0 | 0 |
| Lochaber | PH44.4 | n/a | - | - | - | 0 | 0 | 0 |
| Nairn | IV1.2P | 3 | 108 | 75 | 126 | 4 | 1 | 3 |
| Nairn | IV12.4 | 2 | 101 | 93 | 103 | 198 | 35 | 163 |
| Nairn | IV12.5 | 3 | 104 | 93 | 107 | 228 | 47 | 181 |
| Nairn | IV36.0P | n/a | - | - | - | 0 | 0 | 0 |
| Nairn | PH26.3P | n/a | - | - | - | 0 | 0 | 0 |
| Ross & Cromarty | IV1.1P | 2 | 62* | 87 | 56* | 29 | 8 | 21 |
| Ross & Cromarty | IV10.8 | 2 | 87 | 80 | 89 | 64 | 11 | 53 |
| Ross & Cromarty | IV11.8 | 2 | 72 | 50 | 78 | 29 | 4 | 25 |
| Ross & Cromarty | IV14.9 | 3 | 94 | 117 | 87 | 66 | 20 | 46 |
| Ross & Cromarty | IV15.9 | 3 | 102 | 98 | 103 | 164 | 45 | 119 |
| Ross & Cromarty | IV16.9 | 2 | 99 | 90 | 103 | 42 | 11 | 31 |
| Ross & Cromarty | IV17.0 | 4 | 125* | 121 | 127* | 173 | 59 | 114 |
| Ross & Cromarty | IV18.0 | 3 | 100 | 94 | 102 | 174 | 45 | 129 |
| Ross & Cromarty | IV19.1 | 3 | 87 | 76 | 91 | 126 | 30 | 96 |
| Ross & Cromarty | IV20.1 | 3 | 91 | 80 | 95 | 93 | 21 | 72 |
| Ross & Cromarty | IV21.2 | 4 | 86 | 59 | 92 | 40 | 5 | 35 |
| Ross & Cromarty | IV22.2 | 3 | 93 | 94 | 93 | 53 | 12 | 41 |
| Ross & Cromarty | IV23.2 | 3 | 90 | 69 | 99 | 21 | 5 | 16 |
| Ross & Cromarty | IV24.3P | n/a | - | - | - | 0 | 0 | 0 |
| Ross & Cromarty | IV26.2 | 3 | 85 | 106 | 78 | 47 | 15 | 32 |
| Ross & Cromarty | IV27.4P | n/a | - | - | - | 0 | 0 | 0 |
| Ross & Cromarty | IV4.7P | 3 | 138 | 153 | 132 | 10 | 3 | 7 |
| Ross & Cromarty | IV54.8 | 3 | 87 | 99 | 83 | 49 | 11 | 38 |
| Ross & Cromarty | IV6.7 | 3 | 87 | 84 | 89 | 110 | 24 | 86 |
| Ross & Cromarty | IV7.8 | 2 | 104 | 85 | 111 | 144 | 31 | 113 |
| Ross & Cromarty | IV8.8 | 2 | 108 | 149 | 94 | 22 | 8 | 14 |
| Ross & Cromarty | IV9.8 | 4 | 125 | 116 | 128 | 57 | 12 | 45 |
| Skye & Lochalsh | IV3.6P | n/a | - | - | - | 0 | 0 | 0 |
| Skye & Lochalsh | IV4.7P | n/a | - | - | - | 0 | 0 | 0 |
| Skye & Lochalsh | IV40.8P | 3 | 112 | 91 | 117 | 116 | 20 | 96 |
| Skye & Lochalsh | IV41.8 | 2 | 133 | 158 | 123 | 15 | 5 | 10 |
| Skye & Lochalsh | IV42.8 | 2 | 109 | 93 | 111 | 23 | 3 | 20 |
| Skye & Lochalsh | IV43.8 | 4 | 19 | - | 22 | 2 | 0 | 2 |
| Skye & Lochalsh | IV44.8 | 3 | 14 | 72 | - | 1 | 1 | 0 |
| Skye & Lochalsh | IV45.8 | 3 | 27 | 78 | 21 | 3 | 1 | 2 |
| Skye & Lochalsh | IV46.8 | 3 | 260* | 393 | 231* | 11 | 3 | 8 |
| Skye & Lochalsh | IV47.8 | 4 | 86 | 98 | 84 | 21 | 4 | 17 |
| Skye & Lochalsh | IV48.8 | 4 | 31 | 175 | - | 1 | 1 | 0 |
| Skye & Lochalsh | IV49.9 | 5 | 105 | 138 | 97 | 34 | 9 | 25 |
| Skye & Lochalsh | IV51.9 | 4 | 104 | 123 | 99 | 194 | 45 | 149 |
| Skye & Lochalsh | IV52.8 | 3 | 75 | 35 | 85 | 11 | 1 | 10 |
| Skye & Lochalsh | IV53.8 | 2 | 68 | - | 90 | 2 | 0 | 2 |
| Skye & Lochalsh | IV55.8 | 3 | 48* | 70 | 43* | 27 | 7 | 20 |
| Skye & Lochalsh | IV56.8 | 3 | 91 | 48 | 101 | 10 | 1 | 9 |
| Skye & Lochalsh | PH35.4P | n/a | - | - | - | 0 | 0 | 0 |
| Skye & Lochalsh | PH41.4P | n/a | - | - | - | 0 | 0 | 0 |
| Sutherland | IV24.3P | 3 | 86 | 60 | 92 | 68 | 8 | 60 |
| Sutherland | IV25.3 | 2 | 95 | 116 | 90 | 100 | 23 | 77 |
| Sutherland | IV27.4P | 3 | 102 | 100 | 103 | 173 | 35 | 138 |
| Sutherland | IV28.3 | 2 | 87 | 46 | 96 | 21 | 2 | 19 |
| Sutherland | KW10.6 | 3 | 108 | 96 | 111 | 68 | 15 | 53 |
| Sutherland | KW11.6 | 2 | 66 | 83 | 63 | 5 | 1 | 4 |
| Sutherland | KW13.6 | 2 | 112 | 124 | 110 | 5 | 1 | 4 |
| Sutherland | KW14.7P | 3 | 92 | 65 | 98 | 53 | 7 | 46 |
| Sutherland | KW8.6 | 4 | 120 | 174* | 106 | 61 | 18 | 43 |
| Sutherland | KW9.6 | 4 | 100 | 114 | 96 | 80 | 20 | 60 |

Standardised Mortality Ratios. Health Board: Lanarkshire

| L. A. District | Sector | DEPCAT | SMR | S64 | S65 | Obs | O64 | O65 |
|---|---|---|---|---|---|---|---|---|
| Cumbernauld & Kilsyth | FK1.3P | n/a | - | - | - | 0 | 0 | 0 |
| Cumbernauld & Kilsyth | FK4.2P | n/a | - | - | - | 0 | 0 | 0 |
| Cumbernauld & Kilsyth | FK6.5P | n/a | - | - | - | 0 | 0 | 0 |

| L. A. District | Sector | DEPCAT | SMR | S64 | S65 | Obs | O64 | O65 |
|---|---|---|---|---|---|---|---|---|
| Cumbernauld & Kilsyth | G65.0P | 5 | 104 | 103 | 104 | 274 | 60 | 214 |
| Cumbernauld & Kilsyth | G65.8P | n/a | - | - | - | 0 | 0 | 0 |
| Cumbernauld & Kilsyth | G65.9P | 5 | 108 | 96 | 115 | 205 | 67 | 138 |
| Cumbernauld & Kilsyth | G67.1 | 3 | 106 | 106 | 105 | 174 | 65 | 109 |
| Cumbernauld & Kilsyth | G67.2 | 4 | 106 | 106 | 107 | 335 | 141 | 194 |
| Cumbernauld & Kilsyth | G67.3P | 3 | 107 | 101 | 111 | 186 | 77 | 109 |
| Cumbernauld & Kilsyth | G67.4P | 3 | 98 | 94 | 102 | 162 | 73 | 89 |
| Cumbernauld & Kilsyth | G68.0 | 2 | 137 | - | 320* | 8 | 0 | 8 |
| Cumbernauld & Kilsyth | G68.9P | 3 | 102 | 99 | 104 | 71 | 27 | 44 |
| Cumbernauld & Kilsyth | ML6.7P | n/a | - | - | - | 0 | 0 | 0 |
| East Kilbride | G72.0P | n/a | - | - | - | 0 | 0 | 0 |
| East Kilbride | G72.8P | 1 | - | - | - | 0 | 0 | 0 |
| East Kilbride | G72.9P | 6 | - | - | - | 0 | 0 | 0 |
| East Kilbride | G73.4P | n/a | - | - | - | 0 | 0 | 0 |
| East Kilbride | G73.5P | n/a | - | - | - | 0 | 0 | 0 |
| East Kilbride | G74.1 | 4 | 86 | 67* | 98 | 132 | 38 | 94 |
| East Kilbride | G74.2P | 2 | 93 | 81 | 99 | 239 | 75 | 164 |
| East Kilbride | G74.3 | 3 | 87* | 96 | 82* | 416 | 159 | 257 |
| East Kilbride | G74.4 | 4 | 98 | 90 | 102 | 180 | 55 | 125 |
| East Kilbride | G74.5 | 1 | 132 | 85 | 155 | 19 | 4 | 15 |
| East Kilbride | G75.0 | 4 | 85* | 94 | 80* | 210 | 89 | 121 |
| East Kilbride | G75.8 | 3 | 89 | 80* | 97 | 307 | 120 | 187 |
| East Kilbride | G75.9 | 4 | 99 | 81 | 115 | 147 | 56 | 91 |
| East Kilbride | G76.8P | 2 | 109 | 106 | 110 | 48 | 14 | 34 |
| East Kilbride | G76.9P | 4 | 157 | 147 | 161 | 8 | 2 | 6 |
| East Kilbride | KA17.0P | n/a | - | - | - | 0 | 0 | 0 |
| East Kilbride | ML10.6P | 2 | 89 | 72* | 96 | 257 | 62 | 195 |
| East Kilbride | ML3.7P | n/a | - | - | - | 0 | 0 | 0 |
| East Kilbride | ML3.8P | n/a | - | - | - | 0 | 0 | 0 |
| Hamilton | G71.6P | n/a | - | - | - | 0 | 0 | 0 |
| Hamilton | G71.7P | 3 | 107 | 101 | 109 | 173 | 46 | 127 |
| Hamilton | G71.8P | 3 | 103 | 85 | 110 | 212 | 52 | 160 |
| Hamilton | G72.0P | 6 | 120* | 135* | 113 | 318 | 106 | 212 |
| Hamilton | G72.9P | 4 | 110 | 112 | 110 | 279 | 108 | 171 |
| Hamilton | G74.2P | n/a | - | - | - | 0 | 0 | 0 |
| Hamilton | ML10.6P | 5 | - | - | - | 0 | 0 | 0 |
| Hamilton | ML3.0 | 6 | 105 | 118 | 100 | 224 | 66 | 158 |
| Hamilton | ML3.6 | 4 | 106 | 143* | 98 | 354 | 89 | 265 |
| Hamilton | ML3.7P | 3 | 101 | 77* | 113 | 337 | 83 | 254 |
| Hamilton | ML3.8P | 4 | 107 | 109 | 107 | 308 | 139 | 169 |
| Hamilton | ML3.9 | 5 | 102 | 108 | 99 | 469 | 155 | 314 |
| Hamilton | ML8.5P | 1 | 160 | 230 | 142 | 7 | 2 | 5 |
| Hamilton | ML9.1 | 5 | 112* | 104 | 115* | 315 | 82 | 233 |
| Hamilton | ML9.2 | 3 | 101 | 99 | 101 | 263 | 79 | 184 |
| Hamilton | ML9.3P | 3 | 101 | 89 | 106 | 219 | 61 | 158 |
| Lanark (Clydesdale) | DG10.9P | n/a | - | - | - | 0 | 0 | 0 |
| Lanark (Clydesdale) | EH46.7P | 2 | 63 | - | 79 | 4 | 0 | 4 |
| Lanark (Clydesdale) | EH55.8P | 3 | 139 | 158 | 133 | 19 | 5 | 14 |
| Lanark (Clydesdale) | ML11.0 | 4 | 115* | 103 | 120* | 319 | 83 | 236 |
| Lanark (clydesdale) | ML11.7 | 3 | 100 | 112 | 95 | 278 | 82 | 196 |
| Lanark (Clydesdale) | ML11.8 | 4 | 94 | 95 | 94 | 286 | 80 | 206 |
| Lanark (Clydesdale) | ML11.9 | 3 | 102 | 88 | 107 | 329 | 75 | 254 |
| Lanark (Clydesdale) | ML12.6P | 3 | 102 | 94 | 104 | 276 | 54 | 222 |
| Lanark (Clydesdale) | ML2.9P | n/a | - | - | - | 0 | 0 | 0 |
| Lanark (Clydesdale) | ML8.4 | 4 | 86* | 118 | 73* | 195 | 77 | 118 |
| Lanark (Clydesdale) | ML8.5P | 3 | 103 | 112 | 99 | 291 | 91 | 200 |
| Lanark (Clydesdale) | ML9.3P | n/a | - | - | - | 0 | 0 | 0 |
| Monklands | EH48.3P | n/a | - | - | - | 0 | 0 | 0 |
| Monklands | FK1.3P | n/a | - | - | - | 0 | 0 | 0 |
| Monklands | G67.4P | 3 | 110 | 115 | 107 | 3 | 1 | 2 |
| Monklands | G69.6P | n/a | - | - | - | 0 | 0 | 0 |
| Monklands | G69.7P | 6 | 126* | 145* | 117 | 99 | 37 | 62 |
| Monklands | G69.8P | 2 | - | - | - | 0 | 0 | 0 |
| Monklands | ML1.5P | 1 | 87 | - | 113 | 2 | 0 | 2 |
| Monklands | ML4.1P | n/a | - | - | - | 0 | 0 | 0 |
| Monklands | ML5.1 | 4 | 113* | 122 | 110 | 293 | 84 | 209 |
| Monklands | ML5.2P | 6 | 102 | 101 | 102 | 351 | 100 | 251 |
| Monklands | ML5.3 | 5 | 105 | 99 | 106 | 257 | 52 | 205 |
| Monklands | ML5.4P | 6 | 107 | 114 | 105 | 411 | 131 | 280 |
| Monklands | ML5.5 | 6 | 119* | 120* | 119* | 417 | 183 | 234 |
| Monklands | ML6.0 | 5 | 113* | 103 | 118* | 277 | 82 | 195 |
| Monklands | ML6.6 | 6 | 102 | 125* | 93 | 270 | 101 | 169 |
| Monklands | ML6.7P | 6 | 116* | 108 | 119* | 429 | 110 | 319 |
| Monklands | ML6.8 | 5 | 111 | 112 | 110 | 302 | 126 | 176 |
| Monklands | ML6.9 | 4 | 111* | 107 | 113* | 417 | 125 | 292 |
| Monklands | ML7.4P | 6 | 98 | 100 | 98 | 51 | 16 | 35 |

| | | | | | | | | |
|---|---|---|---|---|---|---|---|---|
| Monklands | ML7.5P | n/a | - | - | - | 0 | 0 | 0 |
| Motherwell | EH47.9P | n/a | - | - | - | 0 | 0 | 0 |
| Motherwell | EH48.3P | 5 | 133 | 168 | 120 | 9 | 3 | 6 |
| Motherwell | G71.5 | 6 | 119* | 128* | 114 | 215 | 90 | 125 |
| Motherwell | G71.6P | 4 | 126* | 117 | 131* | 219 | 69 | 150 |
| Motherwell | G71.7P | 1 | 51 | - | 81 | 1 | 0 | 1 |
| Motherwell | G71.8P | n/a | - | - | - | 0 | 0 | 0 |
| Motherwell | ML1.1 | 5 | 121* | 122 | 120* | 397 | 87 | 310 |
| Motherwell | ML1.2 | 4 | 97 | 96 | 98 | 437 | 100 | 337 |
| Motherwell | ML1.3 | 5 | 104 | 119* | 98 | 475 | 161 | 314 |
| Motherwell | ML1.4 | 6 | 107 | 113 | 105 | 392 | 131 | 261 |
| Motherwell | ML1.5P | 6 | 103 | 113 | 99 | 320 | 106 | 214 |
| Motherwell | ML2.0 | 5 | 104 | 115 | 98 | 358 | 142 | 216 |
| Motherwell | ML2.7 | 5 | 122* | 117 | 124* | 527 | 147 | 380 |
| Motherwell | ML2.8 | 4 | 107 | 106 | 108 | 499 | 138 | 361 |
| Motherwell | ML2.9P | 5 | 115* | 112 | 117* | 236 | 72 | 164 |
| Motherwell | ML4.1P | 4 | 118* | 120 | 117 | 203 | 76 | 127 |
| Motherwell | ML4.2 | 6 | 118* | 132* | 112 | 407 | 145 | 262 |
| Motherwell | ML4.3 | 5 | 120* | 133* | 114 | 189 | 61 | 128 |
| Motherwell | ML5.4P | n/a | - | - | - | 0 | 0 | 0 |
| Motherwell | ML7.4P | 5 | 95 | 135* | 86* | 346 | 96 | 250 |
| Motherwell | ML7.5P | 5 | 117* | 122* | 115* | 361 | 108 | 253 |

Standardised Mortality Ratios. Health Board: Lothian

| L. A. District | Sector | DEPCAT | SMR | S64 | S65 | Obs | O64 | O65 |
|---|---|---|---|---|---|---|---|---|
| East Lothian | EH21.6P | 3 | 92 | 89 | 92 | 325 | 72 | 253 |
| East Lothian | EH21.7 | 4 | 97 | 82 | 101 | 301 | 57 | 244 |
| East Lothian | EH21.8P | 5 | 103 | 110 | 100 | 216 | 82 | 134 |
| East Lothian | EH22.2P | 1 | 133 | 119 | 151 | 2 | 1 | 1 |
| East Lothian | EH31.2 | 1 | 88 | 65 | 92 | 113 | 13 | 100 |
| East Lothian | EH32.0 | 2 | 89 | 75* | 94 | 269 | 58 | 211 |
| East Lothian | EH32.9 | 5 | 102 | 112 | 97 | 262 | 86 | 176 |
| East Lothian | EH33.1 | 4 | 91 | 77 | 96 | 161 | 38 | 123 |
| East Lothian | EH33.2 | 4 | 94 | 94 | 94 | 159 | 50 | 109 |
| East Lothian | EH34.5 | 2 | 88 | 52 | 101 | 57 | 9 | 48 |
| East Lothian | EH35.5 | 3 | 95 | 94 | 96 | 74 | 23 | 51 |
| East Lothian | EH36.5 | 2 | 79 | 87 | 77 | 9 | 2 | 7 |
| East Lothian | EH37.5P | 1 | - | - | - | 0 | 0 | 0 |
| East Lothian | EH39.4 | 2 | 78* | 66* | 81* | 216 | 28 | 188 |
| East Lothian | EH39.5 | 2 | 62* | 82 | 57* | 77 | 19 | 58 |
| East Lothian | EH40.3 | 2 | 83 | 41 | 93 | 61 | 6 | 55 |
| East Lothian | EH41.3 | 3 | 78* | 88 | 75* | 173 | 44 | 129 |
| East Lothian | EH41.4 | 3 | 79* | 64* | 85 | 140 | 33 | 107 |
| East Lothian | EH42.1 | 4 | 101 | 99 | 102 | 302 | 70 | 232 |
| East Lothian | TD11.3P | 5 | - | - | - | 0 | 0 | 0 |
| East Lothian | TD13.5P | 2 | 87 | 45 | 103 | 7 | 1 | 6 |
| Edinburgh City | EH1.1 | 6 | 173* | 205* | 163* | 72 | 21 | 51 |
| Edinburgh City | EH1.2 | 4 | 107 | 134 | 99 | 64 | 20 | 44 |
| Edinburgh City | EH1.3 | 5 | 104 | 65 | 120 | 39 | 7 | 32 |
| Edinburgh City | EH10.4 | 2 | 89* | 81 | 90 | 425 | 52 | 373 |
| Edinburgh City | EH10.5 | 1 | 96 | 67* | 100 | 624 | 50 | 574 |
| Edinburgh City | EH10.6 | 1 | 70* | 52* | 77* | 199 | 41 | 158 |
| Edinburgh City | EH10.7P | 1 | 51* | 26* | 62* | 43 | 7 | 36 |
| Edinburgh City | EH11.1 | 3 | 92 | 112 | 88* | 493 | 102 | 391 |
| Edinburgh City | EH11.2 | 4 | 100 | 91 | 102 | 352 | 58 | 294 |
| Edinburgh City | EH11.3 | 6 | 106 | 112 | 105 | 584 | 133 | 451 |
| Edinburgh City | EH11.4 | 4 | 92 | 108 | 87 | 293 | 79 | 214 |
| Edinburgh City | EH12.0 | 4 | 54 | 70 | 13 | 2 | 1 | 1 |
| Edinburgh City | EH12.5 | 2 | 93 | 91 | 93 | 317 | 55 | 262 |
| Edinburgh City | EH12.6 | 1 | 68* | 43* | 75* | 156 | 21 | 135 |
| Edinburgh City | EH12.7 | 2 | 82* | 65* | 87* | 360 | 66 | 294 |
| Edinburgh City | EH12.8 | 1 | 71* | 66* | 73* | 282 | 76 | 206 |
| Edinburgh City | EH12.9 | 3 | 95 | 126 | 73 | 36 | 20 | 16 |
| Edinburgh City | EH13.0 | 1 | 76* | 43* | 85 | 179 | 22 | 157 |
| Edinburgh City | EH13.9 | 4 | 100 | 77* | 110 | 322 | 77 | 245 |
| Edinburgh City | EH14.1 | 2 | 94 | 70* | 100 | 385 | 54 | 331 |
| Edinburgh City | EH14.2 | 5 | 94 | 92 | 95 | 320 | 88 | 232 |
| Edinburgh City | EH14.3 | 4 | 84 | 88 | 81 | 108 | 46 | 62 |
| Edinburgh City | EH14.4 | 2 | 109 | 180 | 91 | 6 | 2 | 4 |
| Edinburgh City | EH14.5 | 1 | 81* | 76* | 84* | 240 | 74 | 166 |
| Edinburgh City | EH14.6 | 3 | 55 | 94 | 30 | 3 | 2 | 1 |
| Edinburgh City | EH14.7 | 1 | 89 | 81 | 93 | 87 | 29 | 58 |
| Edinburgh City | EH15.1 | 2 | 89 | 81 | 91 | 252 | 52 | 200 |
| Edinburgh City | EH15.2 | 2 | 108 | 108 | 108 | 319 | 56 | 263 |
| Edinburgh City | EH15.3 | 6 | 97 | 102 | 95 | 265 | 83 | 182 |
| Edinburgh City | EH16.4 | 7 | 131* | 158* | 119* | 438 | 165 | 273 |

| L. A. District | Sector | DEPCAT | SMR | S64 | S65 | Obs | O64 | O65 |
|---|---|---|---|---|---|---|---|---|
| Edinburgh City | EH16.5 | 3 | 93 | 88 | 94 | 392 | 91 | 301 |
| Edinburgh City | EH16.6 | 4 | 89* | 84 | 91 | 417 | 99 | 318 |
| Edinburgh City | EH17.7 | 5 | 90 | 84 | 94 | 219 | 73 | 146 |
| Edinburgh City | EH17.8P | 5 | 99 | 101 | 99 | 312 | 100 | 212 |
| Edinburgh City | EH18.IP | n/a | - | - | - | 0 | 0 | 0 |
| Edinburgh City | EH2.1 | 3 | 36 | - | 47 | 2 | 0 | 2 |
| Edinburgh City | EH2.2 | 5 | 90 | 117 | 74 | 4 | 2 | 2 |
| Edinburgh City | EH2.3 | 4 | 94 | 154 | 67 | 4 | 2 | 2 |
| Edinburgh City | EH2.4 | 4 | 72 | 109 | 59 | 10 | 4 | 6 |
| Edinburgh City | EH20.9P | 3 | 103 | 101 | 105 | 9 | 3 | 6 |
| Edinburgh City | EH21.6P | n/a | - | - | - | 0 | 0 | 0 |
| Edinburgh City | EH21.8P | 6 | 177* | 187 | 174* | 28 | 6 | 22 |
| Edinburgh City | EH22.IP | n/a | - | - | - | 0 | 0 | 0 |
| Edinburgh City | EH27.8P | 1 | 55 | 48 | 65 | 2 | 1 | 1 |
| Edinburgh City | EH28.8 | 3 | 91 | 90 | 92 | 88 | 29 | 59 |
| Edinburgh City | EH29.9 | 2 | 114 | 104 | 119 | 90 | 28 | 62 |
| Edinburgh City | EH3.5 | 3 | 83* | 96 | 80* | 244 | 47 | 197 |
| Edinburgh City | EH3.6 | 2 | 91 | 100 | 89 | 195 | 45 | 150 |
| Edinburgh City | EH3.7 | 3 | 71 | 13 | 81 | 39 | 1 | 38 |
| Edinburgh City | EH3.8 | 5 | 136* | 138 | 135* | 104 | 23 | 81 |
| Edinburgh City | EH3.9 | 4 | 110 | 101 | 111 | 299 | 44 | 255 |
| Edinburgh City | EH30.9P | 3 | 77* | 79 | 76* | 143 | 53 | 90 |
| Edinburgh City | EH4.1 | 2 | 93 | 115 | 89 | 304 | 58 | 246 |
| Edinburgh City | EH4.2 | 4 | 87* | 89 | 87* | 371 | 110 | 261 |
| Edinburgh City | EH4.3 | 1 | 87* | 73 | 90 | 245 | 41 | 204 |
| Edinburgh City | EH4.4 | 7 | 109 | 124* | 101 | 386 | 146 | 240 |
| Edinburgh City | EH4.5 | 2 | 85* | 74 | 89 | 170 | 40 | 130 |
| Edinburgh City | EH4.6 | 1 | 74* | 55* | 84 | 131 | 32 | 99 |
| Edinburgh City | EH4.7 | 4 | 84* | 84 | 84* | 291 | 88 | 203 |
| Edinburgh City | EH4.8 | 1 | 82 | 61 | 95 | 66 | 19 | 47 |
| Edinburgh City | EH5.1 | 6 | 106 | 107 | 105 | 273 | 62 | 211 |
| Edinburgh City | EH5.2 | 4 | 80* | 72 | 81* | 270 | 37 | 233 |
| Edinburgh City | EH5.3 | 2 | 95 | 61* | 103 | 284 | 34 | 250 |
| Edinburgh City | EH52.5P | n/a | - | - | - | 0 | 0 | 0 |
| Edinburgh City | EH52.6P | n/a | - | - | - | 0 | 0 | 0 |
| Edinburgh City | EH53.0P | 2 | 92 | - | 100 | 1 | 0 | 1 |
| Edinburgh City | EH6.4 | 4 | 95 | 87 | 97 | 354 | 70 | 284 |
| Edinburgh City | EH6.5 | 4 | 116 | 152* | 105 | 183 | 55 | 128 |
| Edinburgh City | EH6.6 | 6 | 99 | 97 | 99 | 143 | 40 | 103 |
| Edinburgh City | EH6.7 | 3 | 99 | 119 | 94 | 158 | 38 | 120 |
| Edinburgh City | EH6.8 | 4 | 100 | 108 | 98 | 493 | 91 | 402 |
| Edinburgh City | EH7.4 | 4 | 95 | 75 | 100 | 325 | 50 | 275 |
| Edinburgh City | EH7.5 | 4 | 94 | 121 | 88* | 470 | 103 | 367 |
| Edinburgh City | EH7.6 | 4 | 93 | 102 | 91* | 669 | 138 | 531 |
| Edinburgh City | EH8.7 | 3 | 86* | 66* | 93 | 428 | 81 | 347 |
| Edinburgh City | EH8.8 | 4 | 157* | 130 | 162* | 318 | 43 | 275 |
| Edinburgh City | EH8.9 | 5 | 113* | 113 | 113 | 333 | 67 | 266 |
| Edinburgh City | EH9.1 | 2 | 91 | 86 | 92 | 438 | 63 | 375 |
| Edinburgh City | EH9.2 | 1 | 92 | 73 | 95 | 294 | 35 | 259 |
| Edinburgh City | EH9.3 | 1 | 66* | 59* | 68* | 112 | 24 | 88 |
| Midlothian | EH10.7P | 4 | 84 | 121 | 71 | 8 | 3 | 5 |
| Midlothian | EH16.4P | n/a | - | - | - | 0 | 0 | 0 |
| Midlothian | EH17.8P | n/a | - | - | - | 0 | 0 | 0 |
| Midlothian | EH18.1P | 1 | 86 | 68 | 98 | 43 | 13 | 30 |
| Midlothian | EH19.2 | 4 | 90 | 92 | 89 | 175 | 59 | 116 |
| Midlothian | EH19.3 | 3 | 90 | 76 | 96 | 149 | 38 | 111 |
| Midlothian | EH20.9P | 3 | 103 | 90 | 108 | 248 | 58 | 190 |
| Midlothian | EH21.8P | n/a | - | - | - | 0 | 0 | 0 |
| Midlothian | EH22.IP | 4 | 102 | 98 | 103 | 223 | 62 | 161 |
| Midlothian | EH22.2P | 4 | 89 | 78 | 95 | 154 | 51 | 103 |
| Midlothian | EH22.3 | 1 | 100 | 43* | 120 | 109 | 12 | 97 |
| Midlothian | EH22.4 | 4 | 91 | 97 | 89 | 216 | 61 | 155 |
| Midlothian | EH22.5 | 4 | 102 | 96 | 107 | 128 | 64 | 64 |
| Midlothian | EH23.4 | 4 | 102 | 85 | 110 | 265 | 68 | 197 |
| Midlothian | EH24.9 | 5 | 160* | 136 | 173* | 70 | 20 | 50 |
| Midlothian | EH25.9 | 3 | 89 | 104 | 84 | 125 | 36 | 89 |
| Midlothian | EH26.0 | 2 | 78* | 61* | 89 | 110 | 35 | 75 |
| Midlothian | EH26.8P | 3 | 111 | 99 | 116 | 214 | 54 | 160 |
| Midlothian | EH26.9P | 1 | 88 | 56* | 112 | 75 | 20 | 55 |
| Midlothian | EH37.5P | 2 | 74 | 65 | 77 | 46 | 10 | 36 |
| Midlothian | EH38.5P | n/a | - | - | - | 0 | 0 | 0 |
| Midlothian | EH46.7P | n/a | - | - | - | 0 | 0 | 0 |
| West Lothian | EH27.8P | 3 | 110 | 108 | 111 | 47 | 15 | 32 |
| West Lothian | EH30.9P | 2 | 100 | - | 161 | 3 | 0 | 3 |
| West Lothian | EH47.0 | 5 | 98 | 92 | 101 | 222 | 69 | 153 |
| West Lothian | EH47.7 | 6 | 125* | 128* | 123* | 231 | 81 | 150 |

| | | | | | | | | |
|---|---|---|---|---|---|---|---|---|
| West Lothian | EH47.8 | 5 | 95 | 103 | 90 | 164 | 60 | 104 |
| West Lothian | EH47.9P | 6 | 108 | 118 | 104 | 173 | 57 | 116 |
| West Lothian | EH48.1 | 4 | 94 | 81 | 100 | 198 | 52 | 146 |
| West Lothian | EH48.2 | 5 | 104 | 101 | 105 | 291 | 79 | 212 |
| West Lothian | EH48.3P | 4 | 106 | 105 | 107 | 287 | 88 | 199 |
| West Lothian | EH48.4 | 5 | 106 | 114 | 102 | 178 | 53 | 125 |
| West Lothian | EH49.6P | 2 | 81* | 74 | 84 | 158 | 43 | 115 |
| West Lothian | EH49:7P | 2 | 82* | 62* | 89 | 125 | 27 | 98 |
| West Lothian | EH52.5P | 3 | 104 | 99 | 105 | 260 | 55 | 205 |
| West Lothian | EH52.6 | 4 | 101 | 116 | 96 | 406 | 119 | 287 |
| West Lothian | EH53.0P | 3 | 98 | 93 | 101 | 166 | 53 | 113 |
| West Lothian | EH54.5 | 5 | 102 | 106 | 99 | 152 | 65 | 87 |
| West Lothian | EH54.6 | 4 | 104 | 108 | 100 | 216 | 112 | 104 |
| West Lothian | EH54.7 | 1 | 81 | 57 | 95 | 12 | 3 | 9 |
| West Lothian | EH54.8 | 4 | 103 | 113 | 96 | 184 | 85 | 99 |
| West Lothian | EH54.9 | 1 | 59 | 44 | 72 | 11 | 4 | 7 |
| West Lothian | EH55.8P | 4 | 105 | 119 | 100 | 273 | 83 | 190 |
| West Lothian | FK1.2P | 2 | 235* | 680 | 142 | 8 | 4 | 4 |
| West Lothian | ML6.7P | n/a | - | - | - | 0 | 0 | 0 |
| West Lothian | ML7.5P | 4 | 147* | 141 | 151 | 35 | 14 | 21 |

Standardised Mortality Ratios. Health Board: Tayside

| L. A. District | Sector | DEPCAT | SMR | S64 | S65 | Obs | O64 | O65 |
|---|---|---|---|---|---|---|---|---|
| Angus | AB3.1P | 3 | 178 | 511 | 60 | 4 | 3 | 1 |
| Angus | DD10.0P | n/a | - | - | - | 0 | 0 | 0 |
| Angus | DD10.8 | 4 | 89* | 85 | 89 | 350 | 58 | 292 |
| Angus | DD10.9 | 3 | 86* | 78 | 89 | 270 | 62 | 208 |
| Angus | DD11.1 | 5 | 108 | 108 | 108 | 257 | 56 | 201 |
| Angus | DD11.2 | 3 | 86 | 67* | 92 | 161 | 32 | 129 |
| Angus | DD11.3 | 3 | 93 | 93 | 93 | 168 | 35 | 133 |
| Angus | DD11.4 | 4 | 99 | 82 | 104 | 228 | 46 | 182 |
| Angus | DD11.5 | 4 | 107 | 93 | 112 | 244 | 60 | 184 |
| Angus | DD4.0P | n/a | - | - | - | 0 | 0 | 0 |
| Angus | DD5.3P | 1 | 78 | 60 | 87 | 20 | 5 | 15 |
| Angus | DD5.4P | 2 | 122 | - | 219 | 1 | 0 | 1 |
| Angus | DD7.6 | 1 | 75* | 48* | 83 | 100 | 16 | 84 |
| Angus | DD7.7 | 3 | 89 | 60* | 97 | 226 | 33 | 193 |
| Angus | DD8.1P | 4 | 87* | 62* | 95 | 271 | 52 | 219 |
| Angus | DD8.2 | 3 | 92 | 65* | 100 | 248 | 39 | 209 |
| Angus | DD8.3 | 3 | 80* | 84 | 79* | 168 | 39 | 129 |
| Angus | DD8.4 | 2 | 125* | 78 | 136* | 198 | 24 | 174 |
| Angus | DD8.5 | 3 | 85 | 78 | 87 | 132 | 28 | 104 |
| Angus | DD9.6 | 2 | 84* | 61* | 90 | 187 | 30 | 157 |
| Angus | DD9.7P | 4 | 90 | 84 | 91 | 240 | 47 | 193 |
| Angus | PH11.8P | 2 | 47 | 62 | 43 | 7 | 2 | 5 |
| Angus | PH12.8P | 3 | 68 | 43 | 75 | 29 | 4 | 25 |
| Angus | PH13.9P | n/a | - | - | - | 0 | 0 | 0 |
| Dundee City | DD1.1 | 5 | 156* | 116 | 173* | 37 | 8 | 29 |
| Dundee City | DD1.2 | 5 | 131* | 136 | 123* | 79 | 16 | 63 |
| Dundee City | DD1.3 | 3 | 199* | 147 | 223* | 13 | 3 | 10 |
| Dundee City | DD1.4 | 2 | 111 | 61 | 124 | 65 | 7 | 58 |
| Dundee City | DD1.5 | 6 | 121 | 152* | 114 | 100 | 24 | 76 |
| Dundee City | DD2.1 | 2 | 89* | 66* | 94 | 400 | 46 | 354 |
| Dundee City | DD2.2 | 4 | 100 | 84 | 105 | 441 | 76 | 365 |
| Dundee City | DD2.3 | 6 | 101 | 105 | 100 | 552 | 143 | 409 |
| Dundee City | DD2.4 | 5 | 106 | 102 | 109 | 574 | 169 | 405 |
| Dundee City | DD2.5 | 2 | 67* | 70* | 66* | 191 | 37 | 154 |
| Dundee City | DD3.0 | 6 | 95 | 109 | 87 | 210 | 90 | 120 |
| Dundee City | DD3.6 | 5 | 96 | 117 | 92 | 492 | 96 | 396 |
| Dundee City | DD3.7 | 6 | 113* | 112 | 113* | 462 | 81 | 381 |
| Dundee City | DD3.8 | 3 | 92 | 89 | 92 | 372 | 70 | 302 |
| Dundee City | DD3.9 | 4 | 93 | 80 | 100 | 245 | 78 | 167 |
| Dundee City | DD4.0P | 7 | 100 | 117 | 92 | 270 | 101 | 169 |
| Dundee City | DD4.6 | 5 | 90 | 93 | 90 | 268 | 49 | 219 |
| Dundee City | DD4.7 | 2 | 90* | 76* | 94 | 433 | 75 | 358 |
| Dundee City | DD4.8 | 7 | 111* | 106 | 114* | 534 | 174 | 360 |
| Dundee City | DD4.9 | 5 | 89* | 83 | 91 | 357 | 114 | 243 |
| Dundee City | DD5.1 | 1 | 84* | 68* | 89 | 167 | 32 | 135 |
| Dundee City | DD5.2 | 2 | 84* | 54* | 91 | 263 | 36 | 227 |
| Dundee City | DD5.3P | 1 | 82* | 61* | 92 | 180 | 42 | 138 |
| undee City | DD5.4P | 2 | 72* | 70* | 72* | 230 | 44 | 186 |
| Dundee City | DD8.1P | n/a | - | - | - | 0 | 0 | 0 |
| Dundee City | PH13.9P | n/a | - | - | - | 0 | 0 | 0 |
| Dundee City | PH14.9P | 1 | 97 | 87 | 100 | 4 | 1 | 3 |
| Perth & Kinross | DD8.1P | n/a | - | - | - | 0 | 0 | 0 |

316 DEPRIVATION AND HEALTH IN SCOTLAND

| L. A. District | Sector | DEPCAT | SMR | S64 | S65 | Obs | O64 | O65 |
|---|---|---|---|---|---|---|---|---|
| DPerth & Kinross | FK14.7P | 2 | 130 | 108 | 141 | 17 | 5 | 12 |
| Perth & Kinross | FK15.0P | 1 | 61 | - | 119 | 2 | 0 | 2 |
| Perth & Kinross | FK15.9P | 1 | 54* | 14 | 68 | 15 | 1 | 14 |
| Perth & Kinross | FK19.8P | n/a | - | - | - | 0 | 0 | 0 |
| Perth & Kinross | FK21.8P | 1 | 190 | - | 238 | 4 | 0 | 4 |
| Perth & Kinross | KY13.7P | 2 | 100 | 79 | 107 | 271 | 53 | 218 |
| Perth & Kinross | KY14.6P | 2 | - | - | - | 0 | 0 | 0 |
| Perth & Kinross | KY14.7P | 1 | 50 | - | 78 | 1 | 0 | 1 |
| Perth & Kinross | KY4.0P | 1 | 41 | - | 51 | 4 | 0 | 4 |
| Perth & Kinross | KY5.0P | n/a | 278 | - | 1105 | 1 | 0 | 1 |
| Perth & Kinross | KY6.3P | 6 | 28 | - | 34 | 1 | 0 | 1 |
| Perth & Kinross | PH1.1 | 1 | 71* | 62* | 74* | 165 | 39 | 126 |
| Perth & Kinross | PH1.2 | 5 | 100 | 101 | 99 | 400 | 132 | 268 |
| Perth & Kinross | PH1.3 | 4 | 91 | 72* | 98 | 267 | 53 | 214 |
| Perth & Kinross | PH1.4 | 3 | 110 | 94 | 114 | 195 | 38 | 157 |
| Perth & Kinross | PH1.5 | 5 | 110* | 112 | 110 | 406 | 72 | 334 |
| Perth & Kinross | PH10.6 | 2 | 85* | 67* | 90 | 213 | 34 | 179 |
| Perth & Kinross | PH10.7 | 4 | 104 | 100 | 105 | 176 | 36 | 140 |
| Perth & Kinross | PH11.8P | 3 | 94 | 93 | 94 | 121 | 24 | 97 |
| Perth & Kinross | PH12.8P | 3 | 101 | 93 | 103 | 58 | 8 | 50 |
| Perth & Kinross | PH13.9P | 3 | 93 | 96 | 92 | 160 | 37 | 123 |
| Perth & Kinross | PH14.9P | 2 | 102 | 109 | 98 | 28 | 10 | 18 |
| Perth & Kinross | PH15.2 | 3 | 99 | 94 | 101 | 141 | 27 | 114 |
| Perth & Kinross | PH16.5 | 3 | 94 | 74 | 99 | 163 | 25 | 138 |
| Perth & Kinross | PH17.2 | 4 | 75 | 55 | 81 | 6 | 1 | 5 |
| Perth & Kinross | PH18.5 | 3 | 108 | 103 | 109 | 43 | 8 | 35 |
| Perth & Kinross | PH2.0 | 2 | 91 | 97 | 90 | 349 | 67 | 282 |
| Perth & Kinross | PH2.6 | 2 | 86* | 74 | 89 | 254 | 48 | 206 |
| Perth & Kinross | PH2.7 | 2 | 85* | 73* | 87* | 304 | 49 | 255 |
| Perth & Kinross | PH2.8 | 4 | 94 | 96 | 93 | 150 | 29 | 121 |
| Perth & Kinross | PH2.9 | 2 | 75* | 62* | 80* | 129 | 28 | 101 |
| Perth & Kinross | PH3.1 | 3 | 99 | 88 | 102 | 190 | 36 | 154 |
| Perth & Kinross | PH4.1 | 4 | 103 | 120 | 99 | 34 | 7 | 27 |
| Perth & Kinross | PH5.2 | 2 | 103 | 82 | 109 | 41 | 7 | 34 |
| Perth & Kinross | PH6.2 | 3 | 81* | 85 | 81* | 113 | 16 | 97 |
| Perth & Kinross | PH7.3 | 3 | 95 | 90 | 96 | 243 | 41 | 202 |
| Perth & Kinross | PH7.4 | 2 | 83 | 61 | 87 | 92 | 10 | 82 |
| Perth & Kinross | PH8.0 | 2 | 96 | 101 | 94 | 75 | 19 | 56 |
| Perth & Kinross | PH9.0 | 3 | 110 | 56 | 121 | 56 | 5 | 51 |

Standardised Mortality Ratios. Health Board: The Islands

| L. A. District | Sector | DEPCAT | SMR | S64 | S65 | Obs | O64 | O65 |
|---|---|---|---|---|---|---|---|---|
| Orkney | KW15.1 | 3 | 99 | 111 | 96 | 273 | 69 | 204 |
| Orkney | KW16.3 | 3 | 101 | 111 | 99 | 159 | 38 | 121 |
| Orkney | KW17.2 | 2 | 83* | 81 | 83* | 313 | 64 | 249 |
| Shetland | ZE1.0 | 3 | 91 | 81 | 94 | 289 | 60 | 229 |
| Shetland | ZE2.9 | 3 | 90* | 76* | 95 | 474 | 86 | 388 |
| Shetland | ZE3.9 | 2 | 117 | 42 | 145 | 20 | 2 | 18 |
| Western Isles | PA80.5 | 6 | 116 | 184* | 103 | 69 | 18 | 51 |
| Western Isles | PA81.5 | 6 | 100 | 154* | 87 | 106 | 32 | 74 |
| Western Isles | PA82.5 | 4 | 86 | 60 | 91 | 85 | 10 | 75 |
| Western Isles | PA83.3 | 3 | 60 | - | 75 | 13 | 0 | 13 |
| Western Isles | PA84.3 | 4 | 57 | 68 | 55 | 16 | 3 | 13 |
| Western Isles | PA85.3 | 5 | 82 | 107 | 77* | 94 | 19 | 75 |
| Western Isles | PA86.0 | 4 | 101 | 106 | 99 | 481 | 101 | 380 |
| Western Isles | PA86.9 | 4 | 106 | 105 | 107 | 326 | 57 | 269 |
| Western Isles | PA87.2 | 4 | 90 | 94 | 89 | 249 | 50 | 199 |
| Western Isles | PA88.5 | 3 | 107 | 55 | 135 | 39 | 7 | 32 |

TABLE B3.2   ALL CAUSES SMR (ALL AGES) STATISTICS (SECTORS WITH POP GT 500)

| AREA | Population | SMR (All ages) | | | | Sectors |
|---|---|---|---|---|---|---|
| | | Mean | Stan Dev | Minimum | Maximum | |
| Group 1 - WEST | 2315779 | 107 | 15 | 58 | 180 | 338 |
| Group 2 - EAST | 2117570 | 95 | 11 | 51 | 147 | 337 |
| Group 3 - RURAL | 483781 | 97 | 12 | 48 | 145 | 135 |
| SCOTLAND | 4917130 | 101 | 14 | 48 | 180 | 810 |

| AREA | Population | SMR (All ages) | | | | Sectors |
|---|---|---|---|---|---|---|
| | | Mean | Stan Dev | Minimum | Maximum | |
| Group 1 - WEST | | | | | | |
| Argyll & Clyde | 437958 | 107 | 14 | 58 | 148 | 77 |
| Ayr & Arran | 371043 | 106 | 11 | 66 | 134 | 71 |
| Greater Glasgow | 948125 | 108 | 18 | 62 | 180 | 128 |
| Lanarkshire | 558653 | 105 | 10 | 85 | 126 | 62 |
| Group 2 - EAST | | | | | | |
| Fife | 317302 | 98 | 11 | 70 | 127 | 49 |
| Forth Valley | 254887 | 99 | 11 | 74 | 126 | 44 |
| Grampian | 458931 | 92 | 10 | 54 | 110 | 62 |
| Lothian | 706334 | 94 | 12 | 51 | 147 | 113 |
| Tayside | 380116 | 94 | 11 | 54 | 131 | 69 |
| Group 3 - RURAL | | | | | | |
| Borders | 92543 | 94 | 12 | 49 | 126 | 27 |
| Dumfries & Galloway | 141028 | 95 | 13 | 48 | 138 | 35 |
| Highland | 179119 | 100 | 13 | 48 | 145 | 59 |
| The Islands | 71091 | 95 | 8 | 82 | 117 | 14 |
| SCOTLAND | 4917130 | 101 | 14 | 48 | 180 | 810 |

Notes:
   Institutional SMRs have been excluded. Population weighted statistics

# DEPRIVATION AND HEALTH IN SCOTLAND

TABLE B3.2  ALL CAUSES SMR (ALL AGES) STATISTICS (SECTORS WITH POP GT 500)  CONTD.

| AREA | Population | SMR (All ages) | | | | Sectors |
|------|-----------|------|---------|---------|---------|---------|
| | | Mean | Stan Dev | Minimum | Maximum | |
| **Argyll & Clyde** | | | | | | |
| Argyll & Bute | 57760 | 103 | 12 | 81 | 143 | 20 |
| Dumbarton | 76166 | 101 | 14 | 66 | 133 | 13 |
| Inverclyde | 98833 | 114 | 15 | 86 | 148 | 13 |
| Renfrew | 205199 | 107 | 13 | 58 | 136 | 31 |
| **Ayr & Arran** | | | | | | |
| Cumnock & Doon V | 44657 | 110 | 6 | 95 | 122 | 8 |
| Cunninghame | 135412 | 106 | 11 | 66 | 134 | 28 |
| Kilmar. & Loudoun | 81633 | 109 | 10 | 82 | 124 | 16 |
| Kyle & Carrick | 109341 | 102 | 12 | 79 | 124 | 19 |
| **Borders** | | | | | | |
| Berwickshire | 17148 | 86 | 14 | 49 | 115 | 6 |
| Ett.& Lauderdale | 27204 | 98 | 15 | 70 | 126 | 8 |
| Roxburgh | 34518 | 96 | 4 | 91 | 105 | 7 |
| Tweedale | 13673 | 92 | 9 | 66 | 107 | 6 |
| **Dumfries & Galloway** | | | | | | |
| Ann. & Eskdale | 34744 | 87 | 14 | 48 | 104 | 9 |
| Nithsdale | 54437 | 97 | 9 | 75 | 107 | 11 |
| Stewartry | 22310 | 88 | 6 | 77 | 93 | 6 |
| Wigtown | 29537 | 107 | 12 | 92 | 138 | 9 |
| **Fife** | | | | | | |
| Dunfermline | 121692 | 100 | 9 | 81 | 113 | 16 |
| Kirkaldy | 142706 | 101 | 10 | 90 | 127 | 20 |
| N.E.Fife | 52904 | 86 | 7 | 70 | 97 | 13 |
| **Forth Valley** | | | | | | |
| Clackmannan | 47168 | 105 | 12 | 81 | 122 | 8 |
| Falkirk | 132004 | 98 | 8 | 80 | 126 | 20 |
| Stirling | 75715 | 98 | 12 | 74 | 122 | 16 |
| **Grampian** | | | | | | |
| Aberdeen City | 199552 | 96 | 8 | 82 | 110 | 20 |
| Banff & Buchan | 79331 | 93 | 9 | 75 | 107 | 11 |
| Gordon | 61324 | 81 | 8 | 54 | 92 | 11 |
| Kincar.& Deeside | 39277 | 86 | 5 | 75 | 93 | 7 |
| Moray | 79447 | 92 | 7 | 78 | 101 | 13 |
| **Greater Glasgow** | | | | | | |
| Bears. & Milngavie | 39335 | 80 | 7 | 67 | 92 | 7 |
| Clydebank | 51995 | 105 | 9 | 92 | 118 | 7 |
| Eastwood | 53389 | 79 | 10 | 62 | 111 | 9 |
| Glasgow City | 722303 | 114 | 16 | 78 | 180 | 90 |
| Stathkelvin | 8 1103 | 95 | 15 | 75 | 124 | 15 |
| **Highland** | | | | | | |
| Baden.& Strathspey | 8366 | 94 | 14 | 70 | 105 | 5 |
| Caithness | 26076 | 108 | 11 | 97 | 145 | 6 |
| Inverness | 53821 | 97 | 11 | 82 | 135 | 9 |
| Lochaber | 16813 | 105 | 10 | 82 | 116 | 7 |
| Nairn | 9488 | 103 | 2 | 101 | 104 | 2 |
| Ross & Crom. | 44624 | 99 | 14 | 62 | 125 | 19 |
| Skye & Lochalsh | 7603 | 99 | 20 | 48 | 112 | 4 |
| Sutherland | 12328 | 100 | 8 | 86 | 120 | 7 |
| **Lanarkshire** | | | | | | |
| Cumbernauld | 61112 | 105 | 3 | 98 | 108 | 7 |
| E. Kilbride | 81865 | 91 | 5 | 85 | 109 | 9 |
| Hamilton | 107784 | 106 | 6 | 101 | 120 | 12 |
| Clydesdale | 56138 | 100 | 8 | 86 | 115 | 7 |
| Monklands | 109597 | 111 | 6 | 98 | 126 | 12 |
| Motherwell | 142157 | 112 | 8 | 97 | 126 | 15 |
| **Lothian** | | | | | | |
| E.Lothian | 78327 | 91 | 10 | 62 | 103 | 16 |
| Edinburgh City | 410951 | 93 | 13 | 51 | 136 | 61 |
| Midlothian | 80006 | 94 | 9 | 74 | 111 | 15 |
| W. Lothian | 137050 | 101 | 10 | 59 | 147 | 21 |
| **Tayside** | | | | | | |
| Angus | 90927 | 91 | 11 | 68 | 125 | 18 |
| Dundee City | 176668 | 96 | 12 | 67 | 131 | 22 |
| Perth & Kinross | 112521 | 93 | 11 | 54 | 110 | 29 |
| **The Islands** | | | | | | |
| Orkney | 18419 | 93 | 8 | 83 | 101 | 3 |
| Shetland | 22768 | 91 | 4 | 90 | 117 | 3 |
| Western Isles | 29904 | 99 | 8 | 82 | 116 | 8 |
| **SCOTLAND** | 4917130 | 101 | 14 | 48 | 180 | 810 |

Notes:

Institutional SMRs have been excluded. Population weighted statistics

TABLE B3.3   ALL CAUSES SMR (0-64) STATISTICS (SECTORS WITH POP GT 500)

| AREA | Population | SMR (0-64) | | | | Sectors |
|------|-----------|------|----------|---------|---------|---------|
| | | Mean | Stan Dev | Minimum | Maximum | |
| Group 1 - WEST | 2315779 | 110 | 26 | 29 | 200 | 338 |
| Group 2 - EAST | 2117570 | 90 | 20 | 13 | 159 | 337 |
| Group 3 - RURAL | 483781 | 94 | 21 | 42 | 214 | 135 |
| SCOTLAND | 4917130 | 100 | 25 | 13 | 214 | 810 |

| AREA | Population | SMR (0-64) | | | | Sectors |
|------|-----------|------|----------|---------|---------|---------|
| | | Mean | Stan Dev | Minimum | Maximum | |
| Group 1 - WEST | | | | | | |
| Argyll & Clyae | 437958 | 109 | 26 | 29 | 176 | 77 |
| Ayr & Arran | 371043 | 104 | 21 | 49 | 154 | 71 |
| Greater Glasgow | 948125 | 114 | 31 | 46 | 200 | 128 |
| Lanarkshire | 558653 | 106 | 15 | 68 | 145 | 62 |
| Group 2 - EAST | | | | | | |
| Fife | 317302 | 97 | 18 | 53 | 142 | 49 |
| Forth Valley | 254887 | 96 | 19 | 50 | 144 | 44 |
| Grampian | 458931 | 84 | 16 | 47 | 131 | 62 |
| Lothian | 706334 | 92 | 22 | 13 | 159 | 113 |
| Tayside | 380116 | 86 | 19 | 14 | 152 | 69 |
| Group 3 - RURAL | | | | | | |
| Borders | 92543 | 80 | 15 | 50 | 111 | 27 |
| Dumfries & Galloway | 141028 | 97 | 18 | 42 | 148 | 35 |
| Highland | 179119 | 100 | 22 | 50 | 214 | 59 |
| The Islands | 71091 | 94 | 23 | 42 | 184 | 14 |
| SCOTLAND | 4917130 | 100 | 25 | 13 | 214 | 810 |

Notes:
    Institutional SMRs have been excluded. Population weighted statistics

TABLE B3.3    ALL CAUSES SMR (0-64) STATISTICS (SECTORS WITH POP GT 500) CONTD.

| AREA | Population | SMR (0-64) | | | | Sectors |
|---|---|---|---|---|---|---|
| | | Mean | Stan Dev | Minimum | Maximum | |
| Argyll & Clyde | | | | | | |
| Argyll & Bute | 57760 | 101 | 22 | 29 | 139 | 20 |
| Dumbarton | 76166 | 98 | 21 | 46 | 140 | 13 |
| Inverclyde | 98833 | 124 | 32 | 57 | 176 | 13 |
| Renfrew | 205199 | 108 | 23 | 48 | 167 | 31 |
| Ayr & Arran | | | | | | |
| Cumnock & Doon V | 44657 | 109 | 17 | 94 | 146 | 8 |
| Cunninghame | 135412 | 111 | 19 | 55 | 154 | 28 |
| Kilmar. & Loudoun | 81633 | 103 | 19 | 49 | 137 | 16 |
| Kyle & Carrick | 109341 | 94 | 23 | 59 | 137 | 19 |
| Borders | | | | | | |
| Berwickshire | 17148 | 79 | 14 | 64 | 111 | 6 |
| Ett. & Lauderdale | 27204 | 87 | 12 | 68 | 105 | 8 |
| Roxburgh | 34518 | 80 | 13 | 54 | 95 | 7 |
| Tweedale | 13673 | 72 | 18 | 50 | 105 | 6 |
| Dumfries & Galloway | | | | | | |
| Ann. & Eskaale | 34744 | 90 | 17 | 42 | 107 | 9 |
| Nithsdale | 54437 | 100 | 12 | 82 | 122 | 11 |
| Stewartry | 22310 | 85 | 10 | 75 | 114 | 6 |
| Wigtown | 29537 | 108 | 25 | 69 | 148 | 9 |
| Fife | | | | | | |
| Dunfermline | 121692 | 99 | 19 | 53 | 127 | 16 |
| Kirkaldy | 142706 | 102 | 16 | 81 | 142 | 20 |
| N. E. Fife | 52904 | 81 | 11 | 63 | 103 | 13 |
| Forth Valley | | | | | | |
| Clackmannan | 47168 | 103 | 18 | 62 | 125 | 8 |
| Falkirk | 132004 | 97 | 17 | 62 | 144 | 20 |
| Stirling | 75715 | 90 | 21 | 50 | 129 | 16 |
| Grampian | | | | | | |
| Aberdeen City | 199552 | 87 | 17 | 54 | 131 | 20 |
| Banff & Buchan | 79331 | 86 | 10 | 71 | 103 | 11 |
| Gordon | 61324 | 70 | 12 | 47 | 93 | 11 |
| Kincar. & Deeside | 39277 | 73 | 10 | 51 | 93 | 7 |
| Moray | 79447 | 88 | 12 | 53 | 104 | 13 |
| Grester Glasgow | | | | | | |
| Bears. & Milngavie | 39335 | 68 | 9 | 59 | 83 | 7 |
| Clydebank | 51995 | 109 | 18 | 84 | 142 | 7 |
| Eastwood | 53389 | 68 | 16 | 46 | 127 | 9 |
| Glasgow City | 722303 | 124 | 27 | 58 | 200 | 90 |
| Strathkelvin | 81103 | 85 | 19 | 47 | 137 | 15 |
| Highland | | | | | | |
| Baden. & Strathspey | 8366 | 85 | 23 | 51 | 110 | 5 |
| Caithness | 26076 | 112 | 25 | 85 | 214 | 6 |
| Inverness | 53821 | 98 | 22 | 76 | 210 | 9 |
| Lochaber | 16813 | 106 | 9 | 91 | 134 | 2 |
| Nairn | 9488 | 93 | 0 | 93 | 93 | 2 |
| Ross & Crom. | 44624 | 94 | 18 | 50 | 149 | 19 |
| Skye & Lochalsh | 7603 | 109 | 21 | 70 | 139 | 4 |
| Sutherland | 12328 | 103 | 28 | 60 | 174 | 7 |
| Lanarkshire | | | | | | |
| Cumbernauld | 61112 | 101 | 5 | 94 | 107 | 7 |
| E. Kilbride | 81865 | 84 | 9 | 68 | 106 | 9 |
| Hamilton | 107784 | 106 | 17 | 77 | 143 | 12 |
| Clydesdale | 56138 | 103 | 10 | 89 | 119 | 7 |
| Monklands | 109597 | 113 | 9 | 99 | 145 | 12 |
| Motherwell | 142157 | 117 | 9 | 97 | 133 | 15 |
| Lothian | | | | | | |
| E. Lothian | 78327 | 86 | 17 | 41 | 113 | 16 |
| Edinburgh City | 410951 | 91 | 24 | 13 | 159 | 61 |
| Midlothian | 80006 | 84 | 16 | 43 | 104 | 15 |
| W. Lothian | 137050 | 103 | 17 | 44 | 141 | 21 |
| Tayside | | | | | | |
| Angus | 90927 | 76 | 15 | 43 | 109 | 18 |
| Dundee City | 176668 | 92 | 20 | 55 | 152 | 22 |
| Perth & Kinross | 112521 | 85 | 16 | 14 | 121 | 29 |
| The Islands | | | | | | |
| Orkney | 18419 | 98 | 15 | 81 | 111 | 3 |
| Shetland | 22768 | 77 | 6 | 42 | 81 | 3 |
| Western Isles | 29904 | 105 | 28 | 55 | 184 | 8 |
| SCOTLAND | 4917130 | 100 | 25 | 13 | 214 | 810 |

Notes:
    Institutional SMRs have been excluded. Population weighted statistics

# APPENDICES

TABLE B3.4  ALL CAUSES SMR (65+) STATISTICS (SECTORS WITH POP GT 500)

| AREA | Population | SMR (65+) | | | | Sectors |
|------|-----------|------|----------|---------|---------|---------|
| | | Mean | Stan Dev | Minimum | Maximum | |
| Group 1 - WEST | 2315779 | 106 | 13 | 52 | 174 | 338 |
| Group 2 - EAST | 2117570 | 97 | 11 | 53 | 151 | 337 |
| Group 3 - RURAL | 483781 | 98 | 13 | 43 | 152 | 135 |
| SCOTLAND | 4917130 | 101 | 13 | 43 | 174 | 810 |

| AREA | Population | SMR (65+) | | | | Sectors |
|------|-----------|------|----------|---------|---------|---------|
| | | Mean | Stan Dev | Minimum | Maximum | |
| Group 1 - WEST | | | | | | |
|   Argyll & Clyde | 437958 | 106 | 13 | 52 | 150 | 77 |
|   Ayr & Arran | 371043 | 106 | 11 | 59 | 135 | 71 |
|   Greater Glasgow | 948125 | 106 | 15 | 66 | 174 | 128 |
|   Lanarkshire | 558653 | 106 | 10 | 73 | 131 | 62 |
| Group 2 - EAST | | | | | | |
|   Fife | 317302 | 100 | 11 | 71 | 132 | 49 |
|   Forth Valley | 254887 | 100 | 11 | 79 | 127 | 44 |
|   Grampian | 458931 | 95 | 10 | 53 | 114 | 62 |
|   Lothian | 706334 | 95 | 11 | 57 | 151 | 113 |
|   Tayside | 380116 | 96 | 11 | 66 | 136 | 69 |
| Group 3 - RURAL | | | | | | |
|   Borders | 92543 | 98 | 14 | 45 | 131 | 27 |
|   Dumfries & Galloway | 141028 | 94 | 14 | 50 | 152 | 35 |
|   Highland | 179119 | 101 | 13 | 43 | 147 | 59 |
|   The Islands | 71091 | 96 | 10 | 77 | 145 | 14 |
| SCOTLAND | 4917130 | 101 | 13 | 43 | 174 | 810 |

Notes:
   Institutional SMRs have been excluded. Population weighted statistics

TABLE B3.4  ALL CAUSES SMR (65+) STATISTICS (SECTORS WITH POP GT 500)  CONTD.

| AREA | Population | SMR (65+) | | | | Sectors |
|------|-----------|------|----------|---------|---------|---------|
| | | Mean | Stan Dev | Minimum | Maximum | |
| Argyll & Clyde | | | | | | |
| Argyll & Bute | 57760 | 104 | 13 | 78 | 150 | 20 |
| Dumbarton | 76166 | 103 | 13 | 73 | 131 | 13 |
| Inverclyde | 98833 | 108 | 12 | 85 | 136 | 13 |
| Renfrew | 205199 | 107 | 13 | 52 | 132 | 31 |
| Ayr & Arran | | | | | | |
| Cumnock & Doon V | 44657 | 110 | 9 | 94 | 126 | 8 |
| Cunninghame | 135412 | 104 | 11 | 59 | 126 | 28 |
| Kilmar. & Loudoun | 81633 | 111 | 12 | 92 | 135 | 16 |
| Kyle & Carrick | 109341 | 105 | 10 | 86 | 131 | 19 |
| Borders | | | | | | |
| Berwickshire | 17148 | 88 | 15 | 45 | 115 | 6 |
| Ett. & Lauderdale | 27204 | 101 | 18 | 64 | 131 | 8 |
| Roxburgh | 34518 | 101 | 6 | 94 | 111 | 7 |
| Tweedale | 13673 | 98 | 12 | 61 | 112 | 6 |
| Dumfries & Galloway | | | | | | |
| Ann.& Eskdale | 34744 | 86 | 13 | 50 | 104 | 9 |
| Nithsdale | 54437 | 96 | 10 | 69 | 109 | 11 |
| Stewartry | 22310 | 88 | 7 | 74 | 94 | 6 |
| Wigtown | 29537 | 107 | 13 | 91 | 152 | 9 |
| Fife | | | | | | |
| Dunfermline | 121692 | 102 | 8 | 81 | 110 | 16 |
| Kirkaldy | 142706 | 102 | 11 | 87 | 132 | 20 |
| N. E. Fife | 52904 | 88 | 9 | 71 | 106 | 13 |
| Forth Valley | | | | | | |
| Clackmannan | 47168 | 105 | 11 | 88 | 122 | 8 |
| Falkirk | 132004 | 99 | 9 | 82 | 117 | 20 |
| Stirling | 75715 | 101 | 13 | 79 | 127 | 16 |
| Grampian | | | | | | |
| Aberdeen City | 199552 | 100 | 8 | 88 | 114 | 20 |
| Banff & Buchan | 79331 | 95 | 10 | 74 | 109 | 11 |
| Gordon | 61324 | 86 | 8 | 53 | 98 | 11 |
| Kincar. & Deeside | 39277 | 90 | 4 | 79 | 93 | 7 |
| Moray | 79447 | 94 | 10 | 75 | 110 | 13 |
| Greater Glasgow | | | | | | |
| Bears. & Milngavie | 39335 | 85 | 10 | 66 | 103 | 7 |
| Clydebank | 51995 | 104 | 7 | 89 | 116 | 7 |
| Eastwood | 53389 | 83 | 9 | 67 | 107 | 9 |
| Glasgow City | 722303 | 110 | 14 | 82 | 174 | 90 |
| Strathkelvin | 81103 | 102 | 15 | 72 | 138 | 15 |
| Highland | | | | | | |
| Baden. & Strathspey | 8366 | 98 | 10 | 80 | 109 | 5 |
| Caithness | 26076 | 108 | 13 | 94 | 147 | 6 |
| Inverness | 53821 | 96 | 8 | 81 | 115 | 9 |
| Lochaber | 16813 | 105 | 15 | 79 | 122 | 7 |
| Nairn | 9488 | 105 | 2 | 103 | 107 | 2 |
| Ross & Crom. | 44624 | 100 | 15 | 56 | 128 | 19 |
| Skye & Lochalsh | 7603 | 97 | 22 | 43 | 117 | 4 |
| Sutherland | 12328 | 99 | 7 | 90 | 111 | 7 |
| Lanarkshire | | | | | | |
| Cumbernauld | 61112 | 107 | 4 | 102 | 115 | 7 |
| E. Kilbride | 81865 | 95 | 11 | 80 | 115 | 9 |
| Hamilton | 107784 | 107 | 6 | 98 | 115 | 12 |
| Clydesdale | 56138 | 99 | 13 | 73 | 119 | 7 |
| Monklands | 109597 | 110 | 8 | 92 | 119 | 12 |
| Motherwell | 142157 | 109 | 10 | 98 | 131 | 15 |
| Lothian | | | | | | |
| E. Lothian | 78327 | 92 | 10 | 57 | 102 | 16 |
| Edinburgh City | 410951 | 93 | 11 | 62 | 135 | 61 |
| Midlothian | 80006 | 100 | 11 | 77 | 120 | 15 |
| W. Lothian | 137050 | 100 | 9 | 72 | 151 | 21 |
| Tayside | | | | | | |
| Angus | 90927 | 96 | 11 | 75 | 136 | 18 |
| Dundee City | 176668 | 97 | 12 | 66 | 129 | 22 |
| Perth & Kinross | 112521 | 95 | 10 | 68 | 121 | 29 |
| The Islands | | | | | | |
| Orkney | 18419 | 91 | 7 | 83 | 99 | 3 |
| Shetland | 22768 | 96 | 8 | 94 | 145 | 3 |
| Western Isles | 29904 | 98 | 12 | 77 | 135 | 8 |
| SCOTLAND | 4917130 | 101 | 13 | 43 | 174 | 810 |

Notes:

Institutional SMRs have been excluded. Population weighted statistics

TABLE B3.5A   SECTOR SMR (ALL AGES) DISTRIBUTION (POP > 500) BY HEALTH BOARD

| AREA | TOTAL | lt 50 | 50<60 | 60<70 | 70<80 | 80<90 | 90<100 | 100<110 | 110<120 | 120<130 | 130<140 | 140<150 | gt 150 |
|---|---|---|---|---|---|---|---|---|---|---|---|---|---|
| Group 1 - WEST | | | | | | | | | | | | | |
| Argyll & Clyde | 77 | - | 1 | 2 | - | 15 | 16 | 18 | 12 | 8 | 3 | 2 | - |
| Ayr & Arran | 71 | - | - | 1 | 2 | 2 | 15 | 25 | 17 | 8 | 1 | - | - |
| Greater Glasgow | 128 | - | - | 2 | 10 | 13 | 18 | 25 | 27 | 15 | 10 | 7 | 1 |
| Lanarkshire | 62 | - | - | - | - | 6 | 8 | 28 | 16 | 4 | - | - | - |
| Group 2 - EAST | | | | | | | | | | | | | |
| Fife | 49 | - | - | - | 3 | 11 | 14 | 16 | 4 | 1 | - | - | - |
| Forth Valley | 44 | - | - | - | 3 | 8 | 16 | 12 | 1 | 4 | - | - | - |
| Grampian | 62 | - | 1 | 1 | 4 | 30 | 16 | 9 | 1 | - | - | - | - |
| Lothian | 113 | - | 2 | 3 | 12 | 27 | 35 | 26 | 4 | 1 | 2 | 1 | - |
| Tayside | 69 | - | 1 | 2 | 5 | 20 | 19 | 15 | 4 | 2 | 1 | - | - |
| Group 3 - RURAL | | | | | | | | | | | | | |
| Borders | 27 | 1 | - | 2 | - | 7 | 12 | 3 | 1 | 1 | - | - | - |
| Dumfries & Galloway | 35 | 1 | 1 | - | 4 | 5 | 12 | 9 | 1 | 1 | 1 | - | - |
| Highland | 59 | 1 | - | 1 | 2 | 12 | 16 | 18 | 3 | 2 | 3 | 1 | - |
| The Islands | 14 | - | - | - | - | 3 | 4 | 5 | 2 | - | - | - | - |
| SCOTLAND | 810 | 3 | 6 | 14 | 45 | 159 | 201 | 209 | 93 | 47 | 21 | 11 | 1 |

TABLE B3.5B   SECTOR SMR (0-64) DISTRIBUTION (POP > 500) BY HEALTH BOARD

| AREA | TOTAL | lt 50 | 50<60 | 60<70 | 70<80 | 80<90 | 90<100 | 100<110 | 110<120 | 120<130 | 130<140 | 140<150 | gt 150 |
|---|---|---|---|---|---|---|---|---|---|---|---|---|---|
| **Group - WEST** | | | | | | | | | | | | | |
| Argyll & Clyde | 77 | 4 | 3 | 2 | 8 | 11 | 10 | 14 | 6 | 7 | 6 | 2 | 4 |
| Ayr & Arran | 71 | 1 | 3 | - | 8 | 8 | 14 | 10 | 10 | 8 | 5 | 3 | 1 |
| Greater Glasgow | 128 | 2 | 5 | 9 | 7 | 13 | 14 | 9 | 13 | 9 | 18 | 13 | 16 |
| Lanarkshire | 62 | - | - | 1 | 3 | 6 | 10 | 16 | 15 | 6 | 3 | 2 | - |
| **Group 2 - EAST** | | | | | | | | | | | | | |
| Fife | 49 | - | 2 | 3 | 6 | 8 | 10 | 9 | 7 | 2 | 1 | 1 | - |
| Forth Valley | 44 | 2 | - | 6 | 5 | 8 | 3 | 10 | 4 | 5 | - | 1 | - |
| Grampian | 62 | 1 | 5 | 6 | 20 | 16 | 8 | 3 | 2 | - | 1 | - | - |
| Lothian | 113 | 7 | 6 | 14 | 13 | 17 | 19 | 17 | 11 | 4 | 2 | 1 | 2 |
| Tayside | 69 | 3 | 4 | 14 | 9 | 11 | 11 | 10 | 4 | 1 | 1 | - | 1 |
| **Group 3 - RURAL** | | | | | | | | | | | | | |
| Borders | 27 | - | 3 | 4 | 5 | 6 | 6 | 2 | 1 | - | - | - | - |
| Dumfries & Galloway | 35 | 1 | 1 | 1 | 2 | 9 | 7 | 6 | 5 | 1 | 1 | 1 | - |
| Highland | 59 | 1 | 3 | 4 | 2 | 11 | 11 | 7 | 8 | 4 | 3 | 1 | 4 |
| The Islands | 14 | 1 | 1 | 1 | 1 | 2 | 1 | 3 | 2 | - | - | - | 2 |
| SCOTLAND | 810 | 23 | 36 | 65 | 89 | 126 | 124 | 116 | 88 | 47 | 41 | 25 | 30 |

TABLE B3.5c   SECTOR SMR (65+) DISTRIBUTION (POP > 500) BY HEALTH BOARD

| AREA | TOTAL | lt 50 | 50<60 | 60<70 | 70<80 | 80<90 | 90<100 | 100<110 | 110<120 | 120<130 | 130<140 | 140<150 | gt 150 |
|---|---|---|---|---|---|---|---|---|---|---|---|---|---|
| **Group 1 - WEST** | | | | | | | | | | | | | |
| Argyll & Clyde | 77 | - | 1 | - | 6 | 6 | 13 | 21 | 19 | 6 | 4 | - | 1 |
| Ayr & Arran | 71 | 1 | - | 1 | 2 | 17 | 23 | 18 | 6 | 3 | - | - | - |
| Greater Glasgow | 128 | - | - | 2 | 3 | 16 | 18 | 43 | 23 | 13 | 8 | 1 | 1 |
| Lanarkshire | 62 | - | - | - | 1 | 2 | 16 | 20 | 20 | 2 | 1 | - | - |
| **Group 2 - EAST** | | | | | | | | | | | | | |
| Fife | 49 | - | - | - | 3 | 10 | 14 | 18 | 1 | 2 | 1 | - | - |
| Forth Valley | 44 | - | - | - | 2 | 7 | 14 | 13 | 4 | 4 | - | - | - |
| Grampian | 62 | - | 1 | - | 5 | 17 | 24 | 13 | 2 | - | - | - | - |
| Lothian | 113 | - | 1 | 2 | 8 | 24 | 42 | 24 | 8 | 2 | 1 | - | 1 |
| Tayside | 69 | - | - | 2 | 5 | 13 | 27 | 12 | 6 | 3 | 1 | - | - |
| **Group 3 - RURAL** | | | | | | | | | | | | | |
| Borders | 27 | 1 | - | 2 | 2 | 3 | 9 | 6 | 3 | - | 1 | - | - |
| Dumfries & Galloway | 35 | - | 1 | 2 | 3 | 6 | 14 | 5 | 3 | - | - | - | 1 |
| Highland | 59 | 1 | 1 | - | 3 | 8 | 19 | 17 | 6 | 3 | - | 1 | - |
| The Islands | 14 | - | - | - | 1 | 3 | 6 | 2 | - | - | 1 | 1 | - |
| SCOTLAND | 810 | 2 | 6 | 10 | 43 | 117 | 233 | 217 | 113 | 41 | 21 | 3 | 4 |

TABLE B3.6A  SECTOR SMR VALUES SIGNIFICANTLY HIGH OR LOW: ALL AGES BY HEALTH BOARD

| AREA | TOTAL | lt 50 | 50<60 | 60<70 | 70<80 | 80<90 | 90<100 | 100<110 | 110<120 | 120<130 | 130<140 | 140<150 | gt 150 |
|---|---|---|---|---|---|---|---|---|---|---|---|---|---|
| Group 1 - WEST | | | | | | | | | | | | | |
| Argyll & Clyde | 25 | - | - | 1 | - | 2 | - | - | 9 | 8 | 3 | 2 | - |
| Ayr & Arran | 19 | - | - | 1 | 2 | - | - | - | 9 | 7 | - | - | - |
| Greater Glasgow | 75 | - | - | 2 | 10 | 7 | - | - | 24 | 14 | 10 | 7 | 1 |
| Lanarkshire | 21 | - | - | - | - | 3 | - | - | 14 | 4 | - | - | - |
| Group 2 - EAST | | | | | | | | | | | | | |
| Fife | 9 | - | - | - | 3 | 2 | - | - | 3 | 1 | - | - | - |
| Forth Valley | 10 | - | - | - | 2 | 3 | - | - | 1 | 4 | - | - | - |
| Grampian | 24 | - | - | 1 | 3 | 16 | 2 | 1 | 1 | - | - | - | - |
| Lothian | 31 | - | 1 | 3 | 10 | 12 | - | 1 | 1 | 1 | 2 | 1 | - |
| Tayside | 26 | - | 1 | 1 | 4 | 15 | - | - | 3 | 1 | 1 | - | - |
| Group 3 - RURAL | | | | | | | | | | | | | |
| Borders | 6 | 1 | - | 2 | - | 2 | - | - | - | 1 | - | - | - |
| Dumfries & Galloway | 8 | 1 | 1 | - | 3 | 1 | - | - | - | 1 | 1 | - | - |
| Highland | 7 | 1 | - | 1 | - | 1 | - | - | 1 | 1 | 1 | 1 | - |
| The Islands | 2 | - | - | - | - | 1 | 1 | - | - | - | - | - | - |
| SCOTLAND | 263 | 3 | 3 | 12 | 37 | 65 | 3 | 1 | 66 | 43 | 18 | 11 | 1 |

TABLE B3.6B  SECTOR SMR VALUES SIGNIFICANTLY HIGH OR LOW: 0-64 BY HEALTH BOARD

| AREA | TOTAL | lt 50 | 50<60 | 60<70 | 70<80 | 80<90 | 90<100 | 100<110 | 110<120 | 120<130 | 130<140 | 140<150 | gt 150 |
|---|---|---|---|---|---|---|---|---|---|---|---|---|---|
| **Group 1 - WEST** | | | | | | | | | | | | | |
| Argyll & Clyde | 19 | - | 2 | - | 2 | - | - | - | - | 3 | 6 | 2 | 4 |
| Ayr & Arran | 10 | - | 2 | - | - | - | - | - | - | 2 | 4 | 2 | - |
| Greater Glasgow | 72 | 2 | 4 | 9 | 3 | - | - | - | 1 | 7 | 17 | 13 | 16 |
| Lanarkshre | 14 | - | - | 1 | 3 | - | - | - | 2 | 3 | 3 | 2 | - |
| **Group 2 - LAST** | | | | | | | | | | | | | |
| Fife | 7 | - | 1 | - | 1 | 1 | - | - | - | 2 | 1 | 1 | - |
| Forth Valley | 8 | 1 | - | 2 | 2 | - | - | - | - | 2 | - | 1 | - |
| Grampian | 17 | 1 | 3 | 5 | 5 | 2 | - | - | - | - | 1 | - | - |
| Lothian | 24 | 4 | 4 | 9 | 3 | - | - | - | - | 2 | - | - | 2 |
| Tayside | 19 | 1 | 2 | 12 | 3 | - | - | - | - | - | - | - | 1 |
| **Group 3 - RURAL** | | | | | | | | | | | | | |
| Borders | 5 | - | 3 | 2 | - | - | - | - | - | - | - | - | - |
| Dumfries & Galloway | 2 | - | 1 | - | - | - | - | - | - | - | - | 1 | - |
| Highland | 5 | - | - | - | 1 | - | - | - | - | - | - | - | 4 |
| The Islands | 3 | - | - | - | 1 | - | - | - | - | - | - | - | 2 |
| SCOTLAND | 205 | 9 | 22 | 40 | 24 | 3 | - | - | 3 | 21 | 32 | 22 | 29 |

TABLE B3.6C   SECTOR SMR VALUES SIGNIFICANTLY HIGH OR LOW: 65+ BY HEALTH BOARD

| AREA | TOTAL | lt 50 | 50<60 | 60<70 | 70<80 | 80<90 | 90<100 | 100<110 | 110<120 | 120<130 | 130<140 | 140<150 | gt 150 |
|---|---|---|---|---|---|---|---|---|---|---|---|---|---|
| Group 1 - WEST | | | | | | | | | | | | | |
| Argyll & Clyde | 18 | - | - | - | 2 | 1 | - | - | 6 | 5 | 3 | - | 1 |
| Ayr & Arran | 15 | - | 1 | - | - | 1 | - | - | 6 | 4 | 3 | - | - |
| Greater Glasgow | 44 | - | - | 2 | 3 | 4 | 1 | - | 12 | 12 | 8 | 1 | 1 |
| Lanarkshire | 14 | - | - | - | 1 | 2 | - | - | 8 | 2 | 1 | - | - |
| Group 2 - EAST | | | | | | | | | | | | | |
| Fife | 7 | - | - | - | 3 | 1 | - | - | - | 2 | 1 | - | - |
| Forth Valley | 6 | - | - | - | - | 2 | - | - | 1 | 3 | - | - | - |
| Grampian | 13 | - | - | - | 3 | 8 | - | 1 | 1 | - | - | - | - |
| Lothian | 21 | - | 1 | 2 | 5 | 9 | 1 | - | 1 | 1 | 1 | - | - |
| Tayside | 11 | - | - | 1 | 4 | 2 | - | - | 2 | 1 | 1 | - | - |
| Group 3 - RURAL | | | | | | | | | | | | | |
| Borders | 5 | 1 | - | 2 | - | 1 | - | - | - | - | 1 | - | - |
| Dumfries & Galloway | 8 | - | 1 | 2 | 2 | 2 | - | - | - | - | - | - | 1 |
| Highland | 7 | 1 | 1 | - | - | 1 | - | - | 1 | 2 | - | 1 | - |
| The Islands | 2 | - | - | - | 1 | 1 | - | - | - | - | - | - | - |
| SCOTLAND | 171 | 2 | 4 | 9 | 24 | 35 | 2 | 1 | 38 | 32 | 19 | 2 | 3 |

TABLE B4.1   AGE-SEX SPECIFIC DEATH RATIOS INDEX FOR 7 DEPRIVATION CATEGORIES
(Overall death rate each age-sex group = 100) Scotland 1980-82

| | | Least Deprived | | | | | Most Deprived | | No. of Deaths | Rate/ 1000 |
|---|---|---|---|---|---|---|---|---|---|---|
| | | 1 | 2 | 3 | 4 | 5 | 6 | 7 | | |
| 0-4 | M | 79 | 81 | 97 | 102 | 111 | 105 | 124 | 1568 | 9.9 |
| | F | 63 | 87 | 90 | 101 | 112 | 110 | 138 | 1147 | 7.6 |
| 5-14 | M | 73 | 78 | 108 | 105 | 86 | 104 | 141 | 375 | 0.9 |
| | F | 81 | 100 | 102 | 86 | 106 | 117 | 106 | 239 | 0.6 |
| 15-24 | M | 70 | 89 | 111 | 101 | 97 | 94 | 127 | 1247 | 2.9 |
| | F | 66 | 113 | 96 | 84 | 117 | 113 | 113 | 427 | 1.0 |
| 25-34 | M | 53 | 77 | 86 | 105 | 108 | 123 | 173 | 1190 | 3.4 |
| | F | 32 | 79 | 84 | 102 | 126 | 121 | 184 | 625 | 1.8 |
| 35-44 | M | 55 | 68 | 87 | 102 | 110 | 139 | 181 | 2246 | 7.7 |
| | F | 75 | 77 | 88 | 95 | 107 | 138 | 166 | 1460 | 4.9 |
| 45-54 | M | 57 | 72 | 86 | 96 | 115 | 140 | 153 | 6702 | 24.0 |
| | F | 65 | 75 | 92 | 100 | 105 | 130 | 145 | 4325 | 14.6 |
| 55-64 | M | 66 | 81 | 90 | 98 | 110 | 123 | 140 | 16596 | 65.6 |
| | F | 64 | 79 | 92 | 99 | 112 | 125 | 127 | 10588 | 36.7 |
| 65-74 | M | 82 | 87 | 94 | 101 | 105 | 116 | 126 | 30160 | 159.7 |
| | F | 79 | 88 | 104 | 100 | 108 | 114 | 127 | 23120 | 90.5 |
| 75+ | M | 92 | 92 | 97 | 103 | 105 | 105 | 114 | 33971 | 404.8 |
| | F | 96 | 95 | 98 | 100 | 105 | 103 | 110 | 54288 | 297.4 |
| 0-64 | | 64 | 79 | 91 | 98 | 110 | 125 | 141 | 48735 | 3.8 |
| 65+ | | 90 | 92 | 96 | 101 | 105 | 108 | 118 | 141539 | 66.4 |
| All ages | | 83 | 89 | 95 | 100 | 107 | 113 | 125 | 190274 | 12.6 |

TABLE B4.2A   SECTOR SMRS ALL AGES: DISTRIBUTION BY DEPRIVATION CATEGORY
ALL VALUES*

| SMR Group | Low | 2 | 3 | 4 | 5 | 6 | High | Sectors |
|---|---|---|---|---|---|---|---|---|
| lt 50 | - | 1 | 2 | - | - | - | - | 3 |
| 50 < 60 | 5 | - | - | 1 | - | - | - | 6 |
| 60 < 70 | 6 | 5 | 1 | 2 | - | - | - | 14 |
| 70 < 80 | 15 | 14 | 13 | 3 | - | - | - | 45 |
| 80 < 90 | 24 | 52 | 49 | 28 | 5 | 1 | - | 159 |
| 90 < 100 | 10 | 35 | 80 | 54 | 16 | 6 | - | 201 |
| 100 < 110 | 2 | 23 | 53 | 68 | 38 | 21 | 4 | 209 |
| 110 < 120 | - | 3 | 11 | 22 | 25 | 24 | 8 | 93 |
| 120 <130 | - | 2 | 2 | 8 | 10 | 18 | 7 | 47 |
| 130 < 140 | - | - | 2 | 2 | 3 | 5 | 9 | 21 |
| 140 < 150 | - | - | 1 | 2 | - | - | 8 | 11 |
| gt 150 | - | - | - | - | - | - | 1 | 1 |
| Total | 62 | 135 | 214 | 190 | 97 | 75 | 37 | 810 |

* excludes institutional sectors and those with <500 population

TABLE B4.2B   SECTOR SMRS ALL AGES: DISTRIBUTION BY DEPRIVATION CATEGORY
SIGNIFICANT VALUES*

| SMR Group | Low | 2 | 3 | 4 | 5 | 6 | High | Sectors |
|---|---|---|---|---|---|---|---|---|
| lt 50     | -  | 1  | 2  | -  | -  | -  | -  | 3   |
| 50 < 60   | 2  | -  | -  | 1  | -  | -  | -  | 3   |
| 60 < 70   | 6  | 4  | -  | 2  | -  | -  | -  | 12  |
| 70 < 80   | 14 | 10 | 11 | 2  | -  | -  | -  | 37  |
| 80 < 90   | 10 | 27 | 15 | 11 | 2  | -  | -  | 65  |
| 90 < 100  | -  | 1  | 1  | 1  | -  | -  | -  | 3   |
| 100 < 110 | -  | -  | -  | -  | 1  | -  | -  | 1   |
| 110 < 120 | -  | -  | 3  | 12 | 23 | 20 | 8  | 66  |
| 120 < 130 | -  | 2  | 2  | 6  | 10 | 16 | 7  | 43  |
| 130 < 140 | -  | -  | -  | 2  | 2  | 5  | 9  | 18  |
| 140 < 150 | -  | -  | 1  | 2  | -  | -  | 8  | 11  |
| gt 150    | -  | -  | -  | -  | -  | -  | 1  | 1   |
| Total     | 32 | 45 | 35 | 39 | 38 | 41 | 33 | 263 |

* excludes institutional sectors and those with <500 population, P <0.05

TABLE B4.3A   SECTOR SMRS 0 - 64: DISTRIBUTION BY DEPRIVATION CATEGORY
ALL VALUES*

| SMR Group | Low | 2 | 3 | 4 | 5 | 6 | High | Sectors |
|---|---|---|---|---|---|---|---|---|
| lt 50     | 11 | 5   | 7   | -   | -  | -  | -  | 23  |
| 150 < 60  | 18 | 7   | 7   | 4   | -  | -  | -  | 36  |
| 160 < 70  | 15 | 23  | 17  | 8   | 1  | 1  | -  | 65  |
| 170 < 80  | 10 | 35  | 26  | 16  | 2  | -  | -  | 89  |
| 80 < 90   | 6  | 35  | 45  | 33  | 5  | 2  | -  | 126 |
| 90 < 100  | 2  | 12  | 57  | 38  | 14 | 1  | -  | 124 |
| 100 < 110 | -  | 11  | 24  | 42  | 27 | 11 | 1  | 116 |
| 110 < 120 | -  | 3   | 22  | 23  | 22 | 15 | 3  | 88  |
| 120 < 130 | -  | 2   | 6   | 14  | 9  | 13 | 3  | 47  |
| 130 < 140 | -  | 1   | 1   | 5   | 12 | 12 | 10 | 41  |
| 140 < 150 | -  | 1   | -   | 4   | 4  | 10 | 6  | 25  |
| gt 50     | -  | -   | 2   | 3   | 1  | 10 | 14 | 30  |
| Total     | 62 | 135 | 214 | 190 | 97 | 75 | 37 | 810 |

* excludes institutional sectors and those with <500 population

TABLE B4.3B  SECTOR SMRS 0 - 64: DISTRIBUTION BY DEPRIVATION CATEGORY SIGNIFICANT VALUES*

| SMR Group | Low | 2 | 3 | 4 | 5 | 6 | High | Sectors |
|---|---|---|---|---|---|---|---|---|
| lt 50 | 9 | - | - | - | - | - | - | 9 |
| 50 < 60 | 13 | 5 | 3 | 1 | - | - | - | 22 |
| 60 < 70 | 10 | 18 | 7 | 5 | - | - | - | 40 |
| 70 < 80 | 2 | 13 | 5 | 3 | 1 | - | - | 24 |
| 80 < 90 | - | - | 1 | 2 | - | - | - | 3 |
| 110 < 120 | - | - | - | 1 | 1 | 1 | - | 3 |
| 120 < 130 | - | - | 1 | 2 | 6 | 9 | 3 | 21 |
| 130 < 140 | - | - | - | 3 | 9 | 11 | 9 | 32 |
| 140 < 150 | - | - | - | 2 | 4 | 10 | 14 | 29 |
| gt 150 | - | - | 2 | 3 | - | 10 | 14 | 29 |
| Total | 34 | 36 | 19 | 22 | 21 | 41 | 32 | 205 |

* excludes institutional sectors and those with <500 population, P <0.05

TABLE B4.4A  SECTOR SMRS 65+: DISTRIBUTION BY DEPRIVATION CATEGORY ALL VALUES*

| SMR Group | Low | 2 | 3 | 4 | 5 | 6 | High | Sectors |
|---|---|---|---|---|---|---|---|---|
| lt 50 | - | -2 | - | - | - | - | 2 | |
| 50 < 60 | 2 | 4 | - | - | - | - | - | 6 |
| 60 < 70 | 5 | 1 | 1 | 3 | - | - | - | 10 |
| 80 < 90 | 17 | 39 | 35 | 21 | 3 | 2 | - | 117 |
| 90 < 100 | 20 | 38 | 81 | 58 | 24 | 11 | 1 | 233 |
| 110 < 120 | 1 | 6 | 22 | 24 | 21 | 29 | 10 | 113 |
| 120 < 130 | 2 | 1 | 6 | 5 | 12 | 5 | 9 | 41 |
| 130 < 140 | - | 3 | 1 | 7 | 1 | 2 | 7 | 21 |
| 140 < 150 | - | 1 | 1 | - | - | - | 1 | 3 |
| gt 150 | - | - | - | 3 | - | - | 1 | 4 |
| Total | 62 | 135 | 214 | 190 | 97 | 75 | 37 | 810 |

* excludes institutional sectors and those with <500 population

TABLE B4.4B  SECTOR SMRS 65+: DISTRIBUTION BY DEPRIVATION CATEGORY SIGNIFICANT VALUES*

| SMR Group | Low | 2 | 3 | 4 | 5 | 6 | High | Sectors |
|---|---|---|---|---|---|---|---|---|
| lt 50 | - | - | 2 | - | - | - | - | 2 |
| 50 < 60 | - | 4 | - | - | - | - | - | 4 |
| 60 < 70 | 4 | 1 | 1 | 3 | - | - | - | 9 |
| 70 < 80 | 6 | 6 | 8 | 2 | 2 | - | - | 24 |
| 80 < 90 | 2 | 14 | 12 | 7 | - | - | - | 35 |
| 90 < 100 | - | - | - | 1 | - | 1 | - | 2 |
| 100 < 110 | - | - | - | 1 | - | - | - | 1 |
| 110 < 120 | - | 1 | 2 | 7 | 9 | 13 | 6 | 38 |
| 130 < 140 | - | 2 | - | 7 | 1 | 2 | 7 | 19 |
| 140 < 150 | - | - | 1 | - | - | - | 1 | 2 |
| Total | 13 | 28 | 30 | 34 | 23 | 21 | 22 | 171 |

* excludes institutional sectors and those with <500 population, P <0.05

*C - Key Maps*

# HEALTH BOARDS

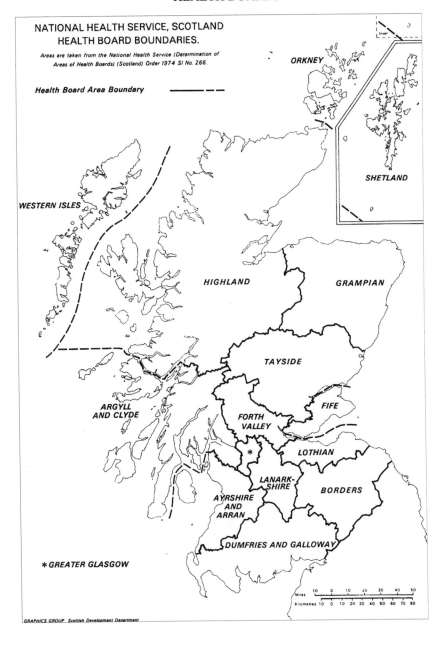

NATIONAL HEALTH SERVICE, SCOTLAND
HEALTH BOARD BOUNDARIES.

Areas are taken from the National Health Service (Determination of
Areas of Health Boards) (Scotland) Order 1974 SI No. 266.

Health Board Area Boundary

ORKNEY

SHETLAND

WESTERN ISLES

HIGHLAND

GRAMPIAN

TAYSIDE

ARGYLL
AND CLYDE

FIFE

FORTH
VALLEY

LOTHIAN

LANARK-
SHIRE

BORDERS

AYRSHIRE
AND
ARRAN

DUMFRIES AND GALLOWAY

*GREATER GLASGOW

Miles
Kilometres

GRAPHICS GROUP  Scottish Development Department

## LOCAL GOVERNMENT DISTRICTS

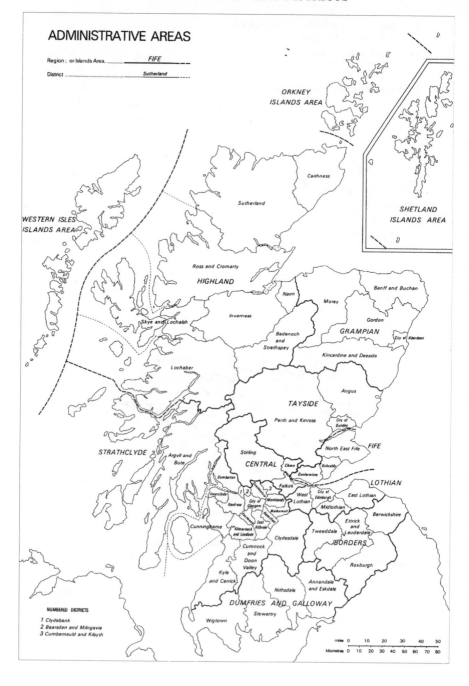

ADMINISTRATIVE AREAS

Region; or Islands Area............ FIFE

District ....................................... Sutherland

ORKNEY
ISLANDS AREA

SHETLAND
ISLANDS AREA

Caithness

Sutherland

WESTERN ISLES
ISLANDS AREA

Ross and Cromarty

HIGHLAND

Nairn

Moray

Banff and Buchan

Gordon

Inverness

City of Aberdeen

Skye and Lochalsh

Badenoch
and
Strathspey

GRAMPIAN

Kincardine and Deeside

Lochaber

Angus

TAYSIDE

Perth and Kinross

City of
Dundee

STRATHCLYDE

Argyll and
Bute

North East Fife

FIFE

Stirling

Clackmannan

CENTRAL

Kirkcaldy

Dumbarton

Dunfermline

Falkirk

LOTHIAN

Inverclyde

City of
Edinburgh

West
Lothian

East Lothian

Renfrew

City of
Glasgow

Monklands

Midlothian

Berwickshire

Motherwell

East
Kilbride

Ettrick
and
Lauderdale

Cunninghame

Kilmarnock
and Loudoun

Tweeddale

Clydesdale

BORDERS

Cumnock
and
Doon
Valley

Roxburgh

Kyle
and Carrick

Annandale
and Eskdale

Nithsdale

DUMFRIES AND GALLOWAY

Wigtown

Stewartry

NUMBERED DISTRICTS

1 Clydebank
2 Bearsden and Milngavie
3 Cumbernauld and Kilsyth

miles 0    10    20    30    40    50
kilometres 0  10  20  30  40  50  60  70  80